W9-CEA-275

COURSE OF THEORETICAL PHYSICS

Volume 3

QUANTUM MECHANICS

Non-relativistic Theory

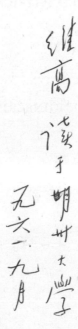

ADDISON-WESLEY PHYSICS SERIES

Bonner and Phillips—Principles of Physical Science
Holton—Introduction to Concepts and Theories in Physical Science
Holton and Roller—Foundations of Modern Physical Science
Knauss—Discovering Physics
Mitchell—Fundamentals of Electronics
Sears and Zemansky—College Physics
Sears and Zemansky—University Physics

PRINCIPLES OF PHYSICS SERIES

Constant—Theoretical Physics—Mechanics
Constant—Theoretical Physics—Electromagnetism
Fowler—Introduction to Electric Theory
Randall—Introduction to Acoustics
Rossi—Optics
Sears—Mechanics, Heat, and Sound
Sears—Electricity and Magnetism
Sears—Optics
Sears—Mechanics, Wave Motion, and Heat
Sears—Thermodynamics, the Kinetic Theory of Gases, and Statistical Mechanics
Symon—Mechanics

ADDISON-WESLEY SERIES IN ADVANCED PHYSICS

Goldstein—Classical Mechanics
Jauch and Rohrlich—The Theory of Photons and Electrons
Landau and Lifshitz—Quantum Mechanics—Non-relativistic Theory
Landau and Lifshitz—The Classical Theory of Fields
Panofsky and Phillips—Classical Electricity and Magnetism
Sachs—Nuclear Theory

A-W SERIES IN NUCLEAR SCIENCE AND ENGINEERING

Goodman—Introduction to Pile Theory
(The Science and Engineering of Nuclear Power, I)
Goodman—Applications of Nuclear Energy
(The Science and Engineering of Nuclear Power, II)
Hughes—Pile Neutron Research
Kaplan—Nuclear Physics

QUANTUM MECHANICS

NON-RELATIVISTIC THEORY

by

L. D. LANDAU AND E. M. LIFSHITZ
INSTITUTE OF PHYSICAL PROBLEMS, USSR ACADEMY OF SCIENCES

Volume 3 of *Course of Theoretical Physics*

Translated from the Russian by

J. B. SYKES AND J. S. BELL

1958
PERGAMON PRESS LTD.
London - Paris

ADDISON-WESLEY PUBLISHING COMPANY, INC.
Reading, Massachusetts, U.S.A.

PERGAMON PRESS LTD.
4 and 5 Fitzroy Square, London W.1

PERGAMON PRESS, S.A.R.L.
24, Rue des Écoles, Paris V^e

Copyright
©
1958
Pergamon Press Ltd.

First published in English 1958

U.S.A. edition distributed by Addison-Wesley Publishing Company, Inc.
Reading, Massachusetts, U.S.A.

Library of Congress Card Number 57-14444

Printed in Great Britain by J. W. Arrowsmith Ltd., Bristol.

CONTENTS

V. MOTION IN A CENTRALLY SYMMETRIC FIELD

VI. PERTURBATION THEORY

VII. THE QUASI-CLASSICAL CASE

VIII. SPIN

IX. IDENTITY OF PARTICLES

X. THE ATOM

XI. THE DIATOMIC MOLECULE

XII. THE THEORY OF SYMMETRY

XIII. POLYATOMIC MOLECULES

XIV. THE THEORY OF ELASTIC COLLISIONS

XV. THE THEORY OF INELASTIC COLLISIONS

XVI. MOTION IN A MAGNETIC FIELD

MATHEMATICAL APPENDICES

PREFACE TO THE ENGLISH EDITION

THE present book is one of the series on *Theoretical Physics*, in which we endeavour to give an up-to-date account of various departments of that science. The complete series will contain the following nine volumes:

1. *Mechanics*. 2. *The classical theory of fields*. 3. *Quantum mechanics (non-relativistic theory)*. 4. *Relativistic quantum theory*. 5. *Statistical physics*. 6. *Fluid mechanics*. 7. *Theory of elasticity*. 8. *Electrodynamics of continuous media*. 9. *Physical kinetics*.

Of these, volumes 4 and 9 remain to be written.

The scope of modern theoretical physics is very wide, and we have, of course, made no attempt to discuss in these books all that is now included in the subject. One of the principles which guided our choice of material was not to deal with those topics which could not properly be expounded without at the same time giving a detailed account of the existing experimental results. For this reason the greater part of nuclear physics, for example, lies outside the scope of these books. Another principle of selection was not to discuss very complicated applications of the theory. Both these criteria are, of course, to some extent subjective.

We have tried to deal as fully as possible with those topics that are included. For this reason we do not, as a rule, give references to the original papers, but simply name their authors. We give bibliographical references only to work which contains matters not fully expounded by us, which by their complexity lie "on the borderline" as regards selection or rejection. We have tried also to indicate sources of material which might be of use for reference. Even with these limitations, however, the bibliography given makes no pretence of being exhaustive.

We attempt to discuss general topics in such a way that the physical significance of the theory is exhibited as clearly as possible, and then to build up the mathematical formalism. In doing so, we do not aim at "mathematical rigour" of exposition, which in theoretical physics often amounts to self-deception.

The present volume is devoted to non-relativistic quantum mechanics. By "relativistic theory" we here mean, in the widest sense, the theory of all quantum phenomena which significantly depend on the velocity of light. The volume on this subject (volume 4) will therefore contain not only Dirac's relativistic theory and what is now known as quantum electrodynamics, but also the whole of the quantum theory of radiation.

The present book was written in 1947, and the Russian edition was published in 1948. Owing to lack of time, we have not had the opportunity of carrying out any considerable revision of the text for the English edition, although after ten years there are probably many points with which we should deal differently. We have simply made a few small additions and corrected some errors that have been noticed.

The Russian text of the book was read in manuscript by Professors V. L. Ginzburg and D. I. Blokhintsev. In the preparation of the English edition, L. P. Pitaevskiĭ has given considerable help in checking all the formulae. Our thanks are due to all three.

We are grateful also to Dr J. B. Sykes and Dr J. S. Bell, who not only translated the book excellently, but also made some useful comments.

Finally, we should like to express our thanks to the Pergamon Press, which always acceded to our requests concerning the translation, and which has produced a book of such pleasing appearance.

Institute of Physical Problems L. D. LANDAU
USSR Academy of Sciences E. M. LIFSHITZ

August 1956

CHAPTER I

THE BASIC CONCEPTS OF QUANTUM MECHANICS

§1. The uncertainty principle

WHEN we attempt to apply classical mechanics and electrodynamics to explain atomic phenomena, they lead to results which are in obvious conflict with experiment. This is very clearly seen from the contradiction obtained on applying ordinary electrodynamics to a model of an atom in which the electrons move round the nucleus in classical orbits. During such motion, as in any accelerated motion of charges, the electrons would have to emit electromagnetic waves continually. By this emission, the electrons would lose their energy, and this would eventually cause them to fall into the nucleus. Thus, according to classical electrodynamics, the atom would be unstable, which does not at all agree with reality.

This marked contradiction between theory and experiment indicates that the construction of a theory applicable to atomic phenomena—that is, phenomena occurring in particles of very small mass at very small distances—demands a fundamental modification of the basic physical concepts and laws.

As a starting-point for an investigation of these modifications, it is convenient to take the experimentally observed phenomenon known as *electron diffraction*†. It is found that, when a homogeneous beam of electrons passes through a crystal, the emergent beam exhibits a pattern of alternate maxima and minima of intensity, wholly similar to the diffraction pattern observed in the diffraction of electromagnetic waves. Thus, under certain conditions, the behaviour of material particles—in this case, the electrons—displays features belonging to wave processes.

How markedly this phenomenon contradicts the usual ideas of motion is best seen from the following imaginary experiment, an idealisation of the experiment of electron diffraction by a crystal. Let us imagine a screen impermeable to electrons, in which two slits are cut. On observing the passage of a beam of electrons‡ through one of the slits, the other being covered, we obtain, on a continuous screen placed behind the slit, some pattern of intensity distribution; in the same way, by uncovering the second slit and covering the first, we obtain another pattern. On observing the passage of the beam through both slits, we should expect, on the basis of ordinary classical ideas, a pattern which is a simple superposition of the other two: each electron, moving in its path, passes through one of the slits and

† The phenomenon of electron diffraction was in fact discovered after quantum mechanics was invented. In our discussion, however, we shall not adhere to the historical sequence of development of the theory, but shall endeavour to construct it in such a way that the connection between the basic principles of quantum mechanics and the experimentally observed phenomena is most clearly shown.

‡ The beam is supposed so rarefied that the interaction of the particles in it plays no part.

has no effect on the electrons passing through the other slit. The phenomenon of electron diffraction shows, however, that in reality we obtain a diffraction pattern which, owing to interference, does not at all correspond to the sum of the patterns given by each slit separately. It is clear that this result can in no way be reconciled with the idea that electrons move in paths.

Thus the mechanics which governs atomic phenomena—*quantum mechanics* or *wave mechanics*—must be based on ideas of motion which are fundamentally different from those of classical mechanics. In quantum mechanics there is no such concept as the path of a particle. This forms the content of what is called the *uncertainty principle*, one of the fundamental principles of quantum mechanics, discovered by W. Heisenberg in 1927†.

In that it rejects the ordinary ideas of classical mechanics, the uncertainty principle might be said to be negative in content. Of course, this principle in itself does not suffice as a basis on which to construct a new mechanics of particles. Such a theory must naturally be founded on some positive assertions, which we shall discuss below (§2). However, in order to formulate these assertions, we must first ascertain the statement of the problems which confront quantum mechanics. To do so, we first examine the special nature of the interrelation between quantum mechanics and classical mechanics. A more general theory can usually be formulated in a logically complete manner, independently of a less general theory which forms a limiting case of it. Thus, relativistic mechanics can be constructed on the basis of its own fundamental principles, without any reference to Newtonian mechanics. It is in principle impossible, however, to formulate the basic concepts of quantum mechanics without using classical mechanics. The fact that an electron‡ has no definite path means that it has also, in itself, no other quantitative dynamical characteristics.‖ Hence it is clear that, for a system composed only of quantum objects, it would be entirely impossible to construct any logically independent mechanics. The possibility of a quantitative description of the motion of an electron requires the presence also of physical objects which obey classical mechanics to a sufficient degree of accuracy. If an electron interacts with such a "classical object", the state of the latter is, generally speaking, altered. The nature and magnitude of this change depend on the state of the electron, and therefore may serve to characterise it quantitatively.

In this connection the "classical object" is usually called *apparatus*, and its interaction with the electron is spoken of as *measurement*. However, it must be most decidedly emphasised that we are here not discussing a process of measurement in which the physicist-observer takes part. By *measurement*, in quantum mechanics, we understand any process of interaction between

† It is of interest to note that the complete mathematical formalism of quantum mechanics was constructed by W. Heisenberg and E. Schrödinger in 1925–6, before the discovery of the uncertainty principle, which revealed the physical content of this formalism.

‡ In this and the following sections we shall, for brevity, speak of "an electron", meaning in general any object of a quantum nature, i.e. a particle or system of particles obeying quantum mechanics and not classical mechanics.

‖ We refer to quantities which characterise the motion of the electron, and not to those, such as the charge and the mass, which relate to it as a particle; these are parameters.

classical and quantum objects, occurring apart from and independently of any observer. The importance of the concept of measurement in quantum mechanics was elucidated by N. BOHR.

We have defined "apparatus" as a physical object which is governed, with sufficient accuracy, by classical mechanics. Such, for instance, is a body of large enough mass. However, it must not be supposed that apparatus is necessarily macroscopic. Under certain conditions, the part of apparatus may also be taken by an object which is microscopic, since the idea of "with sufficient accuracy" depends on the actual problem proposed. Thus, the motion of an electron in a Wilson chamber is observed by means of the cloudy track which it leaves, and the thickness of this is large compared with atomic dimensions; when the path is determined with such low accuracy, the electron is an entirely classical object.

Thus quantum mechanics occupies a very unusual place among physical theories: it contains classical mechanics as a limiting case, yet at the same time it requires this limiting case for its own formulation.

We may now formulate the problem of quantum mechanics. A typical problem consists in predicting the result of a subsequent measurement from the known results of previous measurements. Moreover, we shall see later that, in comparison with classical mechanics, quantum mechanics, generally speaking, restricts the range of values which can be taken by various physical quantities (for example, energy): that is, the values which can be obtained as a result of measuring the quantity concerned. The methods of quantum mechanics must enable us to determine these admissible values.

The measuring process has in quantum mechanics a very important property: it always affects the electron subjected to it, and it is in principle impossible to make its effect arbitrarily small, for a given accuracy of measurement. The more exact the measurement, the stronger the effect exerted by it, and only in measurements of very low accuracy can the effect on the measured object be small. This property of measurements is logically related to the fact that the dynamical characteristics of the electron appear only as a result of the measurement itself, i.e. as a result of its interaction with a classical object. It is clear that, if the effect of the measuring process on the object of it could be made arbitrarily small, this would mean that the measured quantity has in itself a definite value independent of the measurement.

Among the various kinds of measurement, the measurement of the co-ordinates of the electron plays a fundamental part. Within the limits of applicability of quantum mechanics, a measurement of the co-ordinates of an electron can always be performed† with any desired accuracy.

Let us suppose that, at definite time intervals Δt, successive measurements of the co-ordinates of an electron are made. The results will not in general lie on a smooth curve. On the contrary, the more accurately the measurements

† Once again we emphasise that, in speaking of "performing a measurement", we refer to the interaction of an electron with a classical " apparatus", which in no way presupposes the presence of an external observer.

are made, the more discontinuous and disorderly will be the variation of their results, in accordance with the non-existence of a path of the electron. A fairly smooth path is obtained only if the co-ordinates of the electron are measured with a low degree of accuracy, as for instance from the condensation of vapour droplets in a Wilson chamber.

If now, leaving the accuracy of the measurements unchanged, we diminish the intervals Δt between measurements, then adjacent measurements, of course, give neighbouring values of the co-ordinates. However, the results of a series of successive measurements, though they lie in a small region of space, will be distributed in this region in a wholly irregular manner, lying on no smooth curve. In particular, as Δt tends to zero, the results of adjacent measurements by no means tend to lie on one straight line.

This circumstance shows that, in quantum mechanics, there is no such concept as the velocity of a particle in the classical sense of the word, i.e. the limit to which the difference of the co-ordinates at two instants, divided by the interval Δt between these instants, tends as Δt tends to zero. However, we shall see later that in quantum mechanics, nevertheless, a reasonable definition of the velocity of a particle at a given instant can be constructed, and this velocity passes into the classical velocity as we pass to classical mechanics. But whereas in classical mechanics a particle has definite co-ordinates and velocity at any given instant, in quantum mechanics the situation is entirely different. If, as a result of measurement, the electron is found to have definite co-ordinates, then it has no definite velocity whatever. Conversely, if the electron has a definite velocity, it cannot have a definite position in space. For the simultaneous existence of the co-ordinates and velocity would mean the existence of a definite path, which the electron has not. Thus, in quantum mechanics, the co-ordinates and velocity of an electron are quantities which cannot be simultaneously measured exactly, i.e. they cannot simultaneously have definite values. We may say that the co-ordinates and velocity of the electron are quantities which do not exist simultaneously. In what follows we shall derive the quantitative relation which determines the possibility of an inexact measurement of the co-ordinates and velocity at the same instant.

A complete description of the state of a physical system in classical mechanics is effected by stating all its co-ordinates and velocities at a given instant; with these initial data, the equations of motion completely determine the behaviour of the system at all subsequent instants. In quantum mechanics such a description is in principle impossible, since the co-ordinates and the corresponding velocities cannot exist simultaneously. Thus a description of the state of a quantum system is effected by means of a smaller number of quantities than in classical mechanics, i.e. it is less detailed than a classical description.

A very important consequence follows from this regarding the nature of the predictions made in quantum mechanics. Whereas a classical description suffices to predict the future motion of a mechanical system with complete accuracy, the less detailed description given in quantum mechanics evidently cannot be enough to do this. This means that, even if an electron is in a state described in the most complete manner possible in quantum mechanics, its behaviour at subsequent instants is still in principle uncertain. Hence quantum mechanics cannot make completely definite predictions concerning the future behaviour of the electron. For a given initial state of the electron, a subsequent measurement can give various results. The typical problem in quantum mechanics consists in determining the probability of obtaining various results on performing this measurement. It is understood, of course, that in some cases the probability of a given result of measurement may be equal to unity, i.e. certainty, so that the result of that measurement is unique.

All measuring processes in quantum mechanics may be divided into two classes. In one, which contains the majority of measurements, we find those which do not, in any state of the system, lead with certainty to a unique result. The other class contains measurements such that for every possible result of measurement there is a state in which the measurement leads with certainty to that result. These latter measurements, which may be called *predictable*, play an important part in quantum mechanics. The quantitative characteristics of a state which are determined by such measurements are what are called *physical quantities* in quantum mechanics. If in some state a measurement gives with certainty a unique result, we shall say that in this state the corresponding physical quantity has a definite value. In future we shall always understand the expression "physical quantity" in the sense given here.

We shall often find in what follows that by no means every assembly of physical quantities in quantum mechanics can be measured simultaneously, i.e. can all have definite values at the same time. We have already mentioned one example, namely the velocity and co-ordinates of an electron. An important part is played in quantum mechanics by assemblies of physical quantities having the following property: these quantities can be measured simultaneously, but if they simultaneously have definite values, no other physical quantity (not being a function of these) can have a definite value in that state. We shall speak of such assemblies of physical quantities as *complete assemblies*; in particular cases a complete assembly may consist of only one quantity.

Any description of the state of an electron arises as a result of some measurement. We shall now formulate the meaning of a *complete description* of a state in quantum mechanics. Completely described states occur as a result of the simultaneous measurement of a complete assembly of physical quantities. From the results of such a measurement we can, in particular, determine the probability of various results of any subsequent measurement, regardless of the history of the electron prior to the first measurement.

In quantum mechanics we need concern ourselves in practice only with completely described states, and from now on (except in §12) we shall understand by the states of a quantum system just these completely described states.

§2. The principle of superposition

Passing now to an exposition of the fundamental mathematical formalism of quantum mechanics, we shall denote by q the set of co-ordinates of a quantum system, and by $\mathrm{d}q$ the product of the differentials of these co-ordinates. This $\mathrm{d}q$ is often called an element of volume in the *configuration space* of the system; for one particle, $\mathrm{d}q$ coincides with an element of volume $\mathrm{d}V$ in ordinary space.

The basis of the mathematical formalism of quantum mechanics lies in the fact that any state of a system can be described, at a given moment, by a definite (in general complex) function $\Psi(q)$ of the co-ordinates. The square of the modulus of this function determines the probability distribution of the values of the co-ordinates: $|\Psi|^2\mathrm{d}q$ is the probability that a measurement performed on the system will find the values of the co-ordinates to be in the element $\mathrm{d}q$ of configuration space. The function Ψ is called the *wave function* of the system (sometimes also the *probability amplitude*).†

A knowledge of the wave function allows us, in principle, to calculate the probability of the various results of any other measurement (not of the co-ordinates) also. All these probabilities are determined by expressions bilinear in Ψ and Ψ^*. The most general form of such an expression is

$$\iint \Psi(q)\,\Psi^*(q')\,\phi(q, q')\,\mathrm{d}q\mathrm{d}q', \tag{2.1}$$

where the function $\phi(q, q')$ depends on the nature and the result of the measurement, and the integration is extended over all configuration space. The probability $\Psi\Psi^*$ of various values of the co-ordinates is itself an expression of this type.‡

The state of the system, and with it the wave function, in general varies with time. In this sense the wave function can be regarded as a function of time also. If the wave function is known at some initial instant, then, from the very meaning of the concept of complete description of a state, it is in principle determined at every succeeding instant. The actual dependence of the wave function on time is determined by equations which will be derived later.

The sum of the probabilities of all possible values of the co-ordinates of the system must, by definition, be equal to unity. It is therefore necessary that the result of integrating $|\Psi|^2$ over all configuration space should be equal to unity:

$$\int |\Psi|^2\,\mathrm{d}q = 1. \tag{2.2}$$

This equation is what is called the *normalisation condition* for wave functions. If the integral of $|\Psi|^2$ converges, then by choosing an appropriate constant coefficient the function Ψ can always be, as we say, *normalised*. Sometimes,

† It was first introduced into quantum mechanics by SCHRÖDINGER in 1926.

‡ It is obtained from (2.1) when $\phi(q, q') = \delta(q-q_0)\,\delta(q'-q_0)$, where δ denotes the *delta function*, defined in §5 below; q_0 denotes the value of the co-ordinates whose probability is required.

however, wave functions are used which are not normalised; moreover, we shall see later that the integral of $|\Psi|^2$ may diverge, and then Ψ cannot be normalised by the condition (2.2). In such cases $|\Psi|^2$ does not, of course, determine the absolute values of the probability of the co-ordinates, but the ratio of the values of $|\Psi|^2$ at two different points of configuration space determines the relative probability of the corresponding values of the co-ordinates.

Since all quantities calculated by means of the wave function, and having a direct physical meaning, are of the form (2.1), in which Ψ appears multiplied by Ψ^*, it is clear that the normalised wave function is determined only to within a constant *phase factor* of the form $e^{i\alpha}$ (where α is any real number), whose modulus is unity. This indeterminacy is in principle irremovable; it is, however, unimportant, since it has no effect upon any physical results.

The positive content of quantum mechanics is founded on a series of propositions concerning the properties of the wave function. These are as follows.

Suppose that, in a state with wave function $\Psi_1(q)$, some measurement leads with certainty to a definite result (result 1), while in a state with $\Psi_2(q)$ it leads to result 2. Then it is assumed that every linear combination of Ψ_1 and Ψ_2, i.e. every function of the form $c_1\Psi_1+c_2\Psi_2$ (where c_1 and c_2 are constants) gives a state in which that measurement leads to either result 1 or result 2. Moreover, we can assert that, if we know the time dependence of the states, which for the one case is given by the function $\Psi_1(q, t)$, and for the other by $\Psi_2(q, t)$, then any linear combination also gives a possible dependence of a state on time. These propositions can be immediately generalised to any number of different states.

The above set of assertions regarding wave functions constitutes what is called the *principle of superposition of states*, the chief positive principle of quantum mechanics. In particular, it follows at once from this principle that all equations satisfied by wave functions must be linear in Ψ.

Let us consider a system composed of two parts, and suppose that the state of this system is given in such a way that each of its parts is completely described.† Then we can say that the probabilities of the co-ordinates q_1 of the first part are independent of the probabilities of the co-ordinates q_2 of the second part, and therefore the probability distribution for the whole system should be equal to the product of the probabilities of its parts. This means that the wave function $\Psi_{12}(q_1, q_2)$ of the system can be represented in the form of a product of the wave functions $\Psi_1(q_1)$ and $\Psi_2(q_2)$ of its parts:

$$\Psi_{12}(q_1, q_2) = \Psi_1(q_1)\Psi_2(q_2). \tag{2.3}$$

If the two parts do not interact, then this relation between the wave function of the system and those of its parts will be maintained at future instants also,

† This, of course, means that the state of the whole system is completely described also. However, we emphasise that the converse statement is by no means true: a complete description of the state of the whole system does not in general completely determine the states of its individual parts (see also §12).

i.e. we can write

$$\Psi_{12}(q_1, q_2, t) = \Psi_1(q_1, t)\,\Psi_2(q_2, t). \tag{2.4}$$

§3. Operators

Let us consider some physical quantity f which characterises the state of a quantum system. Strictly, we should speak in the following discussion not of one quantity, but of a complete assembly of them at the same time. However, the discussion is not essentially changed by this, and for brevity and simplicity we shall work below in terms of only one physical quantity.

The values which a given physical quantity can take are called in quantum mechanics its *eigenvalues*, and the set of these is referred to as the *spectrum of eigenvalues* of the given quantity. In classical mechanics, generally speak ing, quantities run through a continuous series of values. In quantum mechanics also there are physical quantities (for instance, the co-ordinates) whose eigenvalues occupy a continuous range; in such cases we speak of a *continuous spectrum* of eigenvalues. As well as such quantities, however, there exist in quantum mechanics others whose eigenvalues form some discrete set; in such cases we speak of a *discrete spectrum.*

We shall suppose for simplicity that the quantity f considered here has a discrete spectrum; the case of a continuous spectrum will be discussed in §5. The eigenvalues of the quantity f are denoted by f_n, where the suffix n takes the values 1, 2, 3, ... We also denote the wave function of the system, in the state where the quantity f has the value f_n, by Ψ_n. The wave functions Ψ_n are called the *eigenfunctions* of the given physical quantity f. Each of these functions is supposed normalised, so that

$$\int |\Psi_n|^2 \, dq = 1. \tag{3.1}$$

If the system is in some arbitrary state with wave function Ψ, a measurement of the quantity f carried out on it will give as a result one of the eigenvalues f_n. In accordance with the principle of superposition, we can assert that the wave function Ψ must be a linear combination of those eigenfunctions Ψ_n which correspond to the values f_n that can be obtained, with probability different from zero, when a measurement is made on the system and it is in the state considered. Hence, in the general case of an arbitrary state, the function Ψ can be represented in the form of a series

$$\Psi = \Sigma\, a_n \Psi_n, \tag{3.2}$$

where the summation extends over all n, and the a_n are some constant coefficients.

Thus we reach the conclusion that any wave function can be, as we say, expanded in terms of the eigenfunctions of any physical quantity. A set of functions in terms of which such an expansion can be made is called a *complete* (or *closed*) *set.*

The expansion (3.2) makes it possible to determine the probability of finding (i.e. the probability of getting the corresponding result on measurement), in a system in a state with wave function Ψ, any given value f_n of the quantity f. In fact, according to what was said in the previous section, these probabilities must be determined by some expressions bilinear in Ψ and Ψ^*, and therefore must be bilinear in a_n and a_n^*. Furthermore, these expressions must, of course, be positive. Finally, the probability of the value f_n must become unity if the system is in a state with wave function $\Psi = \Psi_n$, and must become zero if there is no term containing Ψ_n in the expansion (3.2) of the wave function Ψ. This means that the required probability must be unity if all the coefficients a_n except one (with the given n) are zero, that one being unity; the probability must be zero, if the a_n concerned is zero. The only essentially positive quantity satisfying these conditions is the square of the modulus of the coefficient a_n. Thus we reach the result that the squared modulus $|a_n|^2$ of each coefficient in the expansion (3.2) determines the probability of the corresponding value f_n of the quantity f in the state with wave function Ψ. The sum of the probabilities of all possible values f_n must be equal to unity; in other words, the relation

$$\Sigma\, |a_n|^2 = 1 \tag{3.3}$$

must hold.

If the function Ψ were not normalised, then the relation (3.3) would not hold either. The sum $\Sigma\, |a_n|^2$ would then be given by some expression bilinear in Ψ and Ψ^*, and becoming unity when Ψ was normalised. Only the integral $\int \Psi\Psi^*\, dq$ is such an expression. Thus the equation

$$\sum_n a_n a_n^* = \int \Psi\Psi^*\, dq \tag{3.4}$$

must hold.

On the other hand, multiplying by Ψ the expansion $\Psi^* = \Sigma\, a_n^* \Psi_n^*$ of he function Ψ^* (the complex conjugate of Ψ), and integrating, we obtain

$$\int \Psi\Psi^*\, dq = \sum_n a_n^* \int \Psi_n^* \Psi\, dq.$$

Comparing this with (3.4), we have

$$\sum_n a_n a_n^* = \sum_n a_n^* \int \Psi_n^* \Psi\, dq,$$

from which we derive the following formula determining the coefficients a_n in the expansion of the function Ψ in terms of the eigenfunctions Ψ_n:

$$a_n = \int \Psi\Psi_n^*\, dq. \tag{3.5}$$

If we substitute here from (3.2), we obtain

$$a_n = \sum_m a_m \int \Psi_m \Psi_n^*\, dq,$$

from which it is evident that the eigenfunctions must satisfy the conditions

$$\int \Psi_m \Psi_n^* \, dq = \delta_{nm}, \tag{3.6}$$

where $\delta_{nm} = 1$ for $n = m$ and $\delta_{nm} = 0$ for $n \neq m$. The fact that the integrals of the products $\Psi_m \Psi_n^*$ with $m \neq n$ vanish is called the *orthogonality* of the functions Ψ_n. Thus the set of eigenfunctions Ψ_n forms a complete system of normalised and orthogonal functions.

We shall now introduce the concept of the *mean value* $\bar{f}$ of the quantity f in the given state. In accordance with the usual definition of mean values, we define $\bar{f}$ as the sum of all the eigenvalues f_n of the given quantity, each multiplied by the corresponding probability $|a_n|^2$. Thus

$$\bar{f} = \sum_n f_n |a_n|^2. \tag{3.7}$$

We shall write $\bar{f}$ in the form of an expression which does not contain the coefficients a_n in the expansion of the function Ψ, but this function itself. Since the products $a_n a_n^*$ appear in (3.7), it is clear that the required expression must be bilinear in Ψ and Ψ^*. We introduce some mathematical operator, which we denote† by $\hat{f}$ and define as follows. Let $(\hat{f}\Psi)$ denote the result of the operator $\hat{f}$ acting on the function Ψ. We define $\hat{f}$ in such a way that the integral of the product of $(\hat{f}\Psi)$ and the complex conjugate function Ψ^* is equal to the mean value $\bar{f}$:

$$\bar{f} = \int \Psi^* (\hat{f}\Psi) \, dq. \tag{3.8}$$

It is easily seen that, in the general case, the operator $\hat{f}$ is some linear‡ integral operator. For, using the expression (3.5) for a_n, we can rewrite the definition (3.7) of the mean value in the form

$$\bar{f} = \sum_n f_n a_n a_n^* = \int \Psi^* \left(\sum_n a_n f_n \Psi_n\right) dq.$$

Comparing this with (3.8), we see that the result of the operator $\hat{f}$ acting on the function Ψ has the form

$$(\hat{f}\Psi) = \sum_n a_n f_n \Psi_n. \tag{3.9}$$

If we substitute here the expression (3.5) for a_n, we find that $\hat{f}$ is an integral operator of the form

$$(\hat{f}\Psi) = \int K(q, q') \Psi(q') \, dq', \tag{3.10}$$

where the function $K(q, q')$ (called the *kernel* of the operator) is

$$K(q, q') = \sum_n f_n \Psi_n^*(q') \Psi_n(q). \tag{3.11}$$

---

† By convention, we shall always denote operators by letters with circumflexes.

‡ An operator is said to be *linear* if it has the properties

$$\hat{f}(\Psi_1 + \Psi_2) = \hat{f}\Psi_1 + \hat{f}\Psi_2 \text{ and } \hat{f}(a\Psi) = a\hat{f}\Psi,$$

where Ψ_1 and Ψ_2 are arbitrary functions and a is an arbitrary constant.

Thus, for every physical quantity in quantum mechanics, there is a definite corresponding linear operator.

It is seen from (3.9) that, if the function Ψ is one of the eigenfunctions Ψ_n (so that all the a_n except one are zero), then, when the operator $\hat{f}$ acts on it, this function is simply multiplied by the corresponding eigenvalue f_n:

$$\hat{f}\Psi_n = f_n\Psi_n. \tag{3.12}$$

(In what follows we shall always omit the parentheses in the expression $(\hat{f}\Psi)$, where this cannot cause any misunderstanding; the operator is taken to act on the expression which follows it.) Thus we can say that the eigenfunctions of the given physical quantity f are the solutions of the equation

$$\hat{f}\Psi = f\Psi,$$

where f is a constant, and the eigenvalues are the values of this constant for which the above equation has solutions satisfying the required conditions. Of course, while the operator $\hat{f}$ is still defined only by the expressions (3.10) and (3.11), which themselves contain the eigenfunctions Ψ_n, no further conclusions can be drawn from the result we have obtained. However, as we shall see below, the form of the operators for various physical quantities can be determined from direct physical considerations, and then the above property of the operators enables us to find the eigenfunctions and eigenvalues by solving the equations $\hat{f}\Psi = f\Psi$.

The values which can be taken by real physical quantities are obviously real. Hence the mean value of a physical quantity must also be real, in any state. Conversely, if the mean value of a physical quantity is real in every state, its eigenvalues also are all real; to show this, it is sufficient to note that the mean values coincide with the eigenvalues in the states described by the functions Ψ_n.

From the fact that the mean values are real, we can draw some conclusions concerning the properties of operators. Equating the expression (3.8) to its complex conjugate, we obtain the relation

$$\int \Psi^*\hat{f}\Psi \, dq = \int \Psi\hat{f}^*\Psi^* \, dq, \tag{3.13}$$

where $\hat{f}^*$ denotes an operator which is the complex conjugate of $\hat{f}$†. This relation does not hold in general for an arbitrary linear operator, so that it is a restriction on the form of the operator $\hat{f}$. For an arbitrary operator $\hat{f}$ we can find what is called the *transposed operator* $\tilde{\hat{f}}$, defined in such a way that

$$\int \Psi\hat{f}\Phi \, dq = \int \Phi\tilde{\hat{f}}\Psi \, dq, \tag{3.14}$$

where Ψ and Φ are two different functions. If we take, as the function Φ, the function Ψ^* which is the complex conjugate of Ψ, then a comparison with (3.13) shows that we must have

$$\tilde{\hat{f}} = \hat{f}^*. \tag{3.15}$$

† By definition, if for the operator $\hat{f}$ we have $\hat{f}\psi = \phi$, then the complex conjugate operator $\hat{f}^*$ is that for which we have $\hat{f}^*\psi^* = \phi^*$.

Operators satisfying this condition are said to be *Hermitian*†. Thus the operators corresponding, in the mathematical formalism of quantum mechanics, to real physical quantities must be Hermitian.

We can formally consider complex physical quantities also, i.e. those whose eigenvalues are complex. Let f be such a quantity. Then we can introduce its complex conjugate quantity f^*, whose eigenvalues are the complex conjugates of those of f. We denote by $\hat{f}^+$ the operator corresponding to the quantity f^*. It is called the *Hermitian conjugate* of the operator $\hat{f}$ and, in general, will be different from the complex conjugate operator $\hat{f}^*$: from the condition $\overline{f^*} = (\bar{f})^*$ we find at once that

$$\hat{f}^+ = \tilde{\hat{f}}^*, \tag{3.16}$$

from which it is clear that $\hat{f}^+$ is in general not the same as $\hat{f}^*$. For a real physical quantity $\hat{f} = \hat{f}^+$, i.e. the operator is the same as its Hermitian conjugate (Hermitian operators are also called *self-conjugate*).

We shall show how the orthogonality of the eigenfunctions of a Hermitian operator corresponding to different eigenvalues can be directly proved. Let f_n and f_m be two different eigenvalues of the quantity f, and Ψ_n, Ψ_m the corresponding eigenfunctions:

$$\hat{f}\Psi_n = f_n\Psi_n, \quad \hat{f}\Psi_m = f_m\Psi_m.$$

Multiplying both sides of the first of these equations by Ψ_m^*, and both sides of the complex conjugate of the second by Ψ_n, and subtracting corresponding terms, we find

$$\Psi_m^*\hat{f}\Psi_n - \Psi_n\hat{f}^*\Psi_m^* = (f_n - f_m)\Psi_n\Psi_m^*.$$

We integrate both sides of this equation over q. Since $\hat{f}^* = \tilde{\hat{f}}$, by (3.14) the integral on the left-hand side of the equation is zero, so that we have

$$(f_n - f_m)\int \Psi_n\Psi_m^*\, dq = 0,$$

whence, since $f_n \neq f_m$, we obtain the required orthogonality property of the functions Ψ_n and Ψ_m.

We have spoken here of only one physical quantity f, whereas, as we said at the beginning of this section, we should have spoken of a complete system of physical quantities. We should then have found that to each of these quantities $f, g, \ldots$ there corresponds its operator $\hat{f}, \hat{g}, \ldots$. The eigenfunctions Ψ_n then correspond to states in which all the quantities concerned have definite values, i.e. they correspond to definite sets of eigenvalues $f_n, g_n, \ldots$, and are simultaneous solutions of the system of equations

$$\hat{f}\Psi = f\Psi, \quad \hat{g}\Psi = g\Psi, \ldots.$$

† For a linear integral operator of the form (3.10), the Hermitian condition means that the kernel of the operator must be such that $K(q, q') = K^*(q', q)$.

§4. Addition and multiplication of operators

Let f and g be two physical quantities which can simultaneously take definite values, and $\hat{f}$ and $\hat{g}$ their operators. The eigenvalues of the sum $f+g$ of these quantities are equal to the sums of the eigenvalues of f and g. To this new quantity $f+g$ there will obviously correspond an operator equal to the sum of the operators $\hat{f}$ and $\hat{g}$. For, if Ψ_n are the eigenfunctions common to the operators $\hat{f}$ and $\hat{g}$, then it follows from $\hat{f}\Psi_n = f_n\Psi_n$, $\hat{g}\Psi_n = g_n\Psi_n$ that

$$(\hat{f}+\hat{g})\Psi_n = (f_n+g_n)\Psi_n,$$

i.e. the eigenvalues of the operator $\hat{f}+\hat{g}$ are equal to the sums f_n+g_n.

If the quantities f and g cannot simultaneously take definite values, then it is meaningless to speak of their sum in the direct sense just mentioned. It is conventional in quantum mechanics to define the *sum* of the quantities f and g in such cases as the quantity whose mean value in an arbitrary state is equal to the sum of the mean values $\bar{f}$ and $\bar{g}$:

$$\overline{f+g} = \bar{f} + \bar{g}. \tag{4.1}$$

It is clear that, to the quantity $f+g$ so defined, there corresponds an operator $\hat{f}+\hat{g}$. For, by formula (3.8), we have

$$\overline{f+g} = \int \Psi^*(\hat{f}+\hat{g})\Psi \, dq = \int \Psi^*\hat{f}\Psi \, dq + \int \Psi^*\hat{g}\Psi \, dq = \bar{f}+\bar{g}.$$

The eigenvalues and eigenfunctions of the operator $\hat{f}+\hat{g}$ will not, in general, now bear any relation to those of the quantities f and g. It is evident that, if the operators $\hat{f}$ and $\hat{g}$ are self-conjugate, the operator $\hat{f}+\hat{g}$ will be so too, so that its eigenvalues are real and are those of the new quantity $f+g$ thus determined.

The following theorem should be noted. Let f_0 and g_0 be the smallest eigenvalues of the quantities f and g, and $(f+g)_0$ that of the quantity $f+g$. Then

$$(f+g)_0 \geqslant f_0+g_0. \tag{4.2}$$

The equality holds if f and g can be measured simultaneously. The proof follows from the obvious fact that the mean value of a quantity is always greater than or equal to its least eigenvalue. In a state in which the quantity $f+g$ has the value $(f+g)_0$ we have $\overline{f+g} = (f+g)_0$, and since, on the other hand, $\overline{f+g} = \bar{f}+\bar{g} \geqslant f_0+g_0$, we arrive at the inequality (4.2).

Next, let f and g once more be quantities that can be measured simultaneously. Besides their sum, we can also introduce the concept of their *product* as being a quantity whose eigenvalues are equal to the product of those of the quantities f and g. It is easy to see that, to this quantity, there corresponds an operator whose effect consists of the successive action on the function of first one and then the other operator. Such an operator is represented mathematically by the product of the operators $\hat{f}$ and $\hat{g}$. In fact, if Ψ_n are the eigenfunctions common to the operators $\hat{f}$ and $\hat{g}$, we have

$$\hat{f}\hat{g}\Psi_n = \hat{f}(\hat{g}\Psi_n) = \hat{f}g_n\Psi_n = g_n\hat{f}\Psi_n = g_n f_n \Psi_n$$

(the symbol $\hat{f}\hat{g}$ denotes an operator whose effect on a function Ψ consists of the successive action first of the operator $\hat{g}$ on the function Ψ and then of the operator $\hat{f}$ on the function $\hat{g}\Psi$). We could equally well take the operator $\hat{g}\hat{f}$ instead of $\hat{f}\hat{g}$, the former differing from the latter in the order of its factors. It is obvious that the result of the action of either of these operators on the functions Ψ_n will be the same. Since, however, every wave function Ψ can be represented as a linear combination of the functions Ψ_n, it follows that the result of the action of the operators $\hat{f}\hat{g}$ and $\hat{g}\hat{f}$ on an arbitrary function will also be the same. This fact can be written in the form of the symbolic equation $\hat{f}\hat{g} = \hat{g}\hat{f}$ or

$$\hat{f}\hat{g} - \hat{g}\hat{f} = 0. \tag{4.3}$$

Two such operators $\hat{f}$ and $\hat{g}$ are said to *commute* with each other. Thus we arrive at the important result: if two quantities f and g can simultaneously take definite values, then their operators commute with each other.

The converse theorem can also be proved (§11): if the operators $\hat{f}$ and $\hat{g}$ commute, then all their eigenfunctions are common to both; physically, this means that the corresponding physical quantities can be measured simultaneously. Thus the commutability of the operators is a necessary and sufficient condition for the physical quantities to be simultaneously measurable.

A particular case of the product of operators is an operator raised to some power. From the above discussion we can deduce that the eigenvalues of an operator $\hat{f}^p$ (where p is an integer) are equal to the pth powers of the eigenvalues of the operator $\hat{f}$.

If the quantities f and g cannot simultaneously take definite values, the concept of their product cannot be defined in the above manner. This appears in the fact that the operator $\hat{f}\hat{g}$ is not self-conjugate in this case, and hence cannot correspond to any physical quantity. In fact, by the definition of the transpose of an operator we can write

$$\int \Psi\hat{f}\hat{g}\Phi \, dq = \int \Psi\hat{f}(\hat{g}\Phi) \, dq = \int (\hat{g}\Phi)(\tilde{\hat{f}}\Psi) \, dq.$$

Here the operator $\tilde{\hat{f}}$ acts only on the function Ψ, and the operator $\hat{g}$ on Φ, so that the integrand is a simple product of two functions $\hat{g}\Phi$ and $\tilde{\hat{f}}\Psi$. Again using the definition of the transpose of an operator, we can write

$$\int \Psi\hat{f}\hat{g}\Phi \, dq = \int (\tilde{\hat{f}}\Psi)(\hat{g}\Phi) \, dq = \int \Phi\tilde{\hat{g}}\tilde{\hat{f}}\Psi \, dq.$$

Thus we obtain an integral in which the functions Ψ and Φ have changed places as compared with the original one. In other words, the operator $\tilde{\hat{g}}\tilde{\hat{f}}$ is the transpose of $\hat{f}\hat{g}$, and we can write

$$\widetilde{\hat{f}\hat{g}} = \tilde{\hat{g}}\tilde{\hat{f}}, \tag{4.4}$$

i.e. the transpose of the product $\hat{f}\hat{g}$ is the product of the transposes of the factors written in the opposite order.

If each of the operators $\hat{f}$ and $\hat{g}$ is Hermitian, then $(\widetilde{\hat{f}\hat{g}})^* = \tilde{\hat{g}}^*\tilde{\hat{f}}^* = \hat{g}\hat{f}$. It follows from this that the operator $\hat{f}\hat{g}$ is Hermitian if and only if the factors $\hat{f}$ and $\hat{g}$ commute.

We note that, from the products $\hat{f}\hat{g}$ and $\hat{g}\hat{f}$ of two non-commuting Hermitian operators, we can form a Hermitian operator by taking the symmetrical combination

$$\tfrac{1}{2}(\hat{f}\hat{g}+\hat{g}\hat{f}).$$

Such expressions are sometimes needed; they are called *symmetrised products*.

It is easy to see that the difference $\hat{f}\hat{g}-\hat{g}\hat{f}$ is an *anti-Hermitian* operator (i.e. one for which the transpose is equal to the complex conjugate taken with the opposite sign). It can be made Hermitian by multiplying by i; thus

$$i(\hat{f}\hat{g}-\hat{g}\hat{f})$$

is again a Hermitian operator.

In what follows we shall sometimes use for brevity the notation

$$\{\hat{f},\hat{g}\} = \hat{f}\hat{g}-\hat{g}\hat{f}. \tag{4.5}$$

It is easily seen that

$$\{\hat{f}\hat{g}, \hat{h}\} = \{\hat{f}, \hat{h}\}\hat{g}+\hat{f}\{\hat{g}, \hat{h}\}. \tag{4.6}$$

We notice that, if $\{\hat{f}, \hat{h}\} = 0$ and $\{\hat{g}, \hat{h}\} = 0$, it does not in general follow that $\hat{f}$ and $\hat{g}$ commute.

§5. The continuous spectrum

All the relations given in §§3 and 4, describing the properties of the eigenfunctions of a discrete spectrum, can be generalised without difficulty to the case of a continuous spectrum of eigenvalues.

Let f be a physical quantity having a continuous spectrum. We shall denote its eigenvalues by the same letter f simply, without suffix, in accordance with the fact that f takes a continuous range of values. We denote by Ψ_f the eigenfunction corresponding to the eigenvalue f. Just as an arbitrary wave function Ψ can be expanded in a series (3.2) of eigenfunctions of a quantity having a discrete spectrum, it can also be expanded (this time as an integral) in terms of the complete set of eigenfunctions of a quantity with a continuous spectrum. This expansion has the form

$$\Psi(q) = \int a_f \Psi_f(q)\, df, \tag{5.1}$$

where the integration is extended over the whole range of values that can be taken by the quantity f.

The subject of the normalisation of the eigenfunctions of a continuous spectrum is more complex than in the case of a discrete spectrum. The requirement that the integral of the squared modulus of the function should be equal to unity cannot here be satisfied, as we shall see below. Instead, we try to normalise the functions Ψ_f in such a way that $|a_f|^2\,df$ is the probability that the physical quantity concerned, in the state described by the wave function Ψ, has a value between f and $f+df$. This is a direct generalisation of the case of a discrete spectrum, where the square $|a_n|^2$ determines the probability of the eigenvalue f_n. Since the sum of the probabilities of all possible values of f must be equal to unity, we have

$$\int |a_f|^2\,df = 1 \tag{5.2}$$

(similarly to the relation (3.3) for a discrete spectrum).

Proceeding in exactly the same way as in the derivation of formula (3.5), and using the same arguments, we can write, firstly,

$$\int \Psi\Psi^*\,dq = \int |a_f|^2\,df$$

and, secondly,

$$\int \Psi\Psi^*\,dq = \iint a_f^*\Psi_f^*\Psi\,df dq.$$

By comparing these two expressions we find the formula which determines the expansion coefficients,

$$a_f = \int \Psi(q)\Psi_f^*(q)\,dq, \tag{5.3}$$

in exact analogy to (3.5).

To derive the normalisation condition, we now substitute (5.1) in (5.3), and obtain

$$a_f = \int a_{f'}\left(\int \Psi_{f'}\Psi_f^*\,dq\right) df'.$$

This relation must hold for arbitrary a_f, and therefore must be satisfied identically. For this to be so, it is necessary that, first of all, the coefficient of $a_{f'}$ under the integral sign (i.e. the integral $\int \Psi_{f'}\Psi_f^*\,dq$) should be zero for all $f' \neq f$. For $f' = f$, this coefficient must become infinite (otherwise the integral over f' would vanish). Thus the integral $\int \Psi_{f'}\Psi_f^*\,dq$ is a function of the difference $f'-f$, which becomes zero for values of the argument different from zero and is infinite when the argument is zero. We denote this function by $\delta(f'-f)$:

$$\int \Psi_{f'}\Psi_f^*\,dq = \delta(f'-f). \tag{5.4}$$

The manner in which the function $\delta(f'-f)$ becomes infinite for $f'-f = 0$ is determined by the fact that we must have

$$\int \delta(f'-f)\,a_{f'}\,df' = a_f.$$

It is clear that, for this to be so, we must have

$$\int \delta(f'-f)\,df' = 1.$$

The function thus defined is called a *delta function*; it is often needed in quantum mechanics. We shall write out once more the formulae which define it. They are

$$\delta(x) = 0 \text{ for } x \neq 0, \quad \delta(0) = \infty, \tag{5.5}$$

while

$$\int_{-\infty}^{\infty} \delta(x)\,dx = 1. \tag{5.6}$$

We can take as limits of integration any numbers such that $x = 0$ lies between them. If $f(x)$ is some function continuous at $x = 0$, then

$$\int_{-\infty}^{\infty} \delta(x)f(x)\,dx = f(0). \tag{5.7}$$

This formula can be written in the more general form

$$\int \delta(x-a)f(x)\,dx = f(a), \tag{5.8}$$

where the range of integration includes the point $x = a$, and $f(x)$ is continuous at $x = a$. It is also evident that $\delta(-x) = \delta(x)$. Finally, writing

$$\int_{-\infty}^{\infty} \delta(\alpha x)\,dx = \int_{-\infty}^{\infty} \delta(y)\frac{dy}{|\alpha|} = \frac{1}{|\alpha|},$$

we can deduce that

$$\delta(\alpha x) = (1/|\alpha|)\,\delta(x). \tag{5.8a}$$

The formula (5.4) gives the normalisation rule for the eigenfunctions of a continuous spectrum; it replaces the condition (3.6) for a discrete spectrum. We see that the functions Ψ_f and $\Psi_{f'}$ with $f \neq f'$ are, as before, orthogonal. However, the integrals of the squared moduli $|\Psi_f|^2$ of the functions diverge for a continuous spectrum.

The functions $\Psi_f(q)$ satisfy still another relation similar to (5.4). To derive this, we substitute (5.3) in (5.1), which gives

$$\Psi(q) = \int \Psi(q')\left(\int \Psi_f^*(q')\Psi_f(q)\,df\right)dq',$$

whence we can at once deduce that we must have

$$\int \Psi_f^*(q')\Psi_f(q)\,df = \delta(q'-q). \tag{5.9}$$

We shall also give here, for future reference, the analogous relation for a discrete spectrum:

$$\sum_n \Psi_n^*(q')\Psi_n(q) = \delta(q'-q). \tag{5.9a}$$

Comparing the pair of formulae (5.1), (5.4) with the pair (5.3), (5.9), we see that, on the one hand, the function $\Psi(q)$ can be expanded in terms of the functions $\Psi_f(q)$ with expansion coefficients a_f and, on the other hand, formula (5.3) represents an entirely analogous expansion of the function $a_f \equiv a(f)$ in terms of the functions $\Psi_f^*(q)$, while the $\Psi(q)$ play the part of expansion coefficients. The function $a(f)$, like $\Psi(q)$, completely determines the state of the system; it is sometimes called a wave function *in the f representation* (while the function $\Psi(q)$ is called a wave function in the q representation). Just as $|\Psi(q)|^2$ determines the probability for the system to have co-ordinates lying in a given interval dq, so $|a(f)|^2$ determines the probability for the values of the quantity f to lie in a given interval df. On the one hand, the functions $\Psi_f(q)$ are the eigenfunctions of the quantity f in the q representation; on the other hand, their complex conjugates are the eigenfunctions of the co-ordinate q in the f representation.

Let $\phi(f)$ be some function of the quantity f, such that ϕ and f are related in a one-to-one manner. Each of the functions $\Psi_f(q)$ can then be regarded as an eigenfunction of the quantity ϕ, corresponding to a value of the latter determined by $\phi = \phi(f)$. Here, however, the normalisation of these functions must be changed. In fact, the eigenfunctions $\Psi_\phi(q)$ of the quantity ϕ must be normalised by the condition

$$\int \Psi_{\phi(f')}\Psi_{\phi(f)}^* \,\mathrm{d}q = \delta[\phi(f')-\phi(f)],$$

whereas the functions $\Psi_{f'}$ are normalised by the condition (5.4). The argument of the delta function becomes zero only for $f' = f$. As f' approaches f, we have $\phi(f')-\phi(f) = [\mathrm{d}\phi(f)/\mathrm{d}f]\,.\,(f'-f)$. By (5.8a) we can therefore write†

$$\delta[\phi(f')-\phi(f)] = \frac{1}{|\mathrm{d}\phi(f)/\mathrm{d}f|}\delta(f'-f). \tag{5.10}$$

Thus the normalisation condition for the functions Ψ_ϕ can be written in the form

$$\int \Psi_{\phi(f')}\Psi_{\phi(f)}^* \,\mathrm{d}q = \frac{1}{|\mathrm{d}\phi(f)/\mathrm{d}f|}\delta(f'-f).$$

Comparing this with (5.4), we see that the functions Ψ_ϕ and Ψ_f are related by

$$\Psi_{\phi(f)} = \frac{1}{\sqrt{|\mathrm{d}\phi(f)/\mathrm{d}f|}}\Psi_f. \tag{5.11}$$

There are also physical quantities which in one range of values have a

† In general, if $\phi(x)$ is some one-valued function (the inverse function need not be one-valued), we have

$$\delta[\phi(x)] = \sum \frac{1}{|\phi'(\alpha_i)|}\delta(x-\alpha_i),$$

where α_i are the roots of the equation $\phi(x) = 0$.

discrete spectrum, and in another a continuous spectrum. For the eigenfunctions of such a quantity all the relations derived in this and the previous sections are, of course, true. It need only be noted that the complete system of functions is formed by combining the eigenfunctions of both spectra. Hence the expansion of an arbitrary wave function in terms of the eigenfunctions of such a quantity has the form

$$\Psi(q) = \sum_n a_n \Psi_n(q) + \int a_f \Psi_f(q)\, df, \tag{5.12}$$

where the sum is taken over the discrete spectrum and the integral over the whole continuous spectrum.

The co-ordinate q itself is an example of a quantity having a continuous spectrum. It is easy to see that the operator corresponding to it is simply multiplication by q. For, since the probability of the various values of the co-ordinate is determined by the square $|\Psi(q)|^2$, the mean value of the co-ordinate is $\bar{q} = \int q|\Psi|^2\, dq$. On the other hand, the mean value of the co-ordinate must be determined by its operator as $\bar{q} = \int \Psi^* \hat{q} \Psi\, dq$. A comparison of the two expressions shows that the operator q is simply multiplication by q; this may be symbolically written in the form†

$$\hat{q} = q. \tag{5.13}$$

The eigenfunctions of this operator must be determined, according to the usual rule, by the equation $q\Psi_{q_0} = q_0 \Psi_{q_0}$, where q_0 temporarily denotes the actual values of the co-ordinate as distinct from the variable q. Since this equation can be satisfied either by $\Psi_{q_0} = 0$ or by $q = q_0$, it is clear that the eigenfunctions which satisfy the normalisation condition are‡

$$\Psi_{q_0} = \delta(q-q_0).$$

§6. The passage to the limiting case of classical mechanics

Quantum mechanics contains classical mechanics in the form of a certain limiting case. The question arises as to how this passage to the limit is made.

In quantum mechanics an electron is described by a wave function which determines the various values of its co-ordinates; of this function we so far know only that it is the solution of a certain linear partial differential equation. In classical mechanics, on the other hand, an electron is regarded as a material particle, moving in a path which is completely determined by the equations of motion. There is an interrelation, somewhat similar to that between

† In future we shall always, for simplicity, write operators which amount to multiplication by some quantity in the form of that quantity itself.

‡ The expansion coefficients for an arbitrary function Ψ in terms of these eigenfunctions are

$$a_{q_0} = \int \Psi(q)\delta(q-q_0)\, dq = \Psi(q_0).$$

The probability that the value of the co-ordinate lies in a given interval dq_0 is

$$|a_{q_0}|^2\, dq_0 = |\Psi(q_0)|^2\, dq_0,$$

as it should be.

quantum and classical mechanics, in electrodynamics between wave optics and geometrical optics. In wave optics, the electromagnetic waves are described by the electric and magnetic field vectors, which satisfy a definite system of linear differential equations, namely Maxwell's equations. In geometrical optics, however, the propagation of light along definite paths, or rays, is considered. Such an analogy enables us to see that the passage from quantum mechanics to the limit of classical mechanics occurs similarly to the passage from wave optics to geometrical optics.

Let us recall how this latter transition is made mathematically. Let u be any of the field components in the electromagnetic wave. It can be written in the form $u = ae^{i\phi}$ (with a and ϕ real), where a is called the *amplitude* and ϕ the *phase* of the wave. The limiting case of geometrical optics corresponds to small wavelengths; this is expressed mathematically by saying that ϕ (called in geometrical optics the *eikonal*) varies by a large amount over short distances; this means, in particular, that it can be supposed large in absolute value.

Similarly, we start from the hypothesis that, to the limiting case of classical mechanics, there correspond in quantum mechanics wave functions of the form $\Psi = ae^{i\phi}$, where a is a slowly varying function and ϕ takes large values. As is well known, the path of a particle can be determined in mechanics by means of the variational principle, according to which what is called the *action S* of a mechanical system must take its least possible value (the *principle of least action*, or *Hamilton's principle*). In geometrical optics the path of the rays is determined by what is called *Fermat's principle*, according to which the *optical path length* of the ray, i.e. the difference between its phases at the beginning and end of the path, must take its least (or greatest) possible value.

On the basis of this analogy, we can assert that the phase ϕ of the wave function, in the limiting (classical) case, must be proportional to the mechanical action S of the physical system considered, i.e. we must have $S = \text{constant} \times \phi$. The constant of proportionality is called *Planck's constant*† and is denoted by $\hbar$. It has the dimensions of action (since ϕ is dimensionless) and, according to the latest measurements, has the value‡

$$\hbar = 1{\cdot}054 \times 10^{-27} \text{ erg sec.}$$

Thus, the wave function of an "almost classical" (or, as we say, *quasi-classical*) physical system has the form

$$\Psi = ae^{iS/\hbar}. \tag{6.1}$$

Planck's constant $\hbar$ plays a fundamental part in all quantum phenomena. Its relative value (compared with other quantities of the same dimensions) determines the "extent of quantisation" of a given physical system. The transition from quantum mechanics to classical mechanics, corresponding to

† It was introduced into physics by M. Planck in 1900.

‡ The constant $\hbar$, which we use everywhere in this book, is, strictly speaking, Planck's constant divided by 2π.

large phase, can be formally described as a passage to the limit $\hbar \to 0$ (just as the transition from wave optics to geometrical optics corresponds to a passage to the limit of zero wavelength, $\lambda \to 0$).

We have ascertained the limiting form of the wave function, but the question still remains how it is related to classical motion in a path. In general, the motion described by the wave function does not tend to motion in a definite path. Its connection with classical motion is that, if at some initial instant the wave function, and with it the probability distribution of the co-ordinates, is given, then at subsequent instants this distribution will change according to the laws of classical mechanics (for a more detailed discussion of this, see the end of §15).

In order to obtain motion in a definite path, we must start from a wave function of a particular form, which is perceptibly different from zero only in a very small region of space (what is called a *wave packet*); the dimensions of this region must tend to zero with $\hbar$. Then we can say that, in the quasi-classical case, the wave packet will move in space along a classical path of a particle.

Finally, quantum-mechanical operators must reduce, in the limit, simply to multiplication by the corresponding physical quantity.

§7. The wave function and measurements

Let us again return to the process of measurement, whose properties have been qualitatively discussed in §1; we shall show how these properties are related to the mathematical formalism of quantum mechanics.

We consider a system consisting of two parts: a classical apparatus and an electron (regarded as a quantum object). The process of measurement consists in these two parts' coming into interaction with each other, as a result of which the apparatus passes from its initial state into some other; from this change of state we draw conclusions concerning the state of the electron. The states of the apparatus are distinguished by the values of some physical quantity (or quantities) characterising it—the "readings of the apparatus". We conventionally denote this quantity by g, and its eigenvalues by g_n; these take in general, in accordance with the classical nature of the apparatus, a continuous range of values, but we shall—merely in order to simplify the subsequent formulae—suppose the spectrum discrete. The states of the apparatus are described by means of quasi-classical wave functions, which we shall denote by $\Phi_n(\xi)$, where the suffix n corresponds to the "reading" g_n of the apparatus, and ξ denotes the set of its co-ordinates. The classical nature of the apparatus appears in the fact that, at any given instant, we can say with certainty that it is in one of the known states Φ_n with some definite value of the quantity g; for a quantum system such an assertion would, of course, be unjustified.

Let $\Phi_0(\xi)$ be the wave function of the initial state of the apparatus (before the measurement), and $\Psi(q)$ some arbitrary normalised initial wave function of the electron (q denoting its co-ordinates). These functions describe the state of the apparatus and of the electron independently, and therefore the initial wave function of the whole system is the product

$$\Psi(q)\Phi_0(\xi). \tag{7.1}$$

Next, the apparatus and the electron interact with each other. Applying the equations of quantum mechanics, we can in principle follow the change of the wave function of the system with time. After the measuring process it may not, of course, be a product of functions of ξ and q. Expanding the wave function in terms of the eigenfunctions Φ_n of the apparatus (which form a complete set of functions), we obtain a sum of the form

$$\sum_n A_n(q)\Phi_n(\xi), \tag{7.2}$$

where the $A_n(q)$ are some functions of q.

The classical nature of the apparatus, and the double role of classical mechanics as both the limiting case and the foundation of quantum mechanics, now make their appearance. As has been said above, the classical nature of the apparatus means that, at any instant, the quantity g (the "reading of the apparatus") has some definite value. This enables us to say that the state of the system apparatus + electron after the measurement will in actual fact be described, not by the entire sum (7.2), but by only the one term which corresponds to the "reading" g_n of the apparatus,

$$A_n(q)\Phi_n(\xi). \tag{7.3}$$

It follows from this that $A_n(q)$ is the wave function of the electron after the measurement.

We shall suppose that the measurement concerned is such that it gives a complete description of the state of the electron. In other words (see §1), in the resulting state the probabilities of all the quantities must be independent of the previous state of the electron (before the measurement). Mathematically, this means that the form of the functions $A_n(q)$ must be determined by the measuring process itself, and does not depend on the initial wave function $\Psi(q)$ of the electron. Thus the A_n must have the form

$$A_n(q) = a_n\phi_n(q),$$

where the ϕ_n are definite functions, which we suppose normalised, and only the constants a_n depend on $\Psi(q)$. By virtue of the linearity of the equations of quantum mechanics, the dependence of the constants a_n on $\Psi(q)$ is determined by some linear operator, and can be written in its most general form as

$$a_n = \int \Psi(q)\Psi_n{}^*(q)\,dq, \tag{7.4}$$

where the $\Psi_n(q)$ are certain functions depending on the process of measurement.

The functions $\phi_n(q)$ are the normalised wave functions of the electron after measurement. Thus we see how the mathematical formalism of the theory reflects the possibility of finding by measurement a state of the electron described by a definite wave function.

If the measurement is made on an electron with a given wave function $\Psi(q)$, the constants a_n have a simple physical meaning: in accordance with the usual rules, $|a_n|^2$ is the probability that the measurement will give the nth result. The sum of the probabilities of all results is equal to unity:

$$\sum_n |a_n|^2 = 1.$$

Substituting here the expression (7.4) for a_n^*, we have

$$\sum_n a_n a_n^* = \int \Psi^*(q) \sum_n a_n \Psi_n(q)\, dq = 1.$$

In order that this equation should hold for an arbitrary normalised function $\Psi(q)$, we must have

$$\Psi(q) = \sum_n a_n \Psi_n(q),$$

i.e. an arbitrary function $\Psi(q)$ can be expanded in terms of the functions $\Psi_n(q)$. This means that the functions $\Psi_n(q)$ form a complete set of normalised and orthogonal functions (cf. the derivation of (3.6)).

If the initial wave function of the electron coincides with one of the functions $\Psi_n(q)$, then the corresponding constant a_n is evidently equal to unity, while all the others are zero. In other words, a measurement made on an electron in the state $\Psi_n(q)$ gives with certainty the nth result.

All these properties of the functions $\Psi_n(q)$ show that they are the eigenfunctions of some physical quantity (denoted by f) which characterises the electron, and the measurement concerned can be spoken of as a measurement of this quantity.

It is very important to notice that the functions $\Psi_n(q)$ do not, in general, coincide with the functions $\phi_n(q)$; the latter are in general not even mutually orthogonal, and do not form a set of eigenfunctions of any operator. This expresses the fact that the results of measurements in quantum mechanics cannot be reproduced. If the electron was in a state $\Psi_n(q)$, then a measurement of the quantity f carried out on it leads with certainty to the value f_n. After the measurement, however, the electron is in a state $\phi_n(q)$ different from its initial one, and in this state the quantity f does not in general take any definite value. Hence, on carrying out a second measurement on the electron immediately after the first, we should obtain for f a value which did not agree with that obtained from the first measurement. To predict (in the sense of calculating probabilities) the result of the second measurement from the known result of the first, we must take from the first measurement the wave function $\phi_n(q)$ of the state in which it resulted, and from the second measurement the wave function $\Psi_n(q)$ of the state whose probability is required. This means that from the equations of quantum mechanics we determine the wave function $\phi_n(q, t)$ which, at the instant when the first measurement is made, is equal to $\phi_n(q)$; the probability of the mth result of the second measurement, made at time t, is then given by the squared modulus of the integral $\int \phi_n(q, t)\Psi_m^*(q)\, dq$.

We see that the measuring process in quantum mechanics has a "two-faced" character: it plays different parts with respect to the past and future of the electron. With respect to the past, it "verifies" the probabilities of the various possible results predicted from the state brought about by the previous measurement. With respect to the future, it brings about a new state (see also §44).

It must be remarked that there is an important exception to the statement that results of measurements cannot be reproduced: the one quantity the result of whose measurement can be exactly reproduced is the co-ordinate. Two measurements of the co-ordinates of an electron, made at a sufficiently small interval of time, must give neighbouring values; if this were not so, it would mean that the electron had an infinite velocity.†

† Mathematically, this is related to the fact that the co-ordinate commutes with the operator of the interaction energy between the electron and the apparatus, since this energy is (in non-relativistic theory) a function of the co-ordinates only.

CHAPTER II

ENERGY AND MOMENTUM

§8. The Hamiltonian operator

THE wave function Ψ completely determines the state of a physical system in quantum mechanics. This means that, if this function is given at some instant, not only are all the properties of the system at that instant described, but its behaviour at all subsequent instants is determined (only, of course, to the degree of completeness which is generally admissible in quantum mechanics). The mathematical expression of this fact is that the value of the derivative $\partial\Psi/\partial t$ of the wave function with respect to time at any given instant must be determined by the value of the function itself at that instant, and, by the principle of superposition, the relation between them must be linear. In the most general form we can write

$$i\,\partial\Psi/\partial t = \hat{L}\Psi,$$

where $\hat{L}$ is some linear operator; the factor i is introduced here for convenience.

We shall derive some properties of the operator $\hat{L}$. Since the integral $\int \Psi\Psi^* \,\mathrm{d}q$ is a constant independent of time, we have

$$\frac{\partial}{\partial t}\int |\Psi|^2 \,\mathrm{d}q = \int \Psi\frac{\partial\Psi^*}{\partial t}\,\mathrm{d}q + \int \Psi^*\frac{\partial\Psi}{\partial t}\,\mathrm{d}q = 0.$$

Substituting here $\partial\Psi/\partial t = -i\hat{L}\Psi$, $\partial\Psi^*/\partial t = i\hat{L}^*\Psi^*$ and using in the first integral the definition of the transpose of an operator, we can write

$$\int \Psi\hat{L}^*\Psi^* \,\mathrm{d}q - \int \Psi^*\hat{L}\Psi \,\mathrm{d}q = \int \Psi^*\tilde{\hat{L}}^*\Psi \,\mathrm{d}q - \int \Psi^*\hat{L}\Psi \,\mathrm{d}q$$

$$= \int \Psi^*(\tilde{\hat{L}}^* - \hat{L})\Psi \,\mathrm{d}q = 0.$$

Since this equation must hold for an arbitrary function Ψ, it follows that we must have identically $\tilde{\hat{L}}^* - \hat{L} = 0$, or

$$\tilde{\hat{L}} = \hat{L}^*.$$

The operator $\hat{L}$ is therefore Hermitian. Let us find the classical quantity to which the operator $\hat{L}$ corresponds. To do this, we use the limiting expression (6.1) for the wave function and write

$$\frac{\partial\Psi}{\partial t} = \frac{i}{\hbar}\frac{\partial S}{\partial t}\Psi;$$

the slowly varying amplitude a need not be differentiated. Comparing this equation with the definition $\partial\Psi/\partial t = -i\hat{L}\Psi$, we see that, in the limiting case, the operator $\hat{L}$ reduces to simply multiplying by $-(1/\hbar)\,\partial S/\partial t$. This means that $-(1/\hbar)\,\partial S/\partial t$ is the physical quantity into which the Hermitian operator $\hat{L}$ passes.

As is well known from mechanics, the derivative $-\partial S/\partial t$ is just HAMILTON's function H for a mechanical system. Thus the operator $\hbar\hat{L}$ is what corresponds in quantum mechanics to HAMILTON's function; this operator, which we shall denote by $\hat{H}$, is called the *Hamiltonian operator* or, more briefly, the *Hamiltonian* of the system. The relation between $\partial\Psi/\partial t$ and Ψ is

$$i\hbar\,\partial\Psi/\partial t = \hat{H}\Psi. \tag{8.1}$$

If the form of the Hamiltonian is known, equation (8.1) determines the wave functions of the physical system concerned. This fundamental equation of quantum mechanics is called the *wave equation*.

Let us consider a physical system consisting of two non-interacting parts, and let q_1 and q_2 be the co-ordinates of these parts. The wave function $\Psi_{12}(q_1, q_2, t)$ of the system can, in this particular case, be written as the product of the wave functions of its parts (see §2):

$$\Psi_{12}(q_1, q_2, t) = \Psi_1(q_1, t)\Psi_2(q_2, t).$$

Differentiating Ψ_{12} with respect to time, we have

$$\frac{\partial\Psi_{12}}{\partial t} = \Psi_2\frac{\partial\Psi_1}{\partial t} + \Psi_1\frac{\partial\Psi_2}{\partial t} = -\frac{i}{\hbar}(\Psi_2\hat{H}_1\Psi_1 + \Psi_1\hat{H}_2\Psi_2),$$

where $\hat{H}_1$ and $\hat{H}_2$ are the Hamiltonians of the parts of the system. Since the operator $\hat{H}_1$ acts only on functions of q_1, the function Ψ_2 may be regarded as a constant with respect to $\hat{H}_1$ and written after it; similarly Ψ_1 may be written after $\hat{H}_2$. Thus we have†

$$i\hbar\,\partial\Psi_{12}/\partial t = (\hat{H}_1 + \hat{H}_2)\Psi_{12}.$$

Consequently, we arrive at the result that the Hamiltonian of a system consisting of two (or more) non-interacting parts is equal to the sum of the Hamiltonians of each of these parts.

§9. The differentiation of operators with respect to time

The concept of the derivative of a physical quantity with respect to time cannot be defined in quantum mechanics in the same way as in classical mechanics. For the definition of the derivative in classical mechanics involves the consideration of the values of the quantity at two neighbouring but distinct instants of time. In quantum mechanics, however, a quantity which at some instant has a definite value does not in general have definite values at subsequent instants; this was discussed in detail in §1.

Hence the idea of the derivative with respect to time must be differently

† The wave equation thus obtained is evidently valid in the general case also, when Ψ_{12} cannot be written as a product $\Psi_1\Psi_2$.

defined in quantum mechanics. It is natural to define the *derivative* $\dot{f}$ of a quantity f as the quantity whose mean value is equal to the derivative, with respect to time, of the mean value $\bar{f}$. Thus we have the definition

$$\bar{\dot{f}} = \dot{\bar{f}}. \tag{9.1}$$

Starting from this definition, it is easy to obtain an expression for the quantum-mechanical operator $\hat{\dot{f}}$ corresponding to the quantity $\dot{f}$. Since $\bar{f} = \int \Psi^* \hat{f} \Psi \, \mathrm{d}q$,

$$\bar{\dot{f}} = \dot{\bar{f}} = \frac{\partial}{\partial t}\int \Psi^* \hat{f} \Psi \, \mathrm{d}q = \int \Psi^* \frac{\partial \hat{f}}{\partial t} \Psi \, \mathrm{d}q + \int \frac{\partial \Psi^*}{\partial t} \hat{f} \Psi \, \mathrm{d}q + \int \Psi^* \hat{f} \frac{\partial \Psi}{\partial t} \, \mathrm{d}q.$$

Here $\partial \hat{f}/\partial t$ is the operator obtained by differentiating the operator $\hat{f}$ with respect to time; $\hat{f}$ may depend on the time as a parameter. Substituting for $\partial \Psi/\partial t$, $\partial \Psi^*/\partial t$ their expressions according to (8.1), we obtain

$$\bar{\dot{f}} = \int \Psi^* \frac{\partial \hat{f}}{\partial t} \Psi \, \mathrm{d}q + \frac{i}{\hbar}\int (\hat{H}^* \Psi^*) \hat{f} \Psi \, \mathrm{d}q - \frac{i}{\hbar}\int \Psi^* \hat{f} (\hat{H} \Psi) \, \mathrm{d}q.$$

Since the operator $\hat{H}$ is Hermitian, we have

$$\int (\hat{H}^* \Psi^*)(\hat{f} \Psi) \, \mathrm{d}q \equiv \int (\hat{f} \Psi)(\hat{H}^* \Psi^*) \, \mathrm{d}q = \int \Psi^* \hat{H} \hat{f} \Psi \, \mathrm{d}q;$$

thus

$$\bar{\dot{f}} = \int \Psi^* \left(\frac{\partial \hat{f}}{\partial t} + \frac{i}{\hbar} \hat{H} \hat{f} - \frac{i}{\hbar} \hat{f} \hat{H} \right) \Psi \, \mathrm{d}q.$$

Since, on the other hand, we must have, by the definition of mean values, $\bar{\dot{f}} = \int \Psi^* \hat{\dot{f}} \Psi \mathrm{d}q$, it is seen that the expression in parentheses under the integral is the required operator $\hat{\dot{f}}$†:

---

† In classical mechanics we have for the total derivative, with respect to time, of a quantity f which is a function of the generalised co-ordinates q_i and momenta p_i of the system

$$\frac{\mathrm{d}f}{\mathrm{d}t} = \frac{\partial f}{\partial t} + \sum_i \left(\frac{\partial f}{\partial q_i} \dot{q}_i + \frac{\partial f}{\partial p_i} \dot{p}_i \right).$$

Substituting, in accordance with HAMILTON's equations, $\dot{q}_i = \partial H/\partial p_i$ and $\dot{p}_i = -\partial H/\partial q_i$, we obtain

$$\mathrm{d}f/\mathrm{d}t = \partial f/\partial t + [H, f],$$

where

$$[H, f] \equiv \sum_i \left(\frac{\partial f}{\partial q_i} \frac{\partial H}{\partial p_i} - \frac{\partial f}{\partial p_i} \frac{\partial H}{\partial q_i} \right)$$

is what is called the *Poisson bracket* for the quantities f and H. On comparing with the expression (9.2), we see that, as we pass to the limit of classical mechanics, the operator $i(\hat{H}\hat{f} - \hat{f}\hat{H})$ reduces in the first approximation to zero, as it should, and in the second approximation (with respect to $\hbar$) to the quantity $\hbar[H, f]$. This result is true also for any two quantities f and g; the operator $i(\hat{f}\hat{g} - \hat{g}\hat{f})$ tends in the limit to the quantity $\hbar[f, g]$, where $[f, g]$ is the Poisson bracket

$$[f, g] \equiv \sum_i \left(\frac{\partial g}{\partial q_i} \frac{\partial f}{\partial p_i} - \frac{\partial g}{\partial p_i} \frac{\partial f}{\partial q_i} \right).$$

This follows at once from the fact that we can always formally imagine a system whose Hamiltonian is $\hat{g}$.

$$\dot{\hat{f}} = \frac{\partial \hat{f}}{\partial t} + \frac{i}{\hbar}(\hat{H}\hat{f} - \hat{f}\hat{H}). \tag{9.2}$$

We notice that, if the operator $\hat{f}$ is independent of time, $\dot{\hat{f}}$ reduces, apart from a constant factor, to the result of commuting the operator $\hat{f}$ with the Hamiltonian.

A very important class of physical quantities is formed by those whose operators do not depend explicitly on time, and also commute with the Hamiltonian, so that $\dot{\hat{f}} = 0$. Such quantities are said to be *conserved*.

If the operator $\dot{\hat{f}}$ is identically zero, then $\bar{\dot{f}} = \dot{\bar{f}} = 0$, that is, $\bar{f}$ is constant. In other words, the mean value of the quantity remains constant in time. We can also assert that, if in a given state the quantity f has a definite value (i.e. the wave function is an eigenfunction of the operator $\hat{f}$), then it will have a definite value (the same one) at subsequent instants also.

§10. Stationary states

If the system is not in a varying external field, its Hamiltonian cannot contain the time explicitly. This follows at once from the fact that, in the absence of an external field (or in a constant external field) all times are equivalent so far as the given physical system is concerned. Since, on the other hand, any operator of course commutes with itself, we reach the conclusion that HAMILTON's function is conserved for systems which are not in a varying external field. As is well known, a HAMILTON's function which is conserved is called the *energy*. Thus we have the law of conservation of energy in quantum mechanics. Here it signifies that, if in a given state the energy has a definite value, this value remains constant in time.

States in which the energy has definite values are called *stationary states* of a system. They are described by wave functions Ψ_n which are the eigenfunctions of the Hamiltonian operator, i.e. which satisfy the equation $\hat{H}\Psi_n = E_n\Psi_n$, where E_n are the eigenvalues of the energy. Correspondingly, the wave equation (8.1) for the function Ψ_n,

$$i\hbar\, \partial\Psi_n/\partial t = \hat{H}\Psi_n = E_n\Psi_n$$

can be integrated at once with respect to time and gives

$$\Psi_n = e^{-(i/\hbar)E_n t}\psi_n(q), \tag{10.1}$$

where ψ_n is a function of the co-ordinates only. This determines the relation between the wave functions of stationary states and the time.

We shall denote by the small letter ψ the wave functions of stationary states without the time factor. These functions, and also the actual eigenvalues of the energy, are determined by the equation

$$\hat{H}\psi = E\psi. \tag{10.2}$$

The stationary state with the smallest possible value of the energy is called the *normal* or *ground state* of the system.

The expansion of an arbitrary wave function Ψ in terms of the wave functions of stationary states has the form

$$\Psi = \sum_n a_n e^{-(i/\hbar)E_n t}\psi_n(q). \tag{10.3}$$

The squared moduli $|a_n|^2$ of the expansion coefficients, as usual, determine the probabilities of various values of the energy of the system.

The probability distribution for the co-ordinates in a stationary state is determined by the squared modulus $|\Psi_n|^2 = |\psi_n|^2$; we see that it is independent of time. The same is true of the mean values

$$\bar{f} = \int \Psi_n^* \hat{f} \Psi_n \, dq = \int \psi_n^* \hat{f} \psi_n \, dq$$

of any physical quantity f (whose operator does not depend explicitly on the time), and therefore of the probabilities of its various values.

As has been said, the operator of any quantity that is conserved commutes with the Hamiltonian. This means that any physical quantity that is conserved can be measured simultaneously with the energy.

Among the various stationary states, there may be some which correspond to the same value of the energy, but differ in the values of some other physical quantities. Such eigenvalues of the energy (or, as we say, *energy levels* of the system), to which several different stationary states correspond, are said to be *degenerate*. Physically, the possibility that degenerate levels can exist is related to the fact that the energy does not in general form by itself a complete assembly of physical quantities.

In particular, it is easy to see that, if there are two conserved physical quantities f and g whose operators do not commute, then the energy levels of the system are in general degenerate. For, let ψ be the wave function of a stationary state in which, besides the energy, the quantity f also has a definite value. Then we can say that the function $\hat{g}\psi$ does not coincide (apart from a constant factor) with ψ; if it did, this would mean that the quantity g also had a definite value, which is impossible, since f and g cannot be measured simultaneously. On the other hand, the function $\hat{g}\psi$ is an eigenfunction of the Hamiltonian, corresponding to the same value E of the energy as ψ:

$$\hat{H}(\hat{g}\psi) = \hat{g}\hat{H}\psi = E(\hat{g}\psi).$$

Thus we see that the energy E corresponds to more than one eigenfunction, i.e. the energy level is degenerate.

It is clear that any linear combination of wave functions corresponding to the same degenerate energy level is also an eigenfunction for that value of the energy. In other words, the choice of the eigenfunctions of a degenerate energy level is not unique. Arbitrarily selected eigenfunctions of a degenerate energy level are not, in general, orthogonal. By a proper choice of linear combinations of them, however, we can always obtain a set of orthogonal (and normalised) eigenfunctions (and this can be done in infinitely many ways; for the number of independent coefficients in a linear transformation of n functions is n^2, while the number of normalisation and orthogonality conditions for n functions is $\frac{1}{2}n(n+1)$, i.e. less than n^2).

These statements concerning the eigenfunctions of a degenerate energy level relate, of course, not only to eigenfunctions of the energy, but also to those of any operator. Thus only those functions are automatically orthogonal which correspond to different eigenvalues of the operator concerned; functions which correspond to the same degenerate eigenvalue are not in general orthogonal.

If the Hamiltonian of the system is the sum of two (or more) parts, $\hat{H} = \hat{H}_1 + \hat{H}_2$, one of which contains only the co-ordinates q_1 and the other only the co-ordinates q_2, then the eigenfunctions of the operator $\hat{H}$ can be written down as products of the eigenfunctions of the operators $\hat{H}_1$ and $\hat{H}_2$, and the eigenvalues of the energy are equal to the sums of the eigenvalues of these operators.

The spectrum of eigenvalues of the energy may be either discrete or continuous. A stationary state of a discrete spectrum always corresponds to a finite motion of the system, i.e. one in which neither the system nor any part of it moves off to infinity. For, with eigenfunctions of a discrete spectrum, the integral $\int |\Psi|^2\, dq$, taken over all space, is finite. This certainly means that the squared modulus $|\Psi|^2$ decreases quite rapidly, becoming zero at infinity. In other words, the probability of infinite values of the co-ordinates is zero; that is, the system executes a finite motion.

For wave functions of a continuous spectrum, the integral $\int |\Psi|^2\, dq$ diverges. Here the squared modulus $|\Psi|^2$ of the wave function does not directly determine the probability of the various values of the co-ordinates, and must be regarded only as a quantity proportional to this probability. The divergence of the integral $\int |\Psi|^2\, dq$ is always due to the fact that $|\Psi|^2$ does not become zero at infinity (or becomes zero insufficiently rapidly). Hence we can say that the integral $\int |\Psi|^2\, dq$, taken over the region of space outside any arbitrarily large but finite closed surface, will always diverge. This means that, in the state considered, the system (or some part of it) is at infinity. For a wave function which is a superposition of the wave functions of various stationary states of a continuous spectrum, the integral $\int |\Psi|^2\, dq$ may converge, so that the system lies in a finite region of space. However, it can be shown that, in course of time, this region moves unrestrictedly, and eventually the system moves off to infinity†. Thus the stationary states of a continuous spectrum correspond to an infinite motion of the system.

† This can be seen as follows. The superposition of wave functions of a continuous spectrum has the form

$$\Psi = \int a_E e^{-(i/\hbar)Et} \psi_E(q)\, dE.$$

The squared modulus of Ψ can be written in the form of a double integral:

$$|\Psi|^2 = \iint a_E a_{E'}^* e^{(i/\hbar)(E'-E)t} \psi_E(q) \psi_{E'}^*(q)\, dE dE'.$$

§11. Matrices

We shall suppose for convenience that the system considered has a discrete energy spectrum; all the relations obtained below can be generalised at once to the case of a continuous spectrum. Let $\Psi = \Sigma a_n \Psi_n$ be the expansion of an arbitrary wave function in terms of the wave functions Ψ_n of the stationary states. If we substitute this expansion in the definition $\bar{f} = \int \Psi^* \hat{f} \Psi \, dq$ of the mean value of some quantity f, we obtain

$$\bar{f} = \sum_n \sum_m a_n^* a_m f_{nm}(t), \tag{11.1}$$

where $f_{nm}(t)$ denotes the integral

$$f_{nm}(t) = \int \Psi_n^* \hat{f} \Psi_m \, dq. \tag{11.2}$$

The set of quantities $f_{nm}(t)$ with all possible n and m is called the ***matrix*** of the quantity f, and each of the $f_{nm}(t)$ is called the ***matrix element***† corresponding to the transition from state n to state m.

The dependence of the matrix elements $f_{nm}(t)$ on time is determined (if the operator $\hat{f}$ does not contain the time explicitly) by the dependence of the functions Ψ_n on time. Substituting for them the expressions (10.1), we find that

$$f_{nm}(t) = f_{nm} e^{i\omega_{nm} t}, \tag{11.3}$$

where

$$\omega_{nm} = (E_n - E_m)/\hbar \tag{11.4}$$

is what is called the *transition frequency* between the states n and m, and the quantities

$$f_{nm} = \int \psi_n^* \hat{f} \psi_m \, dq \tag{11.5}$$

form the matrix of the quantity f which is independent of time, and which is commonly used.‡ We note that the "frequencies" ω_{nm} satisfy the obvious relation

$$\omega_{nm} + \omega_{ml} = \omega_{nl}. \tag{11.6}$$

† The matrix representation of physical quantities was introduced by HEISENBERG in 1925, before SCHRÖDINGER's discovery of the wave equation. "Matrix mechanics" was later developed by M. BORN, W. HEISENBERG and P. JORDAN.

‡ It must be borne in mind that, because of the indeterminacy of the phase factor in normalised wave functions (see §2), the matrix elements f_{nm} (and $f_{nm}(t)$) also are determined only to within a factor of the form $e^{i(\alpha_m - \alpha_n)}$. Here again this indeterminacy has no effect on any physical results.

In some cases, when each of the suffixes n and m has to be written in the form of several letters, we shall use the notation $f_m{}^n$ instead of f_{nm}.

If we average this expression over some time interval T, and then let T tend to infinity, the mean values of the oscillating factors $e^{(i/\hbar)(E'-E)t}$, and therefore the whole integral, tend to zero in the limit. Thus the mean value, with respect to time, of the probability of finding the system at any given point of configuration space tends to zero. This is possible only if the motion takes place throughout infinite space.

We note that, for a function Ψ which is a superposition of functions of a discrete spectrum, we should have

$$\overline{|\Psi|^2} = \sum_n \sum_m a_n a_m^* \overline{e^{(i/\hbar)(E_m - E_n)t}} \psi_n \psi_m^* = \sum_n |a_n \psi_n(q)|^2,$$

i.e. the required probability remains finite on averaging over time.

The matrix elements of the derivative $\dot{f}$ are obtained by differentiating the matrix elements of the quantity f with respect to time; this follows directly from the fact that the mean value $\bar{\dot{f}}$ is equal to $\dot{\bar{f}}$, i.e.

$$\dot{\bar{f}} = \sum_n \sum_m a_n^* a_m \dot{f}_{nm}(t).$$

From (11.3) we thus have for the matrix elements of $\dot{f}$

$$\dot{f}_{nm}(t) = i\omega_{nm} f_{nm}(t) \tag{11.7}$$

or (cancelling the time factor $e^{i\omega_{nm}t}$ from both sides) for the matrix elements independent of time

$$(\dot{f})_{nm} = i\omega_{nm} f_{nm} = (i/\hbar)(E_n - E_m) f_{nm}. \tag{11.8}$$

To simplify the notation in the formulae, we shall derive all our relations below for the matrix elements independent of time; exactly the same relations hold for the matrices which depend on the time.

For the matrix elements of the complex conjugate f^* of the quantity f we obtain, taking into account the definition of the Hermitian conjugate operator,

$$(f^*)_{nm} = \int \psi_n^* \hat{f}^+ \psi_m \, dq = \int \psi_n^* \tilde{\hat{f}}^* \psi_m \, dq = \int \psi_m \hat{f}^* \psi_n^* \, dq$$

or

$$(f^*)_{nm} = (f_{mn})^*. \tag{11.9}$$

For real physical quantities, which are the only ones we usually consider, we consequently have

$$f_{nm} = f_{mn}^* \tag{11.10}$$

(f_{mn}^* stands for $(f_{mn})^*$). Such matrices, like the corresponding operators, are said to be *Hermitian*.

It is not difficult to obtain the "multiplication rule" for matrices. To do so, we first observe that the formula

$$\hat{f}\psi_n = \sum_m f_{mn}\psi_m \tag{11.11}$$

holds. This is simply the expansion of the function $\hat{f}\psi_n$ in terms of the functions ψ_m, the coefficients being determined in accordance with the general formula (3.5). Remembering this formula, let us write down the result of the product of two operators acting on the function ψ_n:

$$\hat{f}\hat{g}\psi_n = \hat{f}(\hat{g}\psi_n) = \hat{f}\sum_k g_{kn}\psi_k = \sum_k g_{kn}\hat{f}\psi_k = \sum_{k,m} g_{kn} f_{mk}\psi_m.$$

Since, on the other hand, we must have

$$\hat{f}\hat{g}\psi_n = \sum_m (fg)_{mn}\psi_m,$$

we arrive at the result that the matrix elements of the product fg are determined by the formula

$$(fg)_{mn} = \sum_k f_{mk} g_{kn}. \tag{11.12}$$

This rule is the same as that used in mathematics for the multiplication of matrices.

If the matrix is given, then so is the operator itself. In particular, if the matrix is given, it is in principle possible to determine the eigenvalues of the physical quantity concerned and the corresponding eigenfunctions.

We shall now consider the values of all quantities at some definite instant, and expand an arbitrary wave function Ψ (at that instant) in terms of the eigenfunctions of HAMILTON's operator $\hat{H}$, i.e. of the wave functions ψ_m of the stationary states (these wave functions are independent of time):

$$\Psi = \sum_m c_m \psi_m, \tag{11.13}$$

where the expansion coefficients are denoted by c_m. We substitute this expansion in the equation $\hat{f}\Psi = f\Psi$ which determines the eigenvalues and eigenfunctions of the quantity f. We have

$$\sum_m c_m(\hat{f}\psi_m) = f \sum_m c_m \psi_m.$$

We multiply both sides of this equation by ψ_n^* and integrate over q. Each of the integrals $\int \psi_n^* \hat{f} \psi_m \, dq$ on the left-hand side of the equation is the corresponding matrix element f_{nm}. On the right-hand side, all the integrals $\int \psi_n^* \psi_m \, dq$ with $m \neq n$ vanish by virtue of the orthogonality of the functions ψ_m, and $\int \psi_n^* \psi_n \, dq = 1$ by virtue of their normalisation. Thus

$$\sum_m f_{nm} c_m = f c_n,$$

or

$$\sum_m (f_{nm} - f\delta_{nm}) c_m = 0, \tag{11.14}$$

where $\delta_{nm} = 0$ for $m \neq n$ and $= 1$ for $m = n$.

Thus we have obtained a system of algebraic homogeneous equations of the first degree (with the c_m as unknowns). As is well known, such a system has solutions different from zero only if the determinant formed by the coefficients in the equations vanishes, i.e. only if

$$|f_{nm} - f\delta_{nm}| = 0.$$

The roots of this equation (in which f is regarded as the unknown) are the possible values of the quantity f. The set of values c_m satisfying the equations (11.14) when f is equal to any of these values determines the corresponding eigenfunction.

If, in the definition (11.5) of the matrix elements of the quantity f, we take as ψ_n the eigenfunctions of this quantity, then from the equation $\hat{f}\psi_n = f_n \psi_n$ we have

$$f_{nm} = \int \psi_n^* \hat{f} \psi_m \, dq = f_m \int \psi_n^* \psi_m \, dq.$$

By virtue of the orthogonality and normalisation of the functions ψ_m, this gives $f_{nm} = 0$ for $n \neq m$ and $f_{mm} = f_m$. Thus only those matrix elements are different from zero for which $m = n$, and each of these is equal to the corresponding eigenvalue of the quantity f. The matrix elements f_{mm} are said to be *diagonal*, and a matrix with only these elements different from zero is said to be put in *diagonal form*. In particular, in the usual representation, with the wave functions of the stationary states as the functions ψ_n, the energy matrix is diagonal (and so are the matrices of all other physical quantities having definite values in the stationary states). In general, the matrix of a quantity f, defined with respect to the eigenfunctions of some operator $\hat{g}$, is said to be the matrix of *f in a representation in which g is diagonal*. We shall always, except where the subject is specially mentioned, understand in future by the matrix of a physical quantity its matrix in the usual representation, in which the energy is diagonal. Everything that has been said above regarding the dependence of matrices on time refers, of course, only to this usual representation.†

By means of the matrix representation of operators we can prove the theorem mentioned in §4: if two operators commute with each other, they have their entire sets of eigenfunctions in common. Let $\hat{f}$ and $\hat{g}$ be two such operators. From $\hat{f}\hat{g} = \hat{g}\hat{f}$ and the matrix multiplication rule (11.12), it follows that

$$\sum_k f_{mk}g_{kn} = \sum_k g_{mk}f_{kn}.$$

If we take the eigenfunctions of the operator $\hat{f}$ as the set of functions ψ_n with respect to which the matrix elements are calculated, we shall have $f_{mk} = 0$ for $m \neq k$, so that the above equation reduces to $f_{mm}g_{mn} = g_{mn}f_{nn}$, or

$$g_{mn}(f_m - f_n) = 0.$$

If all the eigenvalues f_n of the quantity f are different, then for all $m \neq n$ we have $f_m - f_n \neq 0$, so that we must have $g_{mn} = 0$. Thus the matrix g_{mn} is also diagonal, i.e. the functions ψ_n are eigenfunctions of the physical quantity g also. If, among the values f_n, there are some which are equal (i.e. if there are eigenvalues to which several different eigenfunctions correspond), then the matrix elements g_{mn} corresponding to each such group of functions ψ_n are, in general, different from zero. However, linear combinations of the functions ψ_n which correspond to a single eigenvalue of the quantity f are evidently also eigenfunctions of f; one can always choose these combinations in such a way that the corresponding non-diagonal matrix elements g_{mn} are zero, and thus, in this case also, we obtain a set of functions which are simultaneously the eigenfunctions of the operators $\hat{f}$ and $\hat{g}$.

The matrix f_{nm} can be regarded as the operator $\hat{f}$ in the energy representation. For the set of coefficients c_n in the expansion (11.13) in terms of the eigenfunctions ψ_n of the Hamiltonian can be considered (cf. §5) as the wave function in the "*E* representation" (the variable being the suffix n which gives the number of the stationary state). The formula

$$\bar{f} = \sum_n \sum_m c_n^* f_{nm} c_m$$

† Bearing in mind the diagonality of the energy matrix, it is easy to see that equation (11.8) is the operator relation (9.2) written in matrix form.

for the mean value of the quantity f then corresponds to the general expression for the quantum-mechanical mean value of a quantity in terms of its operator and the wave function of the state concerned.

Finally, we shall prove an important theorem concerning the sum of the diagonal elements of a matrix; this sum is called the *trace* of the matrix.† We have

$$\mathrm{tr}\, f \equiv \sum_n f_{nn} = \sum_n \int \psi_n^*(q) \hat{f} \psi_n(q)\, \mathrm{d}q.$$

This expression can be rewritten in the form

$$\sum_n \int \psi_n^*(q')\{\hat{f}\psi_n(q)\}_{q=q'}\, \mathrm{d}q'.$$

The operator $\hat{f}$ here acts only on functions of q. Hence we have

$$\sum_n \psi_n^*(q')\hat{f}\psi_n(q) = \hat{f} \sum_n \psi_n^*(q')\psi_n(q) = \hat{f}\delta(q-q'),$$

using formula (5.9a). Thus we have finally

$$\sum_n f_{nn} = \int \{\hat{f}\delta(q-q')\}_{q=q'}\, \mathrm{d}q'.$$

Since the functions ψ_n do not appear at all in this expression, we reach the conclusion that the trace of a matrix is independent of the choice of the system of functions with respect to which the matrix elements are defined.‡

§12. The density matrix

Let us consider a system which is a part of some closed system. We suppose that the closed system as a whole is in some state described by the wave function $\Psi(q, x)$, where x denotes the set of co-ordinates of the system considered, and q the remaining co-ordinates of the closed system. This function in general does not fall into a product of functions of x and of q alone, so that the system does not have its own wave function.‖

Let f be some physical quantity pertaining to the system considered. Its operator therefore acts only on the co-ordinates x, and not on q. The mean value of this quantity in the state considered is

$$\bar{f} = \iint \Psi^*(q, x)\hat{f}\Psi(q, x)\, \mathrm{d}q\mathrm{d}x. \tag{12.1}$$

We introduce the function $\rho(x', x)$ defined by

$$\rho(x', x) = \int \Psi^*(q, x')\Psi(q, x)\, \mathrm{d}q, \tag{12.2}$$

† This sum may be examined, of course, only if it converges, which we shall assume below to be the case.

‡ We emphasise, however, that the expression we have obtained is essentially a purely symbolic way of writing the trace, and is not suitable for calculating it in practice. This is usually done by passing to a representation in which the matrix of the operator $\hat{f}$ is diagonal.

‖ In order that $\Psi(q, x)$ should (at a given instant) fall into such a product, the measurement as a result of which this state was brought about must completely describe the system considered and the remainder of the closed system separately. In order that $\Psi(q, x)$ should continue to have this form at subsequent instants, it is necessary in addition that these parts of the closed system should not interact (see §2). Neither of these conditions is now assumed.

where the integration is extended only over the co-ordinates q; this function is called the *density matrix* of the system. From the definition (12.2) it is evident that the function is "Hermitian":

$$\rho^*(x, x') = \rho(x', x). \tag{12.3}$$

The "diagonal elements" of the density matrix

$$\rho(x, x) = \int |\Psi(q, x)|^2 \, dq$$

evidently determine the probability distribution for the co-ordinates of the system.

Using the density matrix, the mean value $\bar{f}$ can be written in the form

$$\bar{f} = \int [\hat{f}\rho(x', x)]_{x'=x} \, dx. \tag{12.4}$$

Here $\hat{f}$ acts only on the variable x in the function $\rho(x', x)$; after calculating the result of its action, we put $x' = x$. We see that, if we know the density matrix, we can calculate the mean value of any quantity characterising the system. It follows from this that, by means of $\rho(x', x)$, we can also determine the probabilities of various values of the physical quantities in the system. Thus we reach the conclusion that the state of a system which does not have a wave function can be described by means of a density matrix. This does not contain the co-ordinates q which do not belong to the system concerned, though, of course, it depends essentially on the state of the closed system as a whole.

The description by means of the density matrix is the most general form of quantum-mechanical description of the system. The description by means of the wave function, on the other hand, is a particular case of this, corresponding to a density matrix of the form $\rho(x', x) = \Psi^*(x')\Psi(x)$. The following important difference exists between this particular case and the general one.† For a state having a wave function there are always measuring processes such that they lead with certainty to definite results (mathematically, this means that Ψ is an eigenfunction of some operator). For states having only a density matrix, on the other hand, there are no such measuring processes whose result can be uniquely predicted.

Let us now suppose that the system is closed, or became so at some instant. Then we can derive an equation giving the change in the density matrix with time, similar to the wave equation for the Ψ function. The derivation can be simplified by noticing that the required linear differential equation for $\rho(x', x, t)$ must be satisfied in the particular case where the system has a wave function, i.e.

$$\rho(x', x, t) = \Psi^*(x', t)\Psi(x, t).$$

† States having a wave function are sometimes called "pure" states, as distinct from "mixed" states, which are described by a density matrix.

Differentiating with respect to time and using the wave equation (8.1), we have

$$i\hbar\frac{\partial\rho}{\partial t} = i\hbar\Psi^*(x',t)\frac{\partial\Psi(x,t)}{\partial t}+i\hbar\Psi(x,t)\frac{\partial\Psi^*(x',t)}{\partial t}$$

$$=\Psi^*(x',t)\hat{H}\Psi(x,t)-\Psi(x,t)\hat{H}'^*\Psi^*(x',t),$$

where $\hat{H}$ is the Hamiltonian of the system, acting on a function of x, and $\hat{H}'$ is the same operator acting on a function of x'. The functions $\Psi^*(x', t)$ and $\Psi(x, t)$ can obviously be placed behind the respective operators $\hat{H}$ and $\hat{H}'$, and we thus obtain the required equation:

$$i\hbar\,\partial\rho(x',x,t)/\partial t = (\hat{H}-\hat{H}'^*)\rho(x',x,t). \tag{12.5}$$

Let $\psi_n(x)$ be the time-independent wave functions of the stationary states of the system, i.e. the eigenfunctions of its Hamiltonian. We expand the density matrix in terms of these functions; the expansion consists of a double series in the functions $\Psi_n(x, t)$ and $\Psi_n(x', t)$, which we write in the form

$$\rho(x',x,t) = \sum_m\sum_n a_{mn}\Psi_n^*(x',t)\Psi_m(x,t)$$
$$= \sum_m\sum_n a_{mn}\psi_n^*(x')\psi_m(x)e^{(i/\hbar)(E_n-E_m)t}. \tag{12.6}$$

For the density matrix, this expansion plays a part analogous to that of the expansion (10.3) for wave functions. Instead of the set of coefficients a_n, we have here the double set of coefficients a_{mn}. These clearly have the property of being "Hermitian", like the density matrix itself:

$$a_{nm}^* = a_{mn}. \tag{12.7}$$

For the mean value of some quantity f we have, substituting (12.6) in (12.4),

$$\bar{f} = \sum_m\sum_n a_{mn}\int\Psi_n^*(x,t)\hat{f}\Psi_m(x,t)\,\mathrm{d}x,$$

or

$$\bar{f} = \sum_m\sum_n a_{mn}f_{nm}(t) = \sum_m\sum_n a_{mn}f_{nm}e^{(i/\hbar)(E_n-E_m)t}, \tag{12.8}$$

where f_{mn} are the matrix elements of the quantity f. This expression is similar to formula (11.1).†

The quantities a_{mn} must satisfy certain inequalities. The "diagonal elements" $\rho(x, x)$ of the density matrix, which determine the probability distribution for the co-ordinates, must obviously be positive quantities. It therefore follows from the expression (12.6) (with $x' = x$) that the quadratic form

$$\sum_n\sum_m a_{mn}\xi_n^*\xi_m$$

constructed with the coefficients a_{nm} (where the ξ_n are arbitrary complex quantities) must be positive. This places certain conditions, known from the theory of quadratic forms, on the quantities a_{nm}. In particular, all the

† The description of a system by means of the quantities a_{mn} was introduced independently by L. Landau and F. Bloch in 1927.

"diagonal" quantities must clearly be positive:

$$a_{nn} \geqslant 0, \tag{12.9}$$

and any three quantities a_{nn}, a_{mm} and a_{mn} must satisfy the inequality

$$a_{nn}a_{mm} \geqslant |a_{mn}|^2. \tag{12.10}$$

To the "pure" case, where the density matrix reduces to a product of functions, there evidently corresponds a matrix a_{mn} of the form

$$a_{mn} = a_m a_n^*.$$

We shall indicate a simple criterion which enables us to decide, from the form of the density matrix, whether we are concerned with a "pure" or a "mixed" state. In the pure case we have

$$\begin{aligned}(a^2)_{mn} &= \sum_k a_{mk}a_{kn} \\ &= \sum_k a_k^* a_m a_n^* a_k \\ &= a_m a_n^* \sum_k |a_k|^2 \\ &= a_m a_n^*,\end{aligned}$$

or

$$(a^2)_{mn} = a_{mn},$$

i.e. the density matrix is equal to its own square.

§13. Momentum

Let us consider a system of particles not in an external field. Since all positions in space of such a system as a whole are equivalent, we can say, in particular, that the Hamiltonian of the system does not vary when the system undergoes a parallel displacement over any distance. It is sufficient that this condition should be fulfilled for an arbitrary small displacement.

An infinitely small parallel displacement over a distance $\delta\mathbf{r}$ signifies a transformation under which the radius vectors $\mathbf{r}_a$ of all the particles (a being the number of the particle) receive the same increment $\delta\mathbf{r} : \mathbf{r}_a \to \mathbf{r}_a + \delta\mathbf{r}$. An arbitrary function $\psi(\mathbf{r}_1, \mathbf{r}_2, \dots)$ of the co-ordinates of the particles, under such a transformation, becomes the function

$$\begin{aligned}\psi(\mathbf{r}_1+\delta\mathbf{r}, \mathbf{r}_2+\delta\mathbf{r}, \dots) &= \psi(\mathbf{r}_1, \mathbf{r}_2, \dots) + \delta\mathbf{r} \cdot \sum_a \nabla_a \psi \\ &= (1+\delta\mathbf{r} \cdot \sum_a \nabla_a)\psi(\mathbf{r}_1, \mathbf{r}_2, \dots)\end{aligned}$$

(∇_a denotes a "vector" whose components are the operators $\partial/\partial x_a$, $\partial/\partial y_a$, $\partial/\partial z_a$). The expression in parentheses, i.e.

$$1+\delta\mathbf{r} \cdot \sum_a \nabla_a,$$

can be regarded as the operator of an infinitely small displacement, which converts the function $\psi(\mathbf{r}_1, \mathbf{r}_2, \dots)$ into the function

$$\psi(\mathbf{r}_1+\delta\mathbf{r}, \mathbf{r}_2+\delta\mathbf{r}, \dots).$$

The statement that some transformation does not change the Hamiltonian means that, if we make this transformation on the function $\hat{H}\psi$, the result is the same as if we make it only on the function ψ and then apply the operator $\hat{H}$. Mathematically, this can be written as follows. Let $\hat{O}$ be the operator which effects the transformation in question. Then we have $\hat{O}(\hat{H}\psi) = \hat{H}(\hat{O}\psi)$, whence

$$\hat{O}\hat{H}-\hat{H}\hat{O} = 0,$$

i.e. the Hamiltonian must commute with the operator $\hat{O}$.

In the case considered, the operator $\hat{O}$ is the above-mentioned operator of an infinitely small displacement. Since the unit operator (the operator of multiplying by unity) commutes, of course, with any operator, and the constant factor $\delta\mathbf{r}$ can be taken in front of $\hat{H}$, the condition $\hat{O}\hat{H}-\hat{H}\hat{O} = 0$ reduces here to

$$(\sum_a \nabla_a)\hat{H}-\hat{H}(\sum_a \nabla_a) = 0. \tag{13.1}$$

As we know, the commutability of an operator (not containing the time explicitly) with $\hat{H}$ means that the physical quantity corresponding to that operator is conserved. The quantity whose conservation for a closed system follows from the homogeneity of space is called *momentum*. Thus the relation (13.1) expresses the law of conservation of momentum in quantum mechanics; the operator $\sum \nabla_a$ must correspond, apart from a constant factor, to the total momentum of the system, and each term ∇_a of the sum to the momentum of an individual particle.

The coefficient of proportionality between the operator $\hat{\mathbf{p}}$ of the momentum of a particle and the operator ∇ can be determined by means of the passage to the limit of classical mechanics. Putting $\hat{\mathbf{p}} = c\nabla$ and using the limiting expression (6.1) for the wave function, we have

$$\hat{\mathbf{p}}\Psi = (i/\hbar)\, cae^{(i/\hbar)S}\nabla S = c(i/\hbar)\Psi\nabla S,$$

i.e. in the classical approximation the effect of the operator $\hat{\mathbf{p}}$ reduces to multiplication by $(i/\hbar)c\nabla S$. The gradient ∇S is, as we know from mechanics, the momentum $\mathbf{p}$ of the particle; hence we must have $(i/\hbar)c = 1$, i.e. $c = -i\hbar$.

Thus the operator of the momentum of a particle is $\hat{\mathbf{p}} = -i\hbar\nabla$, or, in components,

$$\hat{p}_x = -i\hbar\partial/\partial x,\quad \hat{p}_y = -i\hbar\partial/\partial y,\quad \hat{p}_z = -i\hbar\partial/\partial z. \tag{13.2}$$

It is easy to see that these operators are Hermitian, as they should be. For, with arbitrary functions $\psi(x)$ and $\phi(x)$ which vanish at infinity, we have

$$\int \phi\hat{p}_x\psi\, dx = -i\hbar\int \phi\frac{\partial\psi}{\partial x}\, dx = i\hbar\int \psi\frac{\partial\phi}{\partial x}\, dx = \int \psi\hat{p}_x{}^*\phi\, dx,$$

and this is the condition that the operator should be Hermitian.

Since the result of differentiating functions with respect to two different variables is independent of the order of differentiation, it is clear that the operators of the three components of momentum commute with one another:

$$\hat{p}_x\hat{p}_y-\hat{p}_y\hat{p}_x = 0,\quad \hat{p}_x\hat{p}_z-\hat{p}_z\hat{p}_x = 0,\quad \hat{p}_y\hat{p}_z-\hat{p}_z\hat{p}_y = 0. \tag{13.3}$$

This means that all three components of the momentum of a particle can simultaneously have definite values.

Let us find the eigenfunctions and eigenvalues of the momentum operators. They are determined by the equations

$$-i\hbar\, \partial\psi/\partial x = p_x\psi, \quad -i\hbar\, \partial\psi/\partial y = p_y\psi, \quad -i\hbar\partial\psi/\partial z = p_z\psi. \tag{13.4}$$

The solution of the first of these equations is

$$\psi = f(y, z)e^{(i/\hbar)p_x x},$$

where f is independent of x. This solution remains finite for all values of x, for any real value of p_x. Thus the eigenvalues of the component p_x of the momentum form a continuous spectrum extending from $-\infty$ to $+\infty$; the same is true, of course, of the components p_y and p_z.

The three equations (13.4) have, in particular, common solutions, which correspond to states with definite values of all three momentum components forming the vector $\mathbf{p}$. These solutions are of the form

$$\psi = Ce^{(i/\hbar)\mathbf{p}\cdot\mathbf{r}}, \tag{13.5}$$

where C is a constant. If all three components of the momentum are given simultaneously, this completely determines the wave function of the particle, as we shall see. In other words, the quantities p_x, p_y, p_z form one of the possible complete assemblies of physical quantities.

Let us determine the normalisation coefficient in (13.5). According to the rule (5.4) for normalising the eigenfunctions of a continuous spectrum, we must have

$$\int \psi_{\mathbf{p}'}\psi_{\mathbf{p}}^* \,\mathrm{d}V = \delta(\mathbf{p}'-\mathbf{p}) \tag{13.6}$$

(where $\mathrm{d}V = \mathrm{d}x\mathrm{d}y\mathrm{d}z$), the integration being extended over all space; $\delta(\mathbf{p}'-\mathbf{p})$ denotes the product of the three delta functions $\delta(p'_x-p_x)$, $\delta(p'_y-p_y)$, $\delta(p'_z-p_z)$. The integration can be immediately effected by means of the formula†

$$(1/2\pi)\int_{-\infty}^{\infty} e^{i\alpha x}\,\mathrm{d}x = \delta(\alpha). \tag{13.7}$$

† The conventional meaning of this formula is that the function on the left-hand side has the property of the delta function expressed by the equation

$$\int_{-\infty}^{\infty} f(x)\delta(x)\,\mathrm{d}x = f(0).$$

This follows from the Fourier integral formula

$$f(x') = (1/2\pi)\iint f(x)e^{i(x-x')\alpha}\,\mathrm{d}x\mathrm{d}\alpha,$$

if we put $x' = 0$.

Separating the real part, we can also write formula (13.7) in the form

$$(1/2\pi)\int_{-\infty}^{\infty} \cos\alpha x\,\mathrm{d}x = \delta(\alpha). \tag{13.7a}$$

We have

$$\int \psi_{\mathbf{p}'}\psi_{\mathbf{p}}^* \,\mathrm{d}V = C^2 \int e^{(i/\hbar)(\mathbf{p}'-\mathbf{p}).\mathbf{r}}\,\mathrm{d}V$$

$$= C^2 \int_{-\infty}^{\infty} e^{(i/\hbar)(p'_x-p_x)x}\,\mathrm{d}x \int_{-\infty}^{\infty} e^{(i/\hbar)(p'_y-p_y)y}\,\mathrm{d}y \int_{-\infty}^{\infty} e^{(i/\hbar)(p'_z-p_z)z}\,\mathrm{d}z$$

$$= C^2(2\pi\hbar)^3\delta(\mathbf{p}'-\mathbf{p}).$$

Hence we see that we must have $C^2(2\pi\hbar)^3 = 1$. Thus the normalised function $\psi_{\mathbf{p}}$ is

$$\psi_{\mathbf{p}} = (2\pi\hbar)^{-3/2}e^{(i/\hbar)\mathbf{p}.\mathbf{r}}. \tag{13.8}$$

The expansion of an arbitrary wave function $\psi(\mathbf{r})$ of a particle in terms of the eigenfunctions $\psi_{\mathbf{p}}$ of its momentum operator is simply the expansion as a Fourier integral:

$$\psi(\mathbf{r}) = \int a(\mathbf{p})\psi_{\mathbf{p}}(\mathbf{r})\,\mathrm{d}\tau_{\mathbf{p}} = (2\pi\hbar)^{-3/2}\int a(\mathbf{p})e^{(i/\hbar)\mathbf{p}.\mathbf{r}}\,\mathrm{d}\tau_{\mathbf{p}} \tag{13.9}$$

(where $\mathrm{d}\tau_{\mathbf{p}} = \mathrm{d}p_x\mathrm{d}p_y\mathrm{d}p_z$). The expansion coefficients $a(\mathbf{p})$ are, according to formula (5.3),

$$a(\mathbf{p}) = \int \psi(\mathbf{r})\psi_{\mathbf{p}}^*(\mathbf{r})\,\mathrm{d}V = (2\pi\hbar)^{-3/2}\int \psi(\mathbf{r})e^{-(i/\hbar)\mathbf{p}.\mathbf{r}}\,\mathrm{d}V. \tag{13.10}$$

The function $a(\mathbf{p})$ can be regarded (see §5) as the wave function of the particle in the "**p** representation"; $|a(\mathbf{p})|^2\,\mathrm{d}\tau_{\mathbf{p}}$ is the probability that the momentum has a value in the interval $\mathrm{d}\tau_{\mathbf{p}}$. The formulae (13.9) and (13.10) give the relation between the wave functions in the two representations.

Just as the operator $\hat{\mathbf{p}}$ corresponds to the momentum, determining its eigenfunctions in the "**r** representation", we can introduce the idea of the operator $\hat{\mathbf{r}}$ of the radius vector of the particle in the "**p** representation". It must be defined so that the mean value of the co-ordinates can be represented in the form

$$\bar{\mathbf{r}} = \int a^*(\mathbf{p})\hat{\mathbf{r}}a(\mathbf{p})\,\mathrm{d}\tau_{\mathbf{p}}. \tag{13.11}$$

On the other hand, this mean value is determined from the wave function $\psi(\mathbf{r})$ by

$$\bar{\mathbf{r}} = \int \psi^*\mathbf{r}\psi\,\mathrm{d}V.$$

Writing $\psi(\mathbf{r})$ in the form (13.9) we have (integrating by parts)†

$$\mathbf{r}\psi(\mathbf{r}) = (2\pi\hbar)^{-3/2}\int \mathbf{r}a(\mathbf{p})e^{(i/\hbar)\mathbf{p}.\mathbf{r}}\,\mathrm{d}\tau_{\mathbf{p}}$$

$$= (2\pi\hbar)^{-3/2}\int i\hbar e^{(i/\hbar)\mathbf{p}.\mathbf{r}}[\partial a(\mathbf{p})/\partial\mathbf{p}]\,\mathrm{d}\tau_{\mathbf{p}}.$$

† The derivative with respect to the vector **p** is understood as the vector whose components are the derivatives with respect to p_x, p_y, p_z.

Using this expression and (13.10), we find

$$\bar{\mathbf{r}} = \int \psi^* \mathbf{r} \psi \, \mathrm{d}V = (2\pi\hbar)^{-3/2} \iint \psi^*(\mathbf{r}) i\hbar [\partial a(\mathbf{p})/\partial \mathbf{p}] e^{(i/\hbar)\mathbf{p}.\mathbf{r}} \, \mathrm{d}\tau_{\mathbf{p}} \mathrm{d}V$$

$$= \int i\hbar a^*(\mathbf{p}) [\partial a(\mathbf{p})/\partial \mathbf{p}] \, \mathrm{d}\tau_{\mathbf{p}}.$$

Comparing with (13.11), we see that the radius vector operator in the "**p** representation" is

$$\hat{\mathbf{r}} = i\hbar \partial/\partial \mathbf{p}. \tag{13.12}$$

The momentum operator in this representation reduces simply to multiplication by **p**.

PROBLEM

Express the operator $\hat{T}_{\mathbf{a}}$ of a parallel displacement over a finite distance **a** in terms of the momentum operator.

SOLUTION. By the definition of the operator $\hat{T}_{\mathbf{a}}$ we must have

$$\hat{T}_{\mathbf{a}} \psi(\mathbf{r}) = \psi(\mathbf{r}+\mathbf{a}).$$

Expanding the function $\psi(\mathbf{r}+\mathbf{a})$ in a Taylor series, we have

$$\psi(\mathbf{r}+\mathbf{a}) = \psi(\mathbf{r}) + \mathbf{a} \,.\, \partial \psi(\mathbf{r})/\partial \mathbf{r} + \dots,$$

or, introducing the operator $\hat{\mathbf{p}} = -i\hbar \nabla$,

$$\psi(\mathbf{r}+\mathbf{a}) = \left[1 + \frac{i}{\hbar}\mathbf{a} \,.\, \hat{\mathbf{p}} + \frac{1}{2}\left(\frac{i}{\hbar}\mathbf{a} \,.\, \hat{\mathbf{p}}\right)^2 + \dots \right] \psi(\mathbf{r}).$$

The expression in brackets is an operator which can be symbolically written in the form

$$\hat{T}_{\mathbf{a}} = e^{(i/\hbar)\mathbf{a}\,.\,\hat{\mathbf{p}}}.$$

This is the required operator of the finite displacement.

§14. Uncertainty relations

Let us derive the rule for commutation between momentum and coordinate operators. Since the result of successively differentiating with respect to one of the variables x, y, z and multiplying by another of them does not depend on the order of these operations, we have

$$\hat{p}_x y - y \hat{p}_x = 0, \quad \hat{p}_x z - z \hat{p}_x = 0, \tag{14.1}$$

and similarly for $\hat{p}_y$, $\hat{p}_z$.

To derive the commutation rule for $\hat{p}_x$ and x, we write

$$(\hat{p}_x x - x \hat{p}_x)\psi = -i\hbar \, \partial(x\psi)/\partial x + i\hbar x \, \partial\psi/\partial x$$

$$= -i\hbar\psi.$$

We see that the result of the action of the operator $\hat{p}_x x - x\hat{p}_x$ reduces to multiplication by $-i\hbar$; the same is true, of course, of the commutation of $\hat{p}_y$ with y and $\hat{p}_z$ with z. Thus we have†

$$\hat{p}_x x - x\hat{p}_x = -i\hbar, \quad \hat{p}_y y - y\hat{p}_y = -i\hbar, \quad \hat{p}_z z - z\hat{p}_z = -i\hbar. \tag{14.2}$$

All the relations (14.1) and (14.2) can be written in the form

$$\hat{p}_i x_k - x_k \hat{p}_i = -i\hbar\delta_{ik} \qquad (i, k = x, y, z). \tag{14.3}$$

Before going on to examine the physical significance of these relations and their consequences, we shall derive two formulae which will be useful later. Let $f(\mathbf{r})$ be some function of the co-ordinates. Then

$$\hat{\mathbf{p}}f(\mathbf{r}) - f(\mathbf{r})\hat{\mathbf{p}} = -i\hbar\nabla f. \tag{14.4}$$

For

$$(\hat{\mathbf{p}}f - f\hat{\mathbf{p}})\psi = -i\hbar[\nabla(f\psi) - f\nabla\psi] = -i\hbar\psi\nabla f.$$

A similar relation holds for the commutation of $\mathbf{r}$ with a "function" $f(\hat{\mathbf{p}})$ of the momentum operator:

$$f(\hat{\mathbf{p}})\mathbf{r} - \mathbf{r}f(\hat{\mathbf{p}}) = -i\hbar\partial f/\partial\mathbf{p}. \tag{14.5}$$

It can be derived in the same way as (14.4) if we calculate in the $\mathbf{p}$ representation, using the expression (13.12) for the co-ordinate operators.

The relations (14.1) and (14.2) show that the co-ordinate of a particle along one of the axes can have a definite value at the same time as the components of the momentum along the other two axes; the co-ordinate and momentum component along the same axis, however, cannot exist simultaneously. In particular, the particle cannot be at a definite point in space and at the same time have a definite momentum $\mathbf{p}$.

Let us suppose that the particle is in some finite region of space, whose dimensions along the three axes are (of the order of magnitude of) Δx, Δy, Δz. Also, let the mean value of the momentum of the particle be $\mathbf{p}_0$. Mathematically, this means that the wave function has the form $\psi = u(\mathbf{r})e^{(i/\hbar)\mathbf{p}_0\cdot\mathbf{r}}$, where $u(\mathbf{r})$ is a function which differs considerably from zero only in the region of space concerned. We expand the function ψ in terms of the eigenfunctions of the momentum operator (i.e. as a Fourier integral). The coefficients $a(\mathbf{p})$ in this expansion are determined by the integrals (13.10) of functions of the form $u(\mathbf{r})e^{(i/\hbar)(\mathbf{p}_0-\mathbf{p})\cdot\mathbf{r}}$. If this integral is to differ considerably from zero, the periods of the oscillatory factor $e^{(i/\hbar)(\mathbf{p}_0-\mathbf{p})\cdot\mathbf{r}}$ must not be small in comparison with the dimensions Δx, Δy, Δz of the region in which the function $u(\mathbf{r})$ is different from zero. This means that $a(\mathbf{p})$ will be considerably different from zero only for values of $\mathbf{p}$ such that $(1/\hbar)(p_{0x}-p_x)\Delta x \lesssim 1$, etc. Since $|a(\mathbf{p})|^2$ determines the probability of the various values of the momentum, the ranges of values of p_x, p_y, p_z in which $a(\mathbf{p})$ differs from zero are just those in which the components of the momentum of the particle may

† These relations, discovered in matrix form by HEISENBERG in 1925, formed the genesis of modern quantum mechanics.

be found, in the state considered. Denoting these ranges by Δp_x, Δp_y, Δp_z, we thus have

$$\Delta p_x \Delta x \sim \hbar, \quad \Delta p_y \Delta y \sim \hbar, \quad \Delta p_z \Delta z \sim \hbar. \tag{14.6}$$

These relations, known as the *uncertainty relations*, were obtained by HEISENBERG.†

We see that, the greater the accuracy with which the co-ordinate of the particle is known (i.e. the less Δx), the greater the uncertainty Δp_x in the component of the momentum along the same axis, and *vice versa*. In particular, if the particle is at some completely definite point in space ($\Delta x = \Delta y = \Delta z = 0$), then $\Delta p_x = \Delta p_y = \Delta p_z = \infty$. This means that all values of the momentum are equally probable. Conversely, if the particle has a completely definite momentum $\mathbf{p}$, then all positions of it in space are equally probable (this is seen directly from the wave function (13.8), whose squared modulus is quite independent of the co-ordinates).

As an example, let us consider a particle in a state described by the wave function

$$\psi = \text{constant} \times e^{(i/\hbar)p_0 x - \alpha x^2/2\hbar} \tag{14.7}$$

(for simplicity, we consider a one-dimensional case, with the wave function depending on only one co-ordinate). The probabilities of the various values of the co-ordinates are

$$|\psi|^2 = \text{constant} \times e^{-\alpha x^2/\hbar},$$

i.e. are distributed about the origin of co-ordinates (the mean value $\bar{x} = 0$) according to a Gaussian law, with a standard deviation $\sqrt{[\overline{(\Delta x)^2}]} = \sqrt{(\hbar/2\alpha)}$ (Δx denotes the difference $x - \bar{x}$)‡. If the expansion coefficients $a(p_x)$ of this function are calculated as a Fourier integral according to the formula

$$a(p_x) = (2\pi\hbar)^{-\frac{1}{2}} \int_{-\infty}^{\infty} \psi(x) e^{-(i/\hbar)p_x x} \, dx,$$

we obtain an expression of the form

$$a(p_x) = \text{constant} \times e^{-(p_0 - p_x)^2/2\hbar\alpha}.$$

The distribution of probabilities of values of the momentum is $|a|^2 = \text{constant} \times e^{-(p_0 - p_x)^2/\hbar\alpha}$, and consequently is also of Gaussian form, with a standard deviation

$$\sqrt{[\overline{(\Delta p_x)^2}]} = \sqrt{(\tfrac{1}{2}\alpha\hbar)}$$

† A very instructive discussion of various Gedanken-experiments, revealing the origin of the uncertainty relations, has been given by N. BOHR and W. HEISENBERG. See N. BOHR, Discussion with EINSTEIN on epistemological problems in atomic physics, in *Albert Einstein: philosopher-scientist*, ed. P. A. SCHILPP, The Library of Living Philosophers, Tudor Publishing Company, New York 1951; W. HEISENBERG, *Die physikalischen Prinzipien der Quantentheorie*, Hirzel, Leipzig 1930.

‡ As is well known, the Gaussian distribution for the probability $w(x)$ of the values of some quantity x has the form

$$w(x) = [2\pi\overline{(\Delta x)^2}]^{-\frac{1}{2}} e^{-(\Delta x)^2/2\overline{(\Delta x)^2}}.$$

(where $\Delta p_x = p_x - p_0$). The product of the standard deviations of co-ordinate and momentum is thus

$$\sqrt{[\overline{(\Delta p_x)^2}\,\overline{(\Delta x)^2}]} = \tfrac{1}{2}\hbar, \tag{14.8}$$

in agreement with the relation (14.6)†.

Finally, we shall derive another useful relation. Let f and g be two physical quantities whose operators obey the commutation rule

$$\hat{f}\hat{g} - \hat{g}\hat{f} = -i\hbar\hat{c}, \tag{14.9}$$

where $\hat{c}$ is the operator of some physical quantity c. On the right-hand side of the equation the factor $\hbar$ is introduced in accordance with the fact that in the classical limit (i.e. as $\hbar \to 0$) all operators of physical quantities reduce to multiplication by these quantities and commute with one another. Thus, in the "quasi-classical" case, we can, to a first approximation, regard the right-hand side of equation (14.9) as being zero. In the next approximation, the operator $\hat{c}$ can be replaced by the operator of simple multiplication by the quantity c. We then have

$$\hat{f}\hat{g} - \hat{g}\hat{f} = -i\hbar c.$$

This equation is exactly analogous to the relation $\hat{p}_x x - x\hat{p}_x = -i\hbar$, the only

† It can be shown that this value of the product of the standard deviations is the least possible. To do this, we give the following formal derivation (H. Weyl). Let the state of the particle be described by the function $\psi(x)$; for simplicity, we suppose the mean values of co-ordinate and momentum in this state to be zero. We consider the obvious inequality

$$\int_{-\infty}^{\infty} \left| \alpha x\psi + \frac{d\psi}{dx} \right|^2 dx \geqslant 0,$$

where α is an arbitrary real constant (the equality sign holds for a function of the form (14.7), and for no other). On calculating this integral, noticing that

$$\int x^2|\psi|^2\, dx = \overline{(\Delta x)^2},$$

$$\int \left(x\frac{d\psi^*}{dx}\psi + x\psi^*\frac{d\psi}{dx} \right) dx = \int x\frac{d|\psi|^2}{dx}\, dx = -\int |\psi|^2\, dx = -1,$$

$$\int \frac{d\psi^*}{dx}\frac{d\psi}{dx}\, dx = -\int \psi^*\frac{d^2\psi}{dx^2}\, dx = \frac{1}{\hbar^2}\int \psi^*\hat{p}_x^2\psi\, dx = \frac{1}{\hbar^2}\overline{(\Delta p_x)^2},$$

we obtain

$$\alpha^2\overline{(\Delta x)^2} - \alpha + (1/\hbar^2)\overline{(\Delta p_x)^2} \geqslant 0.$$

If this quadratic (in α) trinomial is positive, the condition

$$4\overline{(\Delta x)^2}\,(1/\hbar^2)\overline{(\Delta p_x)^2} \geqslant 1$$

or

$$\sqrt{[\overline{(\Delta x)^2}\,\overline{(\Delta p_x)^2}]} \geqslant \tfrac{1}{2}\hbar \tag{14.8a}$$

must be fulfilled.

difference being that, instead of the constant $\hbar$, we have† the quantity $\hbar c$. We can therefore conclude, by analogy with the relation $\Delta x \Delta p_x \sim \hbar$, that in the quasi-classical case there is an uncertainty relation

$$\Delta f \Delta g \sim \hbar c. \tag{14.10}$$

for the quantities f and g.

In particular, if one of these quantities is the energy ($\hat{f} \equiv \hat{H}$) and the operator ($\hat{g}$) of the other does not depend explicitly on the time, then by (9.2) $\hat{c} = \hat{\dot{g}}$, and the uncertainty relation in the quasi-classical case is

$$\Delta E \Delta g \sim \hbar \dot{g}. \tag{14.11}$$

---

† The classical quantity c is the Poisson bracket of the quantities f and g; see the footnote in §9.

CHAPTER III

SCHRÖDINGER'S EQUATION

§15. Schrödinger's equation

LET us now turn to determining the form of the Hamiltonian—a problem of the greatest importance, since its solution determines the form of the wave equation.

We shall begin by considering one free particle, i.e. a particle which is not in any external field. Because of the complete homogeneity of space for such a particle, its Hamiltonian cannot explicitly contain the co-ordinates, and must be expressible in terms of the momentum operator only. Moreover, for a free particle both the energy and the momentum are conserved, and hence both these quantities can exist simultaneously. Since the value of the momentum vector completely determines the state of the particle, the eigenvalues of the energy E must be expressible in the form of functions of the value of the momentum in the same state. Here E is a function only of the absolute value of the momentum, and not of its direction; this follows from the complete isotropy of space relative to the free particle, i.e. the equivalence of all directions in space. The actual form of the function $E(p)$ is completely determined by the requirements of what is called *Galileo's relativity principle*, which must hold in non-relativistic quantum mechanics just as much as in classical (non-relativistic) mechanics. As is found in mechanics†, this requirement leads to a quadratic dependence of the energy on the momentum: $E = p^2/2\mu$, where the constant μ is called the *mass* of the particle.

If the relation $E = p^2/2\mu$ holds for every eigenvalue of the energy and momentum, the same relation must hold for their operators also:

$$\hat{H} = (1/2\mu)(\hat{p}_x^2+\hat{p}_y^2+\hat{p}_z^2). \tag{15.1}$$

Substituting here from (13.2), we obtain the Hamiltonian of a freely moving particle in the form

$$\hat{H} = -(\hbar^2/2\mu)\Delta, \tag{15.2}$$

where $\Delta = \partial^2/\partial x^2+\partial^2/\partial y^2+\partial^2/\partial z^2$ is the Laplacian operator.

If we have a system of non-interacting particles, its Hamiltonian is equal to the sum of the Hamiltonians of the separate parts (see §8):

$$\hat{H} = -\tfrac{1}{2}\hbar^2 \sum_a (1/\mu_a)\Delta_a \tag{15.3}$$

(the suffix a is the number of the particle; Δ_a is the Laplacian operator in

† See, for instance, volume 1 of this course, *Mechanics*, §4, Moscow 1958.

which the differentiation is with respect to the co-ordinates of the *a*th particle).

The form of the Hamiltonian for a system of particles which interact with one another cannot be derived from the general principles of quantum mechanics alone. It is found that it has in fact a form similar to that of HAMILTON's function in classical mechanics: it is obtained by adding to the Hamiltonian of the non-interacting particles a certain function $U(\mathbf{r}_1, \mathbf{r}_2, \ldots)$ of their co-ordinates:

$$\hat{H} = -\tfrac{1}{2}\hbar^2 \sum_a \Delta_a/\mu_a + U(\mathbf{r}_1, \mathbf{r}_2, \ldots). \tag{15.4}$$

The first term can be regarded as the operator of the kinetic energy and the second as that of the potential energy. The latter reduces to simple multiplication by the function U, and it follows from the passage to the limiting case of classical mechanics that this function must coincide with the one which gives the potential energy in classical mechanics. In particular, the Hamiltonian for a single particle in an external field is

$$\hat{H} = \hat{\mathbf{p}}^2/2\mu + U(x, y, z) = -(\hbar^2/2\mu)\Delta + U(x, y, z), \tag{15.5}$$

where $U(x, y, z)$ is the potential energy of the particle in the external field.

We notice that the eigenvalues of the kinetic energy operator are positive; this follows at once from the fact that this operator is equal to the sum of the squares of the operators of the momentum components with positive coefficients. Hence the mean value of the kinetic energy in any state is also positive.

Substituting the expressions (15.2) to (15.5) in the general equation (8.1), we obtain the wave equations for the corresponding systems. We shall write out here the wave equation for a particle in an external field:

$$i\hbar\, \partial\Psi/\partial t = -(\hbar^2/2\mu)\Delta\Psi + U(x, y, z)\Psi. \tag{15.6}$$

The equation (10.2), which determines the stationary states, takes the form

$$(\hbar^2/2\mu)\Delta\psi + [E - U(x, y, z)]\psi = 0. \tag{15.7}$$

The equations (15.6) and (15.7) were obtained by SCHRÖDINGER in 1926 and are called *Schrödinger's equations*, with and without the time respectively.

For a free particle, SCHRÖDINGER's equation (15.7) has the form

$$(\hbar^2/2\mu)\Delta\psi + E\psi = 0. \tag{15.8}$$

This equation has solutions finite in all space for any positive (or zero) value of the energy E. These solutions can be taken to be the common eigenfunctions (13.5) of the operators of the three momentum components. The complete wave functions of the stationary states will then have the form

$$\Psi = \text{constant} \times e^{-(i/\hbar)Et + (i/\hbar)\mathbf{p}.\mathbf{r}} \quad (E = p^2/2\mu). \tag{15.9}$$

Each such function describes a state in which the particle has a definite energy E and momentum $\mathbf{p}$. This is a plane wave propagated in the direction of $\mathbf{p}$ and having a (circular) frequency $E/\hbar$ and wavelength $2\pi\hbar/p$ (the latter is called the *de Broglie wavelength* of the particle†).

The energy spectrum of a freely moving particle is thus found to be continuous, extending from zero to $+\infty$. Each of these eigenvalues (except $E = 0$) is degenerate, and the degeneracy is infinite. For there corresponds to every value of E, different from zero, an infinite number of eigenfunctions (15.9), differing in the direction of the vector $\mathbf{p}$, which has a constant absolute magnitude.

Let us enquire how the passage to the limit of classical mechanics occurs in SCHRÖDINGER's equation, considering for simplicity only a single particle in an external field. Substituting in SCHRÖDINGER's equation (15.6) the limiting expression (6.1) for the wave function, $\Psi = ae^{(i/\hbar)S}$, we obtain, on performing the differentiation,

$$a\frac{\partial S}{\partial t}-i\hbar\frac{\partial a}{\partial t}+\frac{a}{2\mu}(\nabla S)^2-\frac{i\hbar}{2\mu}a\Delta S-\frac{i\hbar}{\mu}\nabla S\,.\,\nabla a-\frac{\hbar^2}{2\mu}\Delta a+Ua=0.$$

In this equation there are purely real and purely imaginary terms (we recall that S and a are real); equating each separately to zero, we obtain two equations

$$\frac{\partial S}{\partial t}+\frac{1}{2\mu}(\nabla S)^2+U-\frac{\hbar^2}{2\mu a}\Delta a=0,$$

$$\frac{\partial a}{\partial t}+\frac{a}{2\mu}\Delta S+\frac{1}{\mu}\nabla S\,.\,\nabla a=0.$$

Neglecting the term containing $\hbar^2$ in the first of these equations, we obtain

$$\frac{\partial S}{\partial t}+\frac{1}{2\mu}(\nabla S)^2+U=0, \qquad (15.10)$$

that is, the familiar classical Hamilton-Jacobi equation for the action S of a particle, as it should be. We see, incidentally, that, as $\hbar \to 0$, classical mechanics is valid to within quantities of the first (and not the zero) order in $\hbar$ inclusive.

The second equation obtained above, on multiplication by $2a$, can be rewritten in the form

$$\frac{\partial a^2}{\partial t}+\operatorname{div}\left(a^2\frac{\nabla S}{\mu}\right)=0. \qquad (15.11)$$

This equation has an obvious physical meaning: a^2 is the probability density for finding the particle at some point in space ($|\Psi|^2 = a^2$); $\nabla S/\mu = \mathbf{p}/\mu$ is the classical velocity $\mathbf{v}$ of the particle. Hence equation (15.11) is simply the equation of continuity, which shows that the probability density "moves" according to the laws of classical mechanics with the classical velocity $\mathbf{v}$ at every point.

† The idea of a wave related to a particle was first introduced by L. DE BROGLIE in 1924.

§16. The fundamental properties of Schrödinger's equation

The conditions which must be satisfied by solutions of SCHRÖDINGER's equation are very general in character. First of all, the wave function must be one-valued and continuous in all space. The requirement of continuity is maintained even in cases where the field $U(x, y, z)$ itself has a surface of discontinuity. At such a surface both the wave function and its derivatives must remain continuous. Concerning the continuity of the derivatives, however, it must be added that this does not hold if there is some surface beyond which the potential energy U becomes infinite. A particle clearly cannot penetrate at all into a region of space where $U = \infty$, i.e. we must have $\psi = 0$ everywhere in this region. The continuity of ψ means that ψ vanishes at the boundary of this region; the derivatives of ψ, however, in general are discontinuous in this case.

If the field $U(x, y, z)$ nowhere becomes infinite, then the wave function also must be finite in all space. If, however, $U(x, y, z)$ becomes infinite at some point (at the origin, say), then, although ψ may have a singular point there, the integral $\int |\psi|^2 \,\mathrm{d}V$ over a volume round this point must always converge, and the limit to which the integral

$$\oint(\psi_1^* \nabla\psi_2 - \psi_2 \nabla \psi_1^*) \cdot \mathbf{df},$$

taken over the surface of a sphere of radius r about the origin, tends as $r \to 0$ must be zero (ψ_1 and ψ_2 are any two solutions of SCHRÖDINGER's equation corresponding to different eigenvalues of the energy). In other words, we must have

$$|\psi|^2 r^3 \to 0 \text{ and } \left(\psi_1^* \frac{\partial\psi_2}{\partial r} - \psi_2 \frac{\partial\psi_1^*}{\partial r}\right) r^2 \to 0 \text{ as } r \to 0. \tag{16.1}$$

In practice, these conditions usually lead to the requirement that ψ is finite at the origin. The conditions placed on the integral over the surface of an infinitely small sphere are necessary for the different eigenfunctions to be orthogonal (cf. the proof of this orthogonality based on SCHRÖDINGER's equation, at the end of the next section).

Let $U_{\min}$ be the least value of the function $U(x, y, z)$. Since the Hamiltonian of a particle is the sum of two terms, the operators of the kinetic energy ($\hat{T}$) and of the potential energy, the mean value $\bar{E}$ of the energy in any state is equal to the sum $\bar{T} + \bar{U}$. But all the eigenvalues of the operator $\hat{T}$ (which is the Hamiltonian of a free particle) are positive; hence the mean value $T \geqslant 0$. Recalling also the obvious inequality $\bar{U} > U_{\min}$, we find that $\bar{E} > U_{\min}$. Since this inequality holds for any state, it is clear that it is valid for all the eigenvalues of the energy:

$$E_n > U_{\min}. \tag{16.2}$$

Let us consider a particle moving in an external field which vanishes at infinity; we define the function $U(x, y, z)$, in the usual way, so that it vanishes at infinity. It is easy to see that the spectrum of negative eigenvalues of the energy will then be discrete, i.e. all states with $E < 0$ in a field which vanishes at infinity are states of finite motion of the particle. For, in the stationary states of a continuous spectrum, which correspond to infinite motion, the particle reaches infinity (see §10); however, at sufficiently large distances the field may be neglected, the motion of the particle may be regarded as free, and the energy of a freely moving particle can only be positive.

The positive eigenvalues, on the other hand, form a continuous spectrum and correspond to an infinite motion; for $E > 0$, SCHRÖDINGER's equation in general has no solutions (in the field concerned) for which the integral $\int |\psi|^2 \, dV$ converges†.

Attention must be drawn to the fact that, in quantum mechanics, a particle in a finite motion may be found in those regions of space where $E < U$; however, the probability $|\psi|^2$ of finding the particle tends rapidly to zero as the distance into such a region increases, yet it differs from zero at all finite distances. Here there is a fundamental difference from classical mechanics, in which a particle cannot penetrate into a region where $U > E$. In classical mechanics, the impossibility of penetrating into this region is related to the fact that, for $E < U$, the kinetic energy would be negative, that is, the velocity would be imaginary, which is meaningless. In quantum mechanics, the eigenvalues of the kinetic energy are likewise positive; nevertheless, we do not reach a contradiction here, since, if by a process of measurement a particle is localised at some definite point of space, the state of the particle is changed, as a result of this process, in such a way that it ceases in general to have any definite kinetic energy.

If $U(x, y, z) > 0$ in all space (and $U \to 0$ at infinity), then, by the inequality (16.2), we have $E_n > 0$. Since, on the other hand, for $E > 0$ the spectrum must be continuous, we conclude that, in this case, the discrete spectrum is absent altogether, i.e. only an infinite motion of the particle is possible.

Let us suppose that, at some point (which we take as origin), U tends to $-\infty$ in the manner

$$U \approx -\alpha r^{-s} \qquad (\alpha > 0). \tag{16.3}$$

We consider a wave function finite in some small region (of radius r_0) about the origin, and equal to zero outside this region. The uncertainty in the values of the co-ordinates of a particle in such a wave packet is of the order of r_0; hence the uncertainty in the value of the momentum is $\sim \hbar/r_0$. The mean value of the kinetic energy in this state is of the order of $\hbar^2/\mu r_0^2$, and the mean value of the potential energy is $\sim -\alpha/r_0^s$. Let us first suppose that $s > 2$. Then the sum

$$\hbar^2/\mu r_0^2 - \alpha/r_0^s$$

takes arbitrarily large negative values for sufficiently small r_0. If, however, the mean energy can take such values, this always means that the energy has

† However, it must be mentioned that, for some particular forms of the function $U(x, y, z)$, a discrete set of values may be absent from the otherwise continuous spectrum.

negative eigenvalues which are arbitrarily large in absolute value. The motion of the particle in a very small region of space near the origin corresponds to the energy levels with large $|E|$. The "normal" state corresponds to a particle at the origin itself, i.e. the particle "falls" to the point $r = 0$.

If, however, $s < 2$, the energy cannot take arbitrarily large negative values. The discrete spectrum begins at some finite negative value. In this case the particle does not "fall" to the centre. It should be mentioned that, in classical mechanics, the "fall" of a particle to the centre would be possible in any attractive field (i.e. for any positive s). The case $s = 2$ will be specially considered in §35.

Next, let us investigate how the nature of the energy spectrum depends on the behaviour of the field at large distances. We suppose that, as $r \to \infty$, the potential energy, which is negative, tends to zero according to the power law (16.3) (r is now large in this formula), and consider a wave packet "filling" a spherical shell of large radius r_0 and thickness $\Delta r \ll r_0$. Then the order of magnitude of the kinetic energy is again $\hbar^2/\mu(\Delta r)^2$, and of the potential energy, $-\alpha/r_0^s$. We increase r_0, at the same time increasing Δr, in such a way that Δr increases proportionally to r_0. If $s < 2$, then the sum $\hbar^2/\mu(\Delta r)^2 - \alpha/r_0^s$ becomes negative for sufficiently large r_0. Hence it follows that there are stationary states of negative energy, in which the particle may be found, with a fair probability, at large distances from the origin. This, however, means that there are levels of arbitrarily small negative energy (it must be recalled that the wave functions rapidly tend to zero in the region of space where $U > E$). Thus, in this case, the discrete spectrum contains an infinite number of levels, which become denser and denser towards the level $E = 0$.

If the field diminishes as $-1/r^s$ at infinity, with $s > 2$, then there are not levels of arbitrarily small negative energy. The discrete spectrum terminates at a level with a non-zero absolute value, so that the total number of levels is finite.

SCHRÖDINGER's equation (without the time) is real, as are the conditions imposed on its solution. Hence its solutions ψ can always be taken as real†. The eigenfunctions of non-degenerate values of the energy are automatically real, apart from the unimportant phase factor. For ψ^* satisfies the same equation as ψ, and therefore must also be an eigenfunction for the same value of the energy; hence, if this value is not degenerate, ψ and ψ^* must be essentially the same, i.e. they can differ only by a constant factor (of modulus unity). The wave functions corresponding to the same degenerate energy level need not be real, however, but by a suitable choice of linear combinations of them we can always obtain a set of real functions.

The complete wave functions Ψ are determined by an equation in whose coefficients i appears. This equation, however, retains the same form if we replace t in it by $-t$ and at the same time take the complex conjugate.‡

† These assertions are not valid for systems in a magnetic field.

‡ It is assumed that the potential energy U does not depend explicitly on the time: the system is either closed or in a constant (non-magnetic) field.

Hence we can always choose the functions Ψ in such a way that Ψ and Ψ^* differ only by the sign of the time, a result which we know already from formulae (10.1) and (10.3).

As is well known, the equations of classical mechanics are unchanged when the sign of the time is reversed, i.e. when the future is replaced by the past. In quantum mechanics, the symmetry with respect to the two directions of time is expressed, as we see, in the invariance of the wave equation when the sign of t is changed and Ψ is simultaneously replaced by Ψ^*. However, it must be recalled that this symmetry here relates only to the equations, and not to the concept of measurement itself, which plays a fundamental part in quantum mechanics (as we have explained in detail in §7). Thus in quantum mechanics there is no complete physical symmetry of the two directions of time.

§17. The current density

In classical mechanics, the velocity of a particle is equal to its momentum divided by its mass. We shall show that the same relation holds in quantum mechanics, as we should expect.

According to the general formula (9.2) for the differentiation of operators with respect to time, we have for the velocity operator $\hat{\mathbf{v}} \equiv \hat{\dot{\mathbf{r}}}$

$$\hat{\mathbf{v}} = (i/\hbar)(\hat{H}\mathbf{r} - \mathbf{r}\hat{H}).$$

Using the expression (15.5) for $\hat{H}$ and formula (14.5), we obtain

$$\hat{\mathbf{v}} = \hat{\mathbf{p}}/\mu. \tag{17.1}$$

The same relations will clearly hold between the eigenvalues of the velocity and momentum, and between their mean values in any state.

The velocity, like the momentum of a particle, cannot have a definite value simultaneously with the co-ordinates. But the velocity multiplied by an infinitely short time interval dt gives the displacement of the particle in the time dt. Hence the fact that the velocity cannot exist at the same time as the co-ordinates means that, if the particle is at a definite point in space at some instant, it has no definite position at an infinitely close subsequent instant.

We may notice a useful formula for the operator $\hat{\dot{f}}$ of the derivative, with respect to time, of some quantity $f(\mathbf{r})$ which is a function of the radius vector of the particle. Bearing in mind that f commutes with $U(\mathbf{r})$, we find

$$\hat{\dot{f}} = (i/\hbar)(\hat{H}f - f\hat{H}) = (i/2\mu\hbar)(\hat{\mathbf{p}}^2 f - f\hat{\mathbf{p}}^2).$$

Using (14.4), we can write

$$\hat{\mathbf{p}}^2 f = \hat{\mathbf{p}} \cdot (f\hat{\mathbf{p}} - i\hbar\nabla f) = \hat{\mathbf{p}}f \cdot \hat{\mathbf{p}} - i\hbar\hat{\mathbf{p}} \cdot \nabla f,$$

and similarly for $f\hat{\mathbf{p}}^2$. Substituting in the formula for $\hat{\dot{f}}$, we obtain the required expression:

$$\hat{\dot{f}} = (1/2\mu)(\hat{\mathbf{p}} \cdot \nabla f + \nabla f \cdot \hat{\mathbf{p}}). \tag{17.2}$$

Next, let us find the acceleration operator. We have

$$\hat{\dot{\mathbf{v}}} = (i/\hbar)(\hat{H}\hat{\mathbf{v}} - \hat{\mathbf{v}}\hat{H}) = (i/\mu\hbar)(\hat{H}\hat{\mathbf{p}} - \hat{\mathbf{p}}\hat{H}) = (i/\mu\hbar)(U\hat{\mathbf{p}} - \hat{\mathbf{p}}U)$$

(all the terms in $\hat{H}$ except $U(\mathbf{r})$ commute with $\hat{\mathbf{p}}$).

Using formula (14.4), we find

$$\mu\hat{\dot{\mathbf{v}}} = -\nabla U. \tag{17.3}$$

This operator equation is exactly the same in form as the equation of motion (Newton's equation) in classical mechanics.

The integral $\int |\Psi|^2 \,\mathrm{d}V$, taken over some finite volume V, is the probability of finding the particle in this volume. Let us calculate the derivative of this probability with respect to time. We have

$$\frac{\mathrm{d}}{\mathrm{d}t}\int_V |\Psi|^2 \,\mathrm{d}V = \int_V \left(\Psi\frac{\partial\Psi^*}{\partial t} + \Psi^*\frac{\partial\Psi}{\partial t}\right)\mathrm{d}V = \frac{i}{\hbar}\int_V (\Psi\hat{H}^*\Psi^* - \Psi^*\hat{H}\Psi)\,\mathrm{d}V.$$

Substituting here

$$\hat{H} = \hat{H}^* = -(\hbar^2/2\mu)\Delta + U(x, y, z)$$

and using the identity

$$\Psi\Delta\Psi^* - \Psi^*\Delta\Psi = \operatorname{div}(\Psi\nabla\Psi^* - \Psi^*\nabla\Psi),$$

we obtain

$$\frac{\mathrm{d}}{\mathrm{d}t}\int_V |\Psi|^2 \,\mathrm{d}V = -\int_V \operatorname{div}\mathbf{i}\,\mathrm{d}V,$$

where $\mathbf{i}$ denotes the vector

$$\mathbf{i} = (i\hbar/2\mu)(\Psi\nabla\Psi^* - \Psi^*\nabla\Psi). \tag{17.4}$$

The integral of div $\mathbf{i}$ can be transformed by Gauss's theorem into an integral over the closed surface S which bounds† the volume V:

$$\frac{\mathrm{d}}{\mathrm{d}t}\int_V |\Psi|^2 \,\mathrm{d}V = -\int_S \mathbf{i}\,.\,\mathrm{d}\mathbf{f}. \tag{17.5}$$

It is seen from this that the vector $\mathbf{i}$ may be called the ***probability current density*** vector. The integral of this vector over a surface is the probability that the particle will cross the surface during unit time. The vector $\mathbf{i}$ and the probability density $|\Psi|^2$ satisfy the equation

$$\partial|\Psi|^2/\partial t + \operatorname{div}\mathbf{i} = 0, \tag{17.6}$$

which is analogous to the classical equation of continuity.

Introducing the momentum operator, we can write the vector $\mathbf{i}$ in the form

$$\mathbf{i} = (1/2\mu)(\Psi\hat{\mathbf{p}}^*\Psi^* + \Psi^*\hat{\mathbf{p}}\Psi). \tag{17.7}$$

† The surface element $\mathrm{d}\mathbf{f}$ is defined as a vector equal in magnitude to the area $\mathrm{d}f$ of the element and directed along the outward normal.

It is useful to consider how the orthogonality of the wave functions of states with different energies follows immediately from SCHRÖDINGER's equation. Let ψ_m and ψ_n be two such functions; they satisfy the equations

$$-(\hbar^2/2\mu)\Delta\psi_m + U\psi_m = E_m\psi_m,$$
$$-(\hbar^2/2\mu)\Delta\psi_n^* + U\psi_n^* = E_n\psi_n^*.$$

We multiply the first of these by ψ_n^* and the second by ψ_m and subtract corresponding terms; this gives

$$(E_m - E_n)\psi_m\psi_n^* = (\hbar^2/2\mu)(\psi_m\Delta\psi_n^* - \psi_n^*\Delta\psi_m)$$
$$= (\hbar^2/2\mu)\,\mathrm{div}\,(\psi_m\nabla\psi_n^* - \psi_n^*\nabla\psi_m).$$

If we now integrate both sides of this equation over all space, the right-hand side, on transformation by GAUSS's theorem, reduces to zero, and we obtain

$$(E_m - E_n)\int\psi_m\psi_n^*\,\mathrm{d}V = 0,$$

whence, by the hypothesis $E_m \neq E_n$, there follows the required orthogonality relation

$$\int\psi_m\psi_n^*\,\mathrm{d}V = 0.$$

§18. The variational principle

SCHRÖDINGER's equation, in the general form $\hat{H}\psi = E\psi$, can be obtained from the variational principle

$$\delta\int\psi^*(\hat{H} - E)\psi\,\mathrm{d}q = 0. \tag{18.1}$$

Since ψ is complex, we can vary ψ and ψ^* independently. Varying ψ^*, we have

$$\int\delta\psi^*(\hat{H} - E)\psi\,\mathrm{d}q = 0,$$

whence, because $\delta\psi^*$ is arbitrary, we obtain the required equation $\hat{H}\psi = E\psi$. The variation of ψ gives nothing different. For, varying ψ and using the fact that the operator $\hat{H}$ is Hermitian, we have

$$\int\psi^*(\hat{H} - E)\delta\psi\,\mathrm{d}q = \int\delta\psi(\hat{H}^* - E)\psi^*\,\mathrm{d}q = 0,$$

from which we obtain the complex conjugate equation $\hat{H}^*\psi^* = E\psi^*$.

The variational principle (18.1) requires an unconditional extremum of the integral. It can be stated in a different form by regarding E as a Lagrangian multiplier in a problem with the conditional extremum requirement

$$\delta\int\psi^*\hat{H}\psi\,\mathrm{d}q = 0, \tag{18.2}$$

the condition being

$$\int \psi\psi^* \, dq = 1. \tag{18.3}$$

The least value of the integral (18.2) (with the condition (18.3)) is the first eigenvalue of the energy, i.e. the energy E_0 of the normal state. The function ψ which gives this minimum is accordingly the wave function ψ_n of the normal state†. The wave functions $\psi_n(n > 0)$ of the other stationary states correspond only to an extremum, and not to a true minimum of the integral.

In order to obtain, from the condition that the integral (18.2) is a minimum, the wave function ψ_1 and the energy E_1 of the state next to the normal one, we must restrict our choice to those functions ψ which satisfy not only the normalisation condition (18.3) but also the condition of orthogonality with the wave function ψ_0 of the normal state: $\int \psi\psi_0 \, dV = 0$. In general, if the wave functions $\psi_0, \psi_1, \dots, \psi_{n-1}$ of the first n states (arranged in order of increasing energy) are known, the wave function of the next state gives a minimum of the integral (18.2) with the additional conditions

$$\int \psi^2 \, dq = 1, \quad \int \psi\psi_m \, dq = 0 \qquad (m = 0\ 1, 2, \dots, n-1). \tag{18.4}$$

We shall give here some general theorems which can be proved from the variational principle‡.

The wave function ψ_0 of the normal state does not become zero (or, as we say, has no *nodes*) for any finite values of the co-ordinates‖. In other words, it has the same sign in all space. Hence, it follows that the wave functions ψ_n $(n > 0)$ of the other stationary states, being orthogonal to ψ_0, must have nodes (if ψ_n is also of constant sign, the integral $\int \psi_0\psi_n \, dq$ cannot vanish).

Next, from the fact that ψ_0 has no nodes, it follows that the normal energy level cannot be degenerate. For, suppose the contrary to be true, and let ψ_0, ψ_0' be two different eigenfunctions corresponding to the level E_0. Any linear combination $c\psi_0 + c'\psi_0'$ will also be an eigenfunction; but by choosing the appropriate constants c, c', we can always make this function vanish at any given point in space, i.e. we can obtain an eigenfunction with nodes.

If the motion takes place in a bounded region of space, we must have $\psi = 0$ at the boundary of this region (see §16). To determine the energy levels, it is necessary to find, from the variational principle, the minimum value of the integral (18.2) with this boundary condition. The theorem that the wave function of the normal state has no nodes means in this case that ψ_0 does not vanish anywhere inside this region.

We notice that, as the dimensions of the region containing the motion

---

† In the rest of this section we shall suppose the wave functions ψ to be real; they can always be so chosen (if there is no magnetic field).

‡ See, for instance, V. I. Smirnov, *Course of Higher Mathematics* (*Kurs vysshei matematiki*), volume IV, Moscow 1941; P. M. Morse and H. Feshbach, *Methods of Theoretical Physics*, part I, ch. 6, McGraw-Hill, New York 1953.

‖ This theorem is not in general valid for the wave functions of systems composed of several identical particles (see footnote at the end of §61).

increase, all the energy levels E_n decrease; this follows immediately from the fact that an extension of the region increases the range of functions which can make the integral a minimum, and consequently the least value of the integral can only diminish.

The expression

$$E_n = \int \psi_n \hat{H} \psi_n \, dV = \int [-(\hbar^2/2\mu)\psi_n \Delta \psi_n + U(x, y, z)\psi_n^2] \, dV$$

for the energy levels of the discrete spectrum of one particle may be transformed into another expression which is often more convenient. In the first term of the integrand we write

$$\psi_n \Delta \psi_n = \operatorname{div}(\psi_n \nabla \psi_n) - (\nabla \psi_n)^2.$$

The integral of div $(\psi_n \nabla \psi_n)$ over all space is transformed into an integral over an infinitely distant closed surface, and since the wave functions of the states of a discrete spectrum tend to zero sufficiently rapidly at infinity, this integral vanishes. Thus

$$E_n = \int [(\hbar^2/2\mu)(\nabla \psi_n)^2 + U(x, y, z)\psi_n^2] \, dV. \tag{18.5}$$

§19. General properties of motion in one dimension

If the potential energy of a particle depends on only one co-ordinate (x), then the wave function can be sought as the product of a function of y and z and a function of x only. The former of these is determined by SCHRÖDINGER's equation for free motion, and the second by the one-dimensional SCHRÖDINGER's equation

$$\frac{d^2\psi}{dx^2} + \frac{2\mu}{\hbar^2}[E - U(x)]\psi = 0. \tag{19.1}$$

The same one-dimensional equation is evidently obtained for the problem of motion in a field whose potential energy is $U(x, y, z) = U_1(x) + U_2(y) + U_3(z)$, i.e. can be divided into a sum of functions each of which depends on only one of the co-ordinates. In §§20–22 we shall discuss a number of actual examples of such "one-dimensional" motion. Here we shall obtain some general properties of the motion.

We shall show first of all that, in a one-dimensional problem, none of the energy levels of a discrete spectrum is degenerate. To prove this, suppose the contrary to be true, and let ψ_1 and ψ_2 be two different eigenfunctions corresponding to the same value of the energy. Since both of these satisfy the same equation (19.1), we have

$$\psi_1''/\psi_1 = (2\mu/\hbar^2)(U - E) = \psi_2''/\psi_2,$$

or $\psi_1''\psi_2 - \psi_2''\psi_1 = 0$ (the prime denotes differentiation with respect to x).

Integrating this relation, we find

$$\psi_1'\psi_2 - \psi_1\psi_2' = \text{constant}. \tag{19.2}$$

Since $\psi_1 = \psi_2 = 0$ at infinity, the constant must be zero, and so

$$\psi_1'\psi_2 - \psi_1\psi_2' = 0,$$

or $\psi_1'/\psi_1 = \psi_2'/\psi_2$. Integrating again, we obtain $\psi_1 = \text{constant} \times \psi_2$, i.e. the two functions are essentially identical.

The following theorem† (called the *oscillation theorem*) may be stated for the wave functions $\psi_n(x)$ of a discrete spectrum. The function $\psi_n(x)$ corresponding to the $(n+1)$th eigenvalue E_n (the eigenvalues being arranged in order of magnitude), vanishes n times (for finite‡ values of x).

We shall suppose that the function $U(x)$ tends to finite limiting values as $x \to \pm\infty$ (though it need not be a monotonic function). We take the limiting value $U(+\infty)$ as the zero of energy (i.e. we put $U(+\infty) = 0$), and we denote $U(-\infty)$ by U_0, supposing that $U_0 > 0$. The discrete spectrum lies in the range of energy values for which the particle cannot move off to infinity; for this to be so, the energy must be less than both limiting values $U(\pm\infty)$, i.e. it must be negative:

$$E < 0, \tag{19.3}$$

and we must, of course, have in any case $E > U_{\text{min}}$, i.e. the function $U(x)$ must have at least one minimum with $U_{\text{min}} < 0$.

Let us now consider the range of positive energy values less than U_0:

$$0 < E < U_0. \tag{19.4}$$

In this range the spectrum will be continuous, and the motion of the particle in the corresponding stationary states will be infinite, the particle moving off towards $x = +\infty$. It is easy to see that none of the eigenvalues of the energy in this part of the spectrum is degenerate either. To show this, it is sufficient to notice that the proof given above (for the discrete spectrum) still holds if the functions ψ_1, ψ_2 are zero at only one infinity (in the present case they tend to zero as $x \to -\infty$).

For sufficiently large positive values of x, we can neglect $U(x)$ in Schrödinger's equation (19.1):

$$\psi'' + (2\mu/\hbar^2)E\psi = 0.$$

This equation has real solutions in the form of a *stationary plane wave*

$$\psi = a\cos(kx+\delta), \tag{19.5}$$

where a and δ are constants, and the *wave number* $k = p/\hbar = \sqrt{(2\mu E)}/\hbar$. This formula determines the asymptotic form of the wave functions of the

† See, for instance, the references in the second note to §18.
‡ If the particle can be found only on a limited segment of the x-axis, we must consider the zeros of $\psi_n(x)$ within that segment.

non-degenerate energy levels in the range (19.4) of the continuous spectrum. For large negative values of x, SCHRÖDINGER's equation is

$$\psi''-(2\mu/\hbar^2)(U_0-E)\psi = 0.$$

The solution which does not become infinite as $x \to -\infty$ is

$$\psi = be^{\kappa x}, \quad \text{where } \kappa = \sqrt{[2\mu(U_0-E)]}/\hbar. \tag{19.6}$$

This is the asymptotic form of the wave function as $x \to -\infty$. Thus the wave function decreases exponentially in the region where $E < U$.

Finally, for

$$E > U_0 \tag{19.7}$$

the spectrum will be continuous, and the motion will be infinite in both directions. In this part of the spectrum all the levels are doubly degenerate. This follows from the fact that the corresponding wave functions are determined by the second-order equation (19.1), and both of the two independent solutions of this equation satisfy the necessary conditions at infinity (whereas, for instance, in the previous case one of the solutions became infinite as $x \to -\infty$, and therefore had to be rejected). The asymptotic form of the wave function as $x \to +\infty$ is

$$\psi = a_1 e^{ikx} + a_2 e^{-ikx}, \tag{19.8}$$

and similarly for $x \to -\infty$. The term e^{ikx} corresponds to a particle moving to the right, and e^{-ikx} corresponds to one moving to the left.

Let us suppose that the function $U(x)$ is even $[U(-x) = U(x)]$. Then SCHRÖDINGER's equation (19.1) is unchanged when the sign of the coordinate is reversed. It follows that, if $\psi(x)$ is some solution of this equation, then $\psi(-x)$ is also a solution, and coincides with $\psi(x)$ apart from a constant factor: $\psi(-x) = c\psi(x)$. Changing the sign of x again, we obtain $\psi(x) = c^2\psi(x)$, whence $c = \pm 1$. Thus, for a potential energy which is symmetrical (relative to $x = 0$), the wave functions of the stationary states must be either even $[\psi(-x) = \psi(x)]$ or odd $[\psi-(x) = -\psi(x)]$.†

To normalise the wave functions of one-dimensional motion (in a continuous spectrum), there is a simple method of determining the normalisation coefficient directly from the asymptotic expression for the wave function for large values of $|x|$.

First of all, we notice that a free one-dimensional motion of a particle with momentum p is described by a wave function (a plane wave)

$$\psi_p = (2\pi\hbar)^{-\frac{1}{2}} e^{ikx},$$

where $k = p/\hbar$ is the wave number, and ψ_p is normalised by the delta function of momentum. The wave function ψ_E which is normalised by the delta

† In this discussion it is assumed that the stationary state is not degenerate. Otherwise, when the sign of x is changed, two wave functions belonging to the energy level concerned may be transformed into each other. In this case, however, although the wave functions of the stationary states need not be even or odd, they can always be made so (by choosing appropriate linear combinations of the original functions).

function of energy is obtained, according to (5.11), by multiplying ψ_p by $\sqrt{(\mathrm{d}p/\mathrm{d}E)} = 1/\sqrt{v}$ (where v is the velocity):

$$\psi_E = (2\pi\hbar v)^{-\frac{1}{2}} e^{ikx}. \tag{19.9}$$

We note that the probability current density in this wave is

$$v|\psi_E|^2 = 1/2\pi\hbar. \tag{19.10}$$

Let us consider the wave function of a stationary state in the range (19.4) of the continuous spectrum. The normalisation integral diverges as $x \to \infty$ (as $x \to -\infty$, the function decreases exponentially, so that the integral rapidly converges). Hence, to determine the normalisation constant, we can replace ψ by its asymptotic value (for large positive x), and perform the integration, taking as the lower limit any finite value of x, say zero; this amounts to neglecting a finite quantity in comparison with an infinite one. We shall show that the wave function normalised by the delta function of energy must have the asymptotic form (19.5) with $a = \sqrt{(2/\pi\hbar v)}$, i.e.

$$\psi_E \approx \sqrt{(2/\pi\hbar v)} \cos(kx+\delta = \sqrt{(1/2\pi\hbar v)}[e^{i(kx+\delta)}+e^{-i(\ x+\delta)}]. \tag{19.11}$$

Since we do not intend to verify the orthogonality of the functions corresponding to different E, on substituting the functions (19.11) in the normalisation integral $\int \psi_E{}^* \psi_{E'} \,\mathrm{d}x$ we shall suppose the energies E and E' to be arbitrarily close; we can therefore put $v = v'$ and $\delta = \delta'$ (in general δ is a function of the energy). Next, we retain in the integrand only those terms which diverge for $E = E'$; in other words, we omit terms containing the factor $e^{\pm i(k+k')x}$. Thus we obtain

$$\int \psi_E{}^* \psi_{E'} \,\mathrm{d}x = (1/2\pi\hbar v)\left(\int_0^\infty e^{i(k'-k)x}\,\mathrm{d}x + \int_0^\infty e^{-i(k'-k)x}\,\mathrm{d}x\right),$$

or

$$\int \psi_E{}^* \psi_{E'} \,\mathrm{d}x = (1/2\pi\hbar v) \int_{-\infty}^{\infty} e^{i(k'-k)x}\,\mathrm{d}x.$$

This integral, however, is identical with the normalisation integral for the wave function (19.9) of a free motion, normalised by the delta function of energy, and this proves the correctness of the normalisation chosen.

Bearing in mind the equation (19.10), we can formulate our result as follows. Having represented the asymptotic expression for the wave function in the form of a sum of two plane waves travelling in opposite directions, we must choose the normalisation coefficient in such a way that the probability current density in the wave travelling towards (or away from) the origin is $1/2\pi\hbar$.

Similarly, we can obtain an analogous rule for normalising the wave functions of a motion infinite in both directions. The wave function will be normalised by the delta function of energy if the sum of the probability currents in the waves travelling towards the origin from $x = +\infty$ and $x = -\infty$ is $1/2\pi\hbar$.

§20. The potential well

As a simple example of one-dimensional motion, let us consider motion in a square *potential well*, i.e. in a field where $U(x)$ has the form shown in Fig. 1: $U(x) = 0$ for $0 < x < a$, $U(x) = U_0$ for $x < 0$ and $x > a$. It is evident *a priori* that for $E < U_0$ the spectrum will be discrete, while for $E > U_0$ we have a continuous spectrum of doubly degenerate levels.

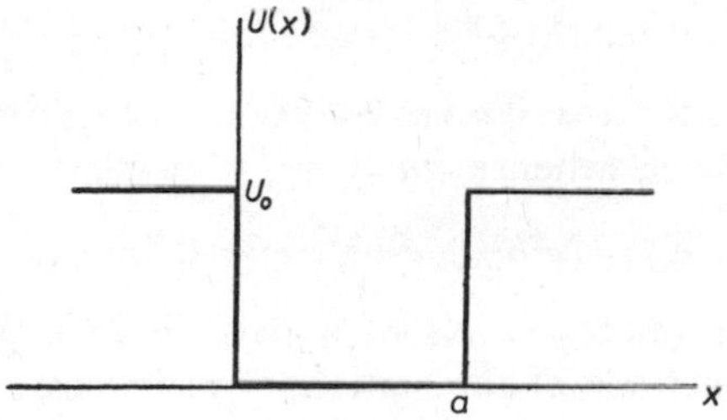

FIG. 1

In the region $0 < x < a$ we have SCHRÖDINGER's equation

$$\psi''+(2\mu/\hbar^2)E\psi = 0 \tag{20.1}$$

(the prime denotes differentiation with respect to x), while in the region outside the well

$$\psi''+(2\mu/\hbar^2)(E-U_0)\psi = 0. \tag{20.2}$$

For $x = 0$ and $x = a$ the solutions of these equations must be continuous together with their derivatives, while for $x = \pm\infty$ the solution of equation (20.2) must remain finite (for the discrete spectrum when $E < U_0$, it must vanish).

For $E < U_0$, the solution of equation (20.2) which vanishes at infinity is

$$\psi = \text{constant} \times e^{\mp\kappa x}, \quad \text{where } \kappa = \sqrt{[(2\mu/\hbar^2)(U_0-E)]}; \tag{20.3}$$

the signs $-$ and $+$ in the exponent refer to the regions $x > a$ and $x < 0$ respectively. The probability $|\psi|^2$ of finding the particle decreases exponentially in the region where $E < U(x)$. Instead of the continuity of ψ and ψ' at the edge of the potential well, it is convenient to require the continuity of ψ and of its logarithmic derivative ψ'/ψ. Taking account of (20.3), we obtain the boundary condition in the form

$$\psi'/\psi = \mp\kappa. \tag{20.4}$$

We shall not pause here to determine the energy levels in a well of arbitrary depth U_0 (see Problem 2), and shall analyse fully only the limiting case of infinitely high walls ($U_0 \to \infty$).

For $U_0 = \infty$, the motion takes place only between the points $x = 0$ and

$x = a$ and, as was pointed out in §16, the boundary condition at these points must be

$$\psi = 0. \tag{20.5}$$

It is easy to see that this condition is also obtained from the general condition (20.4). For, when $U_0 \to \infty$, we have also $\kappa \to \infty$ and hence $\psi'/\psi \to \infty$; since ψ' cannot become infinite, it follows that $\psi = 0$. We seek a solution of equation (20.1) inside the well in the form

$$\psi = c \sin(kx+\delta), \quad \text{where } k = \sqrt{(2\mu E/\hbar^2)}. \tag{20.6}$$

The condition $\psi = 0$ for $x = 0$ gives $\delta = 0$, and then the same condition for $x = a$ gives $\sin ka = 0$, whence $ka = n\pi$, n being a positive integer†, or

$$E_n = (\pi^2\hbar^2/2\mu a^2)n^2, \quad n = 1, 2, 3, \dots. \tag{20.7}$$

This determines the energy levels of a particle in a potential well. The normalised wave functions of the stationary states are

$$\psi_n = \sqrt{(2/a)} \sin(\pi n x/a). \tag{20.8}$$

From these results we can immediately write down the energy levels for a particle in a rectangular "potential box", i.e. for three-dimensional motion in a field whose potential energy $U = 0$ for $0 < x < a, 0 < y < b, 0 < z < c$ and $U = \infty$ outside this region. In fact, these levels are given by the sums

$$E_{n_1 n_2 n_3} = \frac{\pi^2\hbar^2}{2\mu}\left(\frac{n_1^2}{a^2}+\frac{n_2^2}{b^2}+\frac{n_3^2}{c^2}\right) \quad (n_1, n_2, n_3 = 1, 2, 3, \dots), \tag{20.9}$$

and the corresponding wave functions by the products

$$\psi_{n_1 n_2 n_3} = \sqrt{\frac{8}{abc}} \sin\frac{\pi n_1}{a}x \sin\frac{\pi n_2}{b}y \sin\frac{\pi n_3}{c}z. \tag{20.10}$$

PROBLEMS

Problem 1. Determine the probability distribution for various values of the momentum for the normal state of a particle in an infinitely deep square potential well.

Solution. The coefficients $a(p)$ in the expansion of the function ψ_1 (20.8) in terms of the eigenfunctions

$$\psi_p = (2\pi\hbar)^{-\frac{1}{2}} e^{(i/\hbar)px}$$

of the momentum are

$$a(p) = \int \psi_p{}^* \psi_1 \, dx = \frac{1}{\sqrt{(\pi a\hbar)}} \int_0^a \sin\left(\frac{\pi}{a}x\right) e^{-(i/\hbar)px} \, dx.$$

Calculating the integral and squaring its modulus, we obtain the required probability distribution:

$$|a(p)|^2 = \frac{4\pi\hbar^3 a}{(p^2a^2-\pi^2\hbar^2)^2} \cos^2\frac{pa}{2\hbar}.$$

† For $n = 0$ we should have $\psi = 0$ identically.

Problem 2. Determine the energy levels for the potential well shown in Fig. 2.

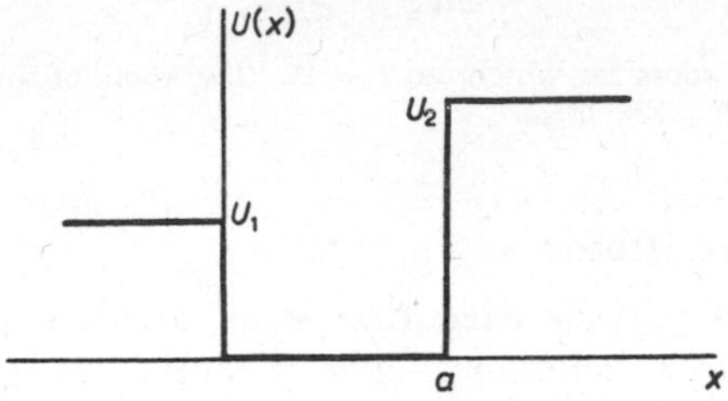

Fig. 2

Solution. The spectrum of energy values $E < U_1$, which we shall consider, is discrete. In the region $x < 0$ the wave function is

$$\psi = c_1 e^{\kappa_1 x}, \text{ where } \kappa_1 = \sqrt{[(2\mu/\hbar^2)(U_1 - E)]},$$

while in the region $x > a$

$$\psi = c_2 e^{-\kappa_2 x}, \quad \text{where } \kappa_2 = \sqrt{[(2\mu/\hbar^2)(U_2 - E)]}.$$

Inside the well $(0 < x < a)$ we look for ψ in the form

$$\psi = c \sin(kx+\delta), \quad \text{where } k = \sqrt{(2\mu E/\hbar^2)}.$$

The condition of the continuity of ψ'/ψ at the edges of the well gives the equations

$$k \cot \delta = \kappa_1 = \sqrt{[(2\mu/\hbar^2)U_1 - k^2]}, \; k \cot(ka+\delta) = -\kappa_2 = -\sqrt{[(2\mu/\hbar^2)U_2 - k^2]},$$

or

$$\sin \delta = k\hbar/\sqrt{(2\mu U_1)}, \; \sin(ka+\delta) = -k\hbar/\sqrt{(2\mu U_2)}.$$

Eliminating δ, we obtain the transcendental equation

$$ka = n\pi - \sin^{-1}[k\hbar/\sqrt{(2\mu U_1)}] - \sin^{-1}[k\hbar/\sqrt{(2\mu U_2)}] \tag{1}$$

(where $n = 1, 2, 3, \ldots$, and the values of the inverse sine are taken between 0 and $\frac{1}{2}\pi$), whose roots determine the energy levels $E = k^2\hbar^2/2\mu$. For each n there is in general one root; the values of n number the levels in order of increasing energy.

Since the argument of the inverse sine cannot exceed unity, it is clear that the values of k can lie only in the range from 0 to $\sqrt{(2\mu U_1/\hbar^2)}$. The left-hand side of equation (1) increases monotonically with k, and the right-hand side decreases monotonically. Hence it is necessary, for a root of equation (1) to exist, that for $k = \sqrt{(2\mu U_1/\hbar^2)}$ the right-hand side should be less than the left-hand side. In particular, the inequality

$$a\sqrt{(2\mu U_1)}/\hbar \geqslant \tfrac{1}{2}\pi - \sin^{-1}\sqrt{(U_1/U_2)}, \tag{2}$$

which is obtained for $n = 1$, is the condition that at least one energy level exists in the well. We see that for given and unequal U_1, U_2 there are always widths a of the well which are so small that there is no discrete energy level. For $U_1 = U_2$, the condition (2) is evidently always satisfied.

For $U_1 = U_2 \equiv U_0$ (a symmetrical well), equation (1) reduces to

$$\sin^{-1}[\hbar k/\sqrt{(2\mu U_0)}] = \tfrac{1}{2}(n\pi - ka). \tag{3}$$

Introducing the variable $\xi = \frac{1}{2}ka$, we obtain for odd n the equation

$$\cos \xi = \pm\gamma\xi, \quad \text{where } \gamma = (\hbar/a)\sqrt{(2/\mu U_0)},$$

and those roots of this equation must be taken for which $\tan\xi > 0$. For even n we obtain the equation

$$\sin\xi = \pm\gamma\xi,$$

and we must take those roots for which $\tan\xi < 0$. The roots of these two equations determine the energy levels $E = 2\xi^2\hbar^2/\mu a^2$.

§21. The linear oscillator

Let us consider a particle executing small oscillations in one dimension (what is called a *linear oscillator*). The potential energy of such a particle is well known to be $\frac{1}{2}\mu\omega^2x^2$, where ω is, in classical mechanics, the characteristic (circular) frequency of the oscillations. Accordingly, the Hamiltonian of the oscillator is

$$\hat{H} = \tfrac{1}{2}\hat{p}^2/\mu + \tfrac{1}{2}\mu\omega^2x^2. \tag{21.1}$$

Since the potential energy becomes infinite for $x = \pm\infty$, while its least value (at $x = 0$) is zero, it is clear from general principles that the energy spectrum of the oscillator is discrete and the energy values are positive.

Let us determine the energy levels of the oscillator, using the matrix method†. We shall start from the "equations of motion" in the form (17.3); in this case they give

$$\hat{\ddot{x}} + \omega^2x = 0. \tag{21.2}$$

In matrix form, this equation reads

$$(\ddot{x})_{mn} + \omega^2x_{mn} = 0.$$

For the matrix elements of the acceleration we have, according to (11.8), $(\ddot{x})_{mn} = i\omega_{mn}(\dot{x})_{mn} = -\omega_{mn}{}^2x_{mn}$. Hence we obtain

$$(\omega_{mn}{}^2 - \omega^2)x_{mn} = 0.$$

This equation is satisfied for $x_{mn} = 0$ or for $\omega_{mn} = \pm\omega$. In other words, all the matrix elements x_{mn} vanish except those for which $\omega_{mn} = \omega$ or $\omega_{mn} = -\omega$.

We number all the stationary states so that the frequency $\omega_{mn} = \omega$ corresponds to the transition $m \to m-1$ (i.e. $n = m-1$), while $\omega_{mn} = -\omega$ corresponds to $m \to m+1$. We thus have

$$x_{mn} = 0 \text{ for } n \neq m\pm1, \quad x_{mn} \neq 0 \text{ for } n = m\pm1.$$

We shall suppose that the wave functions ψ_n are taken real. Since x is a real quantity, all the matrix elements x_{mn} are real. The Hermitian condition (11.10) now shows that the matrix x_{mn} is symmetrical:

$$x_{mn} = x_{nm}.$$

To calculate the matrix elements of the co-ordinate which are different

† This was done by Heisenberg in 1925, before Schrödinger's discovery of the wave equation.

from zero, we use the commutation rule

$$\hat{\dot{x}}\hat{x}-\hat{x}\hat{\dot{x}} = -i\hbar/\mu,$$

written in the matrix form

$$(\dot{x}x)_{mn}-(x\dot{x})_{mn} = -(i\hbar/\mu)\delta_{mn}.$$

By the matrix multiplication rule (11.12) we hence have for $m = n$

$$i\sum_l(\omega_{ml}x_{ml}x_{lm}-x_{ml}\omega_{lm}x_{lm}) = -i\hbar/\mu$$

(we have substituted $\dot{x}_{ml} = i\omega_{ml}x_{ml}$), or, noting that $\omega_{ml} = -\omega_{lm}$ and $x_{ml} = x_{lm}$,

$$\sum_l \omega_{ml}x_{ml}^2 = -\hbar/2\mu.$$

In this sum, only the terms with $l = m+1$, $\omega_{ml} = -\omega$ and $l = m-1$, $\omega_{ml} = \omega$ are different from zero, so that we have

$$(x_{m+1,m})^2-(x_{m\,m-1})^2 = \hbar/2\mu\omega. \tag{21.3}$$

From this equation we deduce that the quantities $(x_{m+1,m})^2$ form an arithmetic progression, which is unbounded above, but is certainly bounded below, since it can contain only positive terms. Since we have as yet fixed only the relative positions of the numbers m of the states, but not their absolute values, we can arbitrarily choose the value of m corresponding to the first (normal) state of the oscillator, and put this value equal to zero. Accordingly $x_{0,-1}$ must be regarded as being zero identically, and the application of equations (21.3) with $m = 0, 1, \ldots$ successively leads to the result

$$(x_{n,n-1})^2 = n\hbar/2\mu\omega.$$

Thus we finally obtain the following expression for the matrix elements of the co-ordinate which are different from zero†:

$$x_{n,n-1} = x_{n-1,n} = \sqrt{(n\hbar/2\mu\omega)} \tag{21.4}$$

The matrix of the operator $\hat{H}$ is diagonal, and the matrix elements H_{nn} are the required eigenvalues E_n of the energy of the oscillator. To calculate them, we write

$$\begin{aligned} H_{nn} = E_n &= \tfrac{1}{2}\mu[(\dot{x}^2)_{nn}+\omega^2(x^2)_{nn}] \\ &= \tfrac{1}{2}\mu[\sum_l i\omega_{nl}x_{nl}i\omega_{ln}x_{ln}+\omega^2\sum_l x_{nl}x_{ln}] \\ &= \tfrac{1}{2}\mu\sum_l(\omega^2+\omega_{nl}^2)x_{ln}^2. \end{aligned}$$

In the sum over l, only the terms with $l = n\pm1$ are different from zero;

† We choose the indeterminate phases α_n (see the second footnote to §11) so as to obtain the plus sign in front of the radical in all the matrix elements (21.4). Such a choice is always possible for a matrix in which only those elements are different from zero which correspond to transitions between states with adjacent numbers.

substituting (21.4), we obtain

$$E_n = (n+\tfrac{1}{2})\hbar\omega, \quad n = 0, 1, 2, \ldots. \tag{21.5}$$

Thus the energy levels of the oscillator lie at equal intervals of $\hbar\omega$ from one another. The energy of the normal state ($n = 0$) is $\frac{1}{2}\hbar\omega$; we call attention to the fact that it is not zero.

The result (21.5) can also be obtained by solving SCHRÖDINGER's equation. For an oscillator, this has the form

$$\frac{d^2\psi}{dx^2}+\frac{2\mu}{\hbar^2}(E-\tfrac{1}{2}\mu\omega^2x^2)\psi = 0. \tag{21.6}$$

Here it is convenient to introduce, instead of the co-ordinate x, the dimensionless variable ξ by the relation

$$\xi = \sqrt{(\mu\omega/\hbar)}x. \tag{21.7}$$

Then we have the equation

$$\psi''+[(2E/\hbar\omega)-\xi^2]\psi = 0; \tag{21.8}$$

here the prime denotes differentiation with respect to ξ.

For large ξ, we can neglect $2E/\hbar\omega$ in comparison with ξ^2; the equation $\psi'' = \xi^2\psi$ has the asymptotic integrals $\psi = e^{\pm\frac{1}{2}\xi^2}$ (for differentiation of this function gives $\psi'' = \xi^2\psi$ on neglecting terms of order less than that of the term retained). Since the wave function ψ must remain finite as $\xi \to \pm\infty$, the index must be taken with the minus sign. It is therefore natural to make in equation (21.8) the substitution

$$\psi = e^{-\frac{1}{2}\xi^2}\chi(\xi). \tag{21.9}$$

For the function $\chi(\xi)$ we obtain the equation (with the notation $(2E/\hbar\omega)-1 = 2n$; since we already know that $E > 0$, we have $n > -\frac{1}{2}$)

$$\chi''-2\xi\chi'+2n\chi = 0, \tag{21.10}$$

where the function χ must be finite for all finite ξ, and for $\xi \to \pm\infty$ must not tend to infinity more rapidly than every finite power of ξ (in order that the function ψ should tend to zero).

Such solutions of equation (21.10) exist only for positive integral (and zero) values of n (see §a of the Mathematical Appendices); this gives the eigenvalues (21.5) for the energy, which we know already. The solutions of equation (21.10) corresponding to various integral values of n are $\chi =$ constant$\times H_n(\xi)$, where $H_n(\xi)$ are what are called *Hermite polynomials*; these are polynomials of the nth degree in ξ, defined by the formula

$$H_n(\xi) = (-1)^n e^{\xi^2} d^n(e^{-\xi^2})/d\xi^n. \tag{21.11}$$

The wave functions of the stationary states of the oscillator consequently have the form $\psi_n = c_n e^{-\frac{1}{2}\xi^2}H_n(\xi)$. Determining the constants c_n so that the functions ψ_n satisfy the normalisation condition

$$\int_{-\infty}^{\infty} \psi_n^2(x)\, dx = 1,$$

we obtain (see (a. 7))

$$\psi_n(x) = \left(\frac{\mu\omega}{\pi\hbar}\right)^{\frac{1}{4}} \frac{1}{2^{\frac{1}{2}n}\sqrt{(n!)}} e^{-\frac{1}{2}\mu\omega x^2/\hbar} H_n(x\sqrt{[\mu\omega/\hbar]}). \tag{21.12}$$

Thus the wave function of the normal state is

$$\psi_0(x) = (\mu\omega/\pi\hbar)^{\frac{1}{4}} e^{-\frac{1}{2}\mu\omega x^2/\hbar}. \tag{21.13}$$

It has no zeros for finite x, which is as it should be.

By calculating the integrals $\int_{-\infty}^{\infty} \psi_n \psi_m \xi \, d\xi$, we can determine the matrix elements of the co-ordinate; this calculation leads, of course, to the same values (21.4).

Finally, we shall show how the wave functions ψ_n may be calculated by the matrix method. We notice that, in the matrices of the operators $\hat{\dot{x}} \pm i\omega\hat{x}$, the only elements different from zero are

$$(\hat{\dot{x}} - i\omega\hat{x})_{n-1\,n} = i\omega_{n-1,n}x_{n-1,n} - i\omega x_{n-1,n} = -2i\omega x_{n-1,n}$$

or

$$(\hat{\dot{x}} - i\omega\hat{x})_{n-1\,n} = -(\hat{\dot{x}} + i\omega\hat{x})_{n,n-1} = -i\sqrt{(2\omega\hbar n/\mu)}. \tag{21.14}$$

Using the general formula $\hat{f}\psi_n = \Sigma f_{mn}\psi_m$ (11.11), and taking into account the fact that $\psi_{-1} \equiv 0$, we conclude that

$$(\hat{\dot{x}} - i\omega\hat{x})\psi_0 = 0.$$

After substituting the expressions $\hat{\dot{x}} = -i(\hbar/\mu)\partial/\partial x$ and $\hat{x} = x$ for the operators, we obtain the equation

$$\partial\psi_0/\partial x = -(\mu\omega/\hbar)x\psi_0,$$

whose normalised solution is (21.13). And, since

$$(\hat{\dot{x}} + i\omega\hat{x})\psi_{n-1} = (\hat{\dot{x}} + i\omega\hat{x})_{n,n-1}\psi_n = i\sqrt{(2\omega\hbar n/\mu)}\psi_n,$$

we obtain the recurrence formula

$$\begin{aligned}\psi_n &= \sqrt{(\mu/2\omega\hbar n)}[-(\hbar/\mu)\,\partial/\partial x + \omega x]\psi_{n-1} \\ &= \frac{1}{\sqrt{(2n)}}\left(-\frac{\partial}{\partial\xi} + \xi\right)\psi_{n-1} = -\frac{1}{\sqrt{(2n)}} e^{\frac{1}{2}\xi^2} \frac{d}{d\xi}(e^{-\frac{1}{2}\xi^2}\psi_{n-1});\end{aligned}$$

when this is applied n times to the function (21.13), we immediately obtain the expression (21.12) for the normalised functions ψ_n.

PROBLEMS

PROBLEM 1. Determine the probability distribution of the various values of the momentum for an oscillator.

SOLUTION. Instead of expanding the wave function of the stationary state in terms of the eigenfunctions of momentum, it is simpler in the case of the oscillator to start directly from SCHRÖDINGER's equation in the "p representation". Substituting in (21.1) the co-ordinate operator $\hat{x} = i\hbar\partial/\partial p$ (13.12), we obtain the Hamiltonian in the p representation,

$$\hat{H} = \tfrac{1}{2}p^2/\mu - \tfrac{1}{2}\mu\omega^2\hbar^2\partial^2/\partial p^2.$$

The corresponding SCHRÖDINGER's equation $\hat{H}a(p) = Ea(p)$ for the wave function $a(p)$ in the p representation is

$$\frac{\mathrm{d}^2 a(p)}{\mathrm{d}p^2} + \frac{2}{\mu\omega^2\hbar^2}\left(E - \frac{p^2}{2\mu}\right)a(p) = 0.$$

This equation is of exactly the same form as (21.6); hence its solutions can be written down at once by analogy with (21.12) (replacing $x\sqrt{(\mu\omega/\hbar)}$ in this formula by $p/\sqrt{(\mu\omega\hbar)}$). Thus we find the required probability distribution to be

$$|a_n(p)|^2 = \frac{1}{2^n n!\sqrt{(\pi\mu\omega\hbar)}} e^{-p^2/\mu\omega\hbar} H_n^2(p/\sqrt{[\mu\omega\hbar]}).$$

PROBLEM 2. Determine the lower limit of the possible values of the energy of an oscillator, using the uncertainty relation (14.8a).

SOLUTION. We have for the mean value of the energy of the oscillator

$$\bar{E} = \tfrac{1}{2}\mu\omega^2\overline{x^2} + \tfrac{1}{2}\overline{p^2}/\mu \geqslant \tfrac{1}{2}\mu\omega^2\overline{(\Delta x)^2} + \tfrac{1}{2}\overline{(\Delta p)^2}/\mu,$$

or, using the relation (14.8a),

$$\bar{E} \geqslant \overline{(\Delta p)^2}/2\mu + \mu\omega^2\hbar^2/8\overline{(\Delta p)^2}.$$

On determining the minimum value of this expression (regarded as a function of $\overline{(\Delta p)^2}$), we find the lower limit of the mean values of the energy, and therefore that of all possible values:

$$E \geqslant \tfrac{1}{2}\hbar\omega.$$

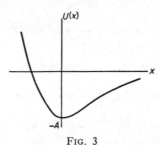

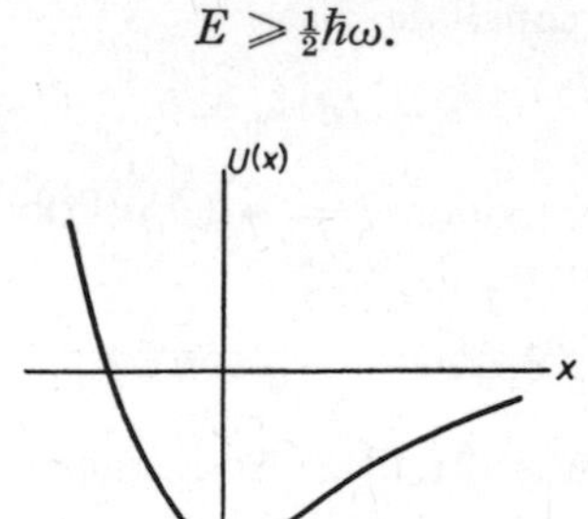

FIG. 3

PROBLEM 3. Determine the energy levels for a particle moving in a field of potential energy (Fig. 3)

$$U(x) = A(e^{-2\alpha x} - 2e^{-\alpha x})$$

(P. M. MORSE).

SOLUTION. The spectrum of positive eigenvalues of the energy is continuous (and the levels are not degenerate), while the spectrum of negative eigenvalues is discrete.

SCHRÖDINGER's equation reads

$$\mathrm{d}^2\psi/\mathrm{d}x^2 + (2\mu/\hbar^2)(E - Ae^{-2\alpha x} + 2Ae^{-\alpha x})\psi = 0.$$

We introduce a new variable

$$\xi = \frac{2\sqrt{(2\mu A)}}{\alpha\hbar}e^{-\alpha x}$$

(taking values from 0 to ∞) and the notation (we consider the discrete spectrum, so that $E < 0$)

$$s = \sqrt{(-2\mu E)}/\alpha\hbar, \quad n = \sqrt{(2\mu A)}/\alpha\hbar-(s+\tfrac{1}{2}). \tag{1}$$

SCHRÖDINGER's equation then takes the form

$$\psi''+\frac{1}{\xi}\psi'+\left(-\tfrac{1}{4}+\frac{n+s+\frac{1}{2}}{\xi}-\frac{s^2}{\xi^2}\right)\psi = 0.$$

As $\xi \to \infty$, the function ψ behaves asymptotically as $e^{\pm\frac{1}{2}\xi}$, while as $\xi \to 0$ it is proportional to $\xi^{\pm s}$. From considerations of finiteness we must choose the solution which behaves as $e^{-\frac{1}{2}\xi}$ as $\xi \to \infty$ and as ξ^s as $\xi \to 0$. We make the substitution

$$\psi = e^{-\frac{1}{2}\xi}\xi^s w(\xi)$$

and obtain for w the equation

$$\xi w''+(2s+1-\xi)w'+nw = 0, \tag{2}$$

which has to be solved with the conditions that w is finite as $\xi \to 0$, while as $\xi \to \infty$, w tends to infinity not more rapidly than every finite power of ξ. Equation (2) is the equation for a confluent hypergeometric function (see §d of the Mathematical Appendices):

$$w = F(-n, 2s+1, \xi).$$

A solution satisfying the required conditions is obtained for non-negative integral n (when the function F reduces to a polynomial). According to the definitions (1), we thus obtain for the energy levels the values

$$-E_n = A\left[1-\frac{\alpha\hbar}{\sqrt{(2\mu A)}}(n+\tfrac{1}{2})\right]^2,$$

where n takes positive integral values from zero to the greatest value for which $\sqrt{(2\mu A)}/\alpha\hbar > n+\frac{1}{2}$ (so that the parameter s is positive in accordance with its definition). Thus the discrete spectrum contains only a limited number of levels. If $\sqrt{(2\mu A)}/\alpha\hbar < \frac{1}{2}$, there is no discrete spectrum at all.

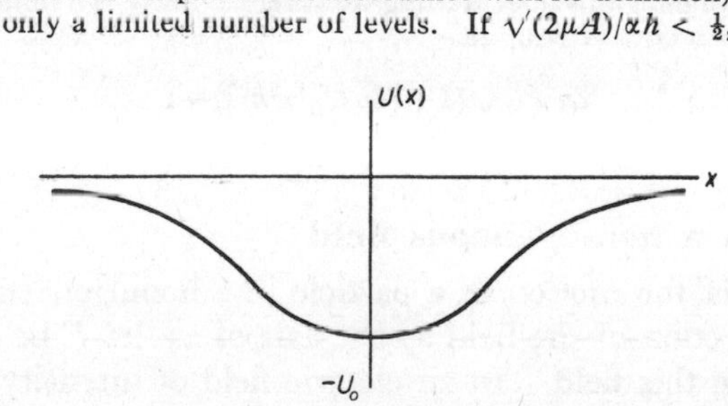

FIG. 4

PROBLEM 4. The same as Problem 3, but with $U = -U_0/\cosh^2 \alpha x$ (Fig. 4).

SOLUTION. The spectrum of positive eigenvalues of the energy is continuous, while that of negative values is discrete; we shall consider the latter. SCHRÖDINGER's equation is

$$\frac{d^2\psi}{dx^2}+\frac{2\mu}{\hbar^2}\left(E+\frac{U_0}{\cosh^2\alpha x}\right)\psi = 0.$$

We make the substitution

$$\psi = \frac{w}{\cosh^s \alpha x}, \quad s = \tfrac{1}{2}\left(-1+\sqrt{\left[1+\frac{8\mu U_0}{\alpha^2\hbar^2}\right]}\right), \tag{1}$$

obtaining

$$\frac{d^2w}{dx^2} - 2s\alpha \tanh(\alpha x)\frac{dw}{dx} + \left(\alpha^2 s^2 + \frac{2\mu E}{\hbar^2}\right)w = 0$$

(s is chosen so that the coefficient of w is constant). This equation can be reduced to a hypergeometric one by introducing the new variable

$$\xi = \sinh^2 \alpha x. \tag{2}$$

Introducing also the constant $\epsilon = \sqrt{(-2\mu E)}/\hbar\alpha$, we obtain

$$\xi(1+\xi)w'' + [(1-s)\xi + \tfrac{1}{2}]w' + \tfrac{1}{4}(s^2-\epsilon^2)w = 0. \tag{3}$$

Since the potential energy $U(\xi)$ is an even function of the co-ordinate, the wave functions of the stationary states must be either even or odd functions (see §19). Since cosh αx is an even function, the parity of ψ is the same as that of $w(x)$. The even and odd (in x) particular integrals of equation (3) are

$$\begin{aligned} w_1 &= F(-\tfrac{1}{2}s+\tfrac{1}{2}\epsilon, -\tfrac{1}{2}s-\tfrac{1}{2}\epsilon, \tfrac{1}{2}, -\xi), \\ w_2 &= \sqrt{\xi}F(-\tfrac{1}{2}s+\tfrac{1}{2}\epsilon+\tfrac{1}{2}, -\tfrac{1}{2}s-\tfrac{1}{2}\epsilon+\tfrac{1}{2}, \tfrac{3}{2}, -\xi) \end{aligned} \tag{4}$$

(when x changes sign, ξ remains the same, while $\sqrt{\xi} = \sinh \alpha x$ changes sign). In order that $\psi = (1+\xi)^{-\frac{1}{2}s}w_1$ should reduce to zero as $\xi \to \infty$, the parameter $\frac{1}{2}\epsilon - \frac{1}{2}s$ must be a negative integer or zero; then F is a polynomial of degree $\frac{1}{2}s - \frac{1}{2}\epsilon$ and ψ tends to zero as $\xi^{-\frac{1}{2}\epsilon}$ as $\xi \to \infty$. Similarly, for $\psi = (1+\xi)^{-\frac{1}{2}s}w_2$, this condition is satisfied if $-\frac{1}{2}s+\frac{1}{2}\epsilon+\frac{1}{2}$ is a negative integer.

Thus the energy levels are determined by $s-\epsilon = n$, or

$$E = -\frac{\hbar^2\alpha^2}{8\mu}\left[-(1+2n)+\sqrt{\left(1+\frac{8\mu U_0}{\alpha^2\hbar^2}\right)}\right]^2,$$

where n takes positive integral values starting from zero. There is a finite number of levels, determined by the condition $\epsilon > 0$, i.e.

$$2n < \sqrt{(1+[8\mu U_0/\alpha^2\hbar^2])}-1.$$

§22. Motion in a homogeneous field

Let us consider the motion of a particle in a homogeneous external field. We take the direction of the field as the axis of x; let F be the force acting on the particle in this field. In an electric field of intensity E, this force is $F = eE$, where e is the charge on the particle.

The potential energy of the particle in the homogeneous field is of the form $U = -Fx + \text{constant}$; choosing the constant so that $U = 0$ for $x = 0$, we have $U = -Fx$. SCHRÖDINGER's equation for this problem is

$$d^2\psi/dx^2 + (2\mu/\hbar^2)(E+Fx)\psi = 0. \tag{22.1}$$

Since U tends to $+\infty$ as $x \to -\infty$, and *vice versa*, it is clear that the energy levels form a continuous spectrum occupying the whole range of energy values E from $-\infty$ to $+\infty$. None of these eigenvalues is degenerate, and they correspond to motion which is finite towards $x = -\infty$ and infinite towards $x = +\infty$.

Instead of the co-ordinate x, we introduce the dimensionless variable

$$\xi = (x+E/F)(2\mu F/\hbar^2)^{1/3}. \tag{22.2}$$

Equation (22.1) then takes the form

$$\psi''+\xi\psi = 0. \tag{22.3}$$

This equation does not contain the energy parameter. Hence, if we obtain a solution of it which satisfies the necessary conditions of finiteness, we at once have the eigenfunction for arbitrary values of the energy.

The solution of equation (22.3) which is finite for all x has the form (see §b of the Mathematical Appendices)

$$\psi(\xi) = A\Phi(-\xi), \tag{22.4}$$

where

$$\Phi(\xi) = \frac{1}{\sqrt{\pi}}\int\limits_0^\infty \cos(\tfrac{1}{3}u^3+u\xi)\,du$$

is called the *Airy function*, while A is a normalisation factor which we shall determine below.

As $\xi \to -\infty$, the function $\psi(\xi)$ tends exponentially to zero. The asymptotic expression which determines $\psi(\xi)$ for large negative values of ξ is (see (b.4))

$$\psi(\xi) \approx \frac{A}{2|\xi|^{1/4}}\exp[-\tfrac{2}{3}|\xi|^{3/2}]. \tag{22.5}$$

For large positive values of ξ, the asymptotic expression for $\psi(\xi)$ is (see (b.5))

$$\psi(\xi) = A\xi^{-1/4}\sin(\tfrac{2}{3}\xi^{3/2}+\tfrac{1}{4}\pi). \tag{22.6}$$

We notice that the argument of the sine is, apart from a constant, the action of the particle divided by $\hbar$:

$$S/\hbar = (1/\hbar)\int p\,dx = (1/\hbar)\int \sqrt{[2\mu(E+Fx)]}\,dx$$

$$= \frac{2\sqrt{(2\mu)}}{3F\hbar}(E+Fx)^{3/2} + \text{constant} = \tfrac{2}{3}\xi^{3/2} + \text{constant}.$$

In other words, the wave function in this region is quasi-classical.

Using the general rule (5.4) for the normalisation of eigenfunctions of a continuous spectrum, let us reduce the function (22.4) to the form normalised by the delta function of energy, for which

$$\int_{-\infty}^{\infty} \psi(\xi)\psi(\xi')\,\mathrm{d}x = \delta(E'-E). \tag{22.7}$$

In §19 we gave a simple method of determining the normalisation coefficient by means of the asymptotic expression for the wave functions. Following this method, we represent the function (22.6) as the sum of two travelling waves:

$$\psi(\xi) \approx \tfrac{1}{2}A\xi^{-1/4}\exp(i[\tfrac{2}{3}\xi^{3/2}-\tfrac{1}{4}\pi])+\tfrac{1}{2}A\xi^{-1/4}\exp(-i[\tfrac{2}{3}\xi^{3/2}-\tfrac{1}{4}\pi]).$$

The probability current density $v|\psi|^2$, calculated from each of these two terms, must be $1/2\pi\hbar$:

$$\sqrt{[2(E+Fx)/\mu]}(A/2\xi^{1/4})^2 = A^2(2\hbar F)^{1/3}/4\mu^{2/3} = 1/2\pi\hbar,$$

whence we find

$$A = \frac{(2\mu)^{1/3}}{\pi^{1/2}F^{1/6}\hbar^{2/3}}. \tag{22.8}$$

PROBLEM

Determine the wave functions in the p representation for a particle in a homogeneous field.

SOLUTION. The Hamiltonian operator in the p representation is

$$\hat{H} = p^2/2\mu - i\hbar F\,\partial/\partial p,$$

so that SCHRÖDINGER's equation for the wave function $a(p)$ has the form

$$-i\hbar F\frac{\mathrm{d}a}{\mathrm{d}p}+\left(\frac{p^2}{2\mu}-E\right)a = 0.$$

Solving this equation, we find the required functions

$$a_E(p) = (2\pi\hbar F)^{-\frac{1}{2}}e^{(i/\hbar F)(Ep-p^3/6\mu)}.$$

These functions are normalised by the condition

$$\int_{-\infty}^{\infty} a_E^*(p)a_{E'}(p)\,\mathrm{d}p = \delta(E'-E).$$

§23. The transmission coefficient

Let us consider the motion of particles in a field of the type shown in Fig. 5: $U(x)$ increases monotonically from one constant limit ($U = 0$ as $x \to -\infty$) to another ($U = U_0$ as $x \to +\infty$). According to classical mechanics, a particle of energy $E < U_0$ moving in such a field from left to right, on reaching such a "potential wall", is "reflected" from it, and begins to move in the opposite direction; if, however, $E > U_0$, the particle continues to move in its original direction, though with diminished velocity. In quantum mechanics, a new phenomenon appears: even for $E > U_0$, the particle may be "reflected" from the potential wall. The probability of reflection must in principle be calculated as follows.

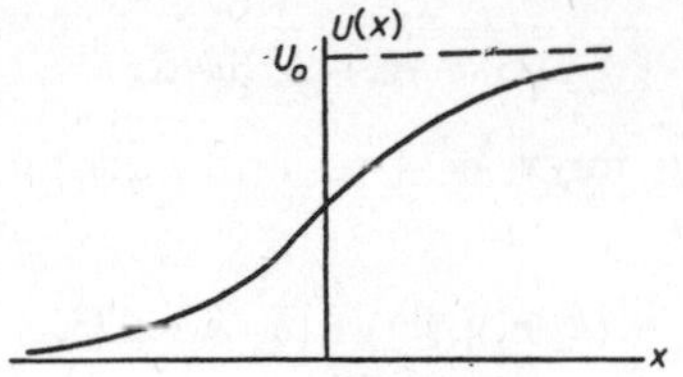

FIG. 5

For large positive values of x, the wave function must describe a particle which has passed "above the wall" and is moving in the positive direction of x, i.e. it must have the asymptotic form

$$\text{for } x \to \infty,\ \psi \approx Ae^{ik_2x}, \quad \text{where } k_2 = (1/\hbar)\sqrt{[2\mu(E-U_0)]} \tag{23.1}$$

and A is a constant. To find the solution of SCHRÖDINGER's equation which satisfies this boundary condition, we calculate the asymptotic expression for $x \to -\infty$; it is a linear combination of the two solutions of the equation of free motion, i.e. it has the form

$$\text{for } x \to -\infty,\ \psi \approx e^{ik_1x}+Be^{-ik_1x}, \quad \text{where } k_1 = \sqrt{(2\mu E)}/\hbar. \tag{23.2}$$

The first term corresponds to a particle incident on the "wall" (we suppose ψ normalised so that the coefficient of this term is unity); the second term represents a particle reflected from the "wall". The probability current density in the incident wave is k_1, in the reflected wave $k_1|B|^2$, and in the transmitted wave $k_2|A|^2$. We define the *transmission coefficient* D of the particle as the ratio of the probability current density in the transmitted wave to that in the incident wave:

$$D = (k_2/k_1)|A|^2. \tag{23.3}$$

Similarly we can define the *reflection coefficient* R as the ratio of the density in the reflected wave to that in the incident wave. Evidently $R = 1-D$:

$$R = |B|^2 = 1-(k_2/k_1)|A|^2 \tag{23.4}$$

(this relation between A and B is automatically satisfied).

An important property of the transmission coefficient (and of the reflection coefficient) is that it is the same (for a given energy $E > U_0$) for particles moving in the positive or negative direction of x. For let us consider a particle moving from right to left, and let ψ' be its wave function. For $x \to -\infty$, this must satisfy the boundary condition

$$\psi' \approx A'e^{-ik_1x} \tag{23.5}$$

(the *transmitted* wave), while the asymptotic form for $x \to +\infty$ is

$$\psi' \approx e^{-ik_2x}+B'e^{ik_2x}. \tag{23.6}$$

Since ψ and ψ' are two different solutions of the same equation, we can use the relation (19.2), taking as ψ_1, ψ_2 the functions ψ, ψ'. Calculating the expression

$$\psi \, \mathrm{d}\psi'/\mathrm{d}x - \psi' \, \mathrm{d}\psi/\mathrm{d}x$$

for $x \to -\infty$ and again for $x \to +\infty$ and equating the results, we obtain $2ik_1A' = 2ik_2A$, whence

$$(k_2/k_1)|A|^2 = (k_1/k_2)|A'|^2,$$

i.e. the transmission coefficients D and D' are equal.

If the particle moves from left to right with energy $E < U_0$, then k_2 is purely imaginary, and the wave function decreases exponentially as $x \to +\infty$. The reflected current is equal to the incident one, i.e. we have "total reflection" of the particle from the potential wall. We emphasise, however, that in this case the probability of finding the particle in the region where $E < U_0$ is still different from zero, though it diminishes rapidly as x increases.

PROBLEMS

PROBLEM 1. Determine the reflection coefficient of a particle from a rectangular potential wall (Fig. 6); the energy of the particle $E > U_0$.

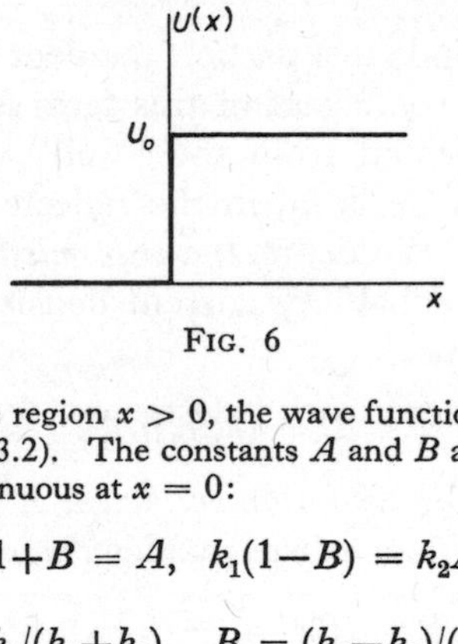

FIG. 6

SOLUTION. Throughout the region $x > 0$, the wave function has the form (23.1), while in the region $x < 0$ its form is (23.2). The constants A and B are determined from the condition that ψ and $\mathrm{d}\psi/\mathrm{d}x$ are continuous at $x = 0$:

$$1+B = A, \quad k_1(1-B) = k_2A,$$

whence

$$A = 2k_1/(k_1+k_2), \quad B = (k_1-k_2)/(k_1+k_2).$$

The reflection coefficient† is (23.4)

$$R = \left(\frac{k_1-k_2}{k_1+k_2}\right)^2 = \left(\frac{p_1-p_2}{p_1+p_2}\right)^2.$$

For $E = U_0$ ($k_2 = 0$), R becomes unity, while for $E \to \infty$ it tends to zero as $(U_0/4E)^2$.

† In the limiting case of classical mechanics, the reflection coefficient must become zero. The expression obtained here, however, does not contain the quantum constant at all. This apparent contradiction is explained as follows. The classical limiting case is that in which the de Broglie wavelength of the particle $\lambda \sim \hbar/p$ is small in comparison with the characteristic dimensions of the problem, i.e. the distances over which the field $U(x)$ changes noticeably. In the schematic example considered, however, this distance is zero (at the point $x = 0$), so that the passage to the limit cannot be effected.

Problem 2. Determine the transmission coefficient for a rectangular potential barrier (Fig. 7).

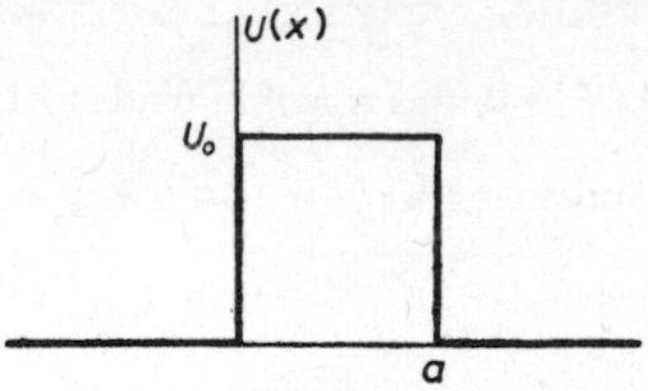

Fig. 7

Solution. Let E be greater than U_0, and suppose that the incident particle is moving from left to right. Then we have for the wave function in the different regions expressions of the form

$$\text{for } x < 0, \qquad \psi = e^{ik_1x}+Ae^{-ik_1x},$$
$$\text{for } 0 < x < a, \ \psi = Be^{ik_2x}+B'e^{-ik_2x},$$
$$\text{for } x > a, \qquad \psi = Ce^{ik_1x}$$

(on the side $x > a$ there can be only the transmitted wave, propagated in the positive direction of x). The constants A, B, B' and C are determined from the conditions of continuity of ψ and $d\psi/dx$ at the points $x = 0$ and a. The penetration coefficient is determined as $D = k_1|C|^2/k_1 = |C|^2$. On calculating this, we obtain

$$D = \frac{4k_1^2k_2^2}{(k_1^2-k_2^2)^2 \sin^2 ak_2+4k_1^2k_2^2}.$$

For $E < U_0$, k_2 is a purely imaginary quantity; the corresponding expression for D is obtained by replacing k_2 by $i\kappa_2$, where $\hbar\kappa_2 = \sqrt{[2\mu(U_0-E)]}$:

$$D = \frac{4k_1^2\kappa_2^2}{(k_1^2+\kappa_2^2)^2 \sinh^2 a\kappa_2+4k_1^2\kappa_2^2}.$$

Problem 3. Determine the reflection coefficient for a potential wall defined by the formula $U(x) = U_0/(1+e^{-\alpha x})$ (Fig. 5); the energy of the particle is $E > U_0$.

Solution. Schrödinger's equation is

$$\frac{d^2\psi}{dx^2}+\frac{2\mu}{\hbar^2}\left(E-\frac{U_0}{1+e^{-\alpha x}}\right)\psi = 0.$$

We have to find a solution which, as $x \to +\infty$, has the form

$$\psi = \text{constant} \times e^{ik_2x}.$$

We introduce a new variable

$$\xi = -e^{-\alpha x}$$

(which takes values from $-\infty$ to 0), and seek a solution of the form

$$\psi = \xi^{-ik_2/\alpha}w(\xi),$$

where $w(\xi)$ tends to a constant as $\xi \to 0$ (i.e., as $x \to \infty$). For $w(\xi)$ we find an equation of hypergeometric type:

$$\xi(1-\xi)w''+(1-2ik_2/\alpha)(1-\xi)w'+(k_2^2-k_1^2)w/\alpha^2 = 0,$$

which has as its solution the hypergeometric function

$$w = F(i[k_1-k_2]/\alpha, \quad -i[k_1+k_2]/\alpha, \quad -2ik_2/\alpha+1, \xi)$$

(we omit a constant factor). As $\xi \to 0$, this function tends to 1, i.e. it satisfies the condition imposed.

The asymptotic form of the function ψ as $\xi \to -\infty$ (i.e. $x \to -\infty$) is†

$$\psi \approx \xi^{-ik_2/\alpha}[C_1(-\xi)^{i(k_2-k_1)/\alpha}+C_2(-\xi)^{i(k_1+k_2)/\alpha}] = (-1)^{-ik_2/\alpha}[C_1e^{ik_1x}+C_2e^{-ik_1x}],$$

where

$$C_1 = \frac{\Gamma(-2ik_1/\alpha)\Gamma(-2ik_2/\alpha+1)}{\Gamma(-i(k_1+k_2)/\alpha)\Gamma(-i(k_1+k_2)/\alpha+1)},$$

$$C_2 = \frac{\Gamma(2ik_1/\alpha)\Gamma(-2ik_2/\alpha+1)}{\Gamma(i(k_1-k_2)/\alpha)\Gamma(i(k_1-k_2)/\alpha+1)}.$$

The required reflection coefficient is $R = |C_2/C_1|^2$; on calculating it by means of the well-known formulae

$$\Gamma(x+1) = x\Gamma(x), \quad \Gamma(x)\Gamma(1-x) = \pi/\sin \pi x,$$

we have

$$R = \left(\frac{\sinh[\pi(k_1-k_2)/\alpha]}{\sinh[\pi(k_1+k_2)/\alpha]}\right)^2.$$

For $E = U_0$ ($k_2 = 0$), R becomes unity, while for $E \to \infty$ it tends to zero as

$$\left(\frac{\pi U_0}{\alpha\hbar}\right)^2 \frac{2\mu}{E} e^{-4\pi\sqrt{(2\mu E)}/\alpha\hbar}.$$

In the limiting case of classical mechanics, R becomes zero, as it should.

PROBLEM 4. Determine the transmission coefficient for a potential barrier defined by the formula

$$U(x) = U_0/\cosh^2\alpha x$$

(Fig. 8); the energy of the particle is $E < U_0$.

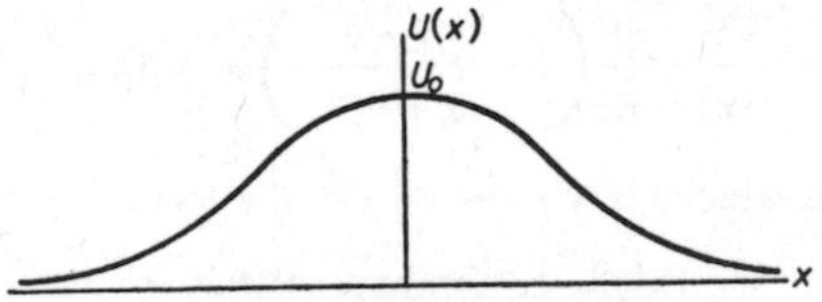

FIG. 8

SOLUTION. The solution of SCHRÖDINGER's equation is the same as that obtained as (4) in the solution of Problem 4, §21; it is necessary merely to alter the sign of the constant U_0 and to regard E as positive. Thus

$$\psi = \cosh^s\alpha x\{C_1F(-\tfrac{1}{2}s+\tfrac{1}{2}ik/\alpha, -\tfrac{1}{2}s-\tfrac{1}{2}ik/\alpha, \tfrac{1}{2}, -\sinh^2\alpha x)+$$
$$+C_2 \sinh \alpha x\, F(-\tfrac{1}{2}s+\tfrac{1}{2}ik/\alpha+\tfrac{1}{2}, -\tfrac{1}{2}s-\tfrac{1}{2}ik/\alpha+\tfrac{1}{2}, \tfrac{3}{2}, -\sinh^2\alpha x)\},$$

† See formula (e.6), in each of whose two terms we must take only the first term of the expansion, i.e. replace the hypergeometric functions of $1/z$ by unity.

where

$$s = \tfrac{1}{2}(-1+\sqrt{(1-8\mu U_0/\alpha^2\hbar^2)}), \quad k = \sqrt{(2\mu E)}/\hbar.$$

The asymptotic form of this solution as $x \to \pm\infty$ is easily found by means of formula (e.6). The ratio of the constants C_1 and C_2 is chosen so that, as $x \to \infty$, the wave function contains only the wave $\sim e^{ikx}$. After some calculation, the following expression is obtained for the penetration coefficient:

$$D = \frac{\sinh^2(\pi k/\alpha)}{\sinh^2(\pi k/\alpha)+\cos^2[\frac{1}{2}\pi\sqrt{(1-8\mu U_0/\hbar^2\alpha^2)}]}$$

(if $8\mu U_0/\hbar^2\alpha^2 < 1$), or

$$D = \frac{\sinh^2(\pi k/\alpha)}{\sinh^2(\pi k/\alpha)+\cosh^2[\frac{1}{2}\pi\sqrt{(8\mu U_0/\hbar^2\alpha^2-1)}]}$$

(if $8\mu U_0/\hbar^2\alpha^2 > 1$).

CHAPTER IV

ANGULAR MOMENTUM

§24. Angular momentum

In §13, to derive the law of conservation of momentum, we have made use of the homogeneity of space relative to a closed system of particles. Besides its homogeneity, space has also the property of isotropy: all directions in it are equivalent. Hence the Hamiltonian of a closed system cannot change when the system rotates as a whole through an arbitrary angle about an arbitrary axis. It is sufficient, as in §13, to require the fulfilment of this condition for an infinitely small rotation.

Let $\delta\boldsymbol{\varphi}$ be the vector of an infinitely small rotation, equal in magnitude to the angle $\delta\phi$ of the rotation and directed along the axis about which the rotation takes place. The changes $\delta\mathbf{r}_a$ (in the radius vectors $\mathbf{r}_a$ of the particles) in such a rotation are well known to be

$$\delta\mathbf{r}_a = \delta\boldsymbol{\varphi}\times\mathbf{r}_a.$$

An arbitrary function $\psi(\mathbf{r}_1, \mathbf{r}_2, \ldots)$ is thereby transformed into the function

$$\begin{aligned}\psi(\mathbf{r}_1+\delta\mathbf{r}_1, \mathbf{r}_2+\delta\mathbf{r}_2, \ldots) &= \psi(\mathbf{r}_1, \mathbf{r}_2, \ldots)+\sum_a \delta\mathbf{r}_a\cdot\nabla_a\psi\\ &= \psi(\mathbf{r}_1, \mathbf{r}_2, \ldots)+\sum_a \delta\boldsymbol{\varphi}\times\mathbf{r}_a\cdot\nabla_a\psi\\ &= (1+\delta\boldsymbol{\varphi}\cdot\sum_a\mathbf{r}_a\times\nabla_a)\psi(\mathbf{r}_1, \mathbf{r}_2, \ldots).\end{aligned}$$

The expression

$$1+\delta\boldsymbol{\varphi}\cdot\sum_a\mathbf{r}_a\times\nabla_a$$

can be regarded as the "operator of an infinitely small rotation". The fact that an infinitely small rotation does not alter the Hamiltonian of the system is expressed (see §13) by the commutability of the "rotation operator" with the operator $\hat{H}$. Since the operator of multiplication by unity commutes with any operator, while $\delta\boldsymbol{\varphi}$ is a constant vector, this condition reduces to the relation

$$(\sum_a\mathbf{r}_a\times\nabla_a)\hat{H}-\hat{H}(\sum_a\mathbf{r}_a\times\nabla_a) = 0, \tag{24.1}$$

which expresses a certain law of conservation.

The quantity whose conservation for a closed system follows from the property of isotropy of space is the *angular momentum* of the system. Thus the operator $\Sigma\mathbf{r}_a\times\nabla_a$ must correspond exactly, apart from a constant factor, to the total angular momentum of the system, and each of the terms $\mathbf{r}_a\times\nabla_a$ of this sum corresponds to the angular momentum of an individual particle

The coefficient of proportionality must be put equal to $-i\hbar$; this follows immediately, because then the expression for the angular momentum operator of a particle is $-i\hbar\mathbf{r}\times\nabla = \mathbf{r}\times\hat{\mathbf{p}}$ and corresponds exactly to the familiar classical expression $\mathbf{r}\times\mathbf{p}$. Henceforward we shall always use the angular momentum measured in units of $\hbar$. The angular momentum operator of a particle, so defined, will be denoted by $\hat{\mathbf{l}}$, and that of the whole system by $\hat{\mathbf{L}}$. Thus we have for the angular momentum component operators of a particle the expressions

$$\hbar\hat{l}_x = y\hat{p}_z - z\hat{p}_y, \quad \hbar\hat{l}_y = z\hat{p}_x - x\hat{p}_z, \quad \hbar\hat{l}_z = x\hat{p}_y - y\hat{p}_x. \tag{24.2}$$

For a system which is in an external field, the angular momentum is in general not conserved. However, it may still be conserved if the field has a certain symmetry. Thus, if the system is in a centrally symmetric field, all directions in space at the centre are equivalent, and hence the angular momentum about this centre will be conserved. Similarly, in an axially symmetric field, the component of angular momentum along the axis of symmetry is conserved. All these conservation laws holding in classical mechanics are valid in quantum mechanics also.

In a system where angular momentum is not conserved, it does not have definite values in the stationary states. In such cases the mean value of the angular momentum in a given stationary state is sometimes of interest. It is easily seen that, in any non-degenerate stationary state, the mean value of the angular momentum is zero. For, when the sign of the time is changed, the energy does not alter, and, since only one stationary state corresponds to a given energy level, it follows that when t is changed into $-t$ the state of the system must remain the same. This means that the mean values of all quantities, and in particular that of the angular momentum, must remain unchanged. But when the sign of the time is changed, so is that of the angular momentum, and we have $\bar{\mathbf{L}} = -\bar{\mathbf{L}}$, whence it follows that $\bar{\mathbf{L}} = 0$. The same result can be obtained by starting from the mathematical definition of the mean value $\bar{\mathbf{L}}$ as being the integral of $\psi^*\hat{\mathbf{L}}\psi$. The wave functions of non-degenerate states are real (see the end of §16). Hence the expression

$$\bar{\mathbf{L}} = -i\hbar \int \psi\left(\sum_a \mathbf{r}_a \times \nabla_a\right)\psi \, dq$$

is purely imaginary, and since $\bar{\mathbf{L}}$ must, of course, be real, it is evident that $\bar{\mathbf{L}} = 0$.

Let us derive the rules for commutation of the angular momentum operators with those of co-ordinates and linear momenta. By means of the relations (14.2) we easily find

$$\left.\begin{aligned} \{\hat{l}_x, x\} &= 0, \quad \{\hat{l}_x, y\} = iz, \quad \{\hat{l}_x, z\} = -iy, \\ \{\hat{l}_y, y\} &= 0, \quad \{\hat{l}_y, z\} = ix, \quad \{\hat{l}_y, x\} = -iz, \\ \{\hat{l}_z, z\} &= 0, \quad \{\hat{l}_z, x\} = iy, \quad \{\hat{l}_z, y\} = -ix. \end{aligned}\right\} \tag{24.3}$$

Thus, for instance,

$$\hat{l}_x y - y\hat{l}_x = (1/\hbar)(y\hat{p}_z - z\hat{p}_y)y - y(y\hat{p}_z - z\hat{p}_y)(1/\hbar)$$
$$= -(z/\hbar)\{\hat{p}_y, y\} = iz.$$

All the relations (24.3) can be written in tensor form as follows:

$$\{\hat{l}_i, x_k\} = ie_{ikl}x_l, \tag{24.4}$$

where e_{ikl} is the antisymmetric unit tensor of rank three†, and summation is implied over those suffixes which appear twice (called *dummy suffixes*).

It is easily seen that a similar commutation rule holds for the angular momentum and linear momentum operators:

$$\{\hat{l}_i, \hat{p}_k\} = ie_{ikl}\hat{p}_l. \tag{24.5}$$

By means of these formulae, it is easy to find the rules for commutation of the operators $\hat{l}_x$, $\hat{l}_y$, $\hat{l}_z$ with one another. We have

$$\hbar(\hat{l}_x\hat{l}_y - \hat{l}_y\hat{l}_x) = \hat{l}_x(z\hat{p}_x - x\hat{p}_z) - (z\hat{p}_x - x\hat{p}_z)\hat{l}_x$$
$$= (\hat{l}_x z - z\hat{l}_x)\hat{p}_x - x(\hat{l}_x\hat{p}_z - \hat{p}_z\hat{l}_x)$$
$$= -iy\hat{p}_x + ix\hat{p}_y = i\hbar\hat{l}_z.$$

Thus

$$\{\hat{l}_y, \hat{l}_z\} = i\hat{l}_x, \quad \{\hat{l}_z, \hat{l}_x\} = i\hat{l}_y, \quad \{\hat{l}_x, \hat{l}_y\} = i\hat{l}_z, \tag{24.6}$$

or

$$\{\hat{l}_i, \hat{l}_k\} = ie_{ikl}\hat{l}_l. \tag{24.7}$$

Exactly the same relations hold for the operators $\hat{L}_x$, $\hat{L}_y$, $\hat{L}_z$ of the total angular momentum of the system. For, since the angular momentum operators of the individual particles commute, we have, for instance,

$$\sum_a \hat{l}_{ay} \sum_a \hat{l}_{az} - \sum_a \hat{l}_{az} \sum_a \hat{l}_{ay} = \sum_a (\hat{l}_{ay}\hat{l}_{az} - \hat{l}_{az}\hat{l}_{ay}) = i\sum_a \hat{l}_{ax}.$$

Thus

$$\{\hat{L}_y, \hat{L}_z\} = i\hat{L}_x, \quad \{\hat{L}_z, \hat{L}_x\} = i\hat{L}_y, \quad \{\hat{L}_x, \hat{L}_y\} = i\hat{L}_z. \tag{24.8}$$

The relations (24.8) show that the three components of the angular momentum cannot simultaneously have definite values (except in the case where all three components simultaneously vanish: see below). In this respect the angular momentum is fundamentally different from the linear momentum, whose three components can simultaneously have definite values.

† The ***antisymmetric unit tensor*** of rank three, e_{ikl} (also called the ***unit axial tensor***) is defined as a tensor antisymmetric in all three suffixes, with $e_{123} = 1$. It is evident that, of its 27 components, only 6 are not zero, namely those in which the suffixes i, k, l form some permutation of 1, 2, 3. Such a component is $+1$ if the permutation i, k, l is obtained from 1, 2, 3 by an even number of transpositions of pairs of figures, and is -1 if the number of transpositions is odd. Clearly $e_{ikl}{}^2 = 6$. The components of the vector $\mathbf{C} = \mathbf{A} \times \mathbf{B}$ which is the vector product of the two vectors $\mathbf{A}$ and $\mathbf{B}$ can be written by means of the tensor e_{ikl} in the form

$$C_i = e_{ikl}A_kB_l.$$

From the operators $\hat{L}_x$, $\hat{L}_y$, $\hat{L}_z$ we can form the operator $\hat{L}_x^2+\hat{L}_y^2+\hat{L}_z^2$, which can be regarded as the operator of the square of the modulus of the angular momentum vector, and which we denote by $\hat{\mathbf{L}}^2$:

$$\hat{\mathbf{L}}^2 = \hat{L}_x^2+\hat{L}_y^2+\hat{L}_z^2 \tag{24.9}$$

(and correspondingly we denote the same operator for a single particle by $\hat{\mathbf{l}}^2$; the operator $\hat{\mathbf{L}}^2$ is not, of course, equal to the sum of the $\hat{\mathbf{l}}_a^2$). We shall show that this operator commutes with each of the operators $\hat{L}_x$, $\hat{L}_y$, $\hat{L}_z$. Using (24.8), we have

$$\begin{aligned}
\{\hat{L}_x^2, \hat{L}_z\} &= \hat{L}_x\{\hat{L}_x, \hat{L}_z\}+\{\hat{L}_x, \hat{L}_z\}\hat{L}_x \\
&= -i(\hat{L}_x\hat{L}_y+\hat{L}_y\hat{L}_x), \\
\{\hat{L}_y^2, \hat{L}_z\} &= i(\hat{L}_x\hat{L}_y+\hat{L}_y\hat{L}_x), \\
\{\hat{L}_z^2, \hat{L}_z\} &= 0.
\end{aligned}$$

Adding these equations, we have $\{\hat{\mathbf{L}}^2, \hat{L}_z\} = 0$; the same clearly holds with $\hat{L}_x$ or $\hat{L}_y$ in place of $\hat{L}_z$. Thus

$$\{\hat{\mathbf{L}}^2, \hat{L}_x\} = 0, \quad \{\hat{\mathbf{L}}^2, \hat{L}_y\} = 0, \quad \{\hat{\mathbf{L}}^2, \hat{L}_z\} = 0. \tag{24.10}$$

Physically, these relations mean that the square of the angular momentum, i.e. its modulus, can have a definite value at the same time as one of its components.

For the operators of the components of angular momentum of a single particle it is often convenient to use their expressions in spherical and not Cartesian co-ordinates. Introducing the spherical co-ordinates r, θ, ϕ in accordance with the usual relations

$$x = r\sin\theta\cos\phi, \quad y = r\sin\theta\sin\phi, \quad z = r\cos\theta,$$

we have after a simple calculation the following expression for the operator of the component l_z of the angular momentum along the polar axis:

$$\hat{l}_z = -i(x\partial/\partial y - y\partial/\partial x) = -i\,\partial/\partial\phi. \tag{24.11}$$

Instead of the operators $\hat{l}_x$, $\hat{l}_y$ it is usually more convenient to use the complex combinations $\hat{l}_x \pm i\hat{l}_y$ of them. For these we have

$$\begin{aligned}
\hat{l}_x+i\hat{l}_y &= e^{i\phi}(\partial/\partial\theta+i\cot\theta\,\partial/\partial\phi), \\
\hat{l}_x-i\hat{l}_y &= e^{-i\phi}(-\partial/\partial\theta+i\cot\theta\,\partial/\partial\phi).
\end{aligned} \tag{24.12}$$

Let us express the operator $\hat{\mathbf{L}}^2$ of the square of the angular momentum of the system in terms of the operators $\hat{L}_x \pm i\hat{L}_y$. Using the third of the relations (24.8), we find

$$\begin{aligned}
(\hat{L}_x+i\hat{L}_y)(\hat{L}_x-i\hat{L}_y) &= \hat{L}_x^2+\hat{L}_y^2-i(\hat{L}_x\hat{L}_y-\hat{L}_y\hat{L}_x) \\
&= \hat{L}_x^2+\hat{L}_y^2+\hat{L}_z.
\end{aligned}$$

Adding $\hat{L}_z^2$ to both sides of the equation, we obtain

$$\mathbf{L}^2 = (\hat{L}_x+i\hat{L}_y)(\hat{L}_x-i\hat{L}_y)+\hat{L}_z^2-\hat{L}_z. \tag{24.13}$$

Similarly

$$\mathbf{L}^2 = (\hat{L}_x-i\hat{L}_y)(\hat{L}_x+i\hat{L}_y)+\hat{L}_z^2+\hat{L}_z. \tag{24.14}$$

Substituting here (24.11) and (24.12), we obtain after a simple calculation the following expression for the operator $\hat{\mathbf{l}}^2$ of the square of the angular momentum of a single particle in spherical co-ordinates:

$$\hat{\mathbf{l}}^2 = -\left[\frac{1}{\sin^2\theta}\frac{\partial^2}{\partial\phi^2}+\frac{1}{\sin\theta}\frac{\partial}{\partial\theta}\left(\sin\theta\frac{\partial}{\partial\theta}\right)\right]. \tag{24.15}$$

It should be noticed that this is, apart from a factor, the angular part of the Laplacian operator.

§25. Eigenvalues of the angular momentum

In order to determine the eigenvalues of the component, in some direction, of the angular momentum of a particle, it is convenient to use the expression for its operator in spherical co-ordinates, taking the direction in question as the polar axis. According to formula (24.11), the equation $\hat{l}_z\psi = l_z\psi$ can be written in the form

$$-i\,\partial\psi/\partial\phi = l_z\psi. \tag{25.1}$$

Its solution is

$$\psi = f(r,\theta)e^{il_z\phi},$$

where $f(r, \theta)$ is an arbitrary function of r and θ. If the function is to be one-valued, it must be periodic in ϕ, with period 2π. Hence we find

$$l_z = m, \quad \text{where } m = 0, \pm 1, \pm 2, \ldots. \tag{25.2}$$

Thus the eigenvalues l_z are the positive and negative integers, including zero. The factor depending on ϕ, which characterises the eigenfunctions of the operator $\hat{l}_z$, is denoted by

$$\Phi_m(\phi) = (2\pi)^{-\frac{1}{2}}e^{im\phi}. \tag{25.3}$$

These functions are normalised so that

$$\int_0^{2\pi} \Phi_m^*(\phi)\Phi_{m'}(\phi)\,d\phi = \delta_{mm'}. \tag{25.4}$$

The eigenvalues of the z-component of the total angular momentum of the system are evidently also equal to the positive and negative integers:

$$L_z = M, \quad \text{where } M = 0, \pm 1, \pm 2, \ldots \tag{25.5}$$

(this follows at once from (25.2), since the operator $\hat{L}_z$ is equal to the sum of the commuting operators $\hat{l}_z$ for the individual particles).

Since the direction of the z-axis is in no way distinctive, it is clear that the same result is obtained for $\hat{L}_x$, $\hat{L}_y$ and in general for the component of the angular momentum in any direction: on measurement, they can all take integral values only. At first sight this result may appear paradoxical, particularly if we apply it to two directions infinitely close to each other. In fact, however, it must be remembered that the only common eigenfunction of the operators $\hat{L}_x$, $\hat{L}_y$, $\hat{L}_z$ corresponds to the simultaneous values

$$L_x = L_y = L_z = 0;$$

in this case the angular momentum vector is zero, and consequently so is its projection upon any direction. If even one of the eigenvalues L_x, L_y, L_z is not zero, the operators $\hat{L}_x$, $\hat{L}_y$, $\hat{L}_z$ have no common eigenfunctions. In other words, there is no state in which two or three of the angular momentum components in different directions simultaneously have definite values different from zero, so that we can say only that one of them is integral.

The stationary states of a system which differ only in the value of L_z have the same energy; this follows from general considerations, together with the fact that the direction of the z-axis is in no way distinctive. Thus the energy levels of a system whose angular momentum is conserved (and is not zero) are always degenerate†.

Let us now look for the eigenvalues of the square $\hat{\mathbf{L}}^2$ of the angular momentum. We shall show how these values may be found, starting from the commutation conditions (24.8) only. We denote by ψ_M the wave functions of the stationary states belonging to one degenerate energy level and distinguished by the value of $L_z = M$. Besides the energy, the square $\hat{\mathbf{L}}^2$ of the angular momentum also has a (single) definite value in these states.‡

First of all, we note that since the difference

$$\hat{\mathbf{L}}^2 - \hat{L}_z^2 = \hat{L}_x^2 + \hat{L}_y^2$$

is equal to the operator of the essentially positive physical quantity $L_x^2 + L_y^2$, it follows that, for a given value of the squared angular momentum $\mathbf{L}^2$ and any possible eigenvalue of the quantity L_z, the inequality $\mathbf{L}^2 \geqslant L_z^2$, or

$$-\sqrt{\mathbf{L}^2} \leqslant L_z \leqslant +\sqrt{\mathbf{L}^2},$$

must hold. Thus the possible values of L_z (for a given $\mathbf{L}^2$) are bounded by certain upper and lower limits; we denote by L the integer corresponding to the greatest value of $|L_z|$.

---

† This is a particular case of the general theorem, mentioned in §10, which states that the levels are degenerate when two or more conserved quantities exist whose operators do not commute. Here the components of the angular momentum are such quantities.

‡ Here it is supposed that there is no additional degeneracy leading to the same value of the energy for different values of the squared angular momentum. This is true for a discrete spectrum (except for the case of what is called *accidental degeneracy* in a Coulomb field: see §36) and in general untrue for the energy levels of a continuous spectrum. However, even when such additional degeneracy is present, we can always choose the eigenfunctions so that they correspond to states with definite values of $\mathbf{L}^2$, and then we can choose from these the states with the same values of E and $\mathbf{L}^2$. This is mathematically expressed by the fact that the matrices of commuting operators can always be simultaneously brought into diagonal form. In what follows we shall, in such cases, speak, for the sake of brevity, as if there were no additional degeneracy, bearing in mind that the results obtained do not in fact depend on this assumption, by what we have just said.

Next, by means of the commutation rules (24.8), it is easy to see that the relation

$$\hat{L}_z(\hat{L}_x \pm i\hat{L}_y) = (\hat{L}_x \pm i\hat{L}_y)(\hat{L}_z \pm 1) \tag{25.6}$$

holds. Applying the operators on both sides of this equation to the function ψ_M, and recalling that $\hat{L}_z\psi_M = M\psi_M$, we obtain

$$\hat{L}_z(\hat{L}_x \pm i\hat{L}_y)\psi_M = (M \pm 1)(\hat{L}_x \pm i\hat{L}_y)\psi_M.$$

Hence we see that the function $(\hat{L}_x \pm i\hat{L}_y)\psi_M$ is (apart from a normalisation constant) the eigenfunction corresponding to the value $M \pm 1$ of the quantity L_z; we can write

$$\begin{aligned} \psi_{M+1} &= \text{constant} \times (\hat{L}_x + i\hat{L}_y)\psi_M \\ \psi_{M-1} &= \text{constant} \times (\hat{L}_x - i\hat{L}_y)\psi_M. \end{aligned} \tag{25.7}$$

If we put $M = L$ in the first of these equations, we must have identically

$$(\hat{L}_x + i\hat{L}_y)\psi_L = 0, \tag{25.8}$$

since there is by definition no state with $M > L$. Applying the operator $\hat{L}_x - i\hat{L}_y$ to this equation and using the relation (24.14), we obtain

$$(\hat{L}_x - i\hat{L}_y)(\hat{L}_x + i\hat{L}_y)\psi_L = (\hat{\mathbf{L}}^2 - \hat{L}_z^2 - \hat{L}_z)\psi_L = 0.$$

Since, however, the ψ_M are common eigenfunctions of the operators $\hat{\mathbf{L}}^2$ and $\hat{L}_z$, we have

$$\hat{\mathbf{L}}^2\psi_L = \mathbf{L}^2\psi_L,\quad \hat{L}_z^2\psi_L = L^2\psi_L,\quad \hat{L}_z\psi_L = L\psi_L,$$

so that the equation found above gives $\mathbf{L}^2 - L^2 - L = 0$ or

$$\mathbf{L}^2 = L(L+1). \tag{25.9}$$

If we understand by L the absolute magnitude of the smallest value of L_z and use the second of formulae (25.7) instead of the first, then we should obtain the same formula (25.9) by proceeding in an exactly similar manner; hence it follows that the greatest and least values of L_z (for a given $\mathbf{L}^2$) are the same in absolute magnitude.

Formula (25.9) determines the required eigenvalues of the square of the angular momentum; the number L takes all positive integral values, including zero. For a given value of L, the component $L_z = M$ of the angular momentum can take the values

$$M = L, L-1, \ldots, -L, \tag{25.10}$$

i.e. $2L+1$ different values in all. The energy level corresponding to the angular momentum† L thus has $(2L+1)$-fold degeneracy. A state with angular momentum $L = 0$ (when all three components are also zero) is not

† We shall often, for the sake of brevity, and in accordance with custom, speak of the "angular momentum L" of a system, understanding by this a momentum whose square is $L(L+1)$.

degenerate; we notice that the wave function of such a state is spherically symmetric. This follows from the mere fact that, when acted on by the angular momentum operator, it becomes zero, i.e. it is unchanged as a result of any infinitely small rotation.

For the angular momentum of a single particle we write formula (25.9) in the form

$$\mathbf{l}^2 = l(l+1), \tag{25.11}$$

i.e. we denote the angular momentum of an individual particle by the small letter l.

Let us calculate the matrix elements of the quantities L_x and L_y in a representation in which L_z and $\mathbf{L}^2$, as well as the energy, are diagonal. First of all, we note that, since the operators $\hat{L}_x$ and $\hat{L}_y$ commute with the operator $\hat{H}$, their matrices are diagonal with respect to the energy, i.e. all matrix elements for transitions between states of different energy (and different angular momentum L) are zero. Thus it is sufficient to consider the matrix elements for transitions within a group of states with different values of M, corresponding to a single degenerate energy level.

It is seen from formulae (25.7) that, in the matrices of the operators $\hat{L}_x+i\hat{L}_y$ and $\hat{L}_x-i\hat{L}_y$, only those elements are different from zero which correspond to transitions $M+1 \rightarrow M$ and $M-1 \rightarrow M$ respectively. Taking this into account, we find the diagonal matrix elements on both sides of the equation (24.13), obtaining†

$$L(L+1) = (L_x+iL_y)_{M,M-1}(L_x-iL_y)_{M-1,M}+M^2-M.$$

Noticing that, since the operators L_x and L_y are Hermitian,

$$(L_x-iL_y)_{M-1,M} = (L_x+iL_y)^*{}_{M,M-1},$$

we can rewrite this equation in the form

$$\begin{aligned}|(L_x+iL_y)_{M,M-1}|^2 &= L(L+1)-M(M-1)\\ &= (L-M+1)(L+M),\end{aligned}$$

whence‡ (Born, Heisenberg and Jordan 1926)

$$\begin{aligned}(L_x+iL_y)_{M,M-1} &= (L_x-iL_y)_{M-1,M}\\ &= \sqrt{[(L+M)(L-M+1)]}.\end{aligned} \tag{25.12}$$

Hence we have for the non-zero matrix elements of the quantities L_x and L_y themselves

$$\begin{aligned}(L_x)_{M,M-1} = (L_x)_{M-1,M} &= \tfrac{1}{2}\sqrt{[(L+M)(L-M+1)]},\\ (L_y)_{M,M-1} = -(L_y)_{M-1,M} &= -\tfrac{1}{2}i\sqrt{[(L+M)(L-M+1)]}.\end{aligned} \tag{25.13}$$

† In the symbols for the matrix elements, we omit for brevity all suffixes with respect to which they are diagonal (including L).

‡ We choose the indeterminate phase factors so as to obtain the + sign in front of the radical in all the matrix elements (cf. the second note to §21).

In the corresponding formulae for the angular momentum of a particle, we must write l, m instead of L, M.

§26. Eigenfunctions of the angular momentum

The wave function of a particle is not completely determined when the values of $\mathbf{l}^2$ and l_z are prescribed. This is seen from the fact that the expressions for the operators of these quantities in spherical co-ordinates contain only the angles θ and ϕ, so that the dependence of their eigenfunctions on r remains undetermined. In fact, the functions ψ_{lm} are of the form $\psi_{lm} = f(r)F(\theta, \phi)$, where the function $f(r)$ is arbitrary. We shall here consider only the angular dependence which characterises the eigenfunctions of the angular momentum, omitting the undetermined factor which depends on r and normalising the functions ψ_{lm} so that

$$\int |\psi_{lm}|^2 \, do = 1,$$

where $do = \sin\theta \, d\theta d\phi$ is an element of solid angle.

We shall see that the problem of determining the common eigenfunctions of the operators $\hat{\mathbf{l}}^2$ and $\hat{l}_z$ admits of separation of the variables θ and ϕ, and these functions can be sought in the form

$$\psi_{lm} = \Phi_m(\phi)\Theta_{lm}(\theta), \tag{26.1}$$

where $\Phi_m(\phi)$ are the eigenfunctions of the operator $\hat{l}_z$, which are given by formula (25.3). Since the functions Φ_m are already normalised by the condition (25.4), the Θ_{lm} must be normalised by the condition

$$\int_0^\pi |\Theta_{lm}|^2 \sin\theta \, d\theta = 1. \tag{26.2}$$

The functions ψ_{lm} with different l or m are automatically orthogonal:

$$\int_0^{2\pi}\int_0^\pi \psi_{l'm'}{}^* \psi_{lm} \sin\theta \, d\theta d\phi = \delta_{ll'}\delta_{mm'}, \tag{26.3}$$

as being the eigenfunctions of angular momentum operators corresponding to different eigenvalues. The functions $\Phi_m(\phi)$ separately are themselves orthogonal (see (25.4)), as being the eigenfunctions of the operator $\hat{l}_z$ corresponding to different eigenvalues m of this operator. The functions $\Theta_{lm}(\theta)$ are not themselves eigenfunctions of any of the angular momentum operators; it follows from (26.3) that they are mutually orthogonal for different l, but not for different m.

The most direct method of calculating the required functions is by directly solving the problem of finding the eigenfunctions of the operator $\hat{\mathbf{l}}^2$ written in spherical co-ordinates (formula (24.15)). The equation $\hat{\mathbf{l}}^2\psi = \mathbf{l}^2\psi$ is

$$\frac{1}{\sin\theta}\frac{\partial}{\partial\theta}\left(\sin\theta\frac{\partial\psi}{\partial\theta}\right) + \frac{1}{\sin^2\theta}\frac{\partial^2\psi}{\partial\phi^2} + l(l+1)\psi = 0.$$

Substituting in this equation the form (26.1) for ψ, we obtain for the function Θ_{lm} the equation

$$\frac{1}{\sin\theta}\frac{\mathrm{d}}{\mathrm{d}\theta}\left(\sin\theta\frac{\mathrm{d}\Theta_{lm}}{\mathrm{d}\theta}\right)-\frac{m^2}{\sin^2\theta}\Theta_{lm}+l(l+1)\Theta_{lm} = 0. \tag{26.4}$$

This equation is well known in the theory of spherical harmonics. It has solutions satisfying the conditions of finiteness and one-valuedness for positive integral values of $l \geqslant |m|$, in agreement with the eigenvalues of the angular momentum obtained above by the matrix method. The corresponding solutions are what are called *associated Legendre polynomials* $P_l^m(\cos\theta)$ (see §c of the Mathematical Appendices). Thus $\Theta_{lm} = \text{constant}\times P_l^m$. Determining the constant from the normalisation condition (26.2), we find

$$\Theta_{lm}(\theta) = (-1)^m\sqrt{[\tfrac{1}{2}(2l+1)(l-m)!/(l+m)!]}P_l^m(\cos\theta) \tag{26.5}$$

(see (c.11)). Here it is supposed that $m \geqslant 0$. For negative m, we determine the constant factor so that

$$\Theta_{l,-|m|} = (-1)^m\Theta_{l|m|}. \tag{26.6}$$

In other words, Θ_{lm} for $m < 0$ is given by (26.5) with $|m|$ instead of m and the factor $(-1)^m$ omitted. This choice of signs in the functions Θ_{lm} corresponds to the choice which we made in the previous section concerning the signs of the matrix elements of the angular momentum†. For $m = 0$, the associated Legendre polynomials are called simply *Legendre polynomials* $P_l(\cos\theta)$; we have

$$\Theta_{l0} = \sqrt{[\tfrac{1}{2}(2l+1)]}P_l(\cos\theta). \tag{26.7}$$

We shall make some remarks concerning the eigenfunctions of the angular momentum. For $l = 0$ (so that $m = 0$ also) this function reduces to a constant. In other words, the wave functions of the states of a particle with zero angular momentum depend only on r, i.e. they have complete spherical symmetry.

For a given m, the values of l starting from $|m|$ denumerate the successive eigenvalues of the quantity l in order of increasing magnitude. Hence, from the general theory of the zeros of eigenfunctions (§19), we can deduce that the function Θ_{lm} becomes zero for $l-|m|$ different values of the angle θ; in other words, it has as nodal lines $l-|m|$ "lines of latitude" on the sphere. If the complete angular functions $\Theta_{lm}(\theta)\,\Phi_m(\phi)$ are taken with the real factors $\cos m\phi$ or $\sin m\phi$ instead of‡ $e^{\pm im\phi}$, they have as further nodal lines $|m|$ "lines of longitude"; the total number of nodal lines is thus l.

---

† The peculiar nature of the sequence of signs should be noticed: the factor -1 in the normalised function Θ_{lm} is found only for odd positive values of m.

The product $\Phi_m(\phi)\Theta_{lm}(\theta)$ is, from the mathematical point of view, a spherical harmonic function normalised in a certain way. We shall sometimes denote it by

$$Y_{lm}(\theta,\phi) = \Phi_m(\phi)\Theta_{lm}(\theta).$$

‡ Each such function corresponds to a state in which l_z does not have a definite value, but can have the values $\pm m$ with equal probability.

Finally, we shall show how the functions Θ_{lm} may be calculated by the matrix method. This is done similarly to the calculation of the wave functions of an oscillator in §21. We start from the equation (25.8):

$$(\hat{l}_x+i\hat{l}_y)\psi_{ll} = 0.$$

Using the expression (24.12) for the operator $\hat{l}_x+i\hat{l}_y$ and substituting $\psi_{ll} = (2\pi)^{-\frac{1}{2}}e^{il\phi}\Theta_{ll}(\theta)$, we obtain for Θ_{ll} the equation

$$\mathrm{d}\Theta_{ll}/\mathrm{d}\theta - l\cot\theta\,\Theta_{ll} = 0,$$

whence $\Theta_{ll} = \text{constant}\times\sin^l\theta$. Determining the constant from the normalisation condition, we find

$$\Theta_{ll} = (-1)^l\sqrt{[\tfrac{1}{2}(2l+1)!]}2^{-l}(1/l!)\sin^l\theta. \tag{26.8}$$

Next, using (25.12), we write

$$\begin{aligned}(\hat{l}_x-i\hat{l}_y)\psi_{l,m+1} &= (l_x-il_y)_{m,m+1}\psi_{lm}\\ &= \sqrt{[(l-m)(l+m+1)]}\psi_{lm}.\end{aligned}$$

A repeated application of this formula gives

$$\sqrt{[(l-m)!/(l+m)!]}\psi_{lm} = [(2l)!]^{-\frac{1}{2}}(\hat{l}_x-i\hat{l}_y)^{l-m}\psi_{ll}.$$

The right-hand side of this equation is easily calculated by means of the expression (24.12) for the operator $\hat{l}_x-i\hat{l}_y$. We have

$$(\hat{l}_x-i\hat{l}_y)e^{il\phi}\Theta_{ll}(\theta) = e^{i(l-1)\phi}\sin^{1-l}\theta\,\mathrm{d}(\sin^l\theta\,.\,\Theta_{ll})/\mathrm{d}(\cos\theta).$$

A repeated application of this formula gives

$$(\hat{l}_x-i\hat{l}_y)^{l-m}e^{il\phi}\Theta_{ll} = e^{im\phi}\sin^{-m}\theta\,\mathrm{d}^{l-m}(\sin^l\theta\,.\,\Theta_{ll})/\mathrm{d}(\cos\theta)^{l-m}.$$

Finally, using these relations and the expression (26.8) for Θ_{ll}, we obtain the formula

$$\Theta_{lm}(\theta) = (-1)^l\sqrt{\left[\frac{(2l+1)(l+m)!}{2(l-m)!}\right]}\frac{1}{2^l l!\sin^m\theta}\frac{\mathrm{d}^{l-m}}{\mathrm{d}(\cos\theta)^{l-m}}\sin^{2l}\theta,$$

which is the same as (26.5).

§27. Matrix elements of vectors

Let us again consider a closed system of particles†; let f be any scalar physical quantity characterising the system, and $\hat{f}$ the operator corresponding to this quantity. Every scalar is invariant with respect to rotation of the co-ordinate system. Hence the scalar operator $\hat{f}$ does not vary when acted on by a rotation operator, i.e. it commutes with a rotation operator. We know, however, that the operator of an infinitely small rotation is the same, apart

† All the results in this section are valid also for a particle in a centrally symmetric field (and in general whenever the total angular momentum of the system is conserved).

from a constant factor, as the angular momentum operator, so that

$$\{f, \hat{L}_x\} = \{f, \hat{L}_y\} = \{f, \hat{L}_z\} = 0 \tag{27.1}$$

(and also $\{f, \hat{\mathbf{L}}^2\} = 0$).

From the commutability of f with the angular momentum operator it follows that, in a representation where $\mathbf{L}^2$ and L_z are diagonal, the matrix of the quantity f will also be diagonal with respect to the suffixes LM. We shall conventionally denote by n all the remaining suffixes which define the state of the system, and we shall show that the matrix elements $f^{nLM}_{n'LM}$ are independent of the suffix M. To do this, we use the commutability of f with $\hat{L}_x + i\hat{L}_y$:

$$f(\hat{L}_x + i\hat{L}_y) - (\hat{L}_x + i\hat{L}_y)f = 0.$$

Let us write down the matrix element of this equation corresponding to the transition $n, L, M \to n', L, M-1$. Taking into account the fact that the matrix of the operator $\hat{L}_x + i\hat{L}_y$ has only elements with $n, L, M \to n, L, M-1$, we obtain

$$f^{nLM}_{n'LM}(L_x + iL_y)^{n'LM}_{n'L,M-1} - (L_x + iL_y)^{nLM}_{nL,M-1} f^{n\,L,M-1}_{n'L,M-1} = 0,$$

and since the matrix elements of the operator $\hat{L}_x + i\hat{L}_y$ are independent of the suffix n, we find

$$f^{nLM}_{n'LM} = f^{nL,M-1}_{n'L,M-1},$$

whence it follows that all the quantities $f^{nLM}_{n'LM}$ for different M (the other suffixes being the same) are equal.

Thus the matrix elements of the quantity f that are different from zero will be

$$f^{nLM}_{n'LM} = f^{nL}_{n'L}, \tag{27.2}$$

where $f^{nL}_{n'L}$ denotes quantities depending on the values of the suffixes n, n', L.

If we apply this result to the Hamiltonian itself, we obtain our previous result that the energy of the stationary states is independent of M, i.e. that the energy levels have $(2L+1)$-fold degeneracy.

Next, let $\mathbf{A}$ be some real vector physical quantity characterising a closed system. When the system of co-ordinates is rotated (and, in particular, when the operator of an infinitely small rotation, i.e. the angular momentum operator, is applied), the components of a vector are transformed into linear functions of one another. Hence, as a result of the commutation of the operators $\hat{L}_i$ with the operators $\hat{A}_i$, we must again obtain components of the same vector, $\hat{A}_i$. The exact form can be found directly by noticing that, in the particular case where $\mathbf{A}$ is the radius vector of the particle, the formulae (24.3) must be obtained. Thus we find the commutation rules

$$\left.\begin{aligned}\{\hat{L}_x,\hat{A}_x\} &= 0, & \{\hat{L}_x,\hat{A}_y\} &= i\hat{A}_z, & \{\hat{L}_x,\hat{A}_z\} &= -i\hat{A}_y,\\ \{\hat{L}_y,\hat{A}_y\} &= 0, & \{\hat{L}_y,\hat{A}_z\} &= i\hat{A}_x, & \{\hat{L}_y,\hat{A}_x\} &= -i\hat{A}_z,\\ \{\hat{L}_z,\hat{A}_z\} &= 0, & \{\hat{L}_z,\hat{A}_x\} &= i\hat{A}_y, & \{\hat{L}_z,\hat{A}_y\} &= -i\hat{A}_x,\end{aligned}\right\} \tag{27.3}$$

or

$$\{\hat{L}_i,\hat{A}_k\} = ie_{ikl}\hat{A}_l. \tag{27.4}$$

These commutation rules enable us to obtain several results concerning the form of the matrices of the quantities A_x, A_y, A_z. For this purpose we must perform the following somewhat lengthy calculations.

By means of the relations (27.3), we find

$$\begin{aligned}\{\hat{L}_x^2,\hat{A}_x\} &= 0,\\ \{\hat{L}_y^2,\hat{A}_x\} &= \hat{L}_y\{\hat{L}_y,\hat{A}_x\}+\{\hat{L}_y,\hat{A}_x\}\hat{L}_y\\ &= -i(\hat{L}_y\hat{A}_z+\hat{A}_z\hat{L}_y)\\ &= -2i\hat{L}_y\hat{A}_z-\hat{A}_x,\\ \{\hat{L}_z^2,\hat{A}_x\} &= 2i\hat{L}_z\hat{A}_y-\hat{A}_x.\end{aligned}$$

Adding these equations, we obtain

$$\{\hat{\mathbf{L}}^2,\hat{A}_x\} = 2i(\hat{L}_z\hat{A}_y-\hat{L}_y\hat{A}_z)-2\hat{A}_x.$$

Next, we commute this operator successively with $\hat{L}_x^2$, $\hat{L}_y^2$, $\hat{L}_z^2$, using again the relations (27.3) and the rules for commuting the operators $\hat{L}_x$, $\hat{L}_y$, $\hat{L}_z$ with one another. After a simple but rather lengthy reduction, which we omit, we have

$$\{\hat{\mathbf{L}}^2,\{\hat{\mathbf{L}}^2,\hat{A}_x\}\} = 2(\hat{\mathbf{L}}^2\hat{A}_x+\hat{A}_x\hat{\mathbf{L}}^2)-4\hat{L}_x(\hat{\mathbf{L}}\cdot\hat{\mathbf{A}}).$$

On the other hand

$$\begin{aligned}\{\hat{\mathbf{L}}^2,\{\hat{\mathbf{L}}^2,\hat{A}_x\}\} &\equiv \{\hat{\mathbf{L}}^2,(\hat{\mathbf{L}}^2\hat{A}_x-\hat{A}_x\hat{\mathbf{L}}^2)\}\\ &\equiv \hat{\mathbf{L}}^4\hat{A}_x-2\hat{\mathbf{L}}^2\hat{A}_x\hat{\mathbf{L}}^2+\hat{A}_x\hat{\mathbf{L}}^4.\end{aligned}$$

Equating these two expressions, we obtain

$$\hat{\mathbf{L}}^4\hat{A}_x-2\hat{\mathbf{L}}^2\hat{A}_x\hat{\mathbf{L}}^2+\hat{A}_x\hat{\mathbf{L}}^4 = 2(\hat{\mathbf{L}}^2\hat{A}_x+\hat{A}_x\hat{\mathbf{L}}^2)-4\hat{L}_x(\hat{L}_x\hat{A}_x+\hat{L}_y\hat{A}_y+\hat{L}_z\hat{A}_z).$$

We take the matrix element of this equation which corresponds to the transition $nLM \to n'L'M'$, where $L' \neq L$. Since the matrix of the scalar $\hat{L}_x\hat{A}_x+\hat{L}_y\hat{A}_y+\hat{L}_z\hat{A}_z$ is diagonal with respect to M and L, while that of $\hat{L}_x$ is diagonal with respect to L and n (see (25.13)), the matrix element of the last term in the equation vanishes for the transition in question. The other terms give

$$[L^2(L+1)^2-2L(L+1)L'(L'+1)+L'^2(L'+1)^2](A_x)_{n'L'M'}^{nLM}$$
$$= 2[L(L+1)+L'(L'+1)](A_x)_{n'L'M'}^{nLM},$$

or, after regrouping and reducing the terms,

$$[(L+L'+1)^2-1][(L-L')^2-1](A_x)^{nLM}_{n'L'M'} = 0 \quad (L' \neq L).$$

The first bracket cannot vanish, since $L \neq L'$ and $L, L' \geqslant 0$. The second vanishes only for $L'-L = \pm 1$. Including also the case $L' = L$ which is not ruled out by these considerations, we arrive at the result that the matrix elements of A_x can be non-zero only for

$$L'-L = 0 \text{ or } \pm 1 \tag{27.5}$$

(this is, of course, a necessary but not sufficient condition). We could similarly calculate for $\hat{A}_y$ and $\hat{A}_z$ instead of $\hat{A}_x$, with the same result, so that the *selection rule*, as it is called, for the suffix L which we have obtained refers to all three components of the vector (the diagonality of L_x with respect to L which was used in the derivation holds also for L_z, whose matrix is diagonal with respect to both L and M).

Besides the selection rule (27.5), there is an additional rule which forbids transitions between any two states with $L = 0$ (if $L = 0$, of course, $M = 0$ also). It is easily obtained, for instance, by taking the matrix element of the equation $\{\hat{L}_y, \hat{A}_z\} = i\hat{A}_x$ which is diagonal with respect to L and M, and then putting $L = M = 0$; this gives at once

$$(A_x)^{n00}_{n'00} \equiv 0.$$

Next we shall derive the selection rule for the suffix M. Instead of $\hat{A}_x$, $\hat{A}_y$ it is here convenient to use the complex conjugates $\hat{A}_x \pm i\hat{A}_y$. We have

$$\{\hat{L}_z, \hat{A}_x - i\hat{A}_y\} = \{\hat{L}_z, \hat{A}_x\} - i\{\hat{L}_z, \hat{A}_y\} = -(\hat{A}_x - i\hat{A}_y),$$

so that

$$\hat{L}_z(\hat{A}_x - i\hat{A}_y) - (\hat{A}_x - i\hat{A}_y)\hat{L}_z = -(\hat{A}_x - i\hat{A}_y). \tag{27.6}$$

Taking the matrix element $nLM \to n'L'M'$, we obtain

$$M(A_x - iA_y)^{nLM}_{n'L'M'} - (A_x - iA_y)^{nLM}_{n'L'M'}M' = -(A_x - iA_y)^{nLM}_{n'L'M'},$$

or

$$(M - M' + 1)(A_x - iA_y)^{nLM}_{n'L'M'} = 0.$$

Hence it follows that the matrix elements of $A_x - iA_y$ can be non-zero only for

$$M' = M+1.$$

Similarly we find that the matrix elements of $A_x + iA_y$ can be non-zero only for

$$M' = M-1.$$

For A_x and A_y themselves, therefore, we have the selection rule

$$M' = M \pm 1. \tag{27.7}$$

It follows from $\hat{A}_z\hat{L}_z - \hat{L}_z\hat{A}_z = 0$ that the matrix of A_z (like the matrix of L_z) is diagonal with respect to M, i.e. the selection rule is

$$M' = M. \tag{27.8}$$

It is possible to determine in general the dependence of the matrix elements of a vector on the number M (BORN, HEISENBERG and JORDAN 1926). To do this, we write

$$\{\hat{L}_x - i\hat{L}_y, \hat{A}_x - i\hat{A}_y\} = \{\hat{L}_x, \hat{A}_x\} - i\{\hat{L}_y, \hat{A}_x\} - i\{\hat{L}_x, \hat{A}_y\} - \{\hat{L}_y, \hat{A}_y\} = 0$$

or

$$(\hat{L}_x - i\hat{L}_y)(\hat{A}_x - i\hat{A}_y) - (\hat{A}_x - i\hat{A}_y)(\hat{L}_x - i\hat{L}_y) = 0. \tag{27.9}$$

Taking the most general matrix element of this equation which satisfies the selection rules, we obtain

$$(L_x - iL_y)_{nLM}^{nL,M-1}(A_x - iA_y)_{n'L',M+1}^{nLM} - (A_x - iA_y)_{n'L'M}^{nL,M-1}(L_x - iL_y)_{n'L',M+1}^{n'L'M} = 0,$$

or, substituting the expression (25.12) for the matrix elements of $L_x - iL_y$,

$$\begin{aligned}(A_x - iA_y)_{n'L',M+1}^{nLM}\sqrt{[(L+M)(L-M+1)]}&\\ &= (A_x - iA_y)_{n'L'M}^{nL,M-1}\sqrt{[(L'+M+1)(L'-M)]}\\ &\qquad (L'-L = 0 \text{ or } \pm 1).\end{aligned} \tag{27.10}$$

Putting here $L' = L$, we have

$$\frac{(A_x - iA_y)_{n'L,M+1}^{nLM}}{\sqrt{[(L-M)(L+M+1)]}} = \frac{(A_x - iA_y)_{n'LM}^{nL,M-1}}{\sqrt{[(L-M+1)(L+M)]}},$$

and since this holds for all M we see that the ratios shown must be independent of M. Denoting their value by $A_{n'L}^{nL}$, we have

$$(A_x - iA_y)_{n L,M+1}^{nLM} = A_{n'L}^{nL}\sqrt{[(L-M)(L+M+1)]}.$$

Similarly, putting $L' = L \pm 1$ in (27.10), we obtain the expressions for the remaining matrix elements of $A_x - iA_y$.

The matrix elements of $A_x + iA_y$ do not need to be specially calculated, since, because $\hat{A}_x$ and $\hat{A}_y$ are Hermitian, we have

$$(A_x + iA_y)_{n'L'M'}^{nLM} = (A_x^* + iA_y^*)_{nLM}^{n'L'M'} = [(A_x - iA_y)_{nLM}^{n'L'M'}]^*.$$

Here it must be noted that, as we shall see below, the quantities $A_{n'L'}^{nL}$ have the property $A_{n'L'}^{nL\,*} = A_{nL}^{n'L'}$. As a result, we obtain the following formulae for the matrix elements of $A_x \pm iA_y$ that are not zero:

$$\left.\begin{aligned}
(A_x - iA_y)_{n'LM}^{nL,M-1} &= (A_x + iA_y)_{n'L,M-1}^{nLM} = A_{n'L}^{nL}\sqrt{[(L-M+1)(L+M)]},\\
(A_x - iA_y)_{n',L-1,M}^{nL,M-1} &= A_{n',L-1}^{nL}\sqrt{[(L-M+1)(L-M)]},\\
(A_x + iA_y)_{n'L,M-1}^{n,L-1,M} &= A_{n'L}^{n,L-1}\sqrt{[(L-M+1)(L-M)]},\\
(A_x - iA_y)_{n'LM}^{n,L-1,M-1} &= -A_{n'L}^{n,L-1}\sqrt{[(L+M-1)(L+M)]},\\
(A_x + iA_y)_{n',L-1,M-1}^{nLM} &= -A_{n',L-1}^{nL}\sqrt{[(L+M-1)(L+M)]}.
\end{aligned}\right\} \tag{27.11}$$

To calculate the matrix elements of A_z, we start from the relation

$$\{\hat{L}_x + i\hat{L}_y, \hat{A}_x - i\hat{A}_y\} = \{\hat{L}_x - i\hat{L}_y, \hat{A}_x - i\hat{A}_y\} + 2i\{\hat{L}_y, \hat{A}_x - i\hat{A}_y\} = 2i\{\hat{L}_y, \hat{A}_x\} = 2\hat{A}_z,$$

or

$$(\hat{L}_x + i\hat{L}_y)(\hat{A}_x - i\hat{A}_y) - (\hat{A}_x - i\hat{A}_y)(\hat{L}_x + i\hat{L}_y) = 2\hat{A}_z. \tag{27.12}$$

Since we already know the matrix elements of $L_x + iL_y$ and $A_x - iA_y$, we can now calculate immediately the matrix elements of A_z. Omitting the easy calculations, we shall give only the final expressions for the matrix elements of A_z that are not zero:

$$\left.\begin{aligned}
(A_z)_{n'LM}^{nLM} &= A_{n'L}^{nL} M,\\
(A_z)_{n',L-1,M}^{nLM} &= A_{n'\,L-1}^{nL}\sqrt{(L^2 - M^2)},\\
(A_z)_{n'LM}^{n,L-1,M} &= A_{n'L}^{n,L-1}\sqrt{(L^2 - M^2)}.
\end{aligned}\right\} \tag{27.13}$$

Since $\hat{A}_z$ is Hermitian, it follows that $(A_z)_{n'L'M}^{nLM} = (A_z)_{nLM}^{n'L'M*}$; substituting the expressions (27.13), we have the relation

$$A_{n'L'}^{nL\,*} = A_{nL}^{n'L'}, \tag{27.14}$$

which we have already utilised above.

Similar formulae for the matrix elements of tensor physical quantities can be obtained at once by using the formulae for vectors. To do so, it is sufficient to consider a vector which is the product of two (or more) vectors, and calculate its matrix elements in accordance with the rule of matrix multiplication†.

It is useful to notice a formula which connects the matrix elements of a scalar **A . B** (where **A**, **B** are two vector physical quantities) with the coefficients $A_{n'L'}^{nL}$, $B_{n\,L}^{nL}$ in formulae (27.11) and (27.13). The calculation is

† Another method, based on group theory, is given at the end of §97.

conveniently effected by writing the operator $\hat{\mathbf{A}} \cdot \hat{\mathbf{B}}$ in the form

$$\hat{\mathbf{A}} \cdot \hat{\mathbf{B}} = \tfrac{1}{2}(\hat{A}_x+i\hat{A}_y)(\hat{B}_x-i\hat{B}_y)+\tfrac{1}{2}(\hat{A}_x-i\hat{A}_y)(\hat{B}_x+i\hat{B}_y)+\hat{A}_z\hat{B}_z.$$

It is evident that the matrix of $\mathbf{A} \cdot \mathbf{B}$ (and of any scalar) is diagonal with respect to L and M. Calculation gives

$$(\mathbf{A} \cdot \mathbf{B})_{n'LM}^{nLM} = (L+1)(2L+3) \sum_{n''} A_{n'',L+1}^{nL} B_{n'L}^{n'',L+1} +$$

$$+L(L+1) \sum_{n''} A_{n''L}^{nL} B_{n'L}^{n''L} + L(2L-1) \sum_{n''} A_{n'',L-1}^{nL} B_{n'L}^{n'',L-1}. \tag{27.15}$$

§28. Parity of a state

Besides the parallel displacement of the co-ordinate system (used in §13) and the rotation of it (used in §24), there is another transformation which leaves unaltered the Hamiltonian of a closed system†. This is what is called the *inversion transformation*, which consists in simultaneously changing the sign of all the co-ordinates. In classical mechanics, the invariance of HAMILTON's function with respect to inversion does not lead to a conservation law, but the situation is different in quantum mechanics.

Let us denote by $\hat{I}$ the inversion operator; its effect on a function is to change the sign of all the co-ordinates. The invariance of $\hat{H}$ with respect to inversion means that

$$\hat{H}\hat{I}-\hat{I}\hat{H} = 0. \tag{28.1}$$

The operator $\hat{I}$ also commutes with the angular momentum operators:

$$\{\hat{I},\hat{L}_x\} = \{\hat{I},\hat{L}_y\} = \{\hat{I},\hat{L}_z\} = 0, \quad \{\hat{I},\hat{\mathbf{L}}^2\} = 0 \tag{28.2}$$

(on inversion, both the co-ordinates themselves and the operators of differentiation with respect to them change sign, so that the angular momentum operators remain unchanged).

It is easy to find the eigenvalues I of the inversion operator, which are determined by the equation

$$\hat{I}\psi = I\psi.$$

To do this, we notice that a double application of the operator $\hat{I}$ amounts to identity: no co-ordinate is altered. In other words, we have

$$\hat{I}^2\psi = I^2\psi = \psi, \text{ i.e. } I^2 = 1, \text{ whence}$$

$$I = \pm 1. \tag{28.3}$$

Thus the eigenfunctions of the inversion operator are either unchanged or change in sign when acted upon by this operator. In the first case, the wave

† The same is true of a system in a centrally symmetric field.

function (and the corresponding state) is said to be *even*, and in the second it is said to be *odd*.

The equation (28.1) thus expresses the "law of conservation of parity"; if the state of a closed system has a given parity (i.e. if it is even, or odd), then this parity is conserved.

The physical meaning of equations (28.2) is that the system can have definite values of L and M and, at the same time, a definite parity of its state. We can also say that all states differing only in the value of M have the same parity. This can be shown by starting from the relation

$$(\hat{L}_x+i\hat{L}_y)\hat{I}-\hat{I}(\hat{L}_x+i\hat{L}_y) = 0$$

and proceeding in exactly the same way as in obtaining the result (27.2).

When the inversion transformation is applied to scalar quantities, either they do not change at all (*true scalars*) or they change sign (what are called *pseudoscalars*)†. If a physical quantity f is a true scalar, its operator commutes with $\hat{I}$:

$$\hat{I}f-f\hat{I} = 0. \tag{28.4}$$

It follows from this that, if the matrix of I is diagonal, then the matrix of f is diagonal with respect to the suffix which shows the parity of the state, i.e. only the matrix elements for transitions $u \to u$ and $g \to g$ are not zero (the suffixes g and u denote even and odd states respectively).

For the operator of a pseudoscalar quantity we have $\hat{I}f = -f\hat{I}$, or

$$\hat{I}f+f\hat{I} = 0; \tag{28.5}$$

$\hat{I}$ *anticommutes* with f. The matrix element of this equation for a transition $g \to g$ is

$$I_{gg}f_{gg}+f_{gg}I_{gg} = 0,$$

and since $I_{gg} = 1$ we have $f_{gg} = 0$ (we omit all suffixes apart from that showing the parity). Similarly we find that $f_{uu} = 0$. Thus, in the matrix of a pseudoscalar quantity, only those elements can be different from zero which are non-diagonal with respect to the parity suffix (transitions with change of parity).

Similar results are obtained for vector quantities. The operators of a polar vector‡ anticommute with $\hat{I}$, and in their matrices (in a representation where $\hat{I}$ is diagonal) only the elements for transitions with change of parity are not zero. The operators of an axial vector, however, commute with $\hat{I}$, and their matrices have non-zero elements only for transitions without change of parity.

---

† An example of a pseudoscalar is the product of an axial and a polar vector.

‡ Ordinary (*polar*) vectors change sign under the inversion transformation, whilst *axial* vectors (for instance, the vector product of two polar vectors) are unchanged by this transformation.

It is useful to point out another method of obtaining these results. For example, the matrix element of a scalar f for a transition between states of opposite parity is the integral $f_{ug} = \int \psi_u{}^* \hat{f} \psi_g \, dq$, where the function ψ_g is even and ψ_u is odd. When all the co-ordinates change sign, the integrand does so if f is a true scalar; on the other hand, the integral taken over all space cannot change when the variables of integration are re-named. Hence it follows that $f_{ug} = -f_{ug}$, i.e. $f_{ug} \equiv 0$.

Let us determine the parity of the state of a single particle with angular momentum l. The inversion transformation $(x \to -x, y \to -y, z \to -z)$ is, in spherical co-ordinates, the transformation

$$r \to r, \quad \theta \to \pi - \theta, \quad \phi \to \pi + \phi. \tag{28.6}$$

The dependence of the wave function of the particle on the angle is given by the eigenfunction Y_{lm} of the angular momentum, which, apart from a constant which is here unimportant, has the form $P_l{}^m(\cos\theta)e^{im\phi}$. When ϕ is replaced by $\pi+\phi$, the factor $e^{im\phi}$ is multiplied by $(-1)^m$, and when θ is replaced by $\pi-\theta$, $P_l{}^m(\cos\theta)$ becomes $P_l{}^m(-\cos\theta) = -(1)^{l-m}P_l{}^m(\cos\theta)$. Thus the whole function is multiplied by $(-1)^l$ (independent of m, in agreement with what was said above), i.e. the parity of a state with a given value of l is

$$I = (-1)^l. \tag{28.7}$$

We see that all states with even l are even, and all those with odd l are odd.

A vector physical quantity relating to an individual particle can have non-zero matrix elements only for transitions with $l \to l$ or $l \pm 1$ (§27). Remembering this, and comparing formula (28.7) with what was said above regarding the change of parity in the matrix elements of vectors, we reach the result that the matrix elements of a polar vector are non-zero only for transitions with $l \to l \pm 1$, and those of an axial vector for transitions with $l \to l$.

§29. Matrix elements of spherical harmonics

Let us calculate the matrix elements of a unit vector **n** in the direction of the radius vector; its components are

$$n_x = \sin\theta\cos\phi, \quad n_y = \sin\theta\sin\phi, \quad n_z = \cos\theta. \tag{29.1}$$

Instead of n_x, n_y it is more convenient to consider the complex combinations

$$n_x \pm i n_y = \sin\theta \, e^{\pm i\phi}.$$

Since **n** is an ordinary (polar) vector, we know already that its matrix elements are non-zero only for transitions with $l \to l \pm 1$ (see the end of §28). Their dependence on the quantum number m is given by the general formulae (27.11) and (27.13), so that, in these formulae, we need calculate only the coefficient A^l_{l-1}, which we shall denote in the present case by n^l_{l-1}. To calculate this quantity it is sufficient to find, for instance, $(\cos\theta)^{l0}_{l-1,0}$. We have

$$(\cos\theta)^{l0}_{l-1,0} = \int_0^\pi \Theta_{l0}\cos\theta\,\Theta_{l-1,0}\sin\theta\,d\theta$$

$$= \tfrac{1}{2}\sqrt{[(2l+1)(2l-1)]}\int_0^\pi P_l(\cos\theta)P_{l-1}(\cos\theta)P_1(\cos\theta)\sin\theta\,d\theta$$

$$= l/\sqrt{(4l^2-1)}$$

$(\cos\theta \equiv P_1(\cos\theta))$; the integral is found at once from formula (c.17) of the Mathematical Appendices. A comparison with the formulae (27.13) shows that $n^l_{l-1} = 1/\sqrt{(4l^2-1)}$. Thus

$$n^{l}_{l-1} = n^{l-1}_{l} = 1/\sqrt{(4l^2-1)}, \quad n^{l}_{l} = 0. \tag{29.2}$$

The components of the vector $\mathbf{n}$ are at the same time three spherical harmonics of order $l = 1$. In calculations concerning the solution of certain problems of quantum mechanics, it is sometimes necessary to consider the matrix elements of other spherical harmonics with respect to the eigenfunctions of the angular momentum of the particle.

The matrix elements of the spherical harmonic $P_l^m(\cos\theta)e^{im\phi}(m > 0)$ have the form

$$(P_l^m e^{im\phi})^{l_1m_1}_{l_2m_2} = \int \Phi_{m_1}{}^*(\phi)\Theta_{l_1m_1}(\theta)P_l^m(\cos\theta)e^{im\phi}\Phi_{m_2}(\phi)\Theta_{l_2m_2}(\theta)\,do$$

$$= (-1)^{\frac{1}{2}(m_1+|m_1|+m_2+|m_2|)}\frac{1}{4\pi}\sqrt{\left\{\frac{(2l_1+1)(2l_2+1)(l_1-|m_1|)!(l_2-|m_2|)!}{(l_1+|m_1|)!(l_2+|m_2|)!}\right\}}\times$$

$$\times\int P_{l_1}^{|m_1|}(\cos\theta)P_{l_2}^{|m_2|}(\cos\theta)P_l^m(\cos\theta)e^{i(m+m_2-m_1)\phi}\,do. \tag{29.3}$$

On integrating over ϕ, the integral vanishes except when $m+m_2-m_1 = 0$. Thus the selection rule for the quantum number m is

$$m_1-m_2 = m. \tag{29.4}$$

The integral of the product of three Legendre polynomials with m_1, m_2 and m satisfying (29.4) vanishes unless† the sum $l+l_1+l_2$ is even:

$$l_1+l_2+l = 2p, \tag{29.5}$$

and unless each of l_1, l_2, l is greater than (or equal to) the difference and less than (or equal to) the sum of the other two:

$$l_1+l_2 \geqslant l \geqslant |l_1-l_2| \text{ (and so } l_1+l \geqslant l_2) \tag{29.6}$$

† See §c of the Mathematical Appendices.

(in other words, l_1, l_2 and l must be the lengths of the sides of a triangle whose perimeter is even).

The matrix elements that are different from zero can be calculated in general from formula (c.14); we shall not pause here to write out this lengthy formula.

Let f be some spherical harmonic. We shall show how to calculate the sums of the squared moduli of the matrix elements, found in certain calculations, of the form

$$\sum_{m_1=-l_1}^{l_1}\sum_{m_2=-l_2}^{l_2}|f^{l_1m_1}_{l_2m_2}|^2$$

$$=\frac{1}{16\pi^2}\sum_{m_1}\sum_{m_2}\frac{(2l_1+1)(2l_2+1)(l_1-|m_1|)!(l_2-|m_2|)!}{(l_1+|m_1|)!(l_2+|m_2|)!}\times$$

$$\times\left|\int fP_{l_1}^{|m_1|}(\cos\theta)P_{l_2}^{|m_2|}(\cos\theta)e^{i(m_2-m_1)\phi}\,\mathrm{d}o\right|^2.$$

We rewrite the squared modulus of the integral as a double integral:

$$\iint ff'P_{l_1}^{|m_1|}(\cos\theta)P_{l_1}^{|m_1|}(\cos\theta')e^{-im_1(\phi-\phi')}P_{l_2}^{|m_2|}(\cos\theta)P_{l_2}^{|m_2|}(\cos\theta')e^{im_2(\phi-\phi')}\,\mathrm{d}o\,\mathrm{d}o'.$$

Substituting this expression and effecting the summation under the integral sign, we obtain as the integrand the product of two sums of the form

$$f\frac{2l_1+1}{4\pi}\sum_{m_1=-l_1}^{l_1}\frac{(l_1-|m_1|)!}{(l_1+|m_1|)!}P_{l_1}^{|m_1|}(\cos\theta)P_{l_1}^{|m_1|}(\cos\theta')e^{-im_1(\phi-\phi')}.$$

According to the addition theorem for spherical harmonics (c.8), this sum is

$$f\frac{2l_1+1}{4\pi}P_{l_1}(\cos\gamma),$$

where γ is the angle between the two directions defined by the angles θ, ϕ and θ', ϕ'. Thus we obtain

$$\sum_{m_1}\sum_{m_2}|f^{l_1m_1}_{l_2m_2}|^2=\frac{(2l_1+1)(2l_2+1)}{16\pi^2}\iint ff'P_{l_1}(\cos\gamma)P_{l_2}(\cos\gamma)\,\mathrm{d}o\,\mathrm{d}o'. \tag{29.7}$$

Let $f = P_l(\cos\theta)$. To calculate the integral, we proceed as follows. We take as a new polar axis the direction (θ, ϕ) and expand the function $f' = P_l(\cos\theta')$ by the addition theorem:

$$P_l(\cos\theta') = P_l(\cos\theta)P_l(\cos\gamma)+2\sum_{m=1}^{l}\frac{(l-m)!}{(l+m)!}P_l^m(\cos\theta)P_l^m(\cos\gamma)\cos m\Phi,$$

where Φ is the azimuthal angle between the direction of the old polar axis and the direction θ', ϕ'. On substituting this expansion in (29.7) and integrating over Φ, all terms except the first vanish, and there remains

$$\sum_{m_1}\sum_{m_2} |(P_l)^{l_1 m_1}_{l_2 m_2}|^2 =$$

$$= \frac{(2l_1+1)(2l_2+1)}{16\pi^2} \iint [P_l(\cos\theta)]^2 P_l(\cos\gamma) P_{l_1}(\cos\gamma) P_{l_2}(\cos\gamma)\, \mathrm{d}o\,\mathrm{d}o'.$$

To integrate, we again take the direction (θ, ϕ) as polar axis and replace $\mathrm{d}o\,\mathrm{d}o'$ by $2\pi \sin\theta\, \mathrm{d}\theta \,.\, 2\pi \sin\gamma\, \mathrm{d}\gamma$. The integrals over θ and γ are given by formulae (c.9) and (c.17). As a result we obtain

$$\sum_{m_1}\sum_{m_2} |(P_l)^{l_1 m_1}_{l_2 m_2}|^2 = \frac{(2l_1+1)(2l_2+1)(p!)^2(l_1+l_2-l)!(l_1-l_2+l)!(l_2+l-l_1)!}{(2l+1)(2p+1)[(p-l)!(p-l_1)!(p-l_2)!]^2}, \tag{29.8}$$

where $2p = l+l_1+l_2$.

The sum (29.8) evidently does not depend on the choice of the axes of co-ordinates. On the other hand, when the system of co-ordinates is rotated, the function $P_l(\cos\theta)$ becomes a linear combination of other spherical harmonics $P_l^m(\cos\theta)e^{im\phi}$ (with the same value of l). From this, it is easy to show that the formula

$$\sum_{m_1}\sum_{m_2} |f^{l_1 m_1}_{l_2 m_2}|^2$$

$$= \frac{(2l_1+1)(2l_2+1)(p!)^2(l_1+l_2-l)!(l_1-l_2+l)!(l_2+l-l_1)!}{4\pi(2p+1)![(p-l)!(p-l_1)!(p-l_2)!]^2} \int |f|^2\, \mathrm{d}o \tag{29.9}$$

(which agrees with (29.8) for $f = P_l(\cos\theta)$) holds for any spherical harmonic function of order l.

§30. Addition of angular momenta

Let us consider a system composed of two parts whose interaction can be neglected, and for each of which the law of conservation of angular momentum holds. The angular momentum $\mathbf{L}$ of the whole system can be regarded as the sum of the angular momenta $\mathbf{L}_1$ and $\mathbf{L}_2$ of its parts.

Let L_1 and L_2 be the quantum numbers which determine the values of the squares $\mathbf{L}_1^2$, $\mathbf{L}_2^2$ of the angular momenta, while M_1, M_2 determine their projections on the z-axis. We denote by L and M the corresponding numbers for the square $\mathbf{L}^2$ and the projection L_z of the total angular momentum. The question arises regarding the "law of addition" of angular momenta: what are the possible values of L for given values of L_1 and L_2? The law of addition for the components of angular momentum is evident: since $\hat{L}_z = \hat{L}_{1z}+\hat{L}_{2z}$, it follows that $M = M_1+M_2$. There is no such simple relation for the operators of the squared angular momenta, however, and to derive their "law of addition" we reason as follows.

If we take the quantities $\mathbf{L}_1^2$, $\mathbf{L}_2^2$, L_{1z}, L_{2z} as a complete assembly of physical quantities†, every state will be determined by the values of the numbers L_1, L_2, M_1, M_2. For given L_1 and L_2, the numbers M_1 and M_2 take $(2L_1+1)$ and $(2L_2+1)$ different values respectively, so that there are altogether $(2L_1+1)(2L_2+1)$ different states with the same L_1 and L_2. We denote the wave functions of the states for this representation by $\phi_{L_1L_2M_1M_2}$.

Instead of the above four quantities, we can take the four quantities $\mathbf{L}_1^2$, $\mathbf{L}_2^2$, $\mathbf{L}^2$, L_z as a complete assembly. Then every state is characterised by the values of the numbers L_1, L_2, L, M (we denote the corresponding wave functions by $\psi_{L_1L_2LM}$). For given L_1 and L_2, there must of course be $(2L_1+1)(2L_2+1)$ different states as before, i.e. for given L_1 and L_2 the pair of numbers L and M must take $(2L_1+1)(2L_2+1)$ pairs of values. These values can be determined as follows.

To each value of L, there correspond $2L+1$ different possible values of M, from $-L$ to $+L$. The greatest possible value of M in the states ϕ (for given L_1 and L_2) is $M = L_1+L_2$, which is obtained when $M_1 = L_1$ and $M_2 = L_2$. Hence the greatest possible value of M in the states ψ is L_1+L_2, and this is therefore the greatest possible value of L also. Next, there are two states ϕ with $M = L_1+L_2-1$, namely those where $M_1 = L_1$, $M_2 = L_2-1$ and $M_1 = L_1-1$, $M_2 = L_2$. Consequently, there must also be two states ψ with this value of M; one of them is the state with $L = L_1+L_2$ (and $M = L-1$), and the other is clearly that with $L = L_1+L_2-1$ (and $M = L$). For the value $M = L_1+L_2-2$ there are three different states ϕ, with the following pairs of values of M_1, M_2 : (L_1, L_2-2), (L_1-1, L_2-1), and (L_1-2, L_2). This means that, besides the values $L = L_1+L_2$, $L = L_1+L_2-1$, the value $L = L_1+L_2-2$ can occur.

Continuing this argument, we arrive at the result that, for given L_1 and L_2, the number L can take the values

$$L = L_1+L_2, L_1+L_2-1, \ldots, |L_1-L_2|, \tag{30.1}$$

that is $2L_2+1$ different values altogether (supposing that $L_2 \leqslant L_1$). It is easy to verify that we do in fact obtain $(2L_1+1)(2L_2+1)$ different values of the pair of numbers M, L. Here it is important to note that, if we regard as different only those states which have different values of L, then only one state will correspond to each of the possible values (30.1) of L.

This result can be illustrated by means of what is called the *vector model.* If we take two vectors $\mathbf{L}_1$, $\mathbf{L}_2$ of lengths L_1 and L_2, then the values of L are represented by the integral lengths of the vectors $\mathbf{L}$ which are obtained by

† Together with such other quantities as form a complete assembly when combined with these four. These other quantities play no part in the subsequent discussion, and for brevity we shall ignore them entirely, and conventionally call the above four quantities a complete assembly.

vector addition of $\mathbf{L}_1$ and $\mathbf{L}_2$; the greatest value of L is L_1+L_2, which is obtained when $\mathbf{L}_1$ and $\mathbf{L}_2$ are parallel, and the least value is $|L_1-L_2|$, when $\mathbf{L}_1$ and $\mathbf{L}_2$ are antiparallel.

The addition rule for angular momenta which we have obtained also makes it possible, of course, to add any number (more than two) of angular momenta by successive applications of this rule.

In states with definite values of the angular momenta L_1, L_2 and of the total angular momentum L, the scalar products $\mathbf{L}_1 \cdot \mathbf{L}_2$, $\mathbf{L} \cdot \mathbf{L}_1$ and $\mathbf{L} \cdot \mathbf{L}_2$ also have definite values. These values are easily found. To calculate $\mathbf{L}_1 \cdot \mathbf{L}_2$, we write $\hat{\mathbf{L}} = \hat{\mathbf{L}}_1 + \hat{\mathbf{L}}_2$ or, squaring and transposing,

$$2\hat{\mathbf{L}}_1 \cdot \mathbf{L}_2 = \mathbf{L}^2 - \hat{\mathbf{L}}_1{}^2 - \hat{\mathbf{L}}_2{}^2.$$

Replacing the operators on the right-hand side of this equation by their eigenvalues, we obtain the eigenvalue of the operator on the left-hand side:

$$\mathbf{L}_1 \cdot \mathbf{L}_2 = \tfrac{1}{2}\{L(L+1) - L_1(L_1+1) - L_2(L_2+1)\}. \tag{30.2}$$

Similarly we find

$$\mathbf{L} \cdot \mathbf{L}_1 = \tfrac{1}{2}\{L(L+1) + L_1(L_1+1) - L_2(L_2+1)\}. \tag{30.3}$$

Let us now determine the "addition rule for parities". As we know, the wave function Ψ of a system consisting of two independent parts is the product of the wave functions Ψ_1 and Ψ_2 of these parts. Hence it is clear that, if both the latter are of the same parity (i.e. both change sign, or both do not change sign, when the sign of all the co-ordinates is reversed), then the wave function of the whole system is even. On the other hand, if Ψ_1 and Ψ_2 are of opposite parity, then the function Ψ is odd.

This rule can, of course, be generalised at once to the case of a system composed of any number n of non-interacting parts. If these parts are in states with definite parities determined by the corresponding eigenvalues $I_i = \pm 1$ of the operator $\hat{I}$, then the parity I of the state of the whole system is given by the product

$$I = I_1 I_2 \ldots I_n. \tag{30.4}$$

In particular, if we are concerned with a system of particles in a centrally symmetric field (the mutual interaction of the particles being supposed weak), then $I_i = (-1)^{l_i}$, where l_i is the angular momentum of the ith particle (see (28.7)), so that the parity of the state of the whole system is given by

$$I = (-1)^{l_1+l_2+\ldots+l_n}. \tag{30.5}$$

We emphasise that the exponent here contains the algebraic sum of the angular momenta l_i, and this is not in general the same as their "vector sum", i.e. the angular momentum $\mathbf{L}$ of the system.

If a closed system disintegrates (under the action of internal forces), the total angular momentum and parity must be conserved. This circumstance may render it impossible for a system to disintegrate, even if this is energetically possible.

For instance, let us consider an atom in an even state with angular momentum $L = 0$, which is able, so far as energy considerations go, to disintegrate into a free electron and an ion in an odd state with the same angular momentum $L = 0$. It is easy to see that in fact no such disintegration can occur (it is, as we say, *forbidden*). For, by virtue of the law of conservation of angular momentum, the free electron would also have to have zero angular momentum, and therefore be in an even state ($I = (-1)^0 = +1$); the state of the system ion+electron would then be odd, however, whereas the original state of the atom was even.

§31. Matrix elements in the addition of angular momenta

In this section we shall derive a number of formulae, which are not so much interesting in themselves as useful in various quantum-mechanical calculations.

Let us again consider a system composed of two parts (which we shall call sub-systems 1 and 2), with angular momenta $\mathbf{L}_1$ and $\mathbf{L}_2$, and suppose the interaction between these parts to be so weak that the angular momenta $\mathbf{L}_1$ and $\mathbf{L}_2$ can be regarded as conserved to a first approximation†.

The matrix elements of the angular momenta $\mathbf{L}_1$ and $\mathbf{L}_2$ in each of the sub-systems are determined by the formulae (25.13), in which we must understand by L, M respectively L_1, M_1 and L_2, M_2. The question arises of how to calculate the matrix elements of these angular momenta with respect to the wave functions of the stationary states of the whole system, in which the absolute value and the z-component of the total angular momentum $\mathbf{L}$ have definite values.

The states of the system are determined by the quantum numbers L_1, L_2, L, M and by other numbers, the assembly of which for each sub-system we conventionally denote by n_1 and n_2. The operators $\hat{\mathbf{L}}_1$ and $\hat{\mathbf{L}}_2$ commute with the Hamiltonian (in which the interaction of the sub-systems is neglected), and with each other (since they belong to two different sub-systems), but not with the operator $\hat{\mathbf{L}}$ of the total angular momentum. Hence their matrices are diagonal with respect to n_1, n_2, L_1, L_2; for brevity, we shall omit these suffixes in writing the matrix elements.

To calculate the matrix elements which interest us, we can use the general formulae (27.11) and (27.13), taking the arbitrary vector $\mathbf{A}$ to be $\mathbf{L}_1$ (or $\mathbf{L}_2$). These formulae give at once the dependence of the matrix elements $(\mathbf{L}_1)_{L'M'}^{LM}$ on the quantum number M, and it remains to calculate the dependence of

† In applications of the formulae derived in this section, one usually deals not with the addition of the orbital angular momenta of two different systems, but with the addition of the orbital angular momentum $\mathbf{L}$ of an atom (or molecule) to its spin $\mathbf{S}$ (see below, Chapter VIII), their interaction being supposed weak. All the formulae here derived are fully applicable to this case, and in general to the addition of any weakly interacting angular momenta which commute with one another.

the coefficients in these formulae on L. We shall denote these coefficients (the quantities $A^{nL}_{n'L'}$ in (27.11), (27.13)) by $(L_1)^L_{L'}$, or by $L_{1,L'}^{\;L}$.

The diagonal component $(L_1)^L_L$ is easily calculated, starting from the identity

$$\hat{\mathbf{L}}_1 \cdot \hat{\mathbf{L}} = \tfrac{1}{2}(\hat{\mathbf{L}}_1^2 - \hat{\mathbf{L}}_2^2 + \hat{\mathbf{L}}^2).$$

We calculate the diagonal matrix elements for both sides of this equation; on the right-hand side we have simply the eigenvalue of the operator there, while on the left we obtain $(L_1)^L_L L(L+1)$, as is seen at once from formula (27.15) (with $\mathbf{L}_1$ and $\mathbf{L}$ in place of $\mathbf{A}$ and $\mathbf{B}$ respectively). As a result we find

$$(L_1)^L_L = \frac{L_1(L_1+1) - L_2(L_2+1) + L(L+1)}{2L(L+1)}. \tag{31.1}$$

The expression for $(L_2)^L_L$ is obtained by interchanging the suffixes 1 and 2.

The calculation of the non-diagonal components is more involved. We start from the identities

$$(\hat{L}_{1x} - i\hat{L}_{1y})\hat{L}_{1z} - \hat{L}_{1z}(\hat{L}_{1x} - i\hat{L}_{1y}) = \hat{L}_{1x} - i\hat{L}_{1y},$$

$$\hat{\mathbf{L}}_1^2 = \tfrac{1}{2}(\hat{L}_{1x} + i\hat{L}_{1y})(\hat{L}_{1x} - i\hat{L}_{1y}) + \tfrac{1}{2}(\hat{L}_{1x} - i\hat{L}_{1y})(\hat{L}_{1x} + i\hat{L}_{1y}) + \hat{L}_{1z}^2.$$

We take the matrix element of the first equation for the transition $L, M \to L, M+1$, and the diagonal matrix element of the second equation. After some computations which we omit here, we find the following two relations:

$$(L_{1,L}^{\;L})^2 - |L_{1,L+1}^{\;L}|^2(2L+3) + |L_{1,L-1}^{\;L}|^2(2L-1) = L_{1,L}^{\;L},$$

$$L_1(L_1+1) = |L_{1,L-1}^{\;L}|^2 L(2L-1) + |L_{1,L+1}^{\;L}|^2(L+1)(2L+3) + (L_{1,L}^{\;L})^2 L(L+1).$$

We already know the component $L_{1,L}^{\;L}$, so that $L_{1,L+1}^{\;L}$ and $L_{1,L-1}^{\;L}$ can be calculated from these two equations. As a result we obtain†

$$(L_1)^L_{L-1} = (L_1)^{L-1}_L$$
$$= \frac{\sqrt{[(L-L_1+L_2)(L+L_1+L_2+1)(L_1+L_2-L+1)(L+L_1-L_2)]}}{2L\sqrt{[(2L+1)(2L-1)]}}. \tag{31.2}$$

The analogous expressions for L_2 are given simply by

$$(L_2)^L_{L-1} = -(L_1)^L_{L-1}. \tag{31.3}$$

This follows at once from the fact that the matrix of the vector $\mathbf{L} = \mathbf{L}_1 + \mathbf{L}_2$ must be diagonal with respect to L.

Next we shall carry out similar calculations for an arbitrary vector physical

---

† We choose the arbitrary phase such that we obtain real positive quantities.

quantity† **A** which characterises sub-system 2. Its matrix elements in this sub-system are determined by formulae (27.11) and (27.13), in which n, L, M must be taken as n_2, L_2, M_2 respectively; the coefficients A in these formulae we denote by $A^{n_2 L_2}_{n_2' L_2'}$. The question arises of how to calculate the matrix elements of the vector **A** relative to the system as a whole. We shall show that they can be expressed in terms of these quantities $A^{n_2 L_2}_{n_2' L_2'}$.

Since the quantity **A** refers to sub-system 2, its operator commutes with the operator $\hat{\mathbf{L}}_1$ of the angular momentum of sub-system 1. Hence the matrix of the quantity **A** is diagonal with respect to L_1; it is also diagonal with respect to the quantum numbers n_1 of sub-system 1. These suffixes can, for the sake of brevity, be omitted, and we shall write the required matrix elements as $A^{n_2 L_2 L M}_{n_2' L_2' L' M'}$. Their dependence on M is determined by the general formulae (27.11) and (27.13), in which n must be taken as the set of numbers n_1, n_2, L_1, L_2. The coefficients A in these formulae are now naturally denoted by $A^{n_2 L_2 L}_{n_2' L_2' L'}$.

First of all, we note that, since **A** obeys the commutation rules (27.3) both with the total angular momentum **L** of the system and with the angular momentum $\mathbf{L}_2$ of the sub-system 2 to which **A** refers, the matrix elements of **A** are different from zero only if both $L' = L \pm 1, L$, and also $L_2' = L_2 \pm 1, L_2$. We shall not pause here to give the subsequent rather lengthy calculations in their entirety; we shall merely point out that we start from the equation

$$(\hat{L}_{1x} - i\hat{L}_{1y})\hat{A}_z = \hat{A}_z(\hat{L}_{1x} - i\hat{L}_{1y}), \tag{31.4}$$

and take the matrix elements for the transitions n, L_2, L', $M \to n'$, L_2', L'', $M+1$, with the following values of L', L'' : $L' = L-1$, $L'' = L+1$; $L' = L$, $L'' = L+1$; $L' = L$, $L'' = L-1$, and the following values of L_2': $L_2' = L_2$; $L_2' = L_2 - 1$. As a result we obtain a series of relations between the various components $A^{n_2 L_2 L}_{n_2' L_2' L'}$, from which we can determine the dependence of these quantities on $A^{n_2 L_2}_{n_2' L_2'}$. We give the final results:

$$A^{n_2 L_2 L}_{n_2' L_2, L-1} = -A^{n_2 L_2}_{n_2' L_2} \frac{\sqrt{[(L-L_1+L_2)(L+L_1+L_2+1)(L_1+L_2-L+1)(L+L_1-L_2)]}}{2L\sqrt{[(2L-1)(2L+1)]}},$$

$$A^{n_2 L_2, L-1}_{n_2', L_2-1, L} = -A^{n_2 L_2}_{n_2', L_2-1} \frac{\sqrt{[(L_1+L_2-L)(L+L_1-L_2+1)(L_1+L_2-L+1)(L+L_1-L_2)]}}{2L\sqrt{[(2L-1)(2L+1)]}},$$

$$A^{n_2 L_2 L}_{n_2', L_2-1, L} = A^{n_2 L_2}_{n_2', L_2-1} \frac{\sqrt{[(L-L_1+L_2)(L+L_1+L_2+1)(L_1+L_2-L)(L+L_1-L_2+1)]}}{2L(L+1)},$$

† If $\mathbf{L}_1$ is taken as the spin **S** of an atom, and $\mathbf{L}_2$ as its orbital angular momentum **L**, then **A** can be the dipole moment of the atom, the orbital angular momentum or the radius vector of an individual electron, etc.

$$A^{n_2L_2L}_{n_2',L_2-1,L-1}$$
$$= A^{n_2L_2}_{n_2',L_2-1}\frac{\sqrt{[(L-L_1+L_2)(L+L_1+L_2+1)(L-L_1+L_2-1)(L+L_1+L_2)]}}{2L\sqrt{[(2L-1)(2L+1)]}},$$

$$A^{n_2L_2L}_{n_2'L_2L}$$
$$= A^{n_2L_2}_{n_2'L_2}\frac{L(L+1)-L_1(L_1+1)+L_2(L_2+1)}{2L(L+1)}. \tag{31.5}$$

The remaining elements which are not zero are equal to the complex conjugates of those given here; for instance,

$$A^{n_2'L_2,L-1}_{n_2L_2L} = (A^{n_2L_2L}_{n_2'L_2,L-1})^*.$$

The coefficients $A^{n_2L_2}_{n_2'L_2'}$ are some functions of L_2, but are independent of L. The notation for them is the same as that for the corresponding coefficients in the matrix elements of **A** in sub-system 2. It is easy to see that the two sets do in fact coincide, so that the formulae obtained give the relation between the matrix elements of one and the same quantity **A** in sub-system 2 and in the whole system. To deduce this, we notice that, if in some state the numbers L and M have their greatest possible values (for given L_1 and L_2), namely $L = M = L_1+L_2$, we can assert that M_1 and M_2 have the values L_1 and L_2 respectively. Hence, for $L = M = L_1+L_2$, and $L' = M' = L_1'+L_2'$, the matrix element of the quantity **A** for the whole system, $A^{n_2L_2LM}_{n_2'L_2'L'M'}$, must be the same as that for sub-system 2, $A^{n_2L_2M_2}_{n_2'L_2'M_2'}$. Calculating each and equating them, we find at once that the coefficients $A^{n_2L_2}_{n_2'L_2'}$ are the same in each case.

Finally, let **B** be another vector physical quantity characterising sub-system 1, and therefore commuting with $\mathbf{L}_2$. The same formulae (31.5) hold for it, except that the suffixes 1 and 2 must be interchanged, and in addition the sign of those components must be altered which are non-diagonal with respect to either the number L_1 or the number L, but not both (i.e. in the first and third formulae)†. We shall give for reference the formulae, which are useful in certain calculations, for the matrix elements of the scalar **A . B** in the representation n_1, n_2, L_1, L_2, L, M. They are found at once by the rule of matrix multiplication, and are

$$(\mathbf{A}\cdot\mathbf{B})^{n_1n_2L_1L_2LM}_{n_1'n_2'L_1L_2LM}$$
$$= \tfrac{1}{2}[L(L+1)-L_1(L_1+1)-L_2(L_2+1)]A^{n_2L_2}_{n_2'L_2}B^{n_1L_1}_{n_1'L_1},$$

$$(\mathbf{A}\cdot\mathbf{B})^{n_1n_2L_1L_2LM}_{n_1'n_2'L_1,L_2-1,LM}$$
$$= \tfrac{1}{2}\sqrt{[(L-L_1+L_2)(L_1+L_2-L)(L+L_1+L_2+1)(L+L_1-L_2+1)]}\times$$
$$\times A^{n_2L_2}_{n_2'L_2-1}B^{n_1L_1}_{n_1'L_1},$$

† The signs in formulae (31.5) are related to the choice of sign in (31.2); the signs given correspond to the choice, which we made above, of the positive sign in front of the radical in (31.2).

$$(\mathbf{A}\,.\,\mathbf{B})^{n_1 n_2 L_1 L_2 LM}_{n_1' n_2', L_1-1, L_2 LM}$$
$$= -\tfrac{1}{2}\sqrt{[(L+L_1-L_2)(L+L_2-L_1+1)(L+L_1+L_2+1)(L_1+L_2-L)]}\times$$
$$\times A^{n_2 L_2}_{n_2' L_2} B^{n_1 L_1}_{n_1', L_1-1},$$

$$(\mathbf{A}\,.\,\mathbf{B})^{n_1 n_2 L_1 L_2 LM}_{n_1' n_2' L_1-1, L_2-1, LM}$$
$$= -\tfrac{1}{2}\sqrt{[(L_1+L_2+L+1)(L_1+L_2+L)(L_1+L_2-L)(L_1+L_2-L-1)]}\times$$
$$\times A^{n_2 L_2}_{n_2', L_2-1} B^{n_1 L_1}_{n_1', L_1-1},$$

$$(\mathbf{A}\,.\,\mathbf{B})^{n_1 n_2, L_1-1, L_2 LM}_{n_1' n_2' L_1, L_2-1, LM}$$
$$= \tfrac{1}{2}\sqrt{[(L+L_2-L_1)(L+L_2-L_1+1)(L+L_1-L_2)(L+L_1-L_2+1)]}\times$$
$$\times A^{n_2 L_2}_{n_2', L_2-1} B^{n_1\, L_1-1}_{n_1' L_1}\,. \tag{31.6}$$

The remaining elements which are not zero are the complex conjugates of those given here.

CHAPTER V

MOTION IN A CENTRALLY SYMMETRIC FIELD

§32. Motion in a centrally symmetric field

THE problem of the motion of two interacting particles can be reduced in quantum mechanics to that of one particle, as can be done in classical mechanics. The Hamiltonian of the two particles (of masses μ_1, μ_2) interacting in accordance with the law $U(r)$ (where r is the distance between the particles) is of the form

$$\hat{H} = -\frac{\hbar^2}{2\mu_1}\Delta_1 - \frac{\hbar^2}{2\mu_2}\Delta_2 + U(r), \tag{32.1}$$

where Δ_1 and Δ_2 are the Laplacian operators with respect to the co-ordinates of the particles. Instead of the radius vectors $\mathbf{r}_1$ and $\mathbf{r}_2$ of the particles, we introduce new variables $\mathbf{R}$ and $\mathbf{r}$:

$$\mathbf{r} = \mathbf{r}_2 - \mathbf{r}_1, \quad \mathbf{R} = (\mu_1\mathbf{r}_1 + \mu_2\mathbf{r}_2)/(\mu_1+\mu_2); \tag{32.2}$$

$\mathbf{r}$ is the vector of the distance between the particles, and $\mathbf{R}$ the radius vector of their centre of mass. A simple calculation gives

$$\hat{H} = -\frac{\hbar^2}{2(\mu_1+\mu_2)}\Delta_R - \frac{\hbar^2}{2\mu}\Delta + U(r), \tag{32.3}$$

where Δ_R and Δ are the Laplacian operators with respect to the components of the vectors $\mathbf{R}$ and $\mathbf{r}$ respectively, $\mu_1+\mu_2$ is the total mass of the system, and $\mu = \mu_1\mu_2/(\mu_1+\mu_2)$ is what is called the *reduced mass*. Thus the Hamiltonian falls into the sum of two independent parts. Hence we can look for $\psi(\mathbf{r}_1, \mathbf{r}_2)$ in the form of a product $\phi(\mathbf{R})\psi(\mathbf{r})$, where the function $\phi(\mathbf{R})$ describes the motion of the centre of mass (as a free particle of mass $\mu_1+\mu_2$), and $\psi(\mathbf{r})$ describes the relative motion of the particles (as a particle of mass μ moving in the centrally symmetric field $U(r)$).

SCHRÖDINGER's equation for the motion of a particle in a centrally symmetric field is

$$\Delta\psi + (2\mu/\hbar^2)[E - U(r)]\psi = 0. \tag{32.4}$$

Using the familiar expression for the Laplacian operator in spherical co-ordinates, we can write this equation in the form

$$\frac{1}{r^2}\frac{\partial}{\partial r}\left(r^2\frac{\partial\psi}{\partial r}\right) + \frac{1}{r^2}\left[\frac{1}{\sin\theta}\frac{\partial}{\partial\theta}\left(\sin\theta\frac{\partial\psi}{\partial\theta}\right) + \frac{1}{\sin^2\theta}\frac{\partial^2\psi}{\partial\phi^2}\right] + \frac{2\mu}{\hbar^2}[E - U(r)]\psi = 0. \tag{32.5}$$

If we introduce here the operator $\hat{\mathbf{l}}^2$ (24.15) of the squared angular momentum we obtain†

$$\frac{\hbar^2}{2\mu}\left[-\frac{1}{r^2}\frac{\partial}{\partial r}\left(r^2\frac{\partial\psi}{\partial r}\right)+\frac{\hat{\mathbf{l}}^2}{r^2}\psi\right]+U(r)\psi = E\psi. \tag{32.6}$$

The angular momentum is conserved during motion in a centrally symmetric field. We shall consider stationary states in which $\mathbf{l}^2$ and l_z have definite values. In other words, we shall seek the common eigenfunctions of the operators $\hat{H}$, $\hat{\mathbf{l}}^2$ and $\hat{l}_z$.

The requirement that ψ is an eigenfunction of the operators $\hat{\mathbf{l}}^2$ and $\hat{l}_z$ determines its angular dependence. We thus seek solutions of equation (32.6) in the form

$$\psi = R(r)Y_{lm}(\theta,\phi), \tag{32.7}$$

where the functions $Y_{lm}(\theta,\phi)$ are defined by the formulae of §26.

Since $\hat{\mathbf{l}}^2 Y_{lm} = l(l+1)Y_{lm}$, we obtain for the *radial function* $R(r)$ the equation

$$\frac{1}{r^2}\frac{\mathrm{d}}{\mathrm{d}r}\left(r^2\frac{\mathrm{d}R}{\mathrm{d}r}\right)-\frac{l(l+1)}{r^2}R+\frac{2\mu}{\hbar^2}[E-U(r)]R = 0. \tag{32.8}$$

We note that this equation does not contain the value of $l_z = m$ at all, in accordance with the $(2l+1)$-fold degeneracy of the levels, with which we are already familiar.

Let us investigate the radial part of the wave functions. By the substitution

$$R(r) = \chi(r)/r \tag{32.9}$$

equation (32.8) is brought to the form

$$\frac{\mathrm{d}^2\chi}{\mathrm{d}r^2}+\left[\frac{2\mu}{\hbar^2}(E-U)-\frac{l(l+1)}{r^2}\right]\chi = 0. \tag{32.10}$$

If the field $U(r)$ is everywhere finite, the wave function ψ must also be finite in all space, including the origin, and consequently so must its radial part

† If we introduce the operator of the radial component p_r of the linear momentum, in the form

$$\hat{p}_r\psi = -i\hbar\frac{1}{r}\frac{\partial}{\partial r}(r\psi) = -i\hbar\left(\frac{\partial}{\partial r}+\frac{1}{r}\right)\psi,$$

the Hamiltonian can be written in the form

$$\hat{H} = (1/2\mu)(\hat{p}_r^{\,2}+\hbar^2\hat{\mathbf{l}}^2/r^2)+U(r),$$

which is the same in form as the classical HAMILTON's function in spherical co-ordinates.

$R(r)$. Hence it follows that $\chi(r)$ must vanish for $r = 0$:

$$\chi(0) = 0. \tag{32.11}$$

This condition actually holds also (see §35) for a field which becomes infinite as $r \to 0$.

The normalisation condition for the radial function $R(r)$ is determined by the integral $\int |R|^2 r^2 \, dr$, and therefore that for the function $\chi(r)$ is determined by the integral $\int |\chi|^2 \, dr$.

Equation (32.10) is formally identical with SCHRÖDINGER's equation for one-dimensional motion in a field of potential energy

$$U_l(r) = U(r) + \frac{\hbar^2}{2\mu}\frac{l(l+1)}{r^2}, \tag{32.12}$$

which is the sum of the energy $U(r)$ and a term

$$\hbar^2 l(l+1)/2\mu r^2 = \hbar^2 \mathbf{l}^2/2\mu r^2,$$

which may be called the *centrifugal energy*. Thus the problem of motion in a centrally symmetric field reduces to that of one-dimensional motion in a region bounded on one side (the boundary condition for $r = 0$).

In one-dimensional motion in a region bounded on one side, the energy levels are not degenerate (§19). Hence we can say that, if the energy is given, the solution of equation (32.10), i.e. the radial part of the wave function, is completely determined. Bearing in mind also that the angular part of the wave function is completely determined by the values of l and m, we reach the conclusion that, for motion in a centrally symmetric field, the wave function is completely determined by the values of E, l and m. In other words, the energy, the squared angular momentum and the z-component of the angular momentum together form a complete assembly of physical quantities for such a motion.

The reduction of the problem of motion in a centrally symmetric field to a one-dimensional problem enables us to apply the oscillation theorem (see §19). It leads to the following result. We arrange the eigenvalues of the energy (discrete spectrum) for a given l in order of increasing magnitude, and give them numbers n_r, the lowest level being given the number $n_r = 0$. Then n_r determines the number of nodes of the radial part of the wave function for finite values of r (excluding the point $r = 0$). The number n_r is called the *radial quantum number*. The number l for motion in a centrally symmetric field is sometimes called the *azimuthal quantum number*, and m the *magnetic quantum number*.

The normal state of a particle moving in a centrally symmetric field is always the state with $l = 0$; for, if $l \neq 0$, the angular part of the wave function invariably has nodes, whereas the wave function of the normal state can have no nodes. We can also say that the least possible eigenvalue of the energy, for a given l, increases with l. This follows from the fact that the presence of an angular momentum involves the addition of the essentially positive term $\hbar^2 l(l+1)/2\mu r^2$, which increases with l, to the Hamiltonian.

Let us determine the form of the radial function near the origin. Here we shall suppose that

$$\lim_{r\to 0} U(r)r^2 = 0.$$

We seek $R(r)$ in the form of a power series in r, retaining only the first term of the series for small r; in other words, we seek $R(r)$ in the form $R = \text{constant} \times r^s$. Substituting this in the equation

$$\mathrm{d}(r^2\, \mathrm{d}R/\mathrm{d}r)/\mathrm{d}r - l(l+1)R = 0,$$

which is obtained from (32.8) by multiplying by r^2 and taking the limit as $r \to 0$, we find

$$s(s+1) = l(l+1).$$

Hence

$$s = l \quad \text{or} \quad s = -(l+1).$$

The solution with $s = -(l+1)$ does not satisfy the necessary conditions; it becomes infinite for $r = 0$ (we recall that $l \geqslant 0$). Thus the solution with $s = l$ remains, i.e. near the origin the wave functions of states with a given l are proportional to r^l:

$$R_l \cong \text{constant} \times r^l. \tag{32.13}$$

The probability of a particle's being at a distance between r and $r+\mathrm{d}r$ from the centre is determined by the value of $r^2|R|^2$ and is thus proportional to $r^{2(l+1)}$. We see that it becomes zero at the origin the more rapidly, the greater the value of l.

§33. Free motion (spherical co-ordinates)

The wave function of a freely moving particle

$$\psi_{\mathbf{p}} = \text{constant} \times e^{(i/\hbar)\mathbf{p}\cdot\mathbf{r}}$$

describes a stationary state in which the particle has a definite momentum $\mathbf{p}$ (and energy $E = p^2/2\mu$). Let us now consider stationary states of a free particle in which it has a definite value, not only of the energy, but also of the absolute value and z-component of the angular momentum. Instead of the energy, it is convenient to introduce the *wave number*

$$k = p/\hbar = \sqrt{(2\mu E)}/\hbar. \tag{33.1}$$

The wave function of a state with angular momentum l and projection thereof m has the form

$$\psi_{klm} = R_{kl}(r)Y_{lm}(\theta,\phi), \tag{33.2}$$

where the radial function is determined by the equation

$$R_{kl}''+\frac{2}{r}R_{kl}'+\left[k^2-\frac{l(l+1)}{r^2}\right]R_{kl} = 0 \tag{33.3}$$

(equation (32.8) with $U(r) \equiv 0$). The wave functions ψ_{klm} satisfy the conditions of normalisation and orthogonality:

$$\int \psi_{k'l'm'}{}^*\psi_{klm}\,\mathrm{d}V = \delta_{ll'}\delta_{mm'}\delta(k'-k).$$

The orthogonality for different l, l' and m, m' is ensured by the angular functions. The radial functions must be normalised by the condition

$$\int_0^\infty r^2R_{k'l}R_{kl}\,\mathrm{d}r = \delta(k'-k). \tag{33.4}$$

If we normalise the wave functions, not on the "k scale", but on the "energy scale", i.e. by the condition

$$\int_0^\infty r^2R_{E'l}R_{El}\,\mathrm{d}r = \delta(E'-E),$$

then, by the general formula (5.11), we have

$$R_{El} = R_{kl}\sqrt{(\mathrm{d}k/\mathrm{d}E)} = (1/\hbar)\sqrt{(\mu/k)}R_{kl}. \tag{33.5}$$

For $l = 0$, equation (33.3) can be written

$$\frac{1}{r}\frac{\mathrm{d}^2(rR_{k0})}{\mathrm{d}r^2}+k^2R_{k0} = 0;$$

its solution finite for $r = 0$ is

$$R_{k0} = A\frac{\sin kr}{r}.$$

To determine the normalisation constant, we calculate the integral

$$\int_0^\infty R_{k0}R_{k'0}r^2\,\mathrm{d}r = A^2\int_0^\infty \sin kr \sin k'r\,\mathrm{d}r$$

$$= \tfrac{1}{2}A^2\int_0^\infty [\cos(k-k')r-\cos(k+k')r]\,\mathrm{d}r.$$

The integral of $\cos(k+k')r$ does not diverge when k, $k' > 0$. The integral of the first term, however, gives by formula (13.7a)

$$\int_0^\infty R_{k0}R_{k'0}r^2\,\mathrm{d}r = \tfrac{1}{2}A^2\pi\delta(k'-k).$$

By comparison with (33.4) we obtain

$$A = \sqrt{(2/\pi)}.$$

Thus the normalised function R_{k0} has the form†

$$R_{k0} = \sqrt{\frac{2}{\pi}}\frac{\sin kr}{r}. \tag{33.6}$$

To solve equation (33.3) with $l \neq 0$, we make the substitution

$$R_{kl} = r^l\chi_{kl}.$$

For χ_{kl} we have the equation

$$\chi_{kl}''+2(l+1)\chi_{kl}'/r+k^2\chi_{kl} = 0.$$

If we differentiate this equation with respect to r, we obtain

$$\chi_{kl}'''+\frac{2(l+1)}{r}\chi_{kl}''+\left[k^2-\frac{2(l+1)}{r^2}\right]\chi_{kl}' = 0.$$

By the substitution $\chi_{kl}' = r\chi_{k,l+1}$ it becomes

$$\chi_{k,l+1}''+\frac{2(l+2)}{r}\chi_{k,l+1}'+k^2\chi_{k,l+1} = 0,$$

which is in fact the equation satisfied by $\chi_{k,l+1}$. Thus the successive functions χ_{kl} are related by

$$\chi_{k,l+1} = \chi_{kl}'/r,$$

and hence

$$\chi_{kl} = \left(\frac{1}{r}\frac{\mathrm{d}}{\mathrm{d}r}\right)^l\chi_{k0},$$

where $\chi_{k0} = R_{k0}$ is determined by formula (33.6) (this expression can, of course, be multiplied by an arbitrary constant).

Thus we finally have the following expression for the radial functions in the free motion of a particle:

$$R_{kl} = (-1)^l\sqrt{\frac{2}{\pi}}\frac{r^l}{k^l}\left(\frac{1}{r}\frac{\mathrm{d}}{\mathrm{d}r}\right)^l\frac{\sin kr}{r} \tag{33.7}$$

† The normalisation could also be effected by the method indicated at the end of §19.

(the factor k^{-l} is introduced for normalisation purposes—see below—and the factor $(-1)^l$ for convenience)†.

To obtain an asymptotic expression for the radial function (33.7) at large distances, we notice that the term which decreases least rapidly as $r \to \infty$ is obtained by differentiating $\sin kr$ l times:

$$R_{kl} \approx (-1)^l \sqrt{\frac{2}{\pi}} \frac{1}{k^l r} \frac{d^l}{dr^l} \sin kr.$$

Since

$$-\frac{d}{dr} \sin kr = k \sin(kr - \tfrac{1}{2}\pi), \ldots, \left(-\frac{d}{dr}\right)^l \sin kr = k^l \sin(kr - \tfrac{1}{2}l\pi),$$

we have the following asymptotic expression:

$$R_{kl} \approx \sqrt{\frac{2}{\pi}} \frac{\sin(kr - \frac{1}{2}l\pi)}{r}. \tag{33.8}$$

The normalisation of the functions R_{kl} can be effected by means of their asymptotic expressions, as was explained in §19. Comparing the asymptotic formula (33.8) with the normalised function R_{k0} (33.6), we see that the functions R_{kl}, with the coefficient used in (33.7), are in fact normalised as they should be.

Near the origin (r small) we have, retaining only the term containing the lowest power of r,

$$\begin{aligned}\left(\frac{1}{r}\frac{d}{dr}\right)^l \frac{\sin kr}{r} &= \left(\frac{1}{r}\frac{d}{dr}\right)^l \sum_{n=0}^{\infty} (-1)^n \frac{k^{2n+1} r^{2n}}{(2n+1)!} \\ &\cong (-1)^l \left(\frac{1}{r}\frac{d}{dr}\right)^l \frac{k^{2l+1} r^{2l}}{(2l+1)!} \\ &= (-1)^l k^{2l+1} \frac{2.4\ldots 2l}{(2l+1)!} \\ &= (-1)^l k^{2l+1}/1.3\ldots(2l+1).\end{aligned}$$

† The functions R_{kl} can be expressed in terms of Bessel functions of half-integral order, in the form

$$R_{kl} = \sqrt{(k/r)} J_{l+\frac{1}{2}}(kr). \tag{33.7a}$$

The first few functions R_k are:

$$R_{k0} = \sqrt{\frac{2}{\pi}} k \frac{\sin kr}{kr},$$

$$R_{k1} = \sqrt{\frac{2}{\pi}} k \left[\frac{\sin kr}{(kr)^2} - \frac{\cos kr}{kr}\right],$$

$$R_{k2} = \sqrt{\frac{2}{\pi}} k \left[\left(\frac{3}{(kr)^3} - \frac{1}{kr}\right)\sin kr - \frac{3\cos kr}{(kr)^2}\right].$$

Thus the functions R_{kl} near the origin have the form

$$R_{kl} \cong \sqrt{\frac{2}{\pi}} \frac{k^{l+1}}{1.3\ldots(2l+1)} r^l, \tag{33.9}$$

in agreement with the general result (32.13).

In some problems it is necessary to consider wave functions which do not satisfy the usual conditions of finiteness, but correspond to a flux of particles from the origin. The wave function which describes such a flux of particles with angular momentum $l = 0$ is obtained by taking, instead of the "stationary spherical wave" (33.6), a solution in the form of an "outgoing spherical wave",

$$R_{k0}^{+} = Ae^{ikr}/r. \tag{33.10}$$

This function becomes infinite at the origin.

Similarly, a flux of particles incident on the centre (with angular momentum $l = 0$) is described by a wave function in the form of an "ingoing spherical wave",

$$R_{k0}^{-} = Ae^{-ikr}/r. \tag{33.11}$$

In the general case of an angular momentum l which is not zero, we obtain a solution of equation (33.3) in the form†

$$R_{kl}^{\pm} = (-1)^l A \frac{r^l}{k^l} \left(\frac{1}{r}\frac{\mathrm{d}}{\mathrm{d}r}\right)^l \frac{e^{\pm ikr}}{r}. \tag{33.12}$$

The asymptotic expression for these functions is

$$R_{kl}^{\pm} \approx Ae^{\pm i(kr - \frac{1}{2}l\pi)}/r. \tag{33.13}$$

Near the origin, it has the form

$$R_{kl}^{\pm} \approx A \frac{1.3\ldots(2l-1)}{k^l} r^{-l-1}. \tag{33.14}$$

We normalise these functions so that they correspond to the emission (or absorption) of one particle per unit time. To do so, we notice that, at large distances, the spherical wave can be regarded as plane in any small interval, and the probability current density in it is $i = v\psi\psi^*$, where $v = k\hbar/\mu$ is the velocity of a particle. The normalisation is determined by the condition

† These functions can be expressed in terms of Hankel functions:

$$R_{kl}^{\pm} = \pm iA\sqrt{(k\pi/2r)}H^{(1,2)}_{l+\frac{1}{2}}(kr), \tag{33.12a}$$

of the first and second kinds for the signs + and − respectively in the exponent in (33.12). The asymptotic expansion of the functions $R_{kl}^{\pm}$ for large r is

$$R_{kl}^{\pm} = A\frac{e^{\pm i(kr-\frac{1}{2}l\pi)}}{r}\left[1 \mp \frac{l(l+1)}{1!\,2ikr} + \frac{(l-1)l(l+1)(l+2)}{2!\,(2ikr)^2} \pm \ldots\right].$$

$\oint i\,df = 1$, where the integration is carried out over a spherical surface of large radius r, i.e. $\int ir^2\,do = 1$, where do is an element of solid angle. If the angular functions are normalised as before, the coefficient A in the radial function must be put equal to

$$A = 1/\sqrt{v} = \sqrt{(\mu/k\hbar)}. \qquad (33.15)$$

An asymptotic expression similar to (33.8) holds, not only for the radial part of the wave function of free motion, but also for motion (with positive energy) in any field which falls off sufficiently rapidly with distance.† At large distances we can neglect both the field and the centrifugal energy in SCHRÖDINGER's equation, and there remains the approximate equation

$$\frac{1}{r}\frac{d^2(rR_{kl})}{dr^2}+k^2R_{kl} = 0.$$

The general solution of this equation is

$$R_{kl} \approx \sqrt{\frac{2}{\pi}}\frac{\sin(kr-\frac{1}{2}l\pi+\delta_l)}{r}, \qquad (33.16)$$

where δ_l is a constant, and the constant factor is chosen in accordance with the normalisation of the wave function on the "k scale".‡ The constant phase δ_l is determined by the boundary condition (R_{kl} is finite as $r \to 0$); to do this, the exact SCHRÖDINGER's equation must be solved, and δ_l cannot be calculated in a general form. The phases δ_l are, of course, functions of both l and k, and are an important property of the eigenfunctions of the continuous spectrum.

PROBLEM

Determine the energy levels for the motion of a particle with angular momentum $l = 0$ in a centrally symmetric potential well:

$$U(r) = -U_0 \text{ for } r < a, \quad U(r) = 0 \text{ for } r > a.$$

SOLUTION. For $l = 0$ the wave functions depend only on r. Inside the well, SCHRÖDINGER's equation has the form

$$\frac{1}{r}\frac{d^2}{dr^2}(r\psi)+k^2\psi = 0, \quad k = \frac{1}{\hbar}\sqrt{[2\mu(U_0-|E|)]}.$$

The solution finite for $r = 0$ is

$$\psi = A\frac{\sin kr}{r}.$$

For $r > a$, we have the equation

$$\frac{1}{r}\frac{d^2}{dr^2}(r\psi)-\kappa^2\psi = 0, \quad \kappa = \frac{1}{\hbar}\sqrt{(2\mu|E|)}.$$

† As we shall show in §106, the field must decrease at least as rapidly as r^{-s} with $s > 1$.
‡ The term $-\frac{1}{2}l\pi$ in the argument of the sine is added so that $\delta_l = 0$ when the field vanishes in all space.

The solution vanishing at infinity is

$$\psi = A'e^{-\kappa r}/r.$$

The condition of the continuity of the logarithmic derivative of $r\psi$ at $r = a$ gives

$$k \cot ka = -\kappa = -\sqrt{[(2\mu U_0/\hbar^2)-k^2]}, \tag{1}$$

or

$$\sin ka = \pm\sqrt{(\hbar^2/2\mu a^2 U_0)}ka. \tag{2}$$

This equation determines in implicit form the required energy levels (we must take those roots of the equation for which $\cot ka < 0$, as follows from (1)). The first of these levels (with $l = 0$) is at the same time the deepest of all energy levels whatsoever (see §32), i.e. it corresponds to the normal state of the particle.

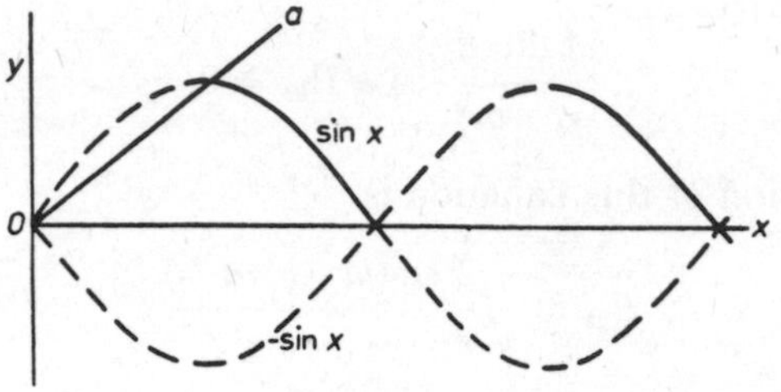

FIG. 9

If the depth U_0 of the potential well is small enough, there are no levels of negative energy, and the particle cannot "stay" in the well. This is easily seen from equation (2), by means of the following graphical construction. The roots of an equation of the form $\pm\sin x = \alpha x$ are given by the points of intersection of the line $y = \alpha x$ with the curves $y = \pm\sin x$, and we must take only those points of intersection for which $\cot x < 0$; the corresponding parts of the curve $y = \sin x$ are shown in Fig. 9 by a continuous line. We see that, if α is sufficiently large (U_0 small), there are no such points of intersection. The first such point appears when the line $y = \alpha x$ occupies the position Oa, i.e. for $\alpha = 2/\pi$, and is at $x = \frac{1}{2}\pi$. Putting $\alpha = \hbar/\sqrt{(2\mu a^2 U_0)}$, $x = ka$, we hence obtain for the minimum well depth to give a single negative level

$$U_{0,\min} = \pi^2\hbar^2/8\mu a^2.$$

This quantity is the greater, the smaller the well radius a. The position of the first level E_1 at the point where it first appears is determined from $ka = \frac{1}{2}\pi$ and is $E_1 = 0$, as we should expect. As the well depth increases further, the normal level E_1 descends, and the next level appears when $U_0 = 9U_{0,\min}$.

§34. Resolution of a plane wave

Let us consider a free particle moving with a given momentum $p = k\hbar$ in the positive direction of the z-axis. The wave function of such a particle is of the form

$$\psi = \text{constant} \times e^{ikz}.$$

Let us expand this function in terms of the wave functions ψ_{klm} of free motion with various angular momenta. Since, in the state considered, the energy has the definite value $k^2\hbar^2/2\mu$, it is clear that only functions with this k will appear in the required expansion. Moreover, since the function e^{ikz} has axial symmetry about the z-axis, its expansion can contain only functions independent of the angle ϕ, i.e. functions with $m = 0$. Thus we must have

$$e^{ikz} = \sum_{l=0}^{\infty} a_l \psi_{kl0} = \sum_{l=0}^{\infty} a_l R_{kl} \Theta_{l0} \Phi_0,$$

where the a_l are constants. Substituting the expressions (25.3), (26.7) and (33.7) for the functions Φ, Θ, R, we obtain

$$e^{ikz} = \sum_{l=0}^{\infty} C_l P_l(\cos\theta) \left(\frac{r}{k}\right)^l \left(\frac{1}{r}\frac{\mathrm{d}}{\mathrm{d}r}\right)^l \frac{\sin kr}{kr} \qquad (z = r\cos\theta),$$

where the C_l are other constants. These constants are conveniently determined by comparing the coefficients of $(r\cos\theta)^n$ in the expansions of the two sides of the equation in powers of r. On the right-hand side of the equation this term occurs only in the nth summand; for $l > n$, the expansion of the radial function begins at a higher power of r, while for $l < n$ the polynomial $P_l(\cos\theta)$ contains only lower powers of $\cos\theta$. The term in $\cos^l\theta$ in $P_l(\cos\theta)$ has the coefficient $(2l)!/2^l(l!)^2$ (see formula (c.2)). Using also formula (33.9), we find the desired term of the expansion of the right-hand side of the equation to be

$$(-1)^l C_l \frac{(2l)!\,(kr\cos\theta)^l}{2^l(l!)^2 1.3\ldots(2l+1)}.$$

On the left-hand side of the equation the corresponding term (in the expansion of $e^{ikr\cos\theta}$) is

$$(ikr\cos\theta)^l/l!$$

Equating these two quantities, we find $C_l = (-i)^l(2l+1)$. Thus we finally obtain the required expansion:

$$e^{ikz} = \sum_{l=0}^{\infty} (-i)^l(2l+1)P_l(\cos\theta)\left(\frac{r}{k}\right)^l \left(\frac{1}{r}\frac{\mathrm{d}}{\mathrm{d}r}\right)^l \frac{\sin kr}{kr}. \qquad (34.1)$$

At large distances this relation takes the asymptotic form

$$e^{ikz} \approx \frac{1}{kr}\sum_{l=0}^{\infty} i^l(2l+1)P_l(\cos\theta)\sin(kr - \tfrac{1}{2}l\pi). \qquad (34.1\text{a})$$

We normalise the wave function e^{ikz} to give a probability current density of unity, i.e. so that it corresponds to a flux of particles (parallel to the z-axis) with one particle passing through unit area in unit time. It is easy to see that this function is

$$\psi = v^{-\frac{1}{2}}e^{ikz} = \sqrt{(\mu/k\hbar)}e^{ikz}, \qquad (34.2)$$

where v is the velocity of the particles. Multiplying both sides of equation (34.1) by $\sqrt{(\mu/k\hbar)}$ and introducing on the right-hand side the normalised functions $\psi_{klm}^{\pm} = R_{kl}^{\pm}(r)Y_{lm}(\theta, \phi)$, we obtain

$$\frac{1}{\sqrt{v}}e^{ikz} = \sum_{l=0}^{\infty} i^{l-1}\sqrt{[\pi(2l+1)]}\frac{1}{k}(\psi_{kl0}^{+}-\psi_{kl0}^{-}).$$

The squared modulus of the coefficient of ψ_{kl0}^{-} (or ψ_{kl0}^{+}) in this expansion determines, according to the usual rules, the probability that a particle in a current converging to (or diverging from) the centre has an angular momentum l (about the origin). Since the wave function $v^{-\frac{1}{2}}e^{ikz}$ corresponds to a current of particles of unit density, this "probability" has the dimensions of length squared; it can be conveniently interpreted as the magnitude of the "cross-section" (in the xy-plane) on which the particle must fall if its angular momentum is l. Denoting this quantity by σ_l, we have

$$\sigma_l = \pi(2l+1)/k^2 = \pi(\lambda/2\pi)^2(2l+1), \tag{34.3}$$

where λ is the de Broglie wavelength of the particle.

For large values of l, the sum of the cross-sections over a range Δl of l (such that $1 \ll \Delta l \ll l$) is

$$\sum_{\Delta l} \sigma_l \cong \frac{\pi}{k^2}2l\Delta l = 2\pi\frac{l\hbar^2}{p^2}\Delta l.$$

On substituting the classical expression for the angular momentum, $\hbar l = \rho p$ (where ρ is what is called the *impact parameter*), this expression becomes

$$2\pi\rho\Delta\rho,$$

in agreement with the classical result. This is no accident; we shall see below that, for large values of l, the motion is quasi-classical (see Chapter VII).

§35. "Fall" of a particle to the centre

To reveal certain properties of quantum-mechanical motion it is useful to examine a case which, it is true, has no direct physical meaning: the motion of a particle in a field where the potential energy becomes infinite at some point (the origin) according to the law $U(r) \approx -\beta/r^2$, $\beta > 0$; the form of the field at large distances from the origin is here immaterial. We have seen in §16 that this is a case intermediate between those where there are ordinary stationary states and those where a "fall" of the particle to the origin takes place.

Near the origin, SCHRÖDINGER's equation in the present case is

$$R''+2R'/r+\gamma R/r^2 = 0, \tag{35.1}$$

where $R(r)$ is the radial part of the wave function, and we have introduced the constant

$$\gamma = 2\mu\beta/\hbar^2 - l(l+1) \tag{35.2}$$

and have omitted all terms of lower orders in $1/r$; the value of the energy E is supposed finite, and so the corresponding term in the equation is omitted also.

Let us seek R in the form $R \sim r^s$; we then obtain for s the quadratic equation

$$s(s+1)+\gamma = 0,$$

which has the two roots

$$s_1 = -\tfrac{1}{2}+\sqrt{(\tfrac{1}{4}-\gamma)}, \quad s_2 = -\tfrac{1}{2}-\sqrt{(\tfrac{1}{4}-\gamma)}. \tag{35.3}$$

For further investigations it is convenient to proceed as follows. We draw a small region of radius r_0 round the origin, and replace the function $-\gamma/r^2$ in this region by the constant $-\gamma/r_0^2$. After determining the wave functions in this "cut off" field, we then examine the result of passing to the limit $r_0 \to 0$.

Let us first suppose that $\gamma < \frac{1}{4}$. Then s_1 and s_2 are real negative quantities, and $s_1 > s_2$. For $r > r_0$, the general solution of SCHRÖDINGER's equation has the form (always restricting ourselves to small r),

$$R = Ar^{s_1}+Br^{s_2}, \tag{35.4}$$

A and B being constants. For $r < r_0$, the solution of the equation

$$R''+2R'/r+\gamma R/r_0^2 = 0$$

which is finite at the origin has the form

$$R = C\frac{\sin kr}{r}, \quad k = \sqrt{\gamma}/r_0. \tag{35.5}$$

For $r = r_0$, the function R and its derivative R' must be continuous. It is convenient to write one of the conditions as a condition of continuity of the logarithmic derivative of rR. This gives the equation

$$\frac{A(s_1+1)r_0^{s_1}+B(s_2+1)r_0^{s_2}}{Ar_0^{s_1+1}+Br_0^{s_2+1}} = k \cot kr_0,$$

or

$$\frac{A(s_1+1)r_0^{s_1}+B(s_2+1)r_0^{s_2}}{Ar_0^{s_1}+Br_0^{s_2}} = \sqrt{\gamma} \cot \sqrt{\gamma}.$$

On solving for the ratio B/A, this equation gives an expression of the form

$$B/A = \text{constant} \times r_0^{s_1-s_2}. \tag{35.6}$$

Passing now to the limit $r_0 \to 0$, we find that $B/A \to 0$ (recalling that

$s_1 > s_2$). Thus, of the two solutions of SCHRÖDINGER's equation (35.1) which diverge at the origin, we must choose that which becomes infinite less rapidly:

$$R = A/r^{|s_1|}. \tag{35.7}$$

Next, let $\gamma > \frac{1}{4}$. Then s_1 and s_2 are complex:

$$s_1 = -\tfrac{1}{2}+i\sqrt{(\gamma-\tfrac{1}{4})}, \quad s_2 = s_1^*.$$

Repeating the above analysis, we again arrive at equation (35.6), which, on substituting the values of s_1 and s_2, gives

$$B/A = \text{constant} \times r_0^{i\sqrt{(4\gamma-1)}}. \tag{35.8}$$

On passing to the limit $r_0 \to 0$, this expression does not tend to any definite limit, so that we do not obtain any criterion for the choice of a solution. The two independent solutions have, near the origin, the form

$$R = \text{constant} \times \frac{1}{\sqrt{r}} e^{\pm i\sqrt{(\gamma-\frac{1}{4})}\log r}.$$

The general form of the real solution can be written

$$R = \text{constant} \times r^{-\frac{1}{2}} \cos(\sqrt{(\gamma-\tfrac{1}{4})} \log r + \text{constant}). \tag{35.9}$$

This function has an infinite number of zeros. Since, on the one hand, the expression (35.9) is valid for the wave function (when r is sufficiently small) with any finite value of the energy E of the particle, and, on the other hand, the wave function of the normal state can have no zeros, we can infer that the "normal state" of a particle in the field considered corresponds to the energy $E = -\infty$. In every state of a discrete spectrum, however, the particle is mainly in a region of space where $E > U$. Hence, for $E \to -\infty$, the particle is in an infinitely small region round the origin, i.e. the particle "falls" to the centre.

The "critical" field U_{cr} for which the "fall" of a particle to the centre becomes possible corresponds to the value $\gamma = \frac{1}{4}$. The smallest value of the coefficient of $-1/r^2$ is obtained for $l = 0$, i.e.

$$U_{cr} = -\hbar^2/8\mu r^2. \tag{35.10}$$

It is seen from formula (35.3) (for s_1) that the permissible solution of SCHRÖDINGER's equation (near the point where $U \sim 1/r^2$) diverges, as $r \to 0$, not more rapidly than $1/\sqrt{r}$. If the field becomes infinite, as $r \to 0$, more slowly than $1/r^2$, we can always neglect $U(r)$, in SCHRÖDINGER's equation near the origin, in comparison with the other terms, and we obtain the same solutions as for free motion, i.e. $\psi \sim r^l$ (see §33). Finally, if the field becomes infinite more rapidly than $1/r^2$ (as $-1/r^s$ with $s > 2$), the wave function near the origin is proportional to $r^{\frac{1}{4}s-1}$ (see §49, Problem 2). In all these cases the product $r\psi$ tends to zero at $r = 0$.

Next, let us investigate the properties of the solution of SCHRÖDINGER's equation in a field which diminishes at large distances according to the law

$U \approx -\beta/r^2$, and has any form at small distances. We first suppose that $\gamma < \frac{1}{4}$. It is easy to see that in this case only a finite number of negative energy levels can exist.† For with energy $E = 0$ SCHRÖDINGER's equation at large distances has the form (35.1), with the general solution (35.4). The function (35.4), however, has no zeros (for $r \neq 0$); hence all zeros of the required radial wave function lie at finite distances from the origin, and their number is always finite. In other words, the ordinal number of the level $E = 0$ which terminates the discrete spectrum is finite.

If $\gamma > \frac{1}{4}$, on the other hand, the discrete spectrum contains an infinite number of negative energy levels. For the wave function of the state with $E = 0$ has, at large distances, the form (35.9), with an infinite number of zeros, so that its ordinal number is always infinite.

Finally, let the field be $U = -\beta/r^2$ in all space. Then, for $\gamma > \frac{1}{4}$, the particle "falls", but if $\gamma < \frac{1}{4}$ there are no negative energy levels. For the wave function of the state with $E = 0$ is of the form (35.7) in all space; it has no zeros at finite distances, i.e. it corresponds to the lowest energy level (for the given l).

§36. Motion in a Coulomb field (spherical co-ordinates)

A very important case of motion in a centrally symmetric field is that of motion in a *Coulomb field*

$$U = \pm\alpha/r$$

(where α is a positive constant). We shall first consider a Coulomb attraction, and shall therefore write $U = -\alpha/r$. It is evident from general considerations that the spectrum of negative eigenvalues of the energy will be discrete (with an infinite number of levels), while that of the positive eigenvalues will be continuous.

Equation (32.8) for the radial functions has the form

$$\frac{d^2R}{dr^2} + \frac{2}{r}\frac{dR}{dr} - \frac{l(l+1)}{r^2}R + \frac{2\mu}{\hbar^2}\left(E + \frac{\alpha}{r}\right)R = 0. \tag{36.1}$$

If we are concerned with the relative motion of two attracting particles, μ must be taken as the reduced mass.

In calculations connected with the Coulomb field it is convenient to use, instead of the ordinary units, special units for the measurement of all quantities, which we shall call *Coulomb units*. As the units of measurement of mass, length and time, we take respectively

$$\mu, \quad \hbar^2/\mu\alpha, \quad \hbar^3/\mu\alpha^2.$$

All the remaining units are derived from these; thus the unit of energy is

$$\mu\alpha^2/\hbar^2.$$

† It is assumed that for small r the field is such that the particle does not "fall".

From now on, in this section and the following one, we shall always (unless explicitly stated) use these units.†

Let us rewrite equation (36.1) in the new units:

$$\frac{d^2R}{dr^2}+\frac{2}{r}\frac{dR}{dr}-\frac{l(l+1)}{r^2}R+2\left(E+\frac{1}{r}\right)R = 0. \tag{36.2}$$

Instead of the parameter E and the variable r, we introduce the new quantities

$$n = 1/\sqrt{(-2E)}, \quad \rho = 2r/n. \tag{36.3}$$

For negative E (which we shall first consider), n is a real positive number. The equation (36.2), on making the substitutions (36.3), becomes

$$R''+\frac{2}{\rho}R'+\left[-\tfrac{1}{4}+\frac{n}{\rho}-\frac{l(l+1)}{\rho^2}\right]R = 0 \tag{36.4}$$

(the primes denote differentiation with respect to ρ).

For small ρ, the solution which satisfies the necessary conditions of finiteness is proportional to ρ^l (see (32.13)). To calculate the asymptotic behaviour of R for large ρ, we omit from (36.4) the terms in $1/\rho$ and $1/\rho^2$ and obtain the equation

$$R'' = \tfrac{1}{4}R,$$

whence $R = e^{\pm\frac{1}{2}\rho}$. The solution in which we are interested, which vanishes at infinity, consequently behaves as $e^{-\frac{1}{2}\rho}$ for large ρ.

It is therefore natural to make the substitution

$$R = \rho^l e^{-\frac{1}{2}\rho} w(\rho), \tag{36.5}$$

when equation (36.4) becomes

$$\rho w''+(2l+2-\rho)w'+(n-l-1)w = 0. \tag{36.6}$$

The solution of this equation must diverge at infinity not more rapidly than every finite power of ρ, while for $\rho = 0$ it must be finite. The solution which satisfies the latter condition is the confluent hypergeometric function

$$w = F(-n+l+1, 2l+2, \rho) \tag{36.7}$$

(see §*d* of the Mathematical Appendices).‡ A solution which satisfies the condition at infinity is obtained for negative integral (or zero) values of

† If $\mu = 9{\cdot}11\times10^{-28}$ g is the mass of the electron, and $\alpha = e^2$ (where e is the charge on the electron), the Coulomb units are the same as what are called *atomic units*. The atomic unit of length is

$$\hbar^2/\mu e^2 = 0{\cdot}529\times10^{-8} \text{ cm}$$

(what is called the *Bohr radius*). The atomic unit of energy is

$$\mu e^4/\hbar^2 = 4{\cdot}304\times10^{-11} \text{ erg} = 27{\cdot}07 \text{ electron-volts.}$$

The atomic unit of charge is $e = 4{\cdot}80\times10^{-10}$ esu. We formally obtain the formulae in atomic units by putting $e = \mu = \hbar = 1$.

‡ The second solution of equation (36.6) diverges as ρ^{-2l-1} as $\rho\to 0$.

$-n+l+1$, when the function (36.7) reduces to a polynomial of degree $n-l-1$. Otherwise it diverges at infinity as e^{ρ} (see (d.14)).

Thus we reach the conclusion that the number n must be a positive integer, and for a given l we must have

$$n \geqslant l+1. \tag{36.8}$$

Recalling the definition (36.3) of the parameter n, we find

$$E = -1/2n^2, \quad n = 1, 2, \ldots. \tag{36.9}$$

This solves the problem of determining the energy levels of the discrete spectrum in a Coulomb field. We see that there are an infinite number of levels between the normal level $E_1 = -\frac{1}{2}$ and zero. The distances between successive levels diminish as n increases; the levels become more crowded as we approach the value $E = 0$, where the discrete spectrum closes up into the continuous spectrum. In ordinary units, formula (36.9) is

$$E = -\mu\alpha^2/2\hbar^2 n^2. \tag{36.10}$$

The integer n is called the ***principal quantum number***. The radial quantum number defined in §32 is

$$n_r = n-l-1.$$

For a given value of the principal quantum number, l can take the values

$$l = 0, 1, \ldots, n-1, \tag{36.11}$$

i.e. n different values in all. Only n appears in the expression (36.9) for the energy. Hence all states with different l but the same n have the same energy. Thus each eigenvalue is degenerate, not only with respect to the magnetic quantum number m (as in any motion in a centrally symmetric field) but also with respect to the number l. This latter degeneracy (called *accidental*) is a specific property of the Coulomb field. To each value of l there correspond, as we know, $2l+1$ different values of m. Hence the degree of degeneracy of the nth energy level is

$$\sum_{l=0}^{n-1}(2l+1) = n^2. \tag{36.12}$$

The wave functions of the stationary states are determined by formulae (36.5) and (36.7).† The confluent hypergeometric functions with both parameters integral are the same, apart from a factor, as what are called the *generalised Laguerre polynomials* (see §d of the Mathematical Appendices). Hence

$$R_{nl} = \text{constant} \times \rho^l e^{-\frac{1}{2}\rho} L_{n+l}^{2l+1}(\rho).$$

† An original method of solving the Coulomb problem in the momentum representation has been given by V. A. Fok (*Izvestiya Akademii Nauk SSSR, Seriya fizicheskaya*, No. 2, 169, 1935). This method also enables us to calculate complicated sums involving Coulomb wave functions.

The radial functions must be normalised by the condition

$$\int_0^\infty R_{nl}^2 r^2 \, dr = 1.$$

Their final form is†

$$R_{nl} = -\frac{2}{n^2}\sqrt{\frac{(n-l-1)!}{[(n+l)!]^3}} e^{-r/n}\left(\frac{2r}{n}\right)^l L_{n+l}^{2l+1}\left(\frac{2r}{n}\right)$$

$$= \frac{2}{n^{l+2}(2l+1)!}\sqrt{\frac{(n+l)!}{(n-l-1)!}}(2r)^l e^{-r/n} F(-n+l+1, 2l+2, 2r/n); \tag{36.13}$$

the normalisation integral is calculated by (f.6).‡

Near the origin, R_{nl} has the form

$$R_{nl} \cong r^l \frac{2^{l+1}}{n^{2+l}(2l+1)!}\sqrt{\frac{(n+l)!}{(n-l-1)!}}. \tag{36.14}$$

At large distances,

$$R_{nl} \approx (-1)^{n-l-1}\frac{2^n}{n^{n+1}\sqrt{[(n+l)!(n-l-1)!]}} r^{n-1}e^{-r/n}. \tag{36.15}$$

The wave function R_{10} of the normal state decreases exponentially at distances of the order $r \sim 1$, i.e. $r \sim \hbar^2/\mu\alpha$ in ordinary units.

The mean values of the various powers of r are calculated from the formula

$$\overline{r^k} = \int_0^\infty r^{k+2} R_{nl}^2 \, dr.$$

---

† We give the first few functions R_{nl} explicitly:

$$R_{10} = 2e^{-r},$$
$$R_{20} = (1/\sqrt{2})e^{-\frac{1}{2}r}(1-\tfrac{1}{2}r),$$
$$R_{21} = (1/2\sqrt{6})e^{-\frac{1}{2}r}r,$$
$$R_{30} = (2/3\sqrt{3})e^{-\frac{1}{3}r}\left(1-\frac{2}{3}r+\frac{2}{27}r^2\right),$$
$$R_{31} = (8/27\sqrt{6})e^{-\frac{1}{3}r}r\left(1-\frac{1}{6}r\right),$$
$$R_{32} = (4/81\sqrt{30})e^{-\frac{1}{3}r}r^2.$$

‡ The normalisation integral can also be calculated by substituting the expression (d.13) for the Laguerre polynomials and integrating by parts (similarly to the calculation of the integral (c.11) for the Legendre polynomials).

The general formula for $\overline{r^k}$ can be obtained by means of formula (f.7). Here we shall give the first few values of $\overline{r^k}$ (for positive and negative k):

$$\bar{r} = \tfrac{1}{2}[3n^2-l(l+1)], \quad \overline{r^2} = \tfrac{1}{2}n^2[5n^2+1-3l(l+1)],$$

$$\overline{r^{-1}} = 1/n^2, \quad \overline{r^{-2}} = 1/n^3(l+\tfrac{1}{2}). \tag{36.16}$$

The spectrum of positive eigenvalues of the energy is continuous and extends from zero to infinity. Each of these eigenvalues is infinitely degenerate; to each value of E there corresponds an infinite number of states, with l taking all integral values from 0 to ∞ (and with all possible values of m for the given l).

The number n and the variables ρ, defined by the formulae (36.3), are now purely imaginary:

$$n = -i/\sqrt{(2E)} = -i/k, \quad \rho = 2ikr \tag{36.17}$$

(we have introduced the *wave number* $k = \sqrt{(2E)}$ in place of the energy). The radial eigenfunctions of the continuous spectrum are of the form

$$R_{kl} = \frac{C_k}{(2l+1)!}(2kr)^l e^{-ikr} F(i/k+l+1, 2l+2, 2ikr), \tag{36.18}$$

where the C_k are normalisation factors. They can be represented as a complex integral (see §d):

$$R_{kl} = C_k(2kr)^l e^{-ikr}\frac{1}{2\pi i}\oint e^{\xi}\left(1-\frac{2ikr}{\xi}\right)^{-i/k-l-1}\xi^{-2l-2}\,d\xi, \tag{36.19}$$

which is taken along the contour† shown in Fig. 10. The substitution

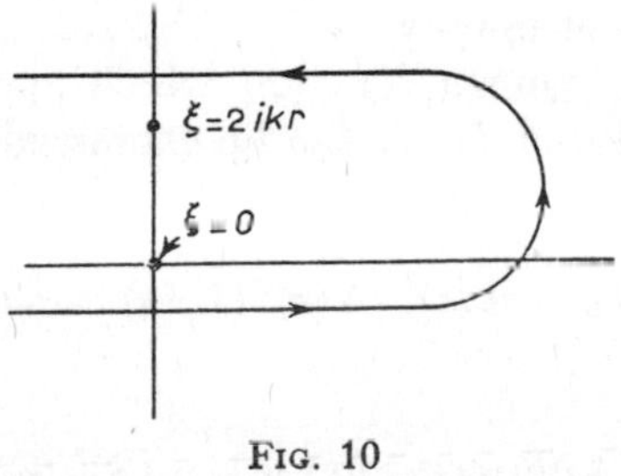

FIG. 10

$\xi = 2ikr(t+\frac{1}{2})$ converts this integral to the more symmetrical form

$$R_{kl} = C_k\frac{(-2kr)^{-l-1}}{2\pi}\oint e^{2iktr}(t+\tfrac{1}{2})^{i/k-l-1}(t-\tfrac{1}{2})^{-i/k-l-1}\,dt; \tag{36.20}$$

† Instead of this contour we could use any closed loop passing round the singular points $\xi = 0$ and $\xi = 2ikr$ in the positive direction. For integral l, the function $V(\xi) = \xi^{-n-l}(\xi-2ikr)^{n-l}$ (see §d) returns to its initial value on passing round such a contour.

the path of integration passes in the positive direction round the points $t = \pm\frac{1}{2}$. It is seen at once from this representation that the functions R_{kl} are real.

The asymptotic expansion (d.14) of the confluent hypergeometric function enables us to obtain immediately a similar expansion for the wave functions R_{kl}. The two terms in (d.14) give two complex conjugate expressions in the function R_{kl}, and as a result we obtain

$$R_{kl} = C_k \frac{e^{-\pi/2k}}{kr} \mathrm{re}\left\{\frac{e^{-i[kr-\frac{1}{2}\pi(l+1)+(1/k)\log 2kr]}}{\Gamma(l+1-i/k)} G(l+1+i/k, i/k-l, -2ikr)\right\}. \tag{36.21}$$

If we normalise the wave functions on the "k scale" (i.e. by the condition (33.4)), the normalisation coefficient is

$$C_k = \sqrt{(2/\pi)}ke^{\pi/2k}|\Gamma(l+1-i/k)|. \tag{36.22}$$

For the asymptotic expression for R_{kl} when r is large (the first term of the expansion (36.21)) is then of the form

$$\begin{aligned} R_{kl} &\approx \sqrt{\frac{2}{\pi}}\frac{1}{r}\sin\left(kr+\frac{1}{k}\log 2kr-\tfrac{1}{2}l\pi+\delta_l\right), \\ \delta_l &= \arg\Gamma(l+1-i/k), \end{aligned} \tag{36.23}$$

in agreement with the general form (33.16) of the normalised wave functions of the continuous spectrum in a centrally symmetric field. The expression (36.23) differs from (33.16) by the presence of a logarithmic term in the argument of the sine; however, since $\log r$ increases only slowly compared with r itself, the presence of this term is immaterial in calculating a normalisation integral which diverges at infinity.

The modulus of the gamma function which appears in the expression (36.22) for the normalisation factor can be expressed in terms of elementary functions. Using the familiar properties of gamma functions:

$$\Gamma(z+1) = z\Gamma(z), \quad \Gamma(z)\Gamma(1-z) = \pi/\sin\pi z,$$

we have

$$\begin{aligned} \Gamma(l+1+i/k) &= (l+i/k)\ldots(1+i/k)(i/k)\Gamma(i/k), \\ \Gamma(l+1-i/k) &= (l-i/k)\ldots(1-i/k)\Gamma(1-i/k), \end{aligned}$$

and also

$$\begin{aligned} |\Gamma(l+1-i/k)| &= [\Gamma(l+1-i/k)\Gamma(l+1+i/k)]^{\frac{1}{2}} \\ &= \sqrt{\frac{\pi}{k}}\prod_{s=1}^{l}\sqrt{\left(s^2+\frac{1}{k^2}\right)}\sinh^{-\frac{1}{2}}\frac{\pi}{k}. \end{aligned}$$

Thus

$$C_k = \frac{2\sqrt{k}}{\sqrt{(1-e^{-2\pi/k})}} \prod_{s=1}^{l} \sqrt{\left(s^2+\frac{1}{k^2}\right)}. \tag{36.24}$$

The radial functions R_{El} normalised on the "energy scale" are obtained from the functions R_{kl} by dividing by $\sqrt{k}$: $R_{El} = k^{-\frac{1}{2}}R_{kl}$ (see (33.5)). By passing to the limit as $E \to 0$ (i.e. $k \to 0$), we can correctly obtain from R_{El} the normalised radial function R_{0l} for the particular case of zero energy.†
The limit of the series $F(i/k+l+1, 2l+2, 2ikr)$ as $k \to 0$ is

$$1-\frac{2r}{(2l+2)1!}+\frac{(2r)^2}{(2l+2)(2l+3)2!}-\ldots = (2l+1)!\,(2r)^{-l-\frac{1}{2}}J_{2l+1}(\sqrt{[8r]}),$$

where J_{2l+1} is the Bessel function of order $2l+1$. We hence easily obtain

$$R_{0l} = \sqrt{(2/r)}J_{2l+1}(\sqrt{[8r]}). \tag{36.25}$$

The asymptotic form of this function for large r is

$$R_{0l} = (2/\pi^2 r^3)^{\frac{1}{4}} \sin(\sqrt{[8r]}-l\pi-\tfrac{1}{4}\pi). \tag{36.26}$$

In a repulsive Coulomb field ($U = \alpha/r$) there is only a continuous spectrum of positive eigenvalues of the energy. SCHRÖDINGER's equation in this field can be formally obtained from the equation for an attractive field by changing the sign of r. Hence the wave functions of the stationary states are found immediately from (36.18) by the same alteration. The normalisation coefficient is again determined from the asymptotic expression, and as a result we obtain

$$R_{kl} = \frac{C_k}{(2l+1)!}(2kr)^l e^{ikr}F(i/k+l+1, 2l+2, -2ikr),$$

$$C_k = \sqrt{\frac{2}{\pi}}ke^{-\pi/2k}|\Gamma(l+1+i/k)|$$

$$= \frac{2\sqrt{k}}{\sqrt{(e^{2\pi/k}-1)}} \prod_{s=1}^{l} \sqrt{\left(s^2+\frac{1}{k^2}\right)}. \tag{36.27}$$

The asymptotic expression for this function for large r is

$$R_{kl} \approx \sqrt{\frac{2}{\pi}}\frac{1}{r} \sin\left(kr-\frac{1}{k}\log 2kr-\tfrac{1}{2}l\pi+\delta_l\right),$$

$$\delta_l = \arg\Gamma(l+1+i/k). \tag{36.28}$$

† It is found that the function R_{El} normalised on the energy scale remains finite as $E \to 0$, while $R_{kl} \to 0$ as $k \to 0$.

PROBLEMS

PROBLEM 1. Determine the energy levels of a particle moving in a centrally symmetric field with potential energy $U = A/r^2 - B/r$ (Fig. 11).

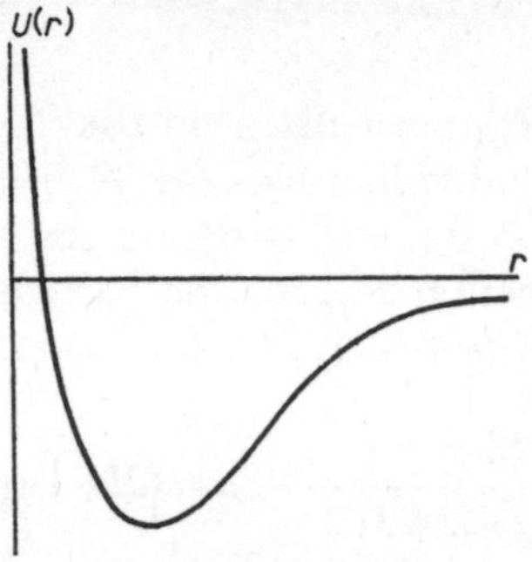

FIG. 11

SOLUTION. The spectrum of positive energy levels is continuous, while that of negative levels is discrete; we shall consider the latter. SCHRÖDINGER's equation for the radial function is

$$\frac{d^2R}{dr^2}+\frac{2}{r}\frac{dR}{dr}+\frac{2\mu}{\hbar^2}\left(E-\frac{\hbar^2}{2\mu}l(l+1)\frac{1}{r^2}-\frac{A}{r^2}+\frac{B}{r}\right)R = 0. \tag{1}$$

We introduce the new variable

$$\rho = 2\sqrt{(-2\mu E)}r/\hbar,$$

and the notation

$$2\mu A/\hbar^2+l(l+1) = s(s+1), \tag{2}$$

$$B\sqrt{(\mu/-2E)}/\hbar = n. \tag{3}$$

Then equation (1) takes the form

$$R''+\frac{2}{\rho}R'+\left(-\frac{1}{4}+\frac{n}{\rho}-\frac{s(s+1)}{\rho^2}\right)R = 0,$$

which is formally identical with (36.4). Hence we can at once conclude that the solution satisfying the necessary conditions is

$$R = \rho^s e^{-\frac{1}{2}\rho}F(-n+s+1, 2s+2, \rho),$$

where $n-s-1 = p$ must be a positive integer (or zero), and s must be taken as the positive root of equation (2). From the definition (3) we consequently obtain the energy levels

$$-E_p = \frac{2B^2\mu}{\hbar^2}[2p+1+\sqrt{\{(2l+1)^2+8\mu A/\hbar^2\}}]^{-2}.$$

PROBLEM 2. The same as Problem 1, but with $U = A/r^2+Br^2$ (Fig. 12).

SOLUTION. There is only a discrete spectrum. SCHRÖDINGER's equation is

$$\frac{d^2R}{dr^2}+\frac{2}{r}\frac{dR}{dr}+\frac{2\mu}{\hbar^2}\left[E-\frac{\hbar^2 l(l+1)}{2\mu r^2}-\frac{A}{r^2}-Br^2\right]R = 0.$$

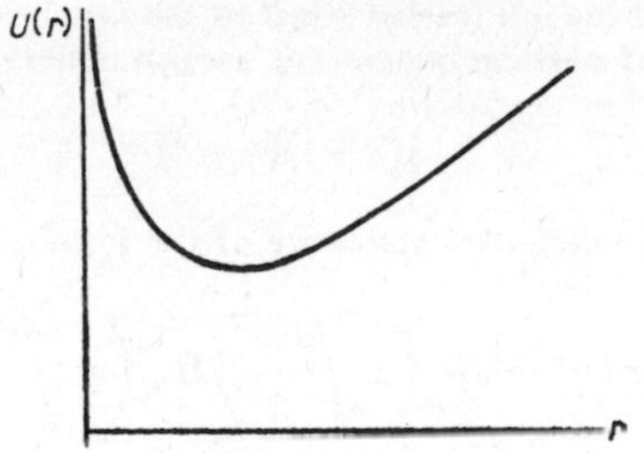

FIG. 12

Introducing the variable

$$\xi = \sqrt{(2\mu B)}r^2/\hbar$$

and the notation

$$l(l+1)+2\mu A/\hbar^2 = 2s(2s+1),$$
$$\sqrt{(2\mu/B)}E/\hbar = 4(n+s)+3,$$

we obtain the equation

$$\xi R''+\frac{3}{2}R'+[n+s+\tfrac{3}{4}-\tfrac{1}{4}\xi-s(s+\tfrac{1}{2})/\xi]R = 0.$$

The solution required behaves asymptotically as $e^{-\frac{1}{2}\xi}$ when $\xi \to \infty$, while for small ξ it is proportional to ξ^s, where s must be taken as the positive quantity

$$s = \tfrac{1}{4}[-1+\sqrt{\{(2l+1)^2+8\mu A/\hbar^2\}}].$$

Hence we seek a solution in the form

$$R = e^{-\frac{1}{2}\xi}\xi^s w,$$

obtaining for w the equation

$$\xi w''+\left(2s+\frac{3}{2}-\xi\right)w'+nw = 0,$$

whence

$$w = F\left(-n, 2s+\frac{3}{2}, \xi\right),$$

where n must be a non-negative integer. We consequently find as the energy levels the infinite set of equidistant values

$$E_n = \hbar\sqrt{(B/2\mu)}[4n+2+\sqrt{\{(2l+1)^2+8\mu A/\hbar^2\}}],\ n = 0, 1, 2, \ldots.$$

PROBLEM 3. Determine the energy levels of a three-dimensional oscillator (a particle in a field $U = \frac{1}{2}\mu\omega^2r^2$), their degrees of degeneracy, and the possible values of the orbital angular momentum in the corresponding stationary states.

SOLUTION. SCHRÖDINGER's equation for a particle in a field $U = \frac{1}{2}\mu\omega^2(x^2+y^2+z^2)$ allows separation of the variables x, y, z. This leads to three equations like that of a linear oscillator. The energy levels are therefore

$$E_n = \hbar\omega(n_1+n_2+n_3+\tfrac{3}{2}) = \hbar\omega(n+\tfrac{3}{2})\quad (n = 0, 1, 2, \ldots).$$

The degree of degeneracy of the nth level is equal to the number of ways in which n can be divided into the sum of three positive integral (or zero) numbers†; this is

$$\tfrac{1}{2}(n+1)(n+2).$$

The wave functions of the stationary states are of the form

$$\psi_{n_1 n_2 n_3} = \text{constant} \times e^{-\mu\omega r^2/2\hbar} H_{n_1}\left(x\sqrt{\frac{\mu\omega}{\hbar}}\right) H_{n_2}\left(y\sqrt{\frac{\mu\omega}{\hbar}}\right) H_{n_3}\left(z\sqrt{\frac{\mu\omega}{\hbar}}\right).$$

Taking suitable linear combinations of these functions with the given sum $n_1+n_2+n_3 = n$, we can form functions

$$\psi_{nlm} = \text{constant} \times e^{-\mu\omega r^2/2\hbar} r^n \Theta_{lm}(\theta) e^{\pm im\phi},$$

where $m = 0, 1, \dots, l$, and l takes the values $0, 2, \dots, n$ for even n and $1, 3, \dots, n$ for odd n. This gives the possible values of the orbital angular momentum corresponding to the energy levels in question.

§37. Motion in a Coulomb field (parabolic co-ordinates)

The separation of the variables in SCHRÖDINGER's equation written in spherical co-ordinates is always possible for motion in any centrally symmetric field. In the case of a Coulomb field, the separation of the variables is also possible in what are called *parabolic co-ordinates.* The solution of the problem of motion in a Coulomb field in terms of parabolic co-ordinates is useful in investigating a number of problems where a certain direction in space is distinctive; for example, for an atom in an external electric field (see §73).

The parabolic co-ordinates ξ, η, ϕ are defined by the equations

$$\begin{aligned} x &= \sqrt{(\xi\eta)}\cos\phi, \quad y = \sqrt{(\xi\eta)}\sin\phi, \quad z = \tfrac{1}{2}(\xi-\eta), \\ r &= \sqrt{(x^2+y^2+z^2)} = \tfrac{1}{2}(\xi+\eta), \end{aligned} \tag{37.1}$$

or conversely

$$\xi = r+z, \quad \eta = r-z, \quad \phi = \tan^{-1}(y/x); \tag{37.2}$$

ξ and η take values from 0 to ∞, and ϕ from 0 to 2π. The surfaces ξ = constant and η = constant are paraboloids of revolution about the z-axis, with focus at the origin. This system of co-ordinates is orthogonal. The element of length is given by the expression

$$(\mathrm{d}l)^2 = \frac{\xi+\eta}{4\xi}(\mathrm{d}\xi)^2 + \frac{\xi+\eta}{4\eta}(\mathrm{d}\eta)^2 + \xi\eta(\mathrm{d}\phi)^2, \tag{37.3}$$

and the element of volume is

$$\mathrm{d}V = \tfrac{1}{4}(\xi+\eta)\mathrm{d}\xi\mathrm{d}\eta\mathrm{d}\phi. \tag{37.4}$$

† In other words, this is the number of ways in which n similar balls can be distributed among three urns.

From (37.3) we have the Laplacian operator

$$\Delta = \frac{4}{\xi+\eta}\left[\frac{\partial}{\partial\xi}\left(\xi\frac{\partial}{\partial\xi}\right)+\frac{\partial}{\partial\eta}\left(\eta\frac{\partial}{\partial\eta}\right)\right]+\frac{1}{\xi\eta}\frac{\partial^2}{\partial\phi^2}. \tag{37.5}$$

SCHRÖDINGER's equation for a particle in an attractive Coulomb field with $U = -1/r = -2/(\xi+\eta)$ is

$$\frac{4}{\xi+\eta}\left[\frac{\partial}{\partial\xi}\left(\xi\frac{\partial\psi}{\partial\xi}\right)+\frac{\partial}{\partial\eta}\left(\eta\frac{\partial\psi}{\partial\eta}\right)\right]+\frac{1}{\xi\eta}\frac{\partial^2\psi}{\partial\phi^2}+2\left(E+\frac{2}{\xi+\eta}\right)\psi = 0. \tag{37.6}$$

Let us seek the eigenfunctions ψ in the form

$$\psi = f_1(\xi)f_2(\eta)e^{im\phi}, \tag{37.7}$$

where m is the magnetic quantum number. Substituting this expression in equation (37.6) multiplied by $\frac{1}{4}(\xi+\eta)$, and separating the variables ξ and η, we obtain for f_1 and f_2 the equations

$$\begin{aligned}\frac{d}{d\xi}\left(\xi\frac{df_1}{d\xi}\right)+[\tfrac{1}{2}E\xi-\tfrac{1}{4}m^2/\xi+\beta_1]f_1 &= 0\\ \frac{d}{d\eta}\left(\eta\frac{df_2}{d\eta}\right)+[\tfrac{1}{2}E\eta-\tfrac{1}{4}m^2/\eta+\beta_2]f_2 &= 0,\end{aligned} \tag{37.8}$$

where the *separation parameters* β_1, β_2 are related by

$$\beta_1+\beta_2 = 1. \tag{37.9}$$

Let us consider the discrete energy spectrum ($E < 0$). We introduce in place of E, ξ, η the quantities

$$n = 1/\sqrt{(-2E)}, \quad \rho_1 = \xi\sqrt{(-2E)} = \xi/n, \quad \rho_2 = \eta/n, \tag{37.10}$$

whereupon we obtain the equation for f_1

$$\frac{d^2f_1}{d\rho_1^2}+\frac{1}{\rho_1}\frac{df_1}{d\rho_1}+\left[-\tfrac{1}{4}+\frac{1}{\rho_1}\left(\frac{|m|+1}{2}+n_1\right)-\frac{m^2}{4\rho_1^2}\right]f_1 = 0, \tag{37.11}$$

and a similar equation for f_2, with the notation

$$n_1 = -\tfrac{1}{2}(|m|+1)+n\beta_1, \quad n_2 = -\tfrac{1}{2}(|m|+1)+n\beta_2. \tag{37.12}$$

Similarly to the calculation for equation (36.4), we find that f_1 behaves as $e^{-\frac{1}{2}\rho_1}$ for large ρ_1 and as $\rho_1^{\frac{1}{2}|m|}$ for small ρ_1. Accordingly, we seek a solution of equation (37.11) in the form

$$f_1(\rho_1) = e^{-\frac{1}{2}\rho_1}\rho_1^{\frac{1}{2}|m|}w_1(\rho_1),$$

and similarly for f_2, obtaining for w_1 the equation

$$\rho_1 w_1''+(|m|+1-\rho_1)w_1'+n_1 w_1 = 0.$$

This is again the equation for a confluent hypergeometric function. The solution satisfying the conditions of finiteness is

$$w_1 = F(-n_1, |m|+1, \rho_1),$$

where n_1 must be a non-negative integer.

Thus each stationary state of the discrete spectrum is determined in parabolic co-ordinates by three integers: the *parabolic quantum numbers* n_1 and n_2, and the magnetic quantum number m. For n, the principal quantum number, we have from (37.9) and (37.12)

$$n = n_1+n_2+|m|+1. \tag{37.13}$$

For the energy levels, of course, we obtain our previous result (36.9).

For given n, the number $|m|$ can take n different values from 0 to $n-1$. For fixed n and $|m|$ the number n_1 takes $n-|m|$ values, from 0 to $n-|m|-1$. Taking into account also that for given $|m|$ we can choose the functions with $m = \pm|m|$, we find that for a given n there are altogether

$$2\sum_{m=1}^{n-1}(n-m)+(n-0) = n^2$$

different states, in agreement with the result obtained in §36.

The wave functions $\psi_{n_1n_2m}$ of the discrete spectrum must be normalised by the condition

$$\int |\psi_{n_1n_2m}|^2\,dV = \tfrac{1}{4}\int_0^\infty\int_0^\infty\int_0^{2\pi} |\psi_{n_1n_2m}|^2(\xi+\eta)\,d\phi\,d\xi\,d\eta = 1. \tag{37.14}$$

The normalised functions are

$$\psi_{n_1n_2m} = \frac{\sqrt{2}}{n^2}f_{n_1m}\left(\frac{\xi}{n}\right)f_{n_2m}\left(\frac{\eta}{n}\right)\frac{e^{im\phi}}{\sqrt{(2\pi)}}, \tag{37.15}$$

where

$$f_{pm}(\rho) = \frac{1}{|m|!}\sqrt{\frac{(p+|m|)!}{p!}}F(-p, |m|+1, \rho)e^{-\frac{1}{2}\rho}\rho^{\frac{1}{2}|m|}. \tag{37.16}$$

The wave functions in parabolic co-ordinates, unlike those in spherical co-ordinates, are not symmetrical about the plane $z = 0$. For $n_1 > n_2$ the probability of finding the particle in the direction $z > 0$ is greater than that for $z < 0$, and *vice versa* for $n_1 < n_2$.

To the continuous spectrum ($E > 0$) there corresponds a continuous spectrum of real values of the parameters β_1, β_2 in equations (37.8) (connected as before, of course, by the relation (37.9)). We shall not pause to write out here the corresponding wave functions, since it is not usually necessary to employ them. Equations (37.8), regarded as equations for the "eigenvalues" of the quantities β_1, β_2, have also (for $E > 0$) a spectrum of complex values of β_1 and β_2. The corresponding wave functions are written out in §112, where we shall use them to solve a problem of scattering in a Coulomb field.

CHAPTER VI

PERTURBATION THEORY

§38. Perturbations independent of time

THE exact solution of SCHRÖDINGER's equation can be found only in a comparatively small number of the simplest cases. The majority of problems in quantum mechanics lead to equations which are too complex to be solved exactly. Often, however, quantities of different orders of magnitude appear in the conditions of the problem; among them there may be small quantities such that, when they are neglected, the problem is so much simplified that its exact solution becomes possible. In such cases, the first step in solving the physical problem concerned is to solve exactly the simplified problem, and the second step is to calculate the errors due to the small terms that have been neglected in the simplified problem. There is a general method of calculating these errors; it is called *perturbation theory*.

Let us suppose that the Hamiltonian of a given physical system is of the form

$$\hat{H} = \hat{H}_0 + \hat{V},$$

where $\hat{V}$ is a small correction (or *perturbation*) to the *unperturbed* operator $\hat{H}_0$. In §§38, 39 we shall consider perturbations $\hat{V}$ which do not depend explicitly on time (the same is assumed regarding $\hat{H}_0$ also). The conditions which are necessary for it to be permissible to regard the operator $\hat{V}$ as "small" compared with the operator $\hat{H}$ will be derived below.

The problem of perturbation theory for a discrete spectrum can be formulated as follows. It is assumed that the eigenfunctions $\psi_n^{(0)}$ and eigenvalues $E_n^{(0)}$ of the discrete spectrum of the unperturbed operator $\hat{H}_0$ are known, i.e. the exact solutions of the equation

$$\hat{H}_0\psi^{(0)} = E^{(0)}\psi^{(0)} \tag{38.1}$$

are known. It is desired to find approximate solutions of the equation

$$\hat{H}\psi = (\hat{H}_0+\hat{V})\psi = E\psi, \tag{38.2}$$

i.e. approximate expressions for the eigenfunctions ψ_n and eigenvalues E_n of the perturbed operator $\hat{H}$.

In this section we shall assume that no eigenvalue of the operator $\hat{H}_0$ is degenerate. Moreover, to simplify our results, we shall suppose that there is only a discrete spectrum of eigenvalues; all the formulae can be at once generalised to the case where there is a continuous spectrum.

The calculations are conveniently performed in matrix form throughout.

To do this, we expand the required function ψ in terms of the functions $\psi_n^{(0)}$:

$$\psi = \sum_m c_m \psi_m^{(0)}. \tag{38.3}$$

Substituting this expansion in (38.2) we obtain

$$\sum_m c_m(E_m^{(0)}+\hat{V})\psi_m^{(0)} = \sum_m c_m E\psi_m^{(0)};$$

multiplying both sides of this equation by $\psi_k^{(0)*}$ and integrating, we find

$$(E-E_k^{(0)})c_k = \sum_m V_{km}c_m. \tag{38.4}$$

Here we have introduced the matrix V_{km} of the perturbation operator $\hat{V}$, defined with respect to the unperturbed functions $\psi_m^{(0)}$:

$$V_{km} = \int \psi_k^{(0)*}\hat{V}\psi_m^{(0)}\,dq. \tag{38.5}$$

We shall seek the values of the coefficients c_m and the energy E in the form of series

$$E = E^{(0)}+E^{(1)}+E^{(2)}+\ldots, \quad c_m = c_m^{(0)}+c_m^{(1)}+c_m^{(2)}+\ldots,$$

where the quantities $E^{(1)}$ and $c_m^{(1)}$ are of the same order of smallness as the perturbation $\hat{V}$, the quantities $E^{(2)}$ and $c_m^{(2)}$ are of the second order of smallness (if $\hat{V}$ is of the first order), and so on.

Let us determine the corrections to the nth eigenvalue and eigenfunction, putting accordingly $c_n^{(0)} = 1$, $c_m^{(0)} = 0$ for $m \neq n$. To find the first approximation, we substitute in equation (38.4) $E = E_n^{(0)}+E_n^{(1)}$, $c_k = c_k^{(0)}+c_k^{(1)}$, and retain only terms of the first order. The equation with $k = n$ gives

$$E_n^{(1)} = V_{nn} = \int \psi_n^{(0)*}\hat{V}\psi_n^{(0)}\,dq. \tag{38.6}$$

Thus the first-order correction to the eigenvalue $E_n^{(0)}$ is equal to the mean value of the perturbation in the state $\psi_n^{(0)}$.

The equation (38.4) with $k \neq n$ gives

$$c_k^{(1)} = V_{kn}/(E_n^{(0)}-E_k^{(0)}) \text{ for } k \neq n,$$

while $c_n^{(1)}$ remains arbitrary; it must be chosen so that the function $\psi_n = \psi_n^{(0)}+\psi_n^{(1)}$ is normalised up to and including terms of the first order. For this we can put $c_n^{(1)} = 0$. For the functions

$$\psi_n^{(1)} = \sum_m{}' \frac{V_{mn}}{E_n^{(0)}-E_m^{(0)}}\psi_m^{(0)} \tag{38.7}$$

(the prime means that the term with $m = n$ is omitted from the sum) are orthogonal to $\psi_n^{(0)}$, and hence the integral of $|\psi_n^{(0)}+\psi_n^{(1)}|^2$ differs from unity only by a quantity of the second order of smallness.

Formula (38.7) determines the correction to the wave functions in the first approximation. Incidentally, we see from this formula the condition for the applicability of the above method of perturbation theory. This condition is that the inequality

$$|V_{mn}| \ll |E_n^{(0)} - E_m^{(0)}| \tag{38.8}$$

must hold, i.e. the matrix elements of the operator $\hat{V}$ must be small compared with the corresponding differences between the unperturbed energy levels.

Next, let us determine the correction to the eigenvalue $E_n^{(0)}$ in the second approximation. To do this, we substitute in (38.4) $E = E_n^{(0)} + E_n^{(1)} + E_n^{(2)}$, $c_k = c_k^{(0)} + c_k^{(1)} + c_k^{(2)}$, and examine the terms of the second order of smallness. The equation with $k = n$ gives

$$E_n^{(2)} c_n^{(0)} = \sum_m{}' V_{nm} c_m^{(1)},$$

whence

$$E_n^{(2)} = \sum_m{}' \frac{|V_{mn}|^2}{E_n^{(0)} - E_m^{(0)}} \tag{38.9}$$

(we have substituted $c_m^{(1)} = V_{mn}/(E_n^{(0)} - E_m^{(0)})$, and used the fact that, since the operator $\hat{V}$ is Hermitian, $V_{mn} = V_{nm}^*$).

We notice that the correction in the second approximation to the energy of the normal state is always negative; for, since $E_n^{(0)}$ then corresponds to the lowest value of the energy, all the terms in the sum (38.9) are negative.

The further approximations can be calculated in an exactly similar manner.

The results obtained can be generalised at once to the case where the operator $\hat{H}_0$ has also a continuous spectrum (but the perturbation is applied, as before, to a state of the discrete spectrum). To do so, we need only add to the sums over the discrete spectrum the corresponding integrals over the continuous spectrum. We shall distinguish the various states of the continuous spectrum by the suffix ν, which takes a continuous range of values; by ν we conventionally understand an assembly of values of quantities sufficient for a complete description of the state (if the states of the continuous spectrum are degenerate, which is almost always the case, the value of the energy alone does not suffice to determine the state). Then, for instance, we must write instead of (38.7)†

$$\psi_n^{(1)} = \sum_m{}' \frac{V_{mn}}{E_n^{(0)} - E_m^{(0)}} \psi_m^{(0)} + \int \frac{V_{\nu n}}{E_n^{(0)} - E_\nu} \psi_\nu^{(0)} \, d\nu, \tag{38.10}$$

and similarly for the other formulae.

It is useful to note also the formula for the perturbed value of the matrix element of a physical quantity f, calculated as far as terms of the first order by using the functions $\psi_n = \psi_n^{(0)} + \psi_n^{(1)}$, with $\psi_n^{(1)}$ given by (38.7). The

† Here the wave functions $\psi_\nu^{(0)}$ must be normalised by delta functions of the quantities ν.

following expression is easily obtained:

$$f_{nm} = f_{nm}^{(0)} + \sum_k{}' \frac{V_{nk} f_{km}^{(0)}}{E_n^{(0)} - E_k^{(0)}} + \sum_k{}' \frac{V_{km} f_{nk}^{(0)}}{E_m^{(0)} - E_k^{(0)}}. \qquad (38.11)$$

In the first sum $k \neq n$, while in the second $k \neq m$.

PROBLEMS

Problem 1. Determine the correction $\psi_n^{(2)}$ in the second approximation to the eigenfunctions.

Solution. The coefficients $c_k^{(2)}$ ($k \neq n$) are calculated from equations (38.4) with $k \neq n$, written out up to terms of the second order, and the coefficient $c_n^{(2)}$ is chosen so that the function $\psi_n = \psi_n^{(0)} + \psi_n^{(1)} + \psi_n^{(2)}$ is normalised up to terms of the second order. As a result we find

$$\psi_n^{(2)} = \sum_m \sum_k{}' \frac{V_{mk} V_{kn}}{\hbar^2 \omega_{nk} \omega_{nm}} \psi_m^{(0)} - \sum_m{}' \frac{V_{nn} V_{mn}}{\hbar^2 \omega_{nm}^2} \psi_m^{(0)} - \tfrac{1}{2} \psi_n^{(0)} \sum_m{}' \frac{|V_{mn}|^2}{\hbar^2 \omega_{nm}^2},$$

where we have introduced the frequencies

$$\omega_{nm} = (E_n^{(0)} - E_m^{(0)})/\hbar.$$

Problem 2. Determine the correction in the third approximation to the eigenvalues of the energy.

Solution. Writing out the terms of the third order of smallness in equation (38.4) with $k = n$, we obtain

$$E_n^{(3)} = \sum_k{}' \sum_m{}' \frac{V_{nm} V_{mk} V_{kn}}{\hbar^2 \omega_{mn} \omega_{kn}} - V_{nn} \sum_m{}' \frac{|V_{nm}|^2}{\hbar^2 \omega_{mn}^2}.$$

Problem 3. Determine the energy levels of an anharmonic linear oscillator whose Hamiltonian is

$$\hat{H} = \tfrac{1}{2}\hat{p}^2/\mu + \tfrac{1}{2}x^2\omega^2\mu + \alpha x^3 + \beta x^4.$$

Solution. The matrix elements of x^3 and x^4 can be obtained directly according to the rule of matrix multiplication, using the expression (21.4) for the matrix elements of x. We find for the matrix elements of x^3 that are not zero

$$(x^3)_{n-3,n} = (x^3)_{n,n-3} = (\hbar/\mu\omega)^{3/2} \sqrt{[\tfrac{1}{8} n(n-1)(n-2)]},$$
$$(x^3)_{n-1,n} = (x^3)_{n,n-1} = (\hbar/\mu\omega)^{3/2} \sqrt{(9n^3/8)}.$$

The diagonal elements in this matrix vanish, so that the correction in the first approximation due to the term αx^3 in the Hamiltonian (regarded as a perturbation of the harmonic oscillator) is zero. The correction in the second approximation due to this term is of the same order as that in the first approximation due to the term βx^4. The diagonal matrix elements of x^4 are

$$(x^4)_{n,n} = (\hbar/\mu\omega)^2 \,.\, \tfrac{3}{4}(2n^2+2n+1).$$

Using the general formulae (38.6) and (38.9), we find the following approximate expression for the energy levels of the anharmonic oscillator:

$$E_n = \hbar\omega(n+\tfrac{1}{2}) - \frac{15}{4}\frac{\alpha^2}{\hbar\omega}\left(\frac{\hbar}{\mu\omega}\right)^3\left(n^2+n+\frac{11}{30}\right) + \frac{3}{2}\beta\left(\frac{\hbar}{\mu\omega}\right)^2 (n^2+n+\tfrac{1}{2}).$$

§39. The secular equation

Let us now turn to the case where the unperturbed operator $\hat{H}_0$ has degenerate eigenvalues. We denote by $\psi_n^{(0)}$, $\psi_{n'}^{(0)}$, ... the eigenfunctions belonging to the same eigenvalue $E_n^{(0)}$ of the energy. The choice of these functions is, as we know, not unique; instead of them we can choose any s (where s is the degree of degeneracy of the level $E_n^{(0)}$) independent linear combinations of these functions. The choice ceases to be arbitrary, however, if we subject the wave functions to the requirement that the change in them under the action of the small applied perturbation should be small.

At present we shall understand by $\psi_n^{(0)}$, $\psi_{n'}^{(0)}$, ... some arbitrarily selected unperturbed eigenfunctions. The correct functions in the zero approximation are linear combinations of the form $c_n^{(0)}\psi_n^{(0)}+c_{n'}^{(0)}\psi_{n'}^{(0)}+\dots$. The coefficients in these combinations are determined, together with the corrections in the first approximation to the eigenvalues, as follows.

We write out equations (38.4) with $k = n, n', \dots$, and substitute in them, in the first approximation, $E = E_n^{(0)}+E^{(1)}$; for the quantities c_k it suffices to take the zero-order values $c_n = c_n^{(0)}$, $c_{n'} = c_{n'}^{(0)}, \dots$; $c_m = 0$ for $m \neq n, n', \dots$. We then obtain

$$E^{(1)}c_n^{(0)} = \sum_{n'} V_{nn'}c_{n'}^{(0)}$$

or

$$\sum_{n'}(V_{nn'}-E^{(1)}\delta_{nn'})c_{n'}^{(0)} = 0, \tag{39.1}$$

where n, n' take all values denumerating states belonging to the given unperturbed eigenvalue $E_n^{(0)}$. This system of homogeneous linear equations for the quantities $c_n^{(0)}$ has solutions which are not all zero if the determinant of the coefficients of the unknowns vanishes. Thus we obtain the equation

$$|V_{nn'}-E^{(1)}\delta_{nn'}| = 0. \tag{39.2}$$

This equation is of the sth degree in $E^{(1)}$ and has, in general, s different real roots. These roots are the required corrections to the eigenvalues in the first approximation. Equation (39.2) is called the *secular equation*.† We notice that the sum of its roots is equal to the sum of the diagonal matrix elements V_{nn}, $V_{n'n'}$, ... (this being the coefficient of $[E^{(1)}]^{s-1}$ in the equation).

Substituting in turn the roots of equation (39.2) in the system (39.1) and solving, we find the coefficients $c_n^{(0)}$ and so determine the eigenfunctions in the zero approximation.

We notice that, as a result of the perturbation, an originally degenerate energy level ceases in general to be degenerate (the roots of equation (39.2) are in general distinct); the perturbation *removes* the degeneracy, as we say. The removal of the degeneracy may be either total or partial (in the latter case, after the perturbation has been applied, there remains a degeneracy of degree less than the original one).

† The name is taken from celestial mechanics.

It may happen that all the matrix elements for transitions between the states $n, n', \ldots$ with a single energy are zero. The correction to the energy then vanishes in the first approximation. Let us calculate the correction in the second approximation for this case. In equation (38.4) with $k = n$ we put on the left-hand side $E = E_n^{(0)} + E^{(2)}$, and write $c_n^{(0)}$ in place of c_n. Only the terms with $m \neq n, n', \ldots$ on the right-hand side are different from zero, and since $c_m^{(0)} = 0$ we have

$$E^{(2)} c_n^{(0)} = \sum_m V_{nm} c_m^{(1)}. \tag{39.3}$$

The equation (38.4) with $k = m \neq n, n', \ldots$, on the other hand, gives, correct to terms of the first order,

$$[E_n^{(0)} - E_m^{(0)}] c_m^{(1)} = \sum_{n'} V_{mn'} c_{n'}^{(0)},$$

whence

$$c_m^{(1)} = \sum_{n'} \frac{V_{mn'}}{E_n^{(0)} - E_m^{(0)}} c_{n'}^{(0)}.$$

Substituting in (39.3), we obtain

$$E^{(2)} c_n^{(0)} = \sum_{n'} c_{n'}^{(0)} \sum_m \frac{V_{nm} V_{mn'}}{E_n^{(0)} - E_m^{(0)}}.$$

This system of equations for the $c_n^{(0)}$ now replaces the system (39.1); the condition that these equations are compatible is

$$\left| \sum_m \frac{V_{nm} V_{mn'}}{E_n^{(0)} - E_m^{(0)}} - E^{(2)} \delta_{nn'} \right| = 0. \tag{39.4}$$

Thus here also the corrections to the energy are calculated as the roots of a secular equation, in which, instead of the matrix elements $V_{nn'}$, we now have the sums

$$\sum_m \frac{V_{nm} V_{mn'}}{E_n^{(0)} - E_m^{(0)}}.$$

PROBLEMS

PROBLEM 1. Determine the corrections to the eigenvalue in the first approximation and the correct functions in the zero approximation, for a doubly degenerate level.

SOLUTION. Equation (39.2) here has the form

$$\begin{vmatrix} V_{11} - E^{(1)} & V_{12} \\ V_{21} & V_{22} - E^{(1)} \end{vmatrix} = 0$$

(the suffixes 1 and 2 correspond to two arbitrarily chosen unperturbed eigenfunctions $\psi_1^{(0)}$

and $\psi_2^{(0)}$ of the doubly degenerate level in question). Solving, we find

$$E^{(1)} = \tfrac{1}{2}[(V_{11}+V_{22})\pm\sqrt{\{(V_{11}-V_{22})^2+4|V_{12}|^2\}}]. \quad (1)$$

Solving also equations (39.1) with these values of $E^{(1)}$, we obtain for the coefficients in the correct normalised functions in the zero approximation, $\psi^{(0)} = c_1^{(0)}\psi_1^{(0)}+c_2^{(0)}\psi_2^{(0)}$, the values

$$c_1^{(0)} = \left\{\frac{V_{12}}{2|V_{12}|}\left[1\pm\frac{V_{11}-V_{22}}{\sqrt{\{(V_{11}-V_{22})^2+4|V_{12}|^2\}}}\right]\right\}^{\frac{1}{2}},$$
$$c_2^{(0)} = \pm\left\{\frac{V_{21}}{2|V_{12}|}\left[1\mp\frac{V_{11}-V_{22}}{\sqrt{\{(V_{11}-V_{22})^2+4|V_{12}|^2\}}}\right]\right\}^{\frac{1}{2}}. \quad (2)$$

PROBLEM 2. Derive the formulae for the correction to the eigenfunctions in the first approximation and to the eigenvalues in the second approximation.

SOLUTION. We shall suppose that the correct functions in the zero approximation are chosen as the functions $\psi_n^{(0)}$. The matrix $V_{nn'}$ defined with respect to these is clearly diagonal with respect to the suffixes n, n' (belonging to the same group of functions of a degenerate level), and the diagonal elements V_{nn}, $V_{n'n'}$ are equal to the corresponding corrections $E_n^{(1)}, E_{n'}^{(1)}, \ldots$ in the first approximation.

Let us consider a perturbation of the eigenfunction $\psi_n^{(0)}$, so that in the zero approximation $E = E_n^{(0)}$, $c_n^{(0)} = 1$, $c_m^{(0)} = 0$ for $m \neq n$. In the first approximation $E = E_n^{(0)}+V_{nn}$, $c_n = 1+c_n^{(1)}$, $c_m = c_m^{(1)}$. We write out from the system (38.4) the equation with $k \neq n, n', \ldots$, retaining in it terms of the first order:

$$(E_n^{0}-E_k^{(0)})c_k^{(1)} = V_{kn}c_n^{(0)} = V_{kn},$$

whence

$$c_k^{(1)} = V_{kn}/(E_n^{(0)}-E_k^{(0)}) \text{ for } k \neq n, n', \ldots . \quad (1)$$

Next we write out the equation with $k = n'$, retaining in it terms of the second order:

$$E_n^{(1)}c_{n'}^{(1)} = V_{n'n'}c_{n'}^{(1)}+ \sum_m{}' V_{n'm}c_m^{(1)}$$

(the terms with $m = n, n', \ldots$ are omitted in the sum over m). Substituting $E_n^{(1)} = V_{nn}$ and the expression (1) for $c_m^{(1)}$, we obtain

$$c_{n'}^{(1)} = \frac{1}{V_{nn}-V_{n'n'}}\sum_m{}' \frac{V_{n'm}V_{mn}}{E_n^{(0)}-E_m^{(0)}}. \quad (2)$$

Formulae (1) and (2) determine the correction $\psi_n^{(1)} = \Sigma c_m^{(1)}\psi_m^{(0)}$ to the eigenfunctions in the first approximation.

Finally, writing out the second-order terms in equation (38.4) with $k = n$, we obtain for the second-order corrections to the energy the formula

$$E_n^{(2)} = \sum_m{}' \frac{V_{nm}V_{mn}}{E_n^{(0)}-E_m^{(0)}}, \quad (3)$$

which is formally identical with (38.9).

PROBLEM 3. At the initial instant $t = 0$, a system is in a state $\psi_1^{(0)}$ which belongs to a doubly degenerate level. Determine the probability that, at a subsequent instant t, the system will be in the state $\psi_2^{(0)}$ with the same energy; the transition occurs under the action of a constant perturbation.

SOLUTION. We form the correct functions in the zero approximation,

$$\psi = c_1\psi_1+c_2\psi_2, \qquad \psi' = c_1'\psi_1+c_2'\psi_2,$$

where $c_1, c_2; c_1', c_2'$ are two pairs of coefficients determined by formulae (2) of Problem 1 (for brevity, we omit the index $^{(0)}$ on all quantities).

Conversely,

$$\psi_1 = \frac{c_2'\psi - c_2\psi'}{c_1c_2' - c_1'c_2}.$$

The functions ψ and ψ' belong to states with perturbed energies $E+E^{(1)}$ and $E+E^{(1)\prime}$, where $E^{(1)}$ and $E^{(1)\prime}$ are the two values of the correction (1) in Problem 1. On introducing the time factors we pass to the time-dependent wave functions:

$$\Psi_1 = \frac{e^{-(i/\hbar)Et}}{c_1c_2' - c_1'c_2}[c_2'\psi e^{-(i/\hbar)E^{(1)}t} - c_2\psi' e^{-(i/\hbar)E^{(1)\prime}t}]$$

(at time $t = 0$, $\Psi_1 = \psi_1$). Finally, again expressing ψ, ψ', in terms of ψ_1, ψ_2, we obtain Ψ_1 as a linear combination of ψ_1 and ψ_2, with coefficients depending on time. The squared modulus of the coefficient of ψ_2 determines the required transition probability w_{12}. Calculation gives

$$w_{12} = \left|\frac{c_2c_2'}{c_1c_2' - c_1'c_2}\right|^2 |e^{-(i/\hbar)E^{(1)}t} - e^{-(i/\hbar)E^{(1)\prime}t}|^2,$$

or, substituting formulae (1) and (2) from Problem 1,

$$w_{12} = \frac{|V_{12}|^2}{2|V_{12}|^2 + \frac{1}{2}(V_{11} - V_{22})^2}\left\{1 - \cos\left(\frac{1}{\hbar}\sqrt{[(V_{11}-V_{22})^2 + 4|V_{12}|^2]}t\right)\right\}. \quad (1)$$

We see that the probability varies periodically with time, with frequency $(E^{(1)} - E^{(1)\prime})/\hbar$.

§40. Perturbations depending on time

Let us now go on to study perturbations depending explicitly on time. In general we cannot speak in this case of corrections to the eigenvalues, since, when the Hamiltonian is time-dependent (as will be the perturbed operator $\hat{H} = \hat{H}_0 + \hat{V}(t)$), the energy is in general not conserved, so that there are no stationary states. The problem here consists in approximately calculating the wave functions from those of the stationary states of the unperturbed system.

To do this, we shall apply a method analogous to the well-known method of varying the constants to solve linear differential equations (P. Dirac 1926). Let $\Psi_k^{(0)}$ be the wave functions (including the time factor) of the stationary states of the unperturbed system. Then an arbitrary solution of the unperturbed wave equation can be written in the form of a sum: $\Psi = \Sigma\, a_k \Psi_k^{(0)}$. We shall now seek the solution of the perturbed equation

$$i\hbar\, \partial\Psi/\partial t = (\hat{H}_0 + \hat{V})\Psi \quad (40.1)$$

in the form of a sum

$$\Psi = \sum_k a_k(t)\Psi_k^{(0)}, \quad (40.2)$$

where the expansion coefficients are functions of time. Substituting (40.2) in (40.1), and recalling that the functions $\Psi_k^{(0)}$ satisfy the equation

$$i\hbar\, \partial\Psi_k^{(0)}/\partial t = \hat{H}_0\Psi_k^{(0)},$$

we obtain

$$i\hbar \sum_k \Psi_k^{(0)} \frac{da_k}{dt} = \sum_k a_k \hat{V}\Psi_k^{(0)}.$$

Multiplying both sides of this equation on the left by $\Psi_m^{(0)*}$ and integrating, we have

$$i\hbar \frac{da_m}{dt} = \sum_k V_{mk}(t) a_k, \tag{40.3}$$

where

$$V_{mk}(t) = \int \Psi_m^{(0)*}\hat{V}\Psi_k^{(0)}\, dq$$
$$= V_{mk} e^{(i/\hbar)(E_m^{(0)}-E_k^{(0)})t}$$

are the matrix elements of the perturbation, including the time factor (and it must be borne in mind that, when $\hat{V}$ depends explicitly on time, the quantities V_{mk} also are functions of time).

As the unperturbed wave function we take the wave function of the nth stationary state, for which the corresponding values of the coefficients in (40.2) are $a_n^{(0)} = 1$, $a_k^{(0)} = 0$ for $k \neq n$. To find the first approximation, we seek a_k in the form $a_k = a_k^{(0)} + a_k^{(1)}$, substituting $a_k = a_k^{(0)}$ on the right-hand side of equation (40.3), which already contains the small quantities V_{mk}. This gives

$$i\hbar\, da_k^{(1)}/dt = V_{kn}(t). \tag{40.4}$$

In order to show the unperturbed function to which the correction is being calculated, we introduce a second suffix in the coefficients a_k, writing

$$\Psi_n = \sum_k a_{kn}(t)\Psi_k^{(0)}.$$

Accordingly, we write the result of integrating equation (40.4) in the form

$$a_{kn}^{(1)} = -(i/\hbar) \int V_{kn}(t)\, dt = -(i/\hbar) \int V_{kn} e^{i\omega_{kn}t}\, dt, \tag{40.5}$$

where we have introduced the frequencies $\omega_{kn} = (E_k^{(0)} - E_n^{(0)})/\hbar$. This determines the wave functions in the first approximation.

We can similarly determine the subsequent approximations (in practice, however, the first approximation is adequate in the majority of cases).

Let us now consider in more detail the case of a perturbation $\hat{V}$ which is periodic with respect to time, of the form

$$\hat{V} = \hat{F}e^{-i\omega t} + \hat{G}e^{i\omega t} \tag{40.6}$$

where $\hat{F}$ and $\hat{G}$ are operators independent of time. Since $\hat{V}$ is Hermitian, we must have $V_{nm} = V_{mn}^*$, or

$$F_{nm}e^{-i\omega t}+G_{nm}e^{i\omega t} = F_{mn}^*e^{i\omega t}+G_{mn}^*e^{-i\omega t},$$

from which

$$G_{nm} = F_{mn}^*, \tag{40.7}$$

which determines the relation between the operators $\hat{G}$ and $\hat{F}$. Using this relation, we have

$$\begin{aligned} V_{kn}(t) &= V_{kn}e^{i\omega_{kn}t} \\ &= F_{kn}e^{i(\omega_{kn}-\omega)t}+F_{nk}^*e^{i(\omega_{kn}+\omega)t}. \end{aligned} \tag{40.8}$$

Substituting in (40.5) and integrating, we obtain the following expression for the expansion coefficients of the wave functions:

$$a_{kn}^{(1)} = -\frac{F_{kn}e^{i(\omega_{kn}-\omega)t}}{\hbar(\omega_{kn}-\omega)}-\frac{F_{nk}^*e^{i(\omega_{kn}+\omega)t}}{\hbar(\omega_{kn}+\omega)}. \tag{40.9}$$

These expressions are applicable if none of the denominators vanishes,† i.e. if for all k (and the given n)

$$E_k^{(0)}-E_n^{(0)} \neq \pm\hbar\omega. \tag{40.10}$$

In a number of applications it is useful to have expressions for the matrix elements of an arbitrary quantity f, defined with respect to the perturbed wave functions. In the first approximation we have

$$f_{nm}(t) = f_{nm}^{(0)}(t)+f_{nm}^{(1)}(t),$$

where

$$f_{nm}^{(0)}(t) = \int \Psi_n^{(0)*}\hat{f}\Psi_m^{(0)}\,dq = f_{nm}^{(0)}e^{i\omega_{nm}t},$$

$$f_{nm}^{(1)}(t) = \int [\Psi_n^{(0)*}\hat{f}\Psi_m^{(1)}+\Psi_n^{(1)*}\hat{f}\Psi_m^{(0)}]\,dq.$$

Substituting here $\Psi_n^{(1)} = \Sigma\, a_{kn}^{(1)}\Psi_k^{(0)}$, with $a_{kn}^{(1)}$ determined by formula (40.9), it is easy to obtain the required expression

$$\begin{aligned} f_{nm}^{(1)}(t) = -e^{i\omega_{nm}t}\sum_k \Bigg\{&\left[\frac{f_{nk}^{(0)}F_{km}}{\hbar(\omega_{km}-\omega)}+\frac{f_{km}^{(0)}F_{nk}}{\hbar(\omega_{kn}+\omega)}\right]e^{-i\omega t}+ \\ &+\left[\frac{f_{nk}^{(0)}F_{mk}^*}{\hbar(\omega_{km}+\omega)}+\frac{f_{km}^{(0)}F_{kn}^*}{\hbar(\omega_{kn}-\omega)}\right]e^{i\omega t}\Bigg\}. \end{aligned} \tag{40.11}$$

† More precisely, if none is so small that the quantities $a_{kn}^{(1)}$ are no longer small compared with unity.

This formula is applicable if none of its terms becomes infinite, i.e. if for all k

$$E_k^{(0)}-E_n^{(0)} \neq \hbar\omega,$$
$$E_k^{(0)}-E_m^{(0)} \neq \hbar\omega. \tag{40.12}$$

In all the formulae given here, it is understood that there is only a discrete spectrum of unperturbed energy levels. However, these formulae can be immediately generalised to the case where there is also a continuous spectrum (as before, we are concerned with the perturbation of states of the discrete spectrum); this is done by simply adding to the sums over the levels of the discrete spectrum the corresponding integrals over the continuous spectrum. Here it is necessary for the denominators $\omega_{kn}\pm\omega$ in formulae (40.9), (40.11) to be non-zero when the energy $E_k^{(0)}$ takes all values, not only of the discrete but also of the continuous spectrum. If, as usually happens, the continuous spectrum lies above all the levels of the discrete spectrum, then, for instance, the condition (40.10) must be supplemented by the condition

$$E_{\min}^{(0)}-E_n^{(0)} > \hbar\omega, \tag{40.13}$$

where $E_{\min}^{(0)}$ is the energy of the lowest level of the continuous spectrum.

PROBLEM

Determine the change in the nth and mth solutions of SCHRÖDINGER's equation in the presence of a periodic perturbation (of the form (40.6)), of frequency ω such that $E_m^{(0)}-E_n^{(0)} = \hbar(\omega+\epsilon)$, where ϵ is a small quantity.

SOLUTION. The method developed in the text is here inapplicable, since the coefficient $a_{mn}^{(1)}$ in (40.9) becomes large. We start afresh from the exact equations (40.3), with $V_{mk}(t)$ given by (40.8). It is evident that the most important effect is due to those terms, in the sums on the right-hand side of equations (40.3), in which the time dependence is determined by the small frequency $\omega_{mn}-\omega$. Omitting all other terms, we obtain a system of two equations:

$$i\hbar \mathrm{d}a_m/\mathrm{d}t = F_{mn}e^{i(\omega_{mn}-\omega)t}a_n = F_{mn}e^{i\epsilon t}a_n,$$
$$i\hbar \mathrm{d}a_n/\mathrm{d}t = F_{mn}^*e^{-i\epsilon t}a_m.$$

We make the substitution

$$a_n e^{i\epsilon t} = b_n$$

and obtain the equations

$$i\hbar\dot{a}_m = F_{mn}b_n, \quad i\hbar(\dot{b}_n - i\epsilon b_n) = F_{mn}^* a_m.$$

Eliminating a_m, we have

$$\ddot{b}_n - i\epsilon\dot{b}_n + |F_{mn}|^2 b_n/\hbar^2 = 0.$$

We can take as two independent solutions of these equations

$$a_n = Ae^{i\alpha_1 t}, \quad a_m = -A\hbar\alpha_1 e^{i\alpha_2 t}/F_{mn}^* \tag{1}$$

and

$$a_n = Be^{-i\alpha_2 t}, \quad a_m = B\hbar\alpha_2 e^{-i\alpha_1 t}/F_{mn}^*, \tag{2}$$

where A and B are constants (which have to be determined from the normalisation condition), and we have used the notation

$$\alpha_1 = -\tfrac{1}{2}\epsilon+\sqrt{[\tfrac{1}{4}\epsilon^2+|F_{mn}|^2/\hbar^2]},\quad \alpha_2 = \tfrac{1}{2}\epsilon+\sqrt{[\tfrac{1}{4}\epsilon^2+|F_{mn}|^2/\hbar^2]}.$$

Thus, under the action of the perturbation, the functions $\Psi_n^{(0)}$, $\Psi_m^{(0)}$ become $a_n\Psi_n^{(0)}+ +a_m\Psi_m^{(0)}$, with a_n and a_m given by (1) and (2).

Let the system be in the state $\Psi_m^{(0)}$ at the initial instant ($t = 0$). The state of the system at subsequent instants is given by a linear combination of the two functions which we have obtained, which becomes $\psi_m^{(0)}$ for $t = 0$:

$$\Psi = \left\{e^{\frac{1}{2}i\epsilon t}\cos\sqrt{[\tfrac{1}{4}\epsilon^2+|F_{mn}|^2/\hbar^2]}t-\frac{\tfrac{1}{2}i\epsilon e^{\frac{1}{2}i\epsilon t}}{\sqrt{[\tfrac{1}{4}\epsilon^2+|F_{mn}|^2/\hbar^2]}}\sin\sqrt{[\tfrac{1}{4}\epsilon^2+|F_{mn}|^2/\hbar^2]}t\right\}\Psi_m^{(0)}-$$
$$-\left\{\frac{iF_{mn}^*}{\sqrt{[\tfrac{1}{4}\hbar^2\epsilon^2+|F_{mn}|^2]}}e^{-\frac{1}{2}i\epsilon t}\sin\sqrt{[\tfrac{1}{4}\epsilon^2+|F_{mn}|^2/\hbar^2]}t\right\}\Psi_n^{(0)}. \tag{3}$$

The squared modulus of the coefficient of $\Psi_n^{(0)}$ is

$$\frac{2|F_{mn}|^2}{\hbar^2\epsilon^2+4|F_{mn}|^2}\{1-\cos\sqrt{[\epsilon^2+4|F_{mn}|^2/\hbar^2]}t\}. \tag{4}$$

This gives the probability of finding the system in the state $\psi_n^{(0)}$ at time t. We see that it is a periodic function with period $2\pi\hbar(\epsilon^2\hbar^2+4|F_{mn}|^2)^{-\frac{1}{2}}$, and varies from 0 to $4|F_{mn}|^2/(\hbar^2\epsilon^2+ +4|F_{mn}|^2)$.

For $\epsilon = 0$ (exact resonance) the probability (4) becomes

$$\tfrac{1}{2}(1-\cos 2|F_{mn}|t/\hbar).$$

It varies periodically, with period $\pi\hbar/|F_{mn}|$, between 0 and 1; in other words, the system makes periodic transitions from the state $\Psi_m^{(0)}$ to the state $\Psi_n^{(0)}$.

§41. The transition probability in a discrete spectrum

Let us suppose that the perturbation $V(t)$ acts only during some finite interval of time (or that $V(t)$ diminishes sufficiently rapidly as $t \to \pm\infty$). Let the system be in the nth stationary state (of a discrete spectrum) before the perturbation begins to act (or in the limit as $t \to -\infty$). At any subsequent instant the state of the system will be determined by the function $\Psi = \Sigma\, a_{kn}\Psi_k^{(0)}$, where, in the first approximation,

$$a_{kn} = a_{kn}^{(1)} = -\frac{i}{\hbar}\int_{-\infty}^{t} V_{kn}e^{i\omega_{kn}t}\,dt \quad \text{for} \quad k \neq n,$$
$$a_{nn} = 1+a_{nn}^{(1)} = 1-\frac{i}{\hbar}\int_{-\infty}^{t} V_{nn}\,dt; \tag{41.1}$$

the limits of integration in (40.5) are taken so that, as $t \to -\infty$, all the $a_{kn}^{(1)}$ tend to zero. After the perturbation has ceased to act (or in the limit $t \to +\infty$), the coefficients a_{kn} take constant values $a_{kn}(\infty)$, and the system is in the state with wave function

$$\Psi = \sum_k a_{kn}(\infty)\Psi_k^{(0)},$$

which again satisfies the unperturbed wave equation, but is different from the original function $\Psi_n^{(0)}$. According to the general rule, the squared modulus of the coefficient $a_{kn}(\infty)$ determines the probability for the system to have an energy $E_k^{(0)}$, i.e. to be in the kth stationary state.

Thus, under the action of the perturbation, the system may pass from its initial stationary state to any other. The probability of a transition from the original (nth) to the kth stationary state is

$$w_{nk} = \frac{1}{\hbar^2}\left|\int_{-\infty}^{\infty} V_{kn}e^{i\omega_{kn}t}\,dt\right|^2. \tag{41.2}$$

Let us now consider a perturbation which, once having begun, continues to act for an indefinite time (always, of course, remaining small). In other words, $V(t)$ tends to zero as $t \to -\infty$ and to a finite non-zero limit as $t \to +\infty$. Formula (41.2) cannot be applied directly here, since the integral in it diverges. This divergence, however, is physically unimportant and can easily be removed. To do this, we integrate by parts:

$$a_{kn} = -\frac{i}{\hbar}\int_{-\infty}^{t} V_{kn}e^{i\omega_{kn}t}\,dt = -\left[\frac{V_{kn}e^{i\omega_{kn}t}}{\hbar\omega_{kn}}\right]_{-\infty}^{t} + \int_{-\infty}^{t}\frac{\partial V_{kn}}{\partial t}\frac{e^{i\omega_{kn}t}}{\hbar\omega_{kn}}\,dt.$$

The value of the first term vanishes at the lower limit, while at the upper limit it is formally identical with the expansion coefficients in formula (38.7); the presence of an additional periodic factor $e^{i\omega_{kn}t}$ is merely due to the fact that the a_{kn} are the expansion coefficients of the complete wave function Ψ, while the c_{kn} in §38 are the expansion coefficients of the time-independent function ψ. Hence it is clear that its limit as $t \to \infty$ gives simply the change in the original wave function $\Psi_n^{(0)}$ under the action of the "constant part" $V(+\infty)$ of the perturbation, and consequently has no relation to transitions into other states. The probability of a transition is given by the squared modulus of the second term and is

$$w_{nk} = \frac{1}{\hbar^2\omega_{kn}^2}\left|\int_{-\infty}^{\infty}\frac{\partial V_{kn}}{\partial t}e^{i\omega_{kn}t}\,dt\right|^2. \tag{41.3}$$

In the limiting case of a very rapid, "instantaneous" application of the perturbation, the derivatives $\partial V_{kn}/\partial t$ become infinite at the "instant of application". In the integral of $(\partial V_{kn}/\partial t)e^{i\omega_{kn}t}$, we can take outside the integral the comparatively slowly varying factor $e^{i\omega_{kn}t}$ and use its value at this instant. The integral is then found at once, and we obtain

$$w_{nk} = |V_{kn}|^2/\hbar^2\omega_{kn}^2. \tag{41.4}$$

If the perturbation $V(t)$ varies little during time intervals of the order of the period $1/\omega_{kn}$ of the periodic factor $e^{i\omega_{kn}t}$, the value of the integral in (41.2) or (41.3) will be very small. In the limit when the applied perturbation varies arbitrarily slowly, the probability of any transition with change of energy (i.e. with a non-zero frequency ω_{kn}) tends to zero. Thus, when the applied perturbation changes sufficiently slowly (*adiabatically*), a system in any non-degenerate stationary state will remain in that state.

§42. The transition probability under the action of a periodic perturbation

The results are different for the probability of transitions to the states of the continuous spectrum under the action of a periodic perturbation. Let us suppose that, at some initial instant $t = 0$, the system is in the nth stationary state of the discrete spectrum. We shall assume that the frequency ω of the periodic perturbation is such that

$$\hbar\omega > E_{\min} - E_n^{(0)}, \tag{42.1}$$

where $E_{\min}$ is the value of the energy where the continuous spectrum begins.

It is evident from the results of §40 that the chief part will be played by states with energies E_ν very close to the *resonance* energy $E_n^{(0)} + \hbar\omega$, i.e. those for which the difference $\omega_{\nu n} - \omega$ is small.† For this reason it is sufficient to consider, in the matrix elements (40.8) of the perturbation, only the first term (with the frequency $\omega_{\nu n} - \omega$ close to zero). Substituting this term in (40.5) and integrating, we obtain

$$a_{\nu n} = -\frac{i}{\hbar}\int_0^t V_{\nu n}(t)\,dt = -F_{\nu n}\frac{e^{i(\omega_{\nu n}-\omega)t} - 1}{\hbar(\omega_{\nu n}-\omega)}. \tag{42.2}$$

The lower limit of integration is chosen so that $a_{\nu n} = 0$ for $t = 0$, in accordance with the initial condition imposed.

Hence we find for the squared modulus of $a_{\nu n}$

$$|a_{\nu n}|^2 = |F_{\nu n}|^2 \,.\, 4\sin^2[\tfrac{1}{2}(\omega_{\nu n}-\omega)t]/\hbar^2(\omega_{\nu n}-\omega)^2. \tag{42.3}$$

It is easy to see that, for large t, this function can be regarded as proportional to t. To show this, we notice that

$$\lim_{t\to\infty}\frac{\sin^2\alpha t}{\pi t\alpha^2} = \delta(\alpha). \tag{42.4}$$

For when $\alpha \neq 0$ this limit is zero, while for $\alpha = 0$ we have $(\sin^2\alpha t)/t\alpha^2 = t$, so that the limit is infinite; finally, integrating over α from $-\infty$ to $+\infty$,

† We recall that the suffix ν refers to the continuous spectrum (see the end of §38).

we have (with the substitution $\alpha t = \xi$)

$$\frac{1}{\pi}\int_{-\infty}^{\infty} \frac{\sin^2 \alpha t}{t\alpha^2}\,d\alpha = \frac{1}{\pi}\int_{-\infty}^{\infty} \frac{\sin^2 \xi}{\xi^2}\,d\xi = 1.$$

Thus the function on the left-hand side of equation (42.4) in fact satisfies all the conditions which define the delta function. Accordingly, we can write for large t

$$|a_{\nu n}|^2 = (1/\hbar^2)|F_{\nu n}|^2 \pi t \delta(\tfrac{1}{2}\omega_{\nu n} - \tfrac{1}{2}\omega),$$

or, substituting $\hbar\omega_{\nu n} = E_\nu - E_n^{(0)}$ and using the fact that $\delta(ax) = (1/a)\delta(x)$,

$$|a_{\nu n}|^2 = (2\pi/\hbar)|F_{\nu n}|^2 \delta(E_\nu - E_n^{(0)} - \hbar\omega)t.$$

The expression $|a_{\nu n}|^2\,d\nu$ is the probability of a transition from the original state to one in the interval from ν to $\nu + d\nu$ (cf. §5). We see that, for large t, it is proportional to the time interval elapsed since $t = 0$. The probability $dw_{n\nu}$ of the transition per unit time is†

$$dw_{n\nu} = (2\pi/\hbar)|F_{\nu n}|^2 \delta(E_\nu - E_n^{(0)} - \hbar\omega)\,d\nu. \tag{42.5}$$

As we should expect, it is zero except for transitions to states with energy $E_\nu = E_n^{(0)} + \hbar\omega$. If the energy levels of the continuous spectrum are not degenerate, so that ν can be taken as the value of the energy alone, then the whole "interval" of states $d\nu$ reduces to a single state with energy $E = E_n^{(0)} + \hbar\omega$, and the probability of a transition to this state is

$$w_{nE} = (2\pi/\hbar)|F_{En}|^2. \tag{42.6}$$

§43. The transition probability under the action of a constant perturbation

One of the most important applications of perturbation theory is to calculate the probability of a transition in the continuous spectrum under the action of a constant (time-independent) perturbation. We have already mentioned that the states of the continuous spectrum are almost always degenerate. Having chosen in some manner the set of unperturbed wave functions corresponding to some given energy level, we can put the problem as follows. It is known that, at the initial instant, the system is in one of these states; it is required to determine the probability of the transition to another state with the same energy. If we denote the initial state by the suffix ν_0, then for transitions to states between ν and $\nu + d\nu$ we have at once from (42.5) (putting $\omega = 0$ and changing the notation)

$$dw_{\nu_0\nu} = (2\pi/\hbar)|V_{\nu\nu_0}|^2 \delta(E_\nu - E_{\nu_0})\,d\nu. \tag{43.1}$$

This expression is, as we should expect, zero except for $E_\nu = E_{\nu_0}$: under

† It is easy to verify that, on taking account of the second term in (40.8), which we have omitted, additional expressions are obtained which, on being divided by t, tend to zero as $t \to +\infty$.

the action of a constant perturbation, transitions occur only between states with the same energy. It must be noticed that, for transitions from states of the continuous spectrum, the quantity $dw_{\nu_0\nu}$ cannot be regarded directly as the transition probability; it is not even of the right dimensions (1/time). In formula (43.1), $dw_{\nu_0\nu}$ represents the number of transitions per unit time, and its dimensions depend on the chosen method of normalisation of the wave functions of the continuous spectrum.

Let us calculate the perturbed wave function which at the initial instant coincides with the initial unperturbed function $\psi_{\nu_0}^{(0)}$. According to formula (42.2) (putting $\omega = 0$ and changing the notation) we have

$$a^{(1)}_{\nu\nu_0} = V_{\nu\nu_0}\frac{e^{(i/\hbar)(E_\nu - E_{\nu_0})t} - 1}{E_{\nu_0} - E_\nu}.$$

The perturbed wave function has the form

$$\Psi_{\nu_0} = \Psi_{\nu_0}^{(0)} + \int a^{(1)}_{\nu\nu_0}\Psi_\nu^{(0)}\,d\nu,$$

or

$$\Psi_{\nu_0} = \left[\psi_{\nu_0}^{(0)} + \int V_{\nu\nu_0}\psi_\nu^{(0)}\frac{1 - e^{(i/\hbar)(E_{\nu_0} - E_\nu)t}}{E_{\nu_0} - E_\nu}\,d\nu\right]e^{-(i/\hbar)E_{\nu_0}t}, \tag{43.2}$$

where the integration is extended over the whole continuous spectrum.†

Let us ascertain the limiting form of this function for large t. To do so, we separate from $d\nu$ the differential dE_ν of the energy (writing $d\nu = dE_\nu\,d\tau$, where $d\tau$ is the product of the differentials of the remaining quantities which determine a state in the continuous spectrum), and formally regard E_ν as a complex variable. The integral

$$\int V_{\nu\nu_0}\psi_\nu^{(0)}\frac{1 - e^{(i/\hbar)(E_{\nu_0} - E_\nu)t}}{E_{\nu_0} - E_\nu}\,dE_\nu$$

in (43.2) is taken along the real axis. We slightly displace the path of integration into the lower half-plane; this can be done without changing the value of the integral, since the integrand has no singularities on the real axis. The integral can then be divided into two parts

$$\int V_{\nu\nu_0}\psi_\nu^{(0)}\frac{dE_\nu}{E_{\nu_0} - E_\nu} \text{ and } -\int \frac{V_{\nu\nu_0}\psi_\nu^{(0)}}{E_{\nu_0} - E_\nu}e^{(i/\hbar)(E_{\nu_0} - E_\nu)t}\,dE_\nu$$

(these integrals have no meaning when the integration is along the real axis, since they diverge at the point $E_\nu = E_{\nu_0}$). Since im $E_\nu < 0$ on the contour of integration, the second of the above integrals tends to zero as t tends to

† If there is also a discrete spectrum, then we must add to the integral in this formula (and subsequent ones) the appropriate sum over the states of the discrete spectrum.

infinity (because of the factor $\exp[\hbar^{-1}\mathrm{im}(E_\nu)t]$ in the integrand). In the first integral, we can again make the path of integration the real axis, but pass round the point $E_\nu = E_{\nu_0}$ below.

Thus we obtain for the wave function the expression

$$\Psi_{\nu_0} = \left[\psi_{\nu_0}{}^{(0)} + \int \frac{V_{\nu\nu_0}}{E_{\nu_0}-E_\nu}\psi_\nu{}^{(0)}\,d\nu\right]e^{-(i/\hbar)E_{\nu_0}t}, \tag{43.3}$$

in which the integration over the variable E_ν is carried out along the path shown in Fig. 13. The time factor shows that this function belongs, as it

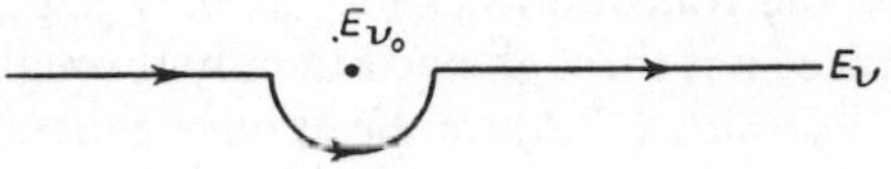

FIG. 13

should, to the same energy E_{ν_0} as the initial unperturbed function. In other words, the function

$$\psi_{\nu_0} = \psi_{\nu_0}{}^{(0)} + \int \frac{V_{\nu\nu_0}}{E_{\nu_0}-E_\nu}\psi_\nu{}^{(0)}\,d\nu$$

satisfies SCHRÖDINGER's equation $(\hat{H}_0+\hat{V})\psi_{\nu_0} = E_{\nu_0}\psi_{\nu_0}$. For this reason it is natural that the expression above should correspond exactly to formula (38.7).†

The calculations given above correspond to the first approximation of perturbation theory. It is not difficult to calculate the second approximation as well. To do this, we must derive the formula for the next approximation to Ψ_{ν_0}; this is easily effected by using the method of §38 (now that we know the method of dealing with the "divergent" integrals). A simple calculation gives the formula

$$\Psi_{\nu_0} = \left\{\psi_{\nu_0}{}^{(0)} + \int \left[V_{\nu\nu_0} + \int \frac{V_{\nu\nu'}V_{\nu'\nu_0}}{E_{\nu_0}-E_{\nu'}}\,d\nu'\right]\frac{\psi_\nu{}^{(0)}\,d\nu}{E_{\nu_0}-E_\nu}\right\}e^{-(i/\hbar)E_{\nu_0}t}. \tag{43.4}$$

Comparing this expression with formula (43.3), we can write down the corresponding formula for the probability (or, more precisely, the number) of transitions, by direct analogy with (43.1):

$$dw_{\nu_0\nu} = \frac{2\pi}{\hbar}\left|V_{\nu\nu_0} + \int \frac{V_{\nu\nu'}V_{\nu'\nu_0}}{E_{\nu_0}-E_{\nu'}}\,d\nu'\right|^2 \delta(E_{\nu_0}-E_\nu)\,d\nu. \tag{43.5}$$

It may happen that the matrix element $V_{\nu\nu_0}$ for the transition considered

† Starting from the latter formula, the way in which the integral must be taken can be found from the condition that the asymptotic expression for ψ_{ν_0} at large distances must contain only an outgoing (and not an ingoing) wave.

vanishes. The effect is then zero in the first approximation, and we have for the number of transitions

$$dw_{\nu_0\nu} = \frac{2\pi}{\hbar}\left|\int \frac{V_{\nu\nu'}V_{\nu'\nu_0}}{E_{\nu_0}-E_{\nu'}}\,d\nu'\right|^2 \delta(E_\nu - E_{\nu_0})\,d\nu. \tag{43.6}$$

In applications of this formula, the point $E_{\nu'} = E_{\nu_0}$ is not usually a singularity of the integrand; the manner of integrating with respect to $E_{\nu'}$ is therefore unimportant in general, and the integral can be taken along the real axis.

The states ν' for which $V_{\nu\nu'}$ and $V_{\nu'\nu_0}$ are not zero are usually called *intermediate* states for the transition $\nu_0 \rightarrow \nu$. It may happen that the transition $\nu_0 \rightarrow \nu$ can take place not through one but only through several successive intermediate states. Formula (43.6) can be at once generalised to such cases. Thus, if two intermediate states are needed, we have

$$dw_{\nu_0\nu} = \frac{2\pi}{\hbar}\left|\int\int \frac{V_{\nu\nu''}V_{\nu''\nu'}V_{\nu'\nu_0}}{(E_{\nu_0}-E_{\nu''})(E_{\nu_0}-E_{\nu'})}\,d\nu'd\nu''\right|^2 \delta(E_\nu - E_{\nu_0})\,d\nu. \tag{43.7}$$

§44. The uncertainty relation for energy

Let us consider a system composed of two weakly interacting parts. We suppose that it is known that at some instant these parts have definite values of the energy, which we denote by E and ϵ respectively. Let the energy be measured again after some time interval Δt; the values E', ϵ' obtained are in general different from E, ϵ. It is easy to determine the order of magnitude of the most probable value of the difference $E'+\epsilon'-E-\epsilon$ which is found as a result of the measurement.

According to formula (42.3) with $\omega = 0$, the probability of a transition of the system (after time t), under the action of a time-independent perturbation, from a state with energy E to one with energy E' is proportional to

$$\sin^2[(E'-E)t/2\hbar]/(E'-E)^2.$$

Hence we see that the most probable value of the difference $E'-E$ is of the order of $\hbar/t$.

Applying this result to the case we are considering (the perturbation being the interaction between the parts of the system), we obtain the relation

$$|E+\epsilon-E'-\epsilon'|\Delta t \sim \hbar. \tag{44.1}$$

Thus the smaller the time interval Δt, the greater the energy change that is observed. It is important to notice that its order of magnitude $\hbar/\Delta t$ is independent of the amount of the perturbation. The energy change determined by the relation (44.1) will be observed, however weak the interaction between the two parts of the system. This result is peculiar to quantum theory and has a deep physical significance. It shows that, in quantum mechanics, the law of conservation of energy can be verified by means of two measurements only to an accuracy of the order of $\hbar/\Delta t$, where Δt is the time interval between the measurements.

The relation (44.1) is often called the *uncertainty relation for energy*. However, it must be emphasised that its significance is entirely different from that of the uncertainty relation $\Delta p \Delta x \sim \hbar$ for the co-ordinate and momentum. In the latter, Δp and Δx are the uncertainties in the values of the momentum and co-ordinate at the same instant; they show that these two quantities can never have entirely definite values simultaneously. The energies E, ϵ, on the other hand, can be measured to any degree of accuracy at any instant. The quantity $(E+\epsilon)-(E'+\epsilon')$ in (44.1) is the difference between two exactly measured values of the energy $E+\epsilon$ at two different instants, and not the uncertainty in the value of the energy at a given instant. The discovery of the physical significance of the uncertainty relation for energy, as well as the following analysis, is due to N. Bohr (1928).

If we regard E as the energy of some system and ϵ as that of a "measuring apparatus", we can say that the energy of interaction between them can be taken into account only to within $\hbar/\Delta t$. Let us denote by ΔE, $\Delta\epsilon$, ... the errors in the measurements of the corresponding quantities. In the favourable case when ϵ, ϵ' are known exactly ($\Delta\epsilon = \Delta\epsilon' = 0$), we have

$$\Delta(E-E') \sim \hbar/\Delta t. \tag{44.2}$$

From this relation we can derive important consequences concerning the measurement of momentum. The process of measuring the momentum of a particle (for definiteness, we shall speak of an electron) consists in a collision of the electron with some other ("measuring") particle, whose momenta before and after the collision can be regarded as known exactly.† If we apply to this collision the law of conservation of momentum, we obtain three equations (the three components of a single vector equation) in six unknowns (the components of the momentum of the electron before and after the collision). The number of equations can be increased by bringing about a series of further collisions between the electron and "measuring" particles, and applying to each collision the law of conservation of momentum. This, however, increases the number of unknowns also (the momenta of the electron between collisions), and it is easy to see that, whatever the number of collisions, the number of unknowns will always be three more than the number of equations. Hence, in order to measure the momentum of the electron, it is necessary to bring in the law of conservation of energy at each collision, as well as that of momentum. The former, however, can be applied, as we have seen, only to an accuracy of the order of $\hbar/\Delta t$, where Δt is the time between the beginning and end of the process in question.

To simplify the subsequent discussion, it is convenient to consider an imaginary idealised experiment in which the "measuring particle" is a

† In the present analysis it is of no importance how the energy of the "measuring" particle is ascertained.

perfectly reflecting plane mirror; only one momentum component is then of importance, namely that perpendicular to the plane of the mirror. To determine the momentum P of the particle, the laws of conservation of momentum and energy give the equations

$$p'+P'-p-P = 0, \tag{44.3}$$

$$|\epsilon'+E'+\epsilon-E| \sim \hbar/\Delta t, \tag{44.4}$$

where P, E are the momentum and energy of the particle, and p, ϵ those of the mirror; the unprimed and primed quantities refer to the instants before and after the collision respectively. The quantities p, p', ϵ, ϵ' relating to the "measuring particle" can be regarded as known exactly, i.e. the errors in them are zero. Then we have for the errors in the remaining quantities, from the above equations:

$$\Delta P = \Delta P', \quad \Delta E'-\Delta E \sim \hbar/\Delta t.$$

But $\Delta E = (\partial E/\partial P)\Delta P = v\Delta P$, where v is the velocity of the electron (before the collision), and similarly $\Delta E' = v'\Delta P' = v'\Delta P$. Hence we obtain

$$(v'_x-v_x)\Delta P_x \sim \hbar/\Delta t. \tag{44.5}$$

We have here added the suffix x to the velocity and momentum, in order to emphasise that this relation holds for each of their components separately.

This is the required relation. It shows that the measurement of the momentum of the electron (with a given degree of accuracy ΔP) necessarily involves a change in its velocity (i.e. in the momentum itself). This change is the greater, the shorter the duration of the measuring process. The change in velocity can be made arbitrarily small only as $\Delta t \to \infty$, but measurements of momentum occupying a long time can be significant only for a free particle. The non-repeatability of a measurement of momentum after short intervals of time, and the "two-faced" nature of measurement in quantum mechanics—the necessity of a sharp distinction between the measured value of a quantity and the value resulting from the process of measurement—are here exhibited with particular clarity.

The conclusion reached at the beginning of this section, which was based on perturbation theory, can also be derived from another standpoint by considering the decay of a system under the action of some perturbation. Let E_0 be some energy level of the system, calculated without any allowance for the possibility of its decay. We denote by τ the *lifetime* of this state of the system, i.e. the reciprocal of the probability of decay per unit time. Then we find by the same method that

$$|E_0-E-\epsilon| \sim \hbar/\tau, \tag{44.6}$$

where E, ϵ are the energies of the two parts into which the system decays. The sum $E+\epsilon$, however, gives us an estimate of the energy of the system before it decays. Hence the above relation shows that the energy of a system, in some "quasi-stationary" state, which is free to decay can be determined only to within a quantity of the order of $\hbar/\tau$. This quantity is usually called the *width* Γ of the level. Thus

$$\Gamma \sim \hbar/\tau. \tag{44.7}$$

§45. Potential energy as a perturbation

The case where the total potential energy of the particle in an external field can be regarded as a perturbation merits special consideration. The unperturbed SCHRÖDINGER's equation is then the equation of free motion of the particle:

$$\Delta\psi^{(0)}+k^2\psi^{(0)} = 0, \qquad k = \sqrt{(2\mu E/\hbar^2)} = p/\hbar, \tag{45.1}$$

and has solutions which represent plane waves. The energy spectrum of free motion is continuous, so that we are concerned with an unusual case of perturbation theory in a continuous spectrum. The solution of the problem is here more conveniently obtained directly, without having recourse to general formulae.

The equation for the correction $\psi^{(1)}$ to the wave function in the first approximation is

$$\Delta\psi^{(1)}+k^2\psi^{(1)} = (2\mu U/\hbar^2)\psi^{(0)}, \tag{45.2}$$

where U is the potential energy. The solution of this equation, as we know from electrodynamics, can be written in the form of *retarded potentials*, i.e. in the form†

$$\psi^{(1)}(x,y,z) = -(\mu/2\pi\hbar^2)\int \psi^{(0)}U(x',y',z')e^{ikR}\,\mathrm{d}V'/R, \tag{45.3}$$

where

$$\mathrm{d}V' = \mathrm{d}x'\mathrm{d}y'\mathrm{d}z', \quad R^2 = (x-x')^2+(y-y')^2+(z-z')^2.$$

Let us find what conditions must be satisfied by the field U in order that it may be regarded as a perturbation. The condition of applicability of perturbation theory is contained in the requirement that $\psi^{(1)} \ll \psi^{(0)}$. Let a be the order of magnitude of the dimensions of the region of space in which the field is noticeably different from zero. We shall first suppose that the energy of the particle is so small that ak is at most of the order of unity. Then the factor e^{ikR} in the integrand of (45.3) is unimportant in an order-of-magnitude estimate, and the integral is of the order of $|\psi^{(0)}|Ua^2$, so that

$$\psi^{(1)} \sim \mu|U|a^2\psi^{(0)}/\hbar^2,$$

† This is a particular integral of equation (45.2), to which we may add any solution of the same equation with zero on the right-hand side, i.e. the unperturbed equation (45.1).

and we have the condition

$$|U| \ll \hbar^2/\mu a^2 \qquad \text{(for } ka \gtrsim 1\text{)}. \tag{45.4}$$

We notice that the expression on the right has a simple physical meaning; it is the order of magnitude of the kinetic energy which the particle would have if enclosed in a volume of linear dimensions a (since, by the uncertainty relation, its momentum would be of the order of $\hbar/a$).

Let us consider, in particular, a potential well so shallow that the condition (45.4) holds for it. It is easy to see that in such a well there are no negative energy levels (R. Peierls 1929); this has been shown, for the particular case of a spherically symmetric well, in §33, Problem. For, when $E = 0$, the unperturbed wave function reduces to a constant, which can be arbitrarily taken as unity: $\psi^{(0)} = 1$. Since $\psi^{(1)} \ll \psi^{(0)}$, it is clear that the wave function $\psi = 1+\psi^{(1)}$ for motion in the well nowhere vanishes; the eigenfunction, being without nodes, belongs to the normal state, so that $E = 0$ remains the least possible value of the energy of the particle. Thus, if the well is sufficiently shallow, only an infinite motion of the particle is possible: the particle cannot be "captured" by the well. Attention must be paid to the fact that this result is peculiar to quantum theory; in classical mechanics a particle can execute a finite motion in any potential well.

It must be emphasised that all that has been said refers only to a three-dimensional well. In a one- or two-dimensional well (i.e. one in which the field is a function of only one or two co-ordinates), there are always negative energy levels (see the Problems at the end of this section). This is related to the fact that, in the one- and two-dimensional cases, the perturbation theory under consideration is inapplicable for an energy E which is zero (or very small).†

For large energies, when $ka \gg 1$, the factor e^{ikr} in the integrand plays an important part, and markedly reduces the value of the integral. The solution (45.3) in this case can be transformed; the alternative form, however, is more conveniently derived by returning to equation (45.2). We take as x-axis the direction of the unperturbed motion; the unperturbed wave function then has the form $\psi^{(0)} = e^{ikx}$ (the constant factor is arbitrarily taken as unity). Let us seek a solution of the equation

$$\Delta\psi^{(1)}+k^2\psi^{(1)} = (2\mu/\hbar^2)Ue^{ikx}$$

in the form $\psi^{(1)} = e^{ikx}f$; in view of the assumed large value of k, it is sufficient to retain in $\Delta\psi^{(1)}$ only those terms in which the factor e^{ikx} is differentiated one or more times. We then obtain for f the equation

$$2ik\, \partial f/\partial x = 2\mu U/\hbar^2,$$

† In the two-dimensional case $\psi^{(1)}$ is expressed (as is known from the theory of the two-dimensional wave equation) as an integral similar to (45.3), in which, instead of $e^{ikR}\,dx'dy'dz'/R$, we have $i\pi H_0^{(1)}(kR)\,dx'dy'$, where $H_0^{(1)}$ is the Hankel function of the first kind, of zero order, and $R^2 = (x-x')^2+(y-y')^2$. As $k\to 0$, the Hankel function, and therefore the whole integral, tends logarithmically to infinity.

Similarly, in the one-dimensional case, we have, in the integrand, $2\pi i e^{ikR}\,dx'/k$, where $R = |x-x'|$, and as $k\to 0$ $\psi^{(1)}$ tends to infinity as $1/k$.

whence

$$\psi^{(1)} = e^{ikx}f = -(i\mu/\hbar^2 k)e^{ikx}\int U\,\mathrm{d}x. \tag{45.5}$$

An estimation of this integral gives $|\psi^{(1)}| \sim \mu Ua/\hbar^2 k$, so that the condition of applicability of perturbation theory in this case is

$$|U| \ll (\hbar^2/\mu a^2)ka = \hbar v/a \qquad (ka \gg 1), \tag{45.6}$$

where $v = k\hbar/\mu$ is the velocity of the particle. It is to be observed that this condition is weaker than (45.4). Hence, if the field can be regarded as a perturbation at small energies of the particle, it can always be so regarded at large energies, whereas the converse is not necessarily true.

The applicability of the perturbation theory developed here to a Coulomb field requires special consideration. In a field where $U = \alpha/r$, it is impossible to separate a finite region of space outside which U is considerably less than inside it. The required condition can be obtained by writing in (45.6) a variable distance r instead of the parameter a; this leads to the inequality

$$\alpha/\hbar v \ll 1. \tag{45.7}$$

Thus, for large energies of the particle, a Coulomb field can be regarded as a perturbation.†

Finally, we shall derive a formula useful in the solution of several problems, which approximately determines the wave function of a particle whose energy E everywhere considerably exceeds the potential energy U (no other conditions being imposed). In the first approximation, the wave function depends on the co-ordinates in the same way as for free motion (whose direction is taken as the x-axis). Accordingly, let us look for ψ in the form $\psi = e^{ikx}F$, where F is a function of the co-ordinates which varies slowly in comparison with the factor e^{ikx} (but we cannot in general say that it is close to unity). Substituting in Schrödinger's equation, we obtain for F the equation

$$2ik\,\partial F/\partial x = (2\mu/\hbar^2)UF,$$

whence

$$\psi = e^{ikx}F = \text{constant} \times e^{ikx}e^{-i\int(U/\hbar v)\mathrm{d}x}. \tag{45.8}$$

This is the required expression.

PROBLEMS

Problem 1. Determine the energy level in a one-dimensional potential well whose depth is small. It is assumed that the condition (45.4) is satisfied, and that the integral $\int_{-\infty}^{\infty} U\,\mathrm{d}x$ converges.

Solution. We make the hypothesis, which will be confirmed by the result, that the energy level $|E| \ll |U|$. Then, on the right-hand side of Schrödinger's equation

$$\mathrm{d}^2\psi/\mathrm{d}x^2 = (2\mu/\hbar^2)[U(x)-E]\psi,$$

† It must be borne in mind that the integral (45.5) with a field $U = \alpha/r$ diverges (logarithmically) when $x/\sqrt{(y^2+z^2)}$ is large. Hence the wave function in a Coulomb field, obtained by means of perturbation theory, is inapplicable within a narrow cone about the x-axis.

we can neglect E in the region of the well, and regard ψ as a constant, which without loss of generality can be taken as unity:

$$d^2\psi/dx^2 = 2\mu U/\hbar^2.$$

We integrate this equation with respect to x between two points $\pm x_1$ such that $a \ll x_1 \ll 1/\kappa$, where a is the width of the well and $\kappa = \sqrt{(2\mu|E|/\hbar^2)}$. Since the integral of $U(x)$ converges, the integration on the right can be extended to the whole range from $-\infty$ to $+\infty$:

$$\left[\frac{d\psi}{dx}\right]_{-x_1}^{x_1} = \frac{2\mu}{\hbar^2}\int_{-\infty}^{\infty} U\,dx. \tag{1}$$

At large distances from the well, the wave function is of the form $\psi = e^{\pm\kappa x}$. Substituting this in (1), we find

$$-2\kappa = (2\mu/\hbar^2)\int_{-\infty}^{\infty} U\,dx$$

$$|E| = (\mu/2\hbar^2)[\int_{-\infty}^{\infty} U\,dx]^2.$$

We see that, in accordance with the hypothesis, the energy of the level is a small quantity of a higher order (the second) than the depth of the well.

PROBLEM 2. Determine the energy level in a two-dimensional potential well $U = U(r)$ (where r is the radius vector in polar co-ordinates in the plane) of small depth; it is assumed that the integral $\int_0^\infty rU\,dr$ converges.

SOLUTION. Proceeding as in the previous problem, we have in the region of the well the equation

$$\frac{1}{r}\frac{d}{dr}\left(r\frac{d\psi}{dr}\right) = \frac{2\mu}{\hbar^2}U.$$

Integrating this with respect to r from 0 to r_1 (where $a \ll r_1 \ll 1/\kappa$), we find

$$\left[\frac{d\psi}{dr}\right]_{r=r_1} = \frac{2\mu}{\hbar^2 r_1}\int_0^{\infty} rU(r)\,dr. \tag{1}$$

At large distances from the well, the equation of free motion in two dimensions is

$$\frac{1}{r}\frac{d}{dr}\left(r\frac{d\psi}{dr}\right)+\frac{2\mu}{\hbar^2}E\psi = 0,$$

and has a solution (vanishing at infinity) $\psi = \text{constant}\times H_0^{(1)}(i\kappa r)$, where $H_0^{(1)}$ is the Hankel function of the first kind, of zero order; for small values of the argument, the leading term in $H_0^{(1)}$ is proportional to $\log \kappa r$. Bearing this in mind, we equate the logarithmic derivatives of ψ for $r \sim a$ inside the well (the right-hand side of (1)) and outside it, obtaining

$$\frac{1}{a\log \kappa a} \cong \frac{2\mu}{\hbar^2 a}\int_0^{\infty} U(r)r\,dr,$$

whence

$$|E| \sim \frac{\hbar^2}{\mu a^2}\exp\left\{-\frac{\hbar^2}{\mu}[\int_0^{\infty} |U|r\,dr]^{-1}\right\}.$$

We see that the energy of the level is exponentially small compared with the depth of the well.

CHAPTER VII

THE QUASI-CLASSICAL CASE

§46. The wave function in the quasi-classical case

If the de Broglie wavelengths of particles are small in comparison with the characteristic dimensions which determine the conditions of a given problem, then the properties of the system are close to being classical,† just as wave optics passes into geometrical optics as the wavelength tends to zero.

Let us now investigate more closely the properties of "quasi-classical" systems. To do this, we make in Schrödinger's equation

$$\sum_a \frac{\hbar^2}{2\mu_a}\Delta_a\psi+(E-U)\psi = 0$$

the substitution

$$\psi = e^{(i/\hbar)\sigma}. \tag{46.1}$$

For the function σ we obtain the equation

$$\sum_a \frac{1}{2\mu_a}(\nabla_a\sigma)^2-\sum_a \frac{i\hbar}{2\mu_a}\Delta_a\sigma = E-U. \tag{46.2}$$

Since the system is supposed almost classical in its properties, we seek σ in the form of a series:

$$\sigma = \sigma_0+(\hbar/i)\sigma_1+(\hbar/i)^2\sigma_2+\ldots, \tag{46.3}$$

expanded in powers of $\hbar$.

We begin by considering the simplest case, that of one-dimensional motion of a single particle. Equation (46.2) then reduces to

$$\sigma'^2/2\mu-i\hbar\sigma''/2\mu = E-U(x), \tag{46.4}$$

where the prime denotes differentiation with respect to the co-ordinate x.

In the first approximation we write $\sigma = \sigma_0$ and omit from the equation the term containing $\hbar$:

$$\sigma_0'^2/2\mu = E-U(x).$$

† We may point out, in particular, that the states of the discrete spectrum with large values of the quantum number n are quasi-classical. For the number n (the ordinal number of the state) determines the number of nodes of the eigenfunction (see §19). The distance between adjoining nodes, however, is of the same order of magnitude as the de Broglie wavelength. For large n this distance is small, so that the wavelength is small in comparison with the dimensions of the region of motion.

Hence we find

$$\sigma_0 = \pm \int \sqrt{\{2\mu[E-U(x)]\}}\, dx.$$

The integrand is simply the classical momentum $p(x)$ of the particle, expressed as a function of the co-ordinate. Defining the function $p(x)$ with the + sign in front of the radical, we have

$$\sigma_0 = \pm \int p\, dx, \quad p = \sqrt{[2\mu(E-U)]}, \tag{46.5}$$

as we should expect from the limiting expression (6.1) for the wave function.† The approximation made in equation (46.4) is legitimate only if the second term on the left-hand side is small compared with the first, i.e. we must have $\hbar|\sigma''/\sigma'^2| \ll 1$ or

$$|d(\hbar/\sigma')/dx| \ll 1.$$

In the first approximation we have, according to (46.5), $\sigma' = p$, so that the condition obtained can be written

$$|d(\lambda/2\pi)/dx| \ll 1, \tag{46.6}$$

where $\lambda(x) = 2\pi\hbar/p(x)$ is the de Broglie wavelength of the particle, expressed as a function of x by means of the classical function $p(x)$. Thus we have obtained a quantitative "quasi-classical" condition: the wavelength of the particle must vary only slightly over distances of the order of itself. The formulae here derived are not applicable in regions of space where this condition is not satisfied.

The condition (46.6) can be written in another form by noticing that

$$\frac{dp}{dx} = \frac{d}{dx}\sqrt{[2\mu(E-U)]} = -\frac{\mu}{p}\frac{dU}{dx} = \frac{\mu F}{p},$$

where $F = -dU/dx$ is the classical force acting on the particle in the external field. In terms of this force we find

$$\mu\hbar F/p^3 \ll 1. \tag{46.7}$$

It is seen from this that the quasi-classical approximation becomes inapplicable if the momentum of the particle is too small. In particular, it is clearly inapplicable near *turning points*, i.e. near points where the particle, according to classical mechanics, would stop and begin to move in the opposite direction. These points are given by the equation $p(x) = 0$, i.e. $E = U(x)$. This fact has a simple and clear significance: as $p \to 0$, the de Broglie wavelength tends to infinity, and hence cannot possibly be supposed small.

† As is well known, $\int p\, dx$ is the time-independent part of the action. The total mechanical action S of a particle is $S = -Et \pm \int p\, dx$. The term $-Et$ is absent from σ_0, since we are considering a time-independent wave function ψ.

Let us now calculate the next term in the expansion (46.3). The first-order terms in $\hbar$ in equation (46.4) give

$$\sigma_0'\sigma_1'+\tfrac{1}{2}\sigma_0'' = 0,$$

whence

$$\sigma_1' = -\sigma_0''/2\sigma_0' = -p'/2p.$$

Integrating, we find

$$\sigma_1 = -\tfrac{1}{2}\log p, \tag{46.8}$$

omitting the constant of integration.

Substituting this expression in (46.1) and (46.3), we find the wave function in the form

$$\psi = C_1 p^{-\frac{1}{2}} e^{(i/\hbar)\int p\,dx} + C_2 p^{-\frac{1}{2}} e^{-(i/\hbar)\int p\,dx}. \tag{46.9}$$

The subsequent terms in the expansion (46.3) lead to the appearance, in the coefficients of the exponentials, of terms in the first and higher powers of $\hbar$; it is not usually necessary to calculate these terms.

The presence of the factor $1/\sqrt{p}$ in the wave function has a simple interpretation. The probability of finding the particle at a point with co-ordinate between x and $x+dx$ is given by the square $|\psi|^2$, i.e. is essentially proportional to $1/p$. This is exactly what we should expect for a "quasi-classical" particle, since, in classical motion, the time spent by a particle in the segment dx is inversely proportional to the velocity (or momentum) of the particle.

In the "classically inaccessible" parts of space, where $E < U(x)$, the function $p(x)$ is purely imaginary, so that the exponents are real. The wave function in these regions can be written in the form

$$\psi = \frac{C_1'}{\sqrt{|p|}} e^{-(1/\hbar)\int |p|\,dx} + \frac{C_2'}{\sqrt{|p|}} e^{(1/\hbar)\int |p|\,dx}. \tag{46.10}$$

PROBLEM

Determine the wave function in the quasi-classical approximation up to terms of the order of $\hbar$ in the coefficient of the exponent.

SOLUTION. The terms of order $\hbar^2$ in equation (46.4) give

$$\sigma_0'\sigma_2'+\tfrac{1}{2}\sigma_1'^2+\tfrac{1}{2}\sigma_1'' = 0,$$

whence (substituting (46.5) and (46.8) for σ_0 and σ_1)

$$\sigma_2' = p''/4p^2-3p'^2/8p^3.$$

Integrating (by parts in the first term) and introducing the force $F = pp'/\mu$, we obtain

$$\sigma_2 = \tfrac{1}{4}\mu F/p^3+\tfrac{1}{8}\mu^2 \int (F^2/p^5)\,dx.$$

The wave function in this approximation is of the form

$$\psi = e^{(i/\hbar)\sigma} = e^{(i/\hbar)\sigma_0+\sigma_1}(1-i\hbar\sigma_2)$$

or

$$\psi = \frac{\text{constant}}{\sqrt{p}}\left[1-\tfrac{1}{4}i\mu\hbar F/p^3-\tfrac{1}{8}i\hbar\mu^2\int (F^2/p^5)\,dx\right]e^{(i/\hbar)\int p\,dx}.$$

§47. Boundary conditions in the quasi-classical case

Let $x = a$ be a turning point (so that $U(a) = E$); we assume that the potential energy curve is such that $U(x) > E$ for all $x < a$. Then the motion will always be finite in the direction where $x-a$ is negative. As we know, the states of a one-dimensional motion finite in even one direction are not degenerate (§19). The wave functions of non-degenerate states, however, must be real (apart from the unimportant phase factor). In the quasi-classical case a real linear combination (46.9) must be taken. We write it

$$\psi = \frac{C}{\sqrt{p}}\sin\left(\frac{1}{\hbar}\int_a^x p\,dx+\alpha\right), \tag{47.1}$$

where α is some constant. We determine this constant from the requirement that, for small $x-a$, where the quasi-classical approximation becomes inapplicable, the function (47.1) should become a solution of the exact SCHRÖDINGER's equation vanishing as $x \to -\infty$ (H. KRAMERS 1926).

To investigate the true form of the wave function near the turning point, we can expand $U(x)$ in powers of $q \equiv x-a$, and in view of the smallness of q it is sufficient to restrict ourselves to the linear form

$$U(q) = E-F_0q \tag{47.2}$$

(we have substituted $U(0) = E$ and introduced the notation

$$F_0 = [-\partial U/\partial q]_{q=0}).$$

SCHRÖDINGER's equation becomes

$$d^2\psi/dq^2+(2\mu/\hbar^2)F_0q\psi = 0.$$

This, however, is just equation (22.1), which we encountered in studying motion in a homogeneous field (in (22.1) we must put $E = 0$); its solution is given by formula (22.4).

Let us consider values of q which, on the one hand, are so small that the expansion (47.2) can be used but, on the other hand, are so large that the asymptotic form (22.6) of the function (22.4) can be used; such values of q always exist if the motion is quasi-classical almost everywhere in the region, as we assume it to be. Substituting in (22.6) the expression for ξ, we can write the wave function in the form

$$\psi = C(2\mu F_0 q)^{-\frac{1}{4}} \sin[\tfrac{2}{3}\sqrt{(2\mu F_0/\hbar^2)} q^{3/2} + \tfrac{1}{4}\pi].$$

In classical motion in a field with potential energy (47.2), the momentum of the particle is

$$p = \sqrt{[2\mu(E-U)]} = \sqrt{(2\mu F_0 q)},$$

and the action is

$$\int_a^x p\, dx = \int_0^q p\, dq = \sqrt{(2\mu F_0)} \int_0^q \sqrt{q}\, dq$$

$$= \tfrac{2}{3}\sqrt{(2\mu F_0)} q^{3/2}.$$

Hence the wave function just obtained can be written in the form

$$\psi = \frac{C}{\sqrt{p}} \sin\left(\frac{1}{\hbar}\int_a^x p\, dx + \tfrac{1}{4}\pi\right)$$

$$= \frac{C}{\sqrt{p}} \cos\left(\frac{1}{\hbar}\int_a^x p\, dx - \tfrac{1}{4}\pi\right). \qquad (47.3)$$

Comparing this function with the quasi-classical function (47.1), we see that they are the same if the constant α in the latter is suitably chosen. Thus the function (47.3) is the required quasi-classical wave function of one-dimensional motion in the region to the right of the turning point (i.e. where $U(x) < E$).†

If the region where $U(x) < E$ lay to the left of the turning point $x = b$, we should have to write

$$\psi = \frac{C}{\sqrt{p}} \sin\left(\frac{1}{\hbar}\int_x^b p\, dx + \tfrac{1}{4}\pi\right)$$

$$= \frac{C}{\sqrt{p}} \cos\left(\frac{1}{\hbar}\int_b^x p\, dx + \tfrac{1}{4}\pi\right). \qquad (47.4)$$

On the other side of the turning point (i.e. in the classically inaccessible

† It must be noticed that the choice of the constant phase in (47.3) is not really unique. Instead of $\frac{1}{4}\pi$ we could put any other number $\frac{1}{4}\pi + n\pi$, where n is an integer. This change of phase either leaves the function ψ unchanged or reverses its sign; the sign of the wave function, however, is physically immaterial.

region where $U > E$), the wave function must diminish as $|q|$ increases. Rejecting the term in the general formula (46.10) which increases without limit, we can write the real wave function for $x < a$ in the form

$$\psi = \frac{C'}{\sqrt{|p|}} \exp\left[-\frac{1}{\hbar}\left|\int_a^x p \, dx\right|\right].$$

In order to bring this function into agreement with the function (47.3) to the right of the turning point,† we must compare it with the asymptotic expression (22.5) for the exact wave function near the turning point. From this comparison we conclude that we must put $C' = \frac{1}{2}C$, where C is the normalisation constant in the function (47.3). Thus the quasi-classical wave function for $x < a$ is of the form

$$\psi = \frac{C}{2\sqrt{|p|}} \exp\left[-\frac{1}{\hbar}\left|\int_a^x p \, dx\right|\right]. \tag{47.5}$$

A different value of the phase is obtained in the case where the classically accessible region of motion is bounded (at $x = a$) by an infinitely high "potential wall". The boundary condition for the wave function at $x = a$ is then $\psi = 0$ (§16). Accordingly, we must take α zero in the quasi-classical function (47.1), so that

$$\begin{aligned} &\text{for } x > a, \quad \psi = \frac{C}{\sqrt{p}} \sin \frac{1}{\hbar} \int_a^x p \, dx, \\ &\text{for } x < a, \quad \psi = 0. \end{aligned} \tag{47.6}$$

§48. Bohr's quantisation rule

The results which we have obtained enable us to derive the condition which determines the quantum energy levels in the quasi-classical case. To do this, we consider the motion in a region $a \leqslant x \leqslant b$ bounded by two turning points ($x = a$ and $x = b$), between which $U(x) < E$; we shall assume that $U(x) > E$ everywhere outside this region.‡ The motion is then finite, and the energy

† i.e. in order that these two functions should represent the approximate expressions, for $x < a$ and $x > a$, of the same exact solution of SCHRÖDINGER's equation.

‡ In classical mechanics, a particle in such a field would execute a periodic motion between the points $x = a$ and $x = b$, with period (time taken in moving from $x = a$ to $x = b$ and back)

$$T = 2\int_a^b dx/v = 2\mu \int_a^b dx/p,$$

where v is the velocity of the particle.

spectrum is accordingly discrete. The boundary condition at $x = a$ gives (in the region right of this point) the wave function (47.3):

$$\frac{C}{\sqrt{p}}\sin\left[\frac{1}{\hbar}\int_a^x p\,\mathrm{d}x+\tfrac{1}{4}\pi\right].$$

Applying formula (47.4) to the region left of the point $x = b$, we obtain the same function in the form

$$\frac{C'}{\sqrt{p}}\sin\left[\frac{1}{\hbar}\int_x^b p\,\mathrm{d}x+\tfrac{1}{4}\pi\right].$$

If these two expressions are the same throughout the region, the sum of their phases (which is a constant) must be an integral multiple of π:

$$\frac{1}{\hbar}\int_a^b p\,\mathrm{d}x+\tfrac{1}{2}\pi = (n+1)\pi,$$

with $C = (-1)^n C'$. Hence

$$\frac{1}{\hbar}\int_a^b p\,\mathrm{d}x = \pi(n+\tfrac{1}{2}),$$

or

$$\oint p\,\mathrm{d}x = 2\pi\hbar(n+\tfrac{1}{2}), \tag{48.1}$$

where $\oint p\,\mathrm{d}x = 2\int_a^b p\,\mathrm{d}x$ is the integral taken over the whole period of the quasi-classical motion of the particle (in this case, along the path from $x = a$ to $x = b$ and back). This is the condition which determines the stationary states of the particle in the quasi-classical case. It corresponds to BOHR's quantisation rule in the old quantum theory.

It is easy to see that the integer n is equal to the number of nodes of the wave function, and hence it is simply the ordinal number of the stationary state. For the phase

$$\frac{1}{\hbar}\int_a^x p\,\mathrm{d}x+\tfrac{1}{4}\pi$$

of the wave function increases from $\tfrac{1}{4}\pi$ at $x = a$ to $(n+\tfrac{3}{4})\pi$ at $x = b$, so that the sine vanishes n times in this range (outside the range $a \leqslant x \leqslant b$, the wave function decreases monotonically and has no zeros at a finite distance).

We recall, incidentally, that the quasi-classical approximation, and therefore the quantisation rule (48.1), are applicable only when n is large.†

In normalising these wave functions, the integration in the normalisation integral $\int |\psi|^2 \, dx$ can be restricted to the range $a \leqslant x \leqslant b$, since outside this range ψ decreases exponentially. Substituting (47.3), we have

$$C^2 \int_a^b \frac{dx}{p(x)} \sin^2\left[\frac{1}{\hbar}\int_a^x p \, dx + \tfrac{1}{4}\pi\right] = 1.$$

The argument of the sine is (in the quasi-classical case) a rapidly varying function; hence we can with sufficient accuracy replace the squared sine by its mean value, i.e. $\frac{1}{2}$. We then obtain

$$\tfrac{1}{2}C^2 \int_a^b \frac{dx}{p(x)} = 1.$$

Introducing the frequency $\omega = 2\pi/T$ of the classical periodic motion, where $T = 2\mu \int_a^b dx/p$ is its period, we have $C = \sqrt{(2\omega\mu/\pi)}$, i.e.

$$\psi = \sqrt{\frac{2\omega}{\pi v}} \sin\left[\frac{1}{\hbar}\int_a^x p \, dx + \tfrac{1}{4}\pi\right]. \qquad (48.2)$$

It must be recalled that the frequency ω is in general different for different levels, being a function of energy.

The relation (48.1) can also be interpreted in another manner. The integral $\oint p \, dx$ is the area enclosed by the closed classical phase trajectory of the particle (i.e. the curve in the px-plane, which is the phase space of the particle). Dividing this area into cells, each of area $2\pi\hbar$, we have n cells altogether; n, however, is the number of states with energies not exceeding the given value (corresponding to the phase trajectory considered). Thus we can say that, in the quasi-classical case, there corresponds to each quantum state a cell in phase space of area $2\pi\hbar$. In other words, the number of states belonging to the volume element $\Delta p \Delta x$ of phase space is

$$\Delta p \Delta x / 2\pi\hbar. \qquad (48.3)$$

If we introduce, instead of the momentum, the *wave number* $k = p/\hbar$, this number can be written

$$\Delta k \Delta x / 2\pi. \qquad (48.4)$$

† In some cases the exact expression for the energy levels $E(n)$ (as a function of the quantum number n), obtained from the exact SCHRÖDINGER's equation, is such that it retains its form as $n \to \infty$; examples are the energy levels in a Coulomb field, and those of a harmonic oscillator. In these cases, of course, BOHR's quantisation rule, although really applicable only for large n, gives for the function $E(n)$ an expression which is the exact one.

It is, as we should expect, the same as the familiar expression for the number of proper vibrations of a wave field.†

Starting from the quantisation rule (48.1), we can ascertain the general nature of the distribution of levels in the energy spectrum. Let ΔE be the distance between two neighbouring levels, i.e. levels whose quantum numbers n differ by unity. Since ΔE is small (for large n) compared with the energy itself of the levels, we can write, from (48.1),

$$\Delta E \oint (\partial p/\partial E)\,\mathrm{d}x = 2\pi\hbar.$$

But $\partial E/\partial p = v$, so that

$$\oint (\partial p/\partial E)\,\mathrm{d}x = \oint \mathrm{d}x/v = T.$$

Hence we have

$$\Delta E = 2\pi\hbar/T = \hbar\omega. \tag{48.5}$$

Thus the distance between two neighbouring levels is $\hbar\omega$. The frequencies ω may be regarded as approximately the same for several adjacent levels (the difference in whose numbers n is small compared with n itself). Hence we reach the conclusion that, in any small range of a quasi-classical part of the spectrum, the levels are equidistant, at intervals of $\hbar\omega$. This result could have been foreseen, since, in the quasi-classical case, the frequencies corresponding to transitions between different energy levels must be integral multiples of the classical frequency ω.

It is of interest to investigate what the matrix elements of any physical quantity f become in the limit of classical mechanics. To do this, we start from the fact that the mean value $\bar{f}$ in any quantum state must become, in the limit, simply the classical value of the quantity, provided that the state itself gives, in the limit, a motion of the particle in a definite path. A wave packet (see §6) corresponds to such a state; it is obtained by superposition of a number of stationary states with nearly the same energy. The wave function of such a state is of the form

$$\Psi = \sum_n a_n \Psi_n,$$

where the coefficients a_n are noticeably different from zero only in some range Δn of values of the quantum number n such that $1 \ll \Delta n \ll n$; the numbers n are supposed large, because the stationary states are quasi-classical. The mean value of f is, by definition,

$$\bar{f} = \int \Psi^* f \Psi\,\mathrm{d}x = \sum_n \sum_m a_m^* a_n f_{mn} e^{i\omega_{mn} t},$$

† See, for example, *The Classical Theory of Fields*, §6–9, Addison-Wesley Press, Cambridge (Mass.) 1951.

or, replacing the summation over n and m by a summation over n and the difference $m - n = s$,

$$\bar{f} = \sum_n \sum_s a_{n+s}{}^* a_n f_{n+s,n} e^{i\omega st},$$

where we have put $\omega_{mn} = s\omega$ in accordance with (48.5).

The matrix elements f_{nm} calculated by means of the quasi-classical wave functions decrease rapidly in magnitude as the difference $m-n$ increases, though at the same time they vary only slowly with n itself ($m-n$ being fixed). Hence we can write approximately

$$\bar{f} = \sum_n \sum_s a_n{}^* a_n f_s e^{i\omega st} = \sum_n |a_n|^2 \sum_s f_s e^{i\omega st},$$

where we have introduced the notation $f_s = f_{\bar{n}+s,\bar{n}}$, $\bar{n}$ being some mean value of the quantum number in the range Δn. But $\Sigma\, |a_n|^2 = 1$; hence

$$\bar{f} = \sum_s f_s e^{i\omega st}.$$

The sum obtained is in the form of an ordinary Fourier series. Since $\bar{f}$ must, in the limit, coincide with the classical quantity $f(t)$, we arrive at the result that the matrix elements f_{mn} in the limit become the components f_{m-n} in the expansion of the classical function $f(t)$ as a Fourier series.

Similarly, the matrix elements for transitions between states of the continuous spectrum become the components in the expansion of $f(t)$ as a Fourier integral. Here the wave functions of the stationary states must be normalised by $(1/\hbar)$ times the delta function of energy.

§49. Quasi-classical motion in a centrally symmetric field

In motion in a centrally symmetric field the wave function of a particle falls, as we know, into an angular and a radial part. Let us first consider the former.

The dependence of the angular wave function on the angle ϕ (determined by the quantum number m) is so simple that the question of finding approximate formulae for it does not arise. The dependence on the polar angle θ is, according to the general rule, quasi-classical if the corresponding quantum number l is large (this condition will be more precisely formulated below).

We shall here confine ourselves to deriving the quasi-classical expression for the angular function for the case (the most important one in applications) of states whose magnetic quantum number is zero ($m = 0$). This function is, apart from a constant factor, the Legendre polynomial $P_l(\cos\theta)$ (see (26.7)), and satisfies the differential equation

$$d^2P_l/d\theta^2 + \cot\theta\, dP_l/d\theta + l(l+1)P_l = 0. \tag{49.1}$$

The substitution

$$P_l(\cos\theta) = \chi(\theta)/\sqrt{\sin\theta} \tag{49.2}$$

reduces this to

$$\chi''+[(l+\tfrac{1}{2})^2+\tfrac{1}{4}\operatorname{cosec}^2\theta]\chi = 0, \tag{49.3}$$

which does not contain the first derivative and is similar in appearance to the one-dimensional SCHRÖDINGER's equation.

In equation (49.3), the part of the de Broglie wavelength is played by

$$\lambda = [(l+\tfrac{1}{2})^2+\tfrac{1}{4}\operatorname{cosec}^2\theta]^{-\frac{1}{2}}.$$

The requirement that the derivative $d\lambda/dx$ is small (the condition (46.6)) gives the inequalities

$$\theta l \gg 1, \qquad (\pi-\theta)l \gg 1, \tag{49.4}$$

which are the conditions that the angular part of the wave function is quasi-classical. For large l these conditions hold for almost all values of θ, excluding only a range of angles very close to 0 or π.

When the conditions (49.4) are satisfied, we can neglect the second term in the brackets in (49.3) compared with the first:

$$\chi''+(l+\tfrac{1}{2})^2\chi = 0.$$

The solution of this equation is

$$\chi = A\sin[(l+\tfrac{1}{2})\theta+\alpha],$$

where A and α are constants. Thus $P_l(\cos\theta)$ is approximately

$$P_l(\cos\theta) = A\frac{\sin[(l+\frac{1}{2})\theta+\alpha]}{\sqrt{\sin\theta}}. \tag{49.5}$$

The constants A and α can be determined as follows. For angles $\theta \ll 1$, we can put in equation (49.1) $\cot\theta \simeq 1/\theta$; replacing also $l(l+1)$ by the approximation $(l+\frac{1}{2})^2$, we obtain the equation

$$\frac{d^2P_l}{d\theta^2}+\frac{1}{\theta}\frac{dP_l}{d\theta}+(l+\tfrac{1}{2})^2P_l = 0,$$

which has as solution the Bessel function of zero order:

$$P_l(\cos\theta) = J_0[(l+\tfrac{1}{2})\theta], \quad \theta \ll 1. \tag{49.6}$$

The constant factor is put equal to unity, since we must have $P_l = 1$ for $\theta = 0$. The approximate expression (49.6) for P_l is valid for all angles $\theta \ll 1$. In particular, it can be applied for angles in the range $1/l \ll \theta \ll 1$, where it must agree with the expression (49.5), which holds for all $\theta \gg 1/l$. For $\theta l \gg 1$ the Bessel function can be replaced by its asymptotic expression for large values of the argument, and we obtain

$$P_l \approx \sqrt{\frac{2}{\pi l}}\frac{\sin[(l+\frac{1}{2})\theta+\frac{1}{4}\pi]}{\sqrt{\theta}}$$

(we can neglect $\frac{1}{2}$ in the coefficient compared with l). On comparison with (49.5), we find that $A = \sqrt{(2/\pi l)}$, $\alpha = \frac{1}{4}\pi$. Thus we obtain finally the following expression for $P_l(\cos\theta)$, applicable in the quasi-classical case:

$$P_l(\cos\theta) \cong \sqrt{\frac{2}{\pi l}}\frac{\sin[(l+\frac{1}{2})\theta+\frac{1}{4}\pi]}{\sqrt{\sin\theta}}. \tag{49.6a}$$

The normalised wave function Θ_{l0} is obtained, according to (26.7), by multiplying by $\sqrt{(l+\frac{1}{2})} \cong \sqrt{l}$:

$$\Theta_{l0}(\theta) \cong \sqrt{\frac{2}{\pi}}\frac{\sin[(l+\frac{1}{2})\theta+\frac{1}{4}\pi]}{\sqrt{\sin\theta}}. \tag{49.7}$$

Let us now turn to the radial part of the wave function. It has been shown in §32 that the function $\chi(r) = rR(r)$ satisfies an equation identical with the one-dimensional SCHRÖDINGER's equation, with the potential energy

$$U_l(r) = U(r)+\frac{\hbar^2}{2\mu}\frac{l(l+1)}{r^2}.$$

Hence we can apply the results obtained in the previous sections, if the potential energy is understood to be the function $U_l(r)$.

The case $l = 0$ is the simplest. The centrifugal energy vanishes and, if the field $U(r)$ satisfies the necessary condition (46.6), (46.7), the radial wave function will be quasi-classical in all space. For $r = 0$ we must have $\chi = 0$, and hence the quasi-classical function $\chi(r)$ is determined by formula (47.6) (with $a = 0$).

If $l \neq 0$, the centrifugal energy also must satisfy the condition (46.6). In the region of small r, where the centrifugal energy is of the same order as the total energy, the wavelength $\lambda = 2\pi\hbar/p \sim r/l$, and the condition (46.6) gives $l \gg 1$. Thus, if l is small, the quasi-classical condition is violated by the centrifugal energy in the region of small r. To calculate the quasi-classical wave function (it is assumed that the field $U(r)$ itself satisfies the quasi-classical condition), we can in the first approximation neglect the centrifugal energy entirely, as being proportional to $\hbar^2$. A better approximation is obtained, however, if the centrifugal energy is written in the form $\hbar^2 s^2/2\mu r^2$, the constant s being chosen so that, as $r \to \infty$, the quasi-classical wave function calculated by the usual rules has the correct phase.

To determine s, let us consider the simplest case, that of free motion. The quasi-classical wave function must, according to (47.3), be given by the formula

$$\chi(r) = \frac{C}{\sqrt{p}}\sin\frac{1}{\hbar}\left(\int_{r_0}^{r} p\,dr+\tfrac{1}{4}\pi\right),$$

where

$$p = \sqrt{[2\mu(E-\hbar^2 s^2/2\mu r^2)]} = \hbar\sqrt{(k^2-s^2/r^2)},$$

and $r_0 = s/k$. Its phase for large r is

$$\frac{1}{\hbar}\int_{r_0}^{r} p\,\mathrm{d}r+\tfrac{1}{4}\pi \cong kr-\tfrac{1}{2}s\pi+\tfrac{1}{4}\pi.$$

In order to obtain the correct value $kr-\frac{1}{2}l\pi$, we must put $s = l+\frac{1}{2}$.

Thus the quasi-classical radial wave function must be calculated from the formulae for the one-dimensional case, the momentum p being understood as the *radial momentum*

$$p_r = \sqrt{[2\mu\{E-U(r)-\hbar^2(l+\tfrac{1}{2})^2/2\mu r^2\}]}. \tag{49.8}$$

The question of the applicability of the quasi-classical approximation to a Coulomb field $U = \pm\alpha/r$ requires special consideration. The most important part of the whole region of the motion is that corresponding to distances r for which $|U(r)| \sim |E|$, i.e. $r \sim \alpha/|E|$. The condition for quasi-classical motion in this region amounts to the requirement that the wavelength $\lambda \sim \hbar/\sqrt{(2\mu|E|)}$ is small compared with the dimensions $r \sim \alpha/|E|$ of the region; this gives

$$|E| \ll \mu\alpha^2/\hbar^2, \tag{49.9}$$

i.e. the absolute value of the energy must be small compared with the energy of the particle in the first Bohr orbit. This condition can also be written in the form

$$\alpha/\hbar v \gg 1, \tag{49.10}$$

where $v \sim \sqrt{(|E|/\mu)}$ is the velocity of the particle. It should be noticed that this condition is the opposite of the condition (45.7) for the applicability of perturbation theory to a Coulomb field.

The region of small distances ($|U(r)| \gg E$) is without interest in a repulsive Coulomb field, since for $U > E$ the quasi-classical wave functions diminish exponentially. In an attractive field, however, when l is small it is possible for the particle to penetrate into the region where $|U| \gg E$, so that we have to consider the limits of applicability of the quasi-classical approximation in this case. We use the general condition (46.7), putting there

$$F = -\mathrm{d}U/\mathrm{d}r = \alpha/r^2, \quad p \cong \sqrt{(2\mu|U|)} \sim \sqrt{(\mu\alpha/r)}.$$

As a result, we find that the region of applicability of the quasi-classical approximation is restricted to distances such that

$$r \gg \hbar^2/\mu\alpha, \tag{49.11}$$

i.e. distances large in comparison with the "radius" of the first Bohr orbit.

PROBLEMS

PROBLEM 1. Calculate the quasi-classical wave functions in an attractive Coulomb field.

SOLUTION. In the discrete spectrum† $E = -1/2n^2$, and the radial momentum is

$$p_r = \sqrt{\left[-\frac{1}{n^2}+\frac{2}{r}-\frac{(l+\frac{1}{2})^2}{r^2}\right]}.$$

The region of classical motion ($p_r^2 > 0$) is $r_1 < r < r_2$, where

$$r_{1,2} = n^2 \mp n\sqrt{[n^2-(l+\tfrac{1}{2})^2]}.$$

The radial wave functions $R(r) = \chi(r)/r$ in this region are calculated from the formula

$$\chi(r) = \frac{C}{\sqrt{p_r}}\sin\Big[\int_{r_1}^{r} p_r\, dr+\tfrac{1}{4}\pi\Big].$$

Calculation gives

$$\chi_{nl} = C_n\left(\frac{2}{r}-\frac{1}{n^2}-\frac{(l+\frac{1}{2})^2}{r^2}\right)^{-\frac{1}{4}} \sin\Bigg[\sqrt{\left\{2r-\frac{r^2}{n^2}-(l+\tfrac{1}{2})^2\right\}}+ +n\sin^{-1}\frac{r-n^2}{n\sqrt{\{n^2-(l+\frac{1}{2})^2\}}}-(l+\tfrac{1}{2})\sin^{-1}\frac{n}{r}\frac{\{r-(l+\frac{1}{2})^2\}}{\sqrt{\{n^2-(l+\frac{1}{2})^2\}}}+\tfrac{1}{2}(n-l)\pi\Bigg]. \tag{1}$$

In calculating the normalisation integral, it is sufficient to integrate over the region between r_1 and r_2, since outside this region the wave functions decrease exponentially. Here the rapidly varying squared sine can be replaced by its mean value $\frac{1}{2}$, so that

$$\int_0^\infty \chi_{nl}^2\, dr \cong \tfrac{1}{2}C_n^2\int_{r_1}^{r_2} dr/p_r = \tfrac{1}{2}C_n^2\pi n^3 = 1,$$

whence

$$C_n = \sqrt{(2/\pi n^3)}. \tag{2}$$

In the continuous spectrum $E = \frac{1}{2}k^2$, and the region of classical motion is $r > r_1$, where

$$r_1 = -\frac{1}{k^2}+\frac{1}{k^2}\sqrt{[1+k^2(l+\tfrac{1}{2})^2]}.$$

The wave function in this region is of the form

$$\chi_{kl} = C_k\left(k^2+\frac{2}{r}-\frac{(l+\frac{1}{2})^2}{r^2}\right)^{-\frac{1}{4}} \sin\Bigg[\sqrt{\{k^2r^2+2r-(l+\tfrac{1}{2})^2\}}+ +\frac{1}{k}\cosh^{-1}\frac{k^2r+1}{\sqrt{\{1+k^2(l+\frac{1}{2})^2\}}}-(l+\tfrac{1}{2})\sin^{-1}\frac{r-(l+\frac{1}{2})^2}{r\sqrt{\{1+k^2(l+\frac{1}{2})^2\}}}-\tfrac{1}{2}l\pi\Bigg] \tag{3}$$

The normalisation coefficient can be chosen so that the asymptotic form of this function as $r \to \infty$ is the same as (36.23):‡

$$C_k = \sqrt{(2k/\pi)}.$$

---

† We are using Coulomb units.

‡ We note that, in the quasi-classical case, $1/k$ is large, and the quantity $\delta_l = \arg\Gamma(l+1-i/k)$ in (36.23) can be approximately calculated by means of Stirling's well-known asymptotic expression for the gamma function.

We note that, for $(l+\frac{1}{2})^2 \ll r \ll 1/k^2$, the function (3) becomes the same as (36.26), as it should.

PROBLEM 2. Determine the behaviour of the wave function near the origin, if the field becomes infinite as α/r^s, with $s > 2$, when $r \to 0$.

SOLUTION. For sufficiently small r, the de Broglie wavelength $\lambda \sim \hbar/\sqrt{(\mu|U|)} \sim \hbar r^{\frac{1}{2}s}/\sqrt{(\mu|\alpha|)}$, so that $d\lambda/dr \sim \hbar r^{\frac{1}{2}s-1}/\sqrt{(\mu|\alpha|)} \ll 1$; thus the quasi-classical condition is satisfied. If $\alpha < 0$ (attractive field), $U \to -\infty$ when $r \to 0$. The region near the origin is in this case classically accessible, and the radial wave function $\chi \sim 1/\sqrt{p}$, whence

$$\psi \sim r^{\frac{1}{4}s-1}.$$

If $\alpha > 0$ (repulsive field), the region of small r is classically inaccessible. In this case the wave function tends exponentially to zero as $r \to 0$. Omitting the coefficient of the exponential function, we have

$$\psi \sim \exp\left[-\frac{1}{\hbar}\left|\int_{r_0}^{r} p\,dr\right|\right], \text{ or } \psi \sim \exp\left\{-\frac{2\sqrt{(2\mu\alpha)}}{(s-2)\hbar} r^{-(\frac{1}{2}s-1)}\right\}.$$

§50. Penetration through a potential barrier

Let us consider the motion of a particle in a field of the type shown in Fig. 14, characterised by the presence of a *potential barrier*, i.e. a region in which the potential energy $U(x)$ exceeds the total energy E of the particle.

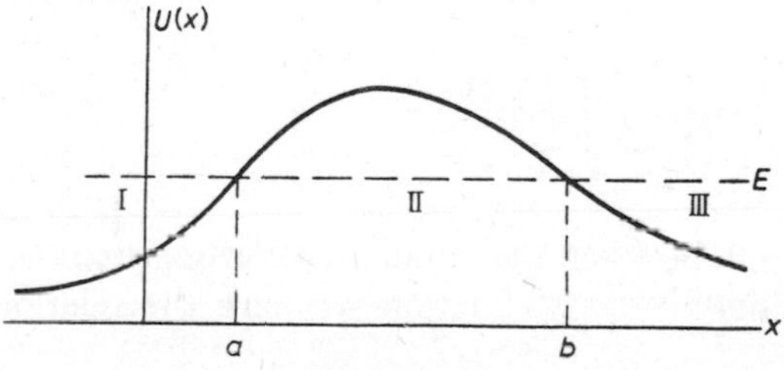

FIG. 14

In classical mechanics, a potential barrier is "impenetrable" to a particle; in quantum mechanics, however, a particle can pass "through the barrier": the probability of this is not zero (see also §23, Problem 2). If the field $U(x)$ satisfies the quasi-classical conditions, the transmission coefficient for the barrier can be calculated in a general form.† We may remark that, in particular, these conditions give the result that the barrier must be "wide", and hence the transmission coefficient is small in the quasi-classical case.

In order not to interrupt the subsequent calculations, we shall first solve

† If the energy E exceeds the height of the barrier, the particle can still be reflected from the barrier; the probability of this is also not zero, although the effect is again absent in classical mechanics. The calculation of the reflection coefficient "above the barrier" in the quasi-classical case requires the use of a special procedure evolved by A. B. MIGDAL and I. I. GOL'DMAN (*Soviet Physics JETP* 1, 304, 1955).

the following problem. Let the quasi-classical wave function in the region to the right of the turning point $x = b$ (where $U(x) < E$) have the form of a travelling wave:

$$\psi = \frac{C}{\sqrt{p}} \exp\left[\frac{i}{\hbar}\int_b^x p\,dx - \tfrac{1}{4}i\pi\right]. \tag{50.1}$$

We require to find the wave function of this state in the region† $x < b$. We shall seek it in the form

$$\psi = \frac{C'}{\sqrt{|p|}} \exp\left[\frac{1}{\hbar}\left|\int_b^x p\,dx\right|\right], \tag{50.2}$$

which increases as we go into the region $x < b$. The exponentially decreasing term is neglected in comparison with the increasing one. To determine the coefficient C' we proceed as follows. We notice that, according to formulae (47.3) and (47.5), there is a correspondence between the functions

$$\psi = \frac{1}{2\sqrt{p}}\left[\exp\left\{\frac{i}{\hbar}\int_b^x p\,dx - \tfrac{1}{4}i\pi\right\} + \exp\left\{-\frac{i}{\hbar}\int_b^x p\,dx + \tfrac{1}{4}i\pi\right\}\right] \text{ for } x > b,$$

$$\psi = \frac{1}{2\sqrt{|p|}} \exp\left\{-\frac{1}{\hbar}\left|\int_b^x p\,dx\right|\right\} \text{ for } x < b. \tag{50.3}$$

On the other hand, between two different exact solutions ψ_1 and ψ_2 of the one-dimensional SCHRÖDINGER's equation we have the relation (19.2)

$$\psi_1\psi_2' - \psi_2\psi_1' = \text{constant}.$$

We apply this relation with ψ_1 the solution given by formulae (50.1), (50.2), and ψ_2 the solution (50.3). To the left of the point $x = b$, we have

$$\psi_1\psi_2' - \psi_2\psi_1' = -\psi_2^2(\psi_1/\psi_2)' = C'/\hbar,$$

while to the right we have

$$\psi_1\psi_2' - \psi_2\psi_1' = \psi_1^2(\psi_2/\psi_1)' = -iC/\hbar.$$

Equating these two expressions, we obtain $C' = -iC$. Thus the required

† In the problem of penetration through a potential barrier, we are concerned with a motion infinite in both directions; the corresponding levels are doubly degenerate (see §19), and hence the wave functions need not be real.

quasi-classical wave function is of the form

$$\begin{aligned} &\text{for } x < b, \quad \psi = -\frac{iC}{\sqrt{|p|}} \exp\left\{\frac{1}{\hbar}\left|\int_b^x p\,\mathrm{d}x\right|\right\}, \\ &\text{for } x > b, \quad \psi = \frac{C}{\sqrt{p}} \exp\left\{\frac{i}{\hbar}\int_b^x p\,\mathrm{d}x - \tfrac{1}{4}i\pi\right\}. \end{aligned} \tag{50.4}$$

Let us now go on to calculate the coefficient for the penetration of the barrier by a particle. Let the particle be incident on the barrier from left to right. Since the probability of penetrating the barrier is small in the quasi-classical case, we can with sufficient accuracy write the wave function in region I (Fig. 14), in front of the barrier, the same as it would be in front of a completely impenetrable potential wall, i.e. in the form (47.4):

$$\psi = \frac{2}{\sqrt{v}} \cos\left[\frac{1}{\hbar}\int_a^x p\,\mathrm{d}x + \tfrac{1}{4}\pi\right], \tag{50.5}$$

where we have introduced the velocity $v = p/\mu$; see below regarding the choice of the normalisation coefficient. If this is written as the sum of two complex expressions,

$$\psi = \frac{1}{\sqrt{v}} \exp\left[\frac{i}{\hbar}\int_a^x p\,\mathrm{d}x + \tfrac{1}{4}i\pi\right] + \frac{1}{\sqrt{v}} \exp\left[-\frac{i}{\hbar}\int_a^x p\,\mathrm{d}x - \tfrac{1}{4}i\pi\right],$$

the first term (which becomes a plane wave $\psi \sim e^{(i/\hbar)px}$ as $x \to -\infty$) represents a particle incident on the barrier, and the second a particle reflected from the barrier. The normalisation chosen corresponds to a unit probability current density in the incident wave.

On the other side of the turning point $x = a$ (in region II, inside the barrier), the wave function (50.5) corresponds, according to the results of §47, to the function

$$\psi = \frac{1}{\sqrt{|v|}} \exp\left[-\frac{1}{\hbar}\left|\int_a^x p\,\mathrm{d}x\right|\right]. \tag{50.6}$$

Writing this in the form

$$\psi = \frac{1}{\sqrt{|v|}} \exp\left[-\frac{1}{\hbar}\left|\int_a^b p\,\mathrm{d}x\right| + \frac{1}{\hbar}\left|\int_b^x p\,\mathrm{d}x\right|\right], \tag{50.7}$$

and applying formula (50.4), we find the wave function in region III:

$$\psi = -\frac{1}{\sqrt{v}}\exp\left[-\frac{1}{\hbar}\left|\int_a^b p\,\mathrm{d}x\right|+\frac{i}{\hbar}\int_b^x p\,\mathrm{d}x+\tfrac{1}{4}i\pi\right]. \tag{50.8}$$

The current density in region III, calculated by means of this function, is

$$D = \exp\left[-\frac{2}{\hbar}\left|\int_a^b p\,\mathrm{d}x\right|\right]. \tag{50.9}$$

Since the current density in the wave incident on the barrier is taken as unity, D is in fact the required transmission coefficient for the barrier. We emphasise that this formula is applicable only when the exponent is large, so that D itself is small.

Let us suppose that a particle is in a potential well, bounded on one side by a quasi-classical potential barrier and on the other by an infinitely high potential wall (Fig. 15). Then, instead of the transmission coefficient, we can

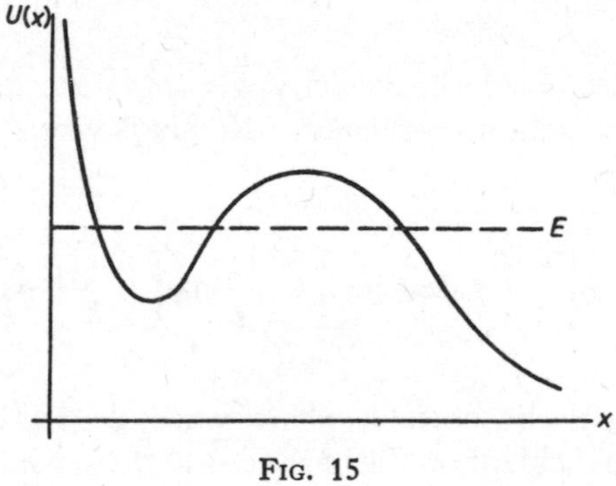

FIG. 15

introduce the probability w that the particle will (during unit time) leave the well through the barrier. Since the problem is quasi-classical, we can reason as follows. During unit time a particle executing classical oscillations within the well approaches the barrier $\omega/2\pi$ times. The probability of emergence is found by multiplying this number by the transmission coefficient D, i.e.

$$w = \frac{\omega}{2\pi}\exp\left[-\frac{2}{\hbar}\left|\int_a^b p\,\mathrm{d}x\right|\right]. \tag{50.10}$$

It has been assumed in the foregoing that the field $U(x)$ satisfies the quasi-classical condition over the whole extent of the barrier (excluding only the immediate neighbourhood of the turning points). In practice, however, we usually have to deal with barriers of the type shown in Fig. 16, where the potential energy curve on one side drops so steeply that the quasi-classical approximation is inapplicable. The exponential factor in D remains the same in this case as in formula (50.9), but the coefficient of the exponential (equal to unity in (50.9)) is different. To calculate it we must, essentially,

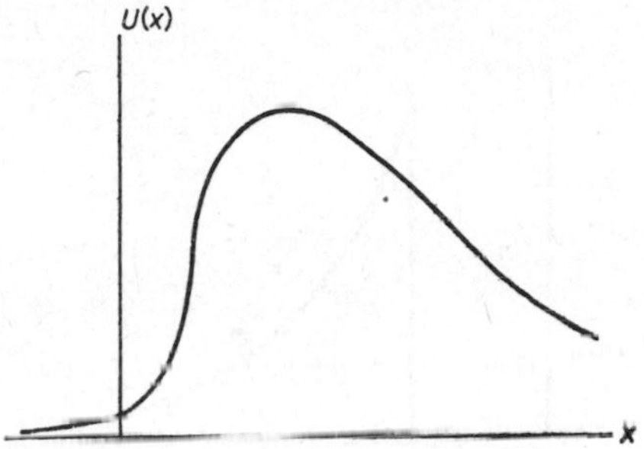

FIG. 16

calculate the exact wave function in the "non-quasi-classical" region and determine the quasi-classical wave function inside the barrier in accordance with this. Instead of (50.6), we obtain for the latter function the expression

$$\psi = \frac{\beta}{\sqrt{|v|}} \exp\left[-\frac{1}{\hbar}\left|\int_a^x p\, dx\right|\right], \tag{50.11}$$

with some value of the coefficient β different from unity. Accordingly we have for the transmission coefficient

$$D = \beta^2 \exp\left[-\frac{2}{\hbar}\left|\int_a^b p\, dx\right|\right]. \tag{50.12}$$

PROBLEMS

PROBLEM 1. Determine the transmission coefficient for the potential barrier shown in Fig. 17: $U(x) = 0$ for $x < 0$, $U(x) = U_0 - Fx$ for $x > 0$; only the exponential factor need be calculated.

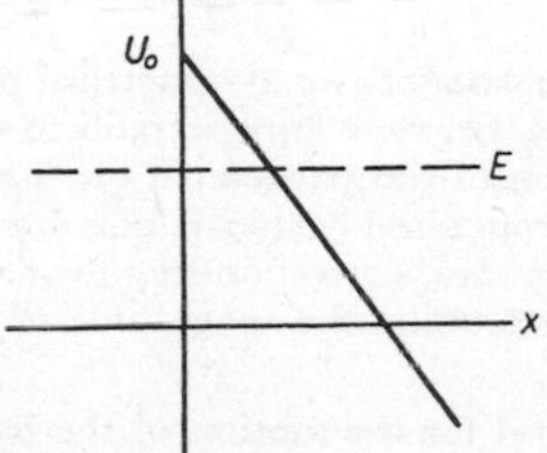

FIG. 17

SOLUTION. A simple calculation gives the result

$$D \sim \exp\left\{-\frac{4\sqrt{(2\mu)}}{3\hbar F}(U_0-E)^{3/2}\right\}.$$

PROBLEM 2. Determine the probability that a particle (with zero angular momentum) will emerge from a centrally symmetric potential well with $U(r) = -U_0$ for $r < r_0$, $U(r) = \alpha/r$ for $r > r_0$ (Fig. 18).

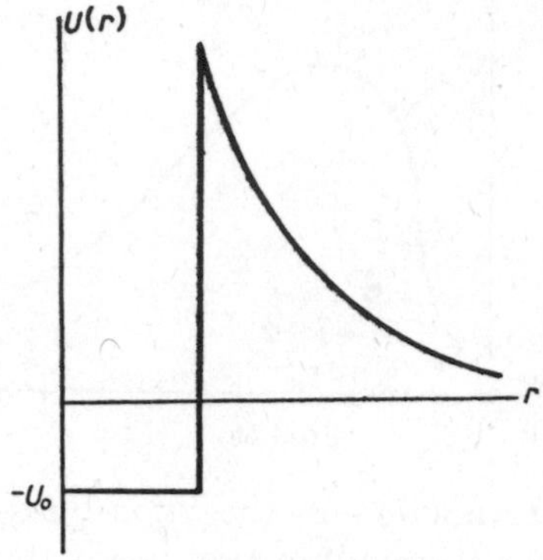

FIG. 18

SOLUTION. The centrally symmetric problem reduces to a one-dimensional one, so that the formulae obtained above can be applied directly. We have

$$w \sim \exp\left\{-\frac{2}{\hbar}\int_{r_0}^{\alpha/E}\sqrt{\left[2\mu\left(\frac{\alpha}{r}-E\right)\right]}\,dr\right\}.$$

Evaluating the integral, we finally obtain *Gamow's formula*

$$w \sim \exp\left\{-\frac{2\alpha}{\hbar}\sqrt{\frac{2\mu}{E}}\left[\cos^{-1}\sqrt{\frac{Er_0}{\alpha}}-\sqrt{\left\{\frac{Er_0}{\alpha}\left(1-\frac{Er_0}{\alpha}\right)\right\}}\right]\right\}.$$

In the limiting case $r_0 \to 0$, this formula becomes

$$w \sim e^{-(\pi\alpha/\hbar)\sqrt{(2\mu/E)}} = e^{-2\pi\alpha/\hbar v}.$$

These formulae are applicable when the exponent is large, i.e. when $\alpha/\hbar v \gg 1$. This condition agrees, as it should, with the condition (49.10) for quasi-classical motion in a Coulomb field.

PROBLEM 3. The field $U(x)$ consists of two symmetrical potential wells (I and II in Fig. 19), separated by a barrier. If the barrier were impenetrable to a particle, there would be energy levels corresponding to the motion of the particle in one or other well, the same for both wells. The fact that a passage through the barrier is possible results in a splitting of each of these levels into two neighbouring ones, corresponding to states in which the particle moves simultaneously in both wells. Determine the magnitude of the splitting (the field $U(x)$ is supposed quasi-classical).

SOLUTION. Let E_0 be some level for the motion of the particle in one well (I, say), and $\psi_0(x)$ the corresponding wave function (so normalised that the integral of ψ_0^2 over well I is unity). When the small probability of penetration through the barrier is taken into account, the level splits into levels E_1 and E_2 with wave functions which are symmetric and antisymmetric combinations of $\psi_0(x)$ and $\psi_0(-x)$:

$$\psi_1(x) = (1/\sqrt{2})[\psi_0(x)+\psi_0(-x)], \quad \psi_2(x) = (1/\sqrt{2})[\psi_0(x)-\psi_0(-x)]. \qquad (1)$$

The quasi-classical function $\psi_0(x)$ diminishes exponentially outside the well, and in particular

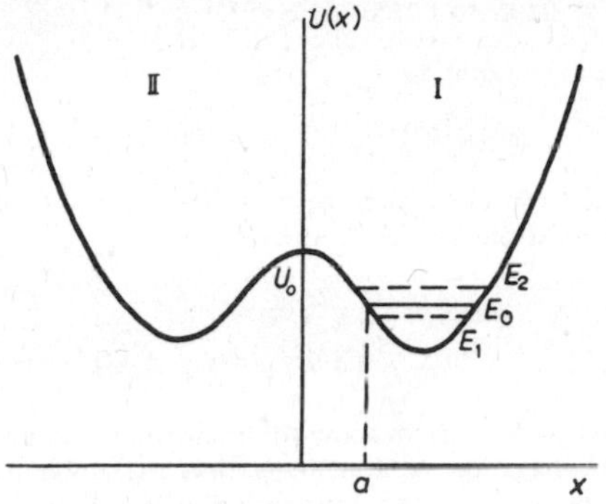

FIG. 19

in the direction of negative x. Hence, within well I, $\psi_0(-x)$ is vanishingly small in comparison with $\psi_0(x)$, and *vice versa* in well II. The functions (1) are so normalised that their squares integrated over wells I and II are unity.

SCHRÖDINGER's equations are

$$\psi_0''+(2\mu/\hbar^2)(E_0-U)\psi_0 = 0, \quad \psi_1''+(2\mu/\hbar^2)(E_1-U)\psi_1 = 0;$$

we multiply the former by ψ_1 and the latter by ψ_0, subtract corresponding terms, and integrate over x from 0 to ∞. Bearing in mind that, for $x = 0$, $\psi_1 = \sqrt{2}\psi_0$ and $\psi_1' = 0$, and that

$$\int_0^\infty \psi_0\psi_1 \,\mathrm{d}x \cong \frac{1}{\sqrt{2}}\int_0^\infty \psi_0^2 \,\mathrm{d}x = 1/\sqrt{2},$$

we find

$$E_1-E_0 = -(\hbar^2/\mu)\psi_0(0)\psi_0'(0).$$

Similarly, we find for E_2-E_0 the same expression with the sign changed. Thus

$$E_2-E_1 = (2\hbar^2/\mu)\psi_0(0)\psi_0'(0).$$

By means of formula (47.5), with the coefficient C from (48.2), we find that

$$\psi_0(0) = \sqrt{\frac{\omega}{2\pi v_0}}\exp\left[-\frac{1}{\hbar}\int_0^a |p|\,\mathrm{d}x\right], \quad \psi_0'(0) = \frac{\mu v_0}{\hbar}\psi_0(0),$$

where $v_0 = \sqrt{[2(U_0-E_0)/\mu]}$. Thus

$$E_2-E_1 = \frac{\omega\hbar}{\pi}\exp\left[-\frac{1}{\hbar}\int_{-a}^{a} |p|\,\mathrm{d}x\right].$$

PROBLEM 4. Determine the exact value of the transmission coefficient D for the passage of a particle through a parabolic potential barrier $U(x) = -\frac{1}{2}\kappa x^2$ (supposing that D is *not* small).

SOLUTION. Whatever the values of κ and E, the motion is quasi-classical at sufficiently large distances $|x|$, with

$$p = \sqrt{[2\mu(E+\tfrac{1}{2}\kappa x^2)]} \cong x\sqrt{(\mu\kappa)}+E\sqrt{(\mu/\kappa)}/x,$$

and the asymptotic form of the solutions of SCHRÖDINGER's equation is

$$\psi = \text{constant} \times e^{\pm \frac{1}{2}i\xi^2}\xi^{\pm i\epsilon - \frac{1}{2}},$$

where we have introduced the notation

$$\xi = x(\mu\kappa/\hbar^2)^{1/4}, \qquad \epsilon = (E/\hbar)\sqrt{(\mu/\kappa)}.$$

We are interested in the solution which, as $x \to +\infty$, contains only a wave which moves off to the right (having passed the barrier). We put

$$\text{as } x \to \infty, \quad \psi = Be^{\frac{1}{2}i\xi^2}\xi^{i\epsilon-\frac{1}{2}}, \tag{1}$$

$$\text{as } x \to -\infty, \quad \psi = e^{-\frac{1}{2}i\xi^2}|\xi|^{-i\epsilon-\frac{1}{2}}+Ae^{\frac{1}{2}i\xi^2}|\xi|^{i\epsilon-\frac{1}{2}}. \tag{2}$$

In the expression (2), the first term represents the incident wave, and the second the reflected wave (the direction of propagation of a wave is that in which its phase increases). The relation between A and B can be found by using the fact that in this case the asymptotic expression for ψ is valid in the whole of a sufficiently distant region of the plane of the complex variable ξ. Let us follow the variation of the function (1) as we go round a semicircle of large radius in the upper half-plane of ξ. Over the whole of this path the term in $e^{\frac{1}{2}i\xi^2}$ is the dominant part of the solution, and hence the function (1) must be converted, by traversing this path, into the second term of the function (2). Hence we find

$$A = B(e^{i\pi})^{i\epsilon-\frac{1}{2}} = -iBe^{-\pi\epsilon}.$$

On the other hand, the condition that the number of particles should be conserved is

$$|A|^2+|B|^2 = 1.$$

From these two relations we find the required penetration coefficient $D = |B|^2$:

$$D = 1/(1+e^{-2\pi\epsilon}).$$

This formula holds for any E. When E is large and negative, it gives $D \cong e^{-2\pi|\epsilon|}$, in accordance with formula (50.9).

§51. Calculation of the quasi-classical matrix elements

A direct calculation of the matrix elements of any physical quantity f with respect to the quasi-classical wave functions presents great difficulty. We may suppose that the energies of the states between which the matrix element is calculated are not close to each other, so that the element does not reduce to the Fourier component of the quantity f (§48). The difficulties arise because, owing to the fact that the wave functions are exponential (with a large imaginary exponent), the integrand oscillates rapidly, and this makes it very troublesome to obtain even an approximate estimate of the integral.

We shall consider a one-dimensional case (motion in a field $U(x)$), and suppose for simplicity that the operator of the physical quantity is merely a function $f(x)$ of the co-ordinate. Let ψ_1 and ψ_2 be the wave functions corresponding to some values E_1 and E_2 of the energy of the particle (with $E_2 > E_1$, Fig. 20); we shall suppose that ψ_1 and ψ_2 are taken real. We have to calculate

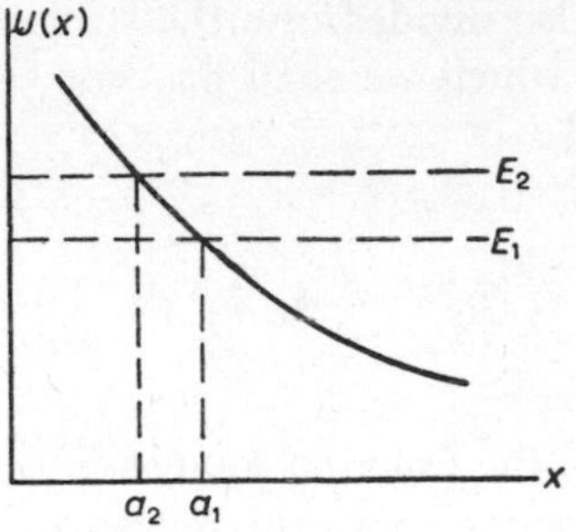

FIG. 20

the integral

$$f_{12} = \int_{-\infty}^{\infty} \psi_1 f \psi_2 \, dx. \tag{51.1}$$

The wave function ψ_1 in the regions on both sides of the turning point $x = a_1$, but not in its immediate neighbourhood, is of the form (47.3), (47.5):

$$\text{for } x < a_1, \quad \psi_1 = \frac{C_1}{2\sqrt{|p_1|}} \exp\left[-\frac{1}{\hbar}\left|\int_{a_1}^{x} p_1 \, dx\right|\right],$$

$$\text{for } x > a_1, \quad \psi_1 = \frac{C_1}{\sqrt{p_1}} \cos\left(\frac{1}{\hbar}\int_{a_1}^{x} p_1 \, dx - \tfrac{1}{4}\pi\right), \tag{51.2}$$

and similarly for ψ_2 (replacing the suffix 1 by 2).

However, the calculation of the integral (51.1) by substituting in it these asymptotic expressions for the wave functions would not give the correct result. The reason is, as we shall see below, that this integral is an exponentially small quantity, whereas the integrand is not itself small. Hence even a relatively small change in the integrand will in general change the order of magnitude of the integral. This difficulty can be circumvented as follows.

We represent the function ψ_2 as a sum $\psi_2 = \psi_2^+ + \psi_2^-$, expressing the cosine (in the region $x > a_2$) as the sum of two exponentials. According to formulae (50.4), we have

$$\text{for } x < a_2, \quad \psi_2^+ = \frac{-iC_2}{2\sqrt{|p_2|}} \exp\left[\frac{1}{\hbar}\left|\int_{a_2}^{x} p_2 \, dx\right|\right],$$

$$\text{for } x > a_2, \quad \psi_2^+ = \frac{C_2}{2\sqrt{|p_2|}} \exp\left[\frac{i}{\hbar}\int_{a_2}^{x} p_2 \, dx - \tfrac{1}{4}i\pi\right]; \tag{51.3}$$

the function ψ_2^- is the complex conjugate of $\psi_2^+ : \psi_2^- = (\psi_2^+)^*$.

The integral (51.1) is also divided into the sum of two complex conjugate integrals $f_{12} = f_{12}^{+} + f_{12}^{-}$, which we shall proceed to calculate. First of all, we note that the integral

$$f_{12}^{+} = \int_{-\infty}^{\infty} \psi_1 f \psi_2^{+} \, dx$$

converges. For, although the function ψ_2^{+} tends exponentially to infinity in the region $x < a_2$, the function ψ_1, in the region $x < a_1$, tends exponentially to zero still more rapidly (since we have $|p_1| > |p_2|$ everywhere in the region $x < a_2$).

We shall regard the co-ordinate x as a complex variable, and displace the path of integration off the real axis into the upper half-plane. When x receives a positive imaginary increment, an increasing term appears in the function ψ_1 (in the region $x > a_1$), but the function ψ_2^{+} decreases still more rapidly, since we have $p_2 > p_1$ everywhere in the region $x > a_1$. Hence the integrand decreases.

The displaced path of integration does not pass through the points $x = a_1$, a_2 on the real axis, near which the quasi-classical approximation is inapplicable. Hence we can use for ψ_1 and ψ_2^{+}, over the whole path, the functions which are their asymptotic expressions in the upper half-plane. These are

$$\psi_1 = \frac{C_1}{2[2\mu(U-E_1)]^{1/4}} \exp\left[\frac{1}{\hbar}\int_{a_1}^{x} \sqrt{\{2\mu(U-E_1)\}}\, dx\right], \qquad (51.4)$$

$$\psi_2^{+} = \frac{-iC_2}{2[2\mu(U-E_2)]^{1/4}} \exp\left[-\frac{1}{\hbar}\int_{a_2}^{x} \sqrt{\{2\mu(U-E_2)\}}\, dx\right],$$

where the roots are taken so as to be positive on the real axis for $x < a_2$.

In the integral

$$f_{12}^{+} = \frac{-iC_1C_2}{4\sqrt{(2\mu)}} \int \exp\left[\frac{1}{\hbar}\int_{a_1}^{x} \sqrt{\{2\mu(U-E_1)\}}\, dx - \frac{1}{\hbar}\int_{a_2}^{x} \sqrt{\{2\mu(U-E_2)\}}\, dx\right] \times$$
$$\times \frac{f(x)\, dx}{[(U-E_1)(U-E_2)]^{1/4}} \qquad (51.5)$$

we desire to displace the path of integration in such a way that the exponential factor is diminished as much as possible. The exponent has an extreme value only where $U(x) = \infty$ (for $E_1 \neq E_2$, its derivative with respect to x vanishes at no other point). Hence the displacement of the contour of integration into the upper half-plane is restricted only by the necessity of passing round the singular points of the function $U(x)$; according to the general theory of linear differential equations, these coincide with the singular points of the wave function $\psi(x)$. The actual choice of the contour depends on the actual form of the field $U(x)$. Thus, if the function $U(x)$ has only one singular point $x = x_0$ in the upper half-plane, the integration can be effected along the type of path shown in Fig. 21. The immediate neighbourhood of the singular

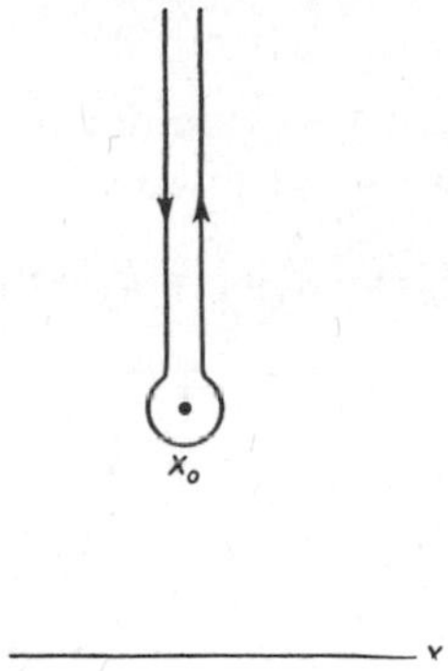

FIG. 21

point plays an important part in the integral, so that the matrix element $f_{12} = 2 \operatorname{re} f_{12}^{+}$ required is practically proportional to an exponential expression of the form†

$$f_{12} \sim \exp\left\{\frac{1}{\hbar}\int_{a_1}^{x_0} \sqrt{[2\mu(U-E_1)]}\,\mathrm{d}x - \frac{1}{\hbar}\int_{a_2}^{x_0} \sqrt{[2\mu(U-E_2)]}\,\mathrm{d}x\right\} \tag{51.6}$$

(L. LANDAU 1932).

The calculation of the exponential factor depends on the actual form of $U(x)$. If $U(x)$ has several singular points, it will clearly be necessary to select the one for which the exponent in (51.6) has its greatest value.

In formula (51.6), only the real part of the exponent (which is always negative) is of interest; the imaginary part gives only an unimportant phase factor. Hence we could put for the exponent the absolute value, with the negative sign, of the real part of the expression given in (51.6).

The quasi-classical radial wave functions for motion in a centrally symmetric field (or, more precisely, the functions $\chi = rR(r)$) have, as we know, the same form as those for one-dimensional motion, and the matrix elements of the quantity $f(r)$ must be calculated by the same method. However, we must now replace $U(r)$ by the effective potential energy (the sum of $U(r)$ and the centrifugal energy), which will be different for states with different l.

† In deriving formula (51.6), we have replaced the wave functions in the integrand by their asymptotic expressions. This is legitimate, since, in the integral taken along the contour shown in Fig. 21, the order of magnitude of the integral is determined by that of the integrand; hence a relatively small change in the latter does not have any great effect on the value of the integral (see the remarks following (51.2)).

In view of further applications of the method in question (see §87), we shall write the potential energies corresponding to the wave functions χ_1 and χ_2 in a general form, as $U_1(r)$ and $U_2(r)$. Then the exponential factor in the integrand is of the form

$$\exp\left\{\frac{1}{\hbar}\int_{a_1}^{r}\sqrt{[2\mu(U_1-E_1)]}\,dr-\frac{1}{\hbar}\int_{a_2}^{r}\sqrt{[2\mu(U_2-E_2)]}\,dr\right\}.$$

The exponent now has an extreme value not only at the points where $U_1(r)$ or $U_2(r)$ becomes infinite, but also at those where

$$U_2(r)-U_1(r) = E_2-E_1. \tag{51.7}$$

Hence, in the formula

$$f_{12} \sim \exp\left\{\frac{1}{\hbar}\int_{a_1}^{r_0}\sqrt{[2\mu(U_1-E_1)]}\,dr-\frac{1}{\hbar}\int_{a_2}^{r_0}\sqrt{[2\mu(U_2-E_2)]}\,dr\right\}, \tag{51.8}$$

the possible values of r_0 include not only the singular points of $U_1(r)$ and $U_2(r)$, but also the roots of equation (51.7).

The centrally symmetric case differs also in that the integration over r in (51.1) is taken from 0 (and not from $-\infty$) to ∞:

$$f_{12} = \int_0^\infty \chi_1 f \chi_2\,dr.$$

Here two cases must be distinguished. If the integrand is an even function of r, the integration can be formally extended to the whole range from $-\infty$ to ∞, so that there is no difference from the previous case. This may occur if $U_1(r)$ and $U_2(r)$ are even functions of r $[U(-r) = U(r)]$. Then the wave functions $\chi_1(r)$ and $\chi_2(r)$ are either even or odd functions† (see the end of §19), and, if the function $f(r)$ is also even or odd, the product $\chi_1 f \chi_2$ may be even.

If, on the other hand, the integrand is not even (as always happens if $U(r)$ is not even), the start of the path of integration cannot be moved away from the point $r = 0$, and this point must be included among the possible values of r_0 in (51.8).

PROBLEMS

PROBLEM 1. Calculate the quasi-classical matrix elements (exponential factor only) in a field $U = U_0 e^{-\alpha x}$.

SOLUTION. $U(x)$ becomes infinite only for $x \to -\infty$. Accordingly, we put $x_0 = -\infty$ in (51.6). Bearing in mind that, for $x > a_1$ (or $x > a_2$), the integrands become imaginary,

† For even $U(r)$, the radial wave function $R(r)$ is even (or odd) when l is even (or odd), as is seen from its behaviour for small r (where $R \sim r^l$).

we can extend the integration to $x = +\infty$, writing the exponent in (51.6) in the form

$$\frac{\sqrt{(2\mu)}}{\hbar}\,\mathrm{re}\{\int\limits_{-\infty}^{\infty}[\sqrt{(U_0e^{-\alpha x}-E_2)}-\sqrt{(U_0e^{-\alpha x}-E_1)}]\,dx\}.$$

The integral of each of the two terms in the brackets diverges at the lower limit. Hence we first calculate them from $-x$ to ∞, and then pass to the limit $x \to \infty$. We find

$$f_{12} \sim e^{-(\pi/\alpha\hbar)(p_2-p_1)},$$

where $p_1 = \sqrt{(2\mu E_1)}$, $p_2 = \sqrt{(2\mu E_2)}$ are the momenta of the particle at infinity ($x \to \infty$), where the motion is free.

PROBLEM 2. The same as Problem 1, but in a Coulomb field $U = \alpha/r$, for transitions between states with $l = 0$.

SOLUTION. The only singular point of the function $U(r)$ is $r = 0$. The corresponding integrals have been calculated in §50, Problem 2. As a result we have by formula (51.8)

$$f_{12} \sim \exp\left[\frac{\pi\alpha}{\hbar}\left(\frac{1}{v_2}-\frac{1}{v_1}\right)\right],$$

with the velocities $v_1 = \sqrt{(2E_1/\mu)}$, $v_2 = \sqrt{(2E_2/\mu)}$.

§52. The case of several degrees of freedom

The results obtained in §48 can easily be generalised to systems with several degrees of freedom. First of all, let us recall some properties of finite motion in classical mechanics.† A finite motion of a closed system is, as we say, *conditionally periodic*, and any function of the co-ordinates and momenta can be expanded in a generalised Fourier series, in which the frequencies are the sums $\sum_{i=1}^{s} p_i\omega_i$, p_i being integers and ω_i the fundamental frequencies, whose number s is equal to the number of degrees of freedom of the system. The action S of such a system is a many-valued quantity, determined only to within sums of the form $\sum_{i=1}^{s} m_i I_i$, where m_i are integers and I_i are certain parameters called *action variables*. The energy of the system can be expressed as a function of the action variables, and the frequencies ω_i are then given by the derivatives

$$\omega_i = 2\pi\,\partial E/\partial I_i. \tag{52.1}$$

The wave function of the system must be a one-valued function. In the quasi-classical case, it has the form $\psi \sim e^{(i/\hbar)S}$, and it follows from the above-mentioned many-valuedness of the action that the I_i can only be integral multiples of $2\pi\hbar$:

$$I_i = 2\pi\hbar n_i. \tag{52.2}$$

† See, for example, volume 1 of this course, *Mechanics*, §50, Moscow 1958.

These equations are the required formulation of the quasi-classical Bohr's quantisation conditions for systems with several degrees of freedom. In the next approximation we should have to put

$$I_i = 2\pi\hbar(n_i+\gamma_i),$$

where the γ_i are constants (cf. (48.1)). As is well known, if the variables in the classical Hamilton-Jacobi equation are separable, the action variables are equal to the integrals

$$I_i = \oint p_i \, dq_i,$$

taken over complete periods of the variation of the generalised co-ordinates q_i. Then the quantisation conditions become

$$\oint p_i \, dq_i = 2\pi\hbar(n_i+\gamma_i). \tag{52.3}$$

For one degree of freedom, this agrees with (48.1), putting $\gamma = \frac{1}{2}$.

The numbers $n_1, n_2, \ldots$ are the quantum numbers determining the stationary states of the system†; the large values of these numbers correspond to the quasi-classical case. The difference in energy between the levels of states whose quantum numbers differ by $\Delta n_1, \Delta n_2, \ldots$ (with $\Delta n_i \ll n_i$) can be written in the form

$$\Delta E = \sum_{i=1}^{s} \Delta n_i \frac{\partial E}{\partial n_i}.$$

E is the energy regarded as a function of the numbers $n_1, n_2, \ldots$. The corresponding frequencies are

$$\frac{\Delta E}{\hbar} = \sum_i \frac{\Delta n_i}{\hbar} \frac{\partial E}{\partial n_i}.$$

In the limit, these frequencies must coincide with the classical frequencies; it is easy to see that this requirement is satisfied. Replacing the differentiation with respect to n_i by one with respect to I_i, in accordance with (52.2), we obtain the energy differences in the form

$$\Delta E = \sum_i \Delta n_i 2\pi\hbar \, \partial E/\partial I_i$$

or, using (52.1),

$$\Delta E = \sum_i \hbar\omega_i \Delta n_i. \tag{52.4}$$

Thus the frequencies $\Delta E/\hbar$ are quantities of the form $\Sigma p_i\omega_i$, as they should be.

† States of the discrete spectrum are always meant.

It is also easy to generalise the concept of "cells" in phase space, introduced in §48. The number of states ΔN with quantum numbers in the intervals Δn_i is given by the product $\Pi\, \Delta n_i$. Putting, from (52.2), $\Delta n_i = \Delta I_i/2\pi\hbar$, we have

$$\Delta N = \prod_i \Delta I_i/(2\pi\hbar)^s.$$

We shall describe the system (regarded as classical) by what are called the *canonical variables*†—the action variables I_i and the *angle variables* w_i (defined by $w_i = \partial S(q_i, I_i)/\partial I_i$). As is well known, the latter take values between 0 and 1, i.e. the ranges over which they vary are $\Delta w_i = 1$. Hence we can write ΔN in the form

$$\Delta N = \prod_i \Delta I_i \Delta w_i/(2\pi\hbar)^s.$$

The transition from the usual variables q_i, p_i (generalised co-ordinates and momenta) to the canonical variables is effected by means of a canonical transformation. This, as is well known, does not alter the volume of phase space (its Jacobian is unity). Hence we can replace the product $\Delta I_i \Delta w_i$ by $\Delta q_i \Delta p_i$, and so we obtain the formula

$$\Delta N = \prod_i \Delta q_i \Delta p_i/(2\pi\hbar)^s, \tag{52.5}$$

which is a direct generalisation of the result (48.3). We may say that, to each quantum state of a system with s degrees of freedom, there "belongs" a "cell" of volume $(2\pi\hbar)^s$ in its phase space.

PROBLEM

Determine (approximately) the number of discrete energy levels of a particle in a centrally symmetric field $U(r)$ satisfying the quasi-classical condition.

SOLUTION. The number of states "belonging" to a volume of phase space corresponding to momenta in the range $0 \leqslant p \leqslant p_0$ and radius vectors in the range from r to $r+dr$ is

$$\tfrac{4}{3}\pi p_0^3 \,.\, 4\pi r^2\, dr/(2\pi\hbar)^3$$

(the number of degrees of freedom $s = 3$). For a given r, the particle can have (in its classical motion) momenta satisfying the condition $E = p^2/2\mu - |U(r)| \leqslant 0$ (we suppose that the potential $U(r)$ is negative in all space, so that negative energies correspond to the finite motion). Substituting

$$p_0 = \sqrt{(2\mu|U(r)|)}$$

and integrating over all r, we obtain the total number of states of the discrete spectrum:

$$\frac{4\sqrt{2}}{3\pi}\frac{\mu^{3/2}}{\hbar^3}\int_0^\infty |U(r)|^{3/2}\, r^2\, dr.$$

This integral diverges (i.e. the number of levels is infinite) if $U(r)$ decreases at infinity as r^{-s} with $s < 2$, in accordance with the results of §16.

† See *Mechanics*, §50, Moscow 1958.

CHAPTER VIII

SPIN

§53. Spin

LET us consider a system consisting of several parts, such as an atomic nucleus, which executes some motion as a whole. We shall suppose that the internal energy of the nucleus has a definite value. The internal state of the nucleus, however, is in general not completely determined by this value; for the "internal" angular momentum L of the nucleus (i.e. the angular momentum of the particles in their motion within the nucleus) may still have various directions in space. The number of different possible orientations of this angular momentum is, as we know, $2L+1$. Thus, in considering the motion of the nucleus (in a given internal state) as a whole, we must examine, as well as its co-ordinates, another discrete variable: the projection of its internal angular momentum on some chosen direction in space.

Consequently, we see that the formalism of quantum mechanics allows us, in considering the motion of any particle, to introduce, besides its co-ordinates, another variable quantity specific to any given particle, which can take a limited number of discrete values. We have no reason to suppose, *a priori*, that this variable is absent when the particle is elementary. In other words, we must in general suppose that, in quantum mechanics, some "intrinsic" angular momentum must be ascribed to an elementary particle, regardless of its motion in space. This property of elementary particles is peculiar to quantum theory (it disappears in the limit $\hbar \rightarrow 0$; see the third footnote to this section), and hence is essentially incapable of a classical interpretation. In particular, it would be wholly meaningless to imagine the "intrinsic" angular momentum of an elementary particle as being the result of its rotation about "its own axis", if only because we cannot ascribe any finite dimensions to an elementary particle.

The intrinsic angular momentum of a particle† is called its *spin*‡, as distinct from the angular momentum due to the motion of the particle in space, called the *orbital angular momentum*. The spin of a particle (measured, like the orbital angular momentum, in units of $\hbar$) will be denoted by s.

In the preceding chapters we have always supposed that the three co-ordinates of a particle form a complete system of quantities, so that, if they are given, its state is completely determined. We now see that this is in general

† The particle concerned may be either elementary, or composite but behaving in some respect as an elementary particle (e.g. an atomic nucleus).

‡ The physical idea that an electron has an intrinsic angular momentum was put forward by G. UHLENBECK and S. GOUDSMIT in 1925. Spin was introduced into quantum mechanics in 1927 by W. PAULI.

not true: for a complete description of the state of a particle, not only its co-ordinates, but also the direction of the spin vector, must be specified. Hence the wave function of a particle must be a function of four variables: the three co-ordinates, and the ***spin variable*** which gives the value of the projection of the spin on a selected direction in space, and takes a limited number of discrete values. These values can be added as a suffix to the wave functions. Thus the wave function of a particle which has a non-zero spin is in fact not one function, but a set of several different functions of the co-ordinates, differing in their *spin suffixes*.

The quantum-mechanical operator corresponding to the spin of the particle, on being applied to the wave function, acts on the spin variable. In other words, it in some way linearly transforms the functions differing only in the spin suffix into one another. The form of this operator will be established later. However, it is easy to see from very general considerations that the operators $\hat{s}_x$, $\hat{s}_y$, $\hat{s}_z$ satisfy the same commutation conditions as the operators of the orbital angular momentum.

The angular momentum operator is essentially the same as that of an infinitely small rotation. In deriving, in §24, the expression for the orbital angular momentum operator, we considered the result of applying the rotation operator to a function of the co-ordinates. In the case of the spin, this derivation becomes invalid, since the spin operator acts on the spin variable, and not on the co-ordinates. Hence, to obtain the required commutation relations, we must consider the operation of an infinitely small rotation in a general form, as a rotation of the system of co-ordinates. If we successively perform infinitely small rotations about the x-axis and the y-axis, and then about the same axes in the reverse order, it is easy to see by direct calculation that the difference between the results of these two operations is equivalent to an infinitely small rotation about the z-axis (through an angle equal to the product of the angles of rotation about the x and y-axes). We shall not pause here to carry out these simple calculations, as a result of which we again obtain the usual commutation relations between the operators of the components of angular momentum; these must therefore hold for the spin operators also:

$$\{\hat{s}_y, \hat{s}_z\} = i\hat{s}_x, \quad \{\hat{s}_z, \hat{s}_x\} = i\hat{s}_y, \quad \{\hat{s}_x, \hat{s}_y\} = i\hat{s}_z, \tag{53.1}$$

together with all the physical consequences resulting from them.

The commutation relations (53.1) enable us to determine the possible values of the absolute magnitude and components of the spin. All the results derived in §25 (formulae (25.6)–(25.9)) were based only on the commutation relations, and hence are fully applicable here also; we need only replace $\mathbf{L}$ in formulae (25.6)–(25.9) by $\mathbf{s}$. It follows from formula (25.7) that the eigenvalues of the z-component of the spin form a sequence of numbers differing by unity. However, we cannot now assert that these values must be integral, as we could for the component L_z of the orbital angular momentum (the derivation given at the beginning of §25 is invalid here, since it was based on the expression (24.11) for the operator $\hat{l}_z$, which holds only for the orbital angular momentum).

Moreover, we find that the sequence of eigenvalues s_z is limited above and below by values equal in absolute magnitude and opposite in sign, which we denote by $\pm s$. The difference $2s$ between the greatest and least values of s_z must be an integer or zero. Consequently s can take the values 0, $\frac{1}{2}$, 1, $\frac{3}{2}$, ...

Thus the eigenvalues of the square of the spin are

$$\mathbf{s}^2 = s(s+1), \tag{53.2}$$

where s can be either an integer (including zero) or half an integer. For given s, the component s_z of the spin can take the values $s, s-1, \dots, -s$, i.e. $2s+1$ values in all. From what was said above, we conclude that the state of a particle whose spin is s must be described by a wave function which is a set of $2s+1$ functions.†

Experiment shows that the majority of the elementary particles (electrons, positrons, protons and neutrons) have a spin of $\frac{1}{2}$. The most probable value of the spin of the μ-mesons is also $\frac{1}{2}$, while π-mesons have zero spin.

The total angular momentum of a particle is composed of its orbital angular momentum $\mathbf{l}$ and its spin $\mathbf{s}$. It is evident that the operator of the total angular momentum is simply the sum of the operators of the orbital angular momentum and the spin. This follows at once from the fact that these operators act on different variables, and are therefore independent of each other. The eigenvalues of the total angular momentum

$$\mathbf{j} = \mathbf{l}+\mathbf{s} \tag{53.3}$$

are therefore determined by the same "vector model" rule as the sum of the orbital angular momenta of two different particles (§30). That is, for given values of l and s, the total angular momentum can take the values $l+s$, $l+s-1, \dots, |l-s|$. Thus, for an electron (spin $\frac{1}{2}$) with orbital angular momentum l, the total angular momentum can be $j = l\pm\frac{1}{2}$.

The operator of the total angular momentum $\mathbf{J}$ of a system of particles is equal to the sum of the operators of the angular momentum $\mathbf{j}$ of each particle, so that its values are again determined by the vector model rules. The angular momentum $\mathbf{J}$ can be put in the form

$$\mathbf{J} = \mathbf{L}+\mathbf{S}, \qquad \mathbf{L} = \sum_a \mathbf{l}_a, \qquad \mathbf{S} = \sum_a \mathbf{s}_a, \tag{53.4}$$

where $\mathbf{S}$ may be called the *total spin* and $\mathbf{L}$ the *total orbital angular momentum* of the system. We notice that, if the total spin of the system is half-integral (or integral), the same is true of the total angular momentum, since the orbital angular momentum is always integral. In particular, if the system consists of an even number of similar particles, its total spin is always integral, and therefore so is the total angular momentum.

† Since s is fixed for each kind of particle, the spin angular momentum $\hbar s$ becomes zero in the limit of classical mechanics ($\hbar \to 0$). This consideration does not apply to the orbital angular momentum, since l can take any value. The transition to classical mechanics is represented by $\hbar$ tending to zero and l simultaneously tending to infinity, in such a way that the product $\hbar l$ remains finite.

The operators of the total angular momentum **j** of a particle (or **J**, of a system of particles) satisfy the same commutation rules as the operators of the orbital angular momentum or the spin, since these rules are general commutation rules holding for any angular momentum. The formulae (25.13) for the matrix elements of angular momentum, which follow from the commutation rules, are also valid for any angular momentum, provided that the matrix elements are defined with respect to the eigenstates of this angular momentum. We, however, have agreed to define the matrix elements with respect to the set of wave functions of the stationary states. If we follow this rule, the formulae (25.13) will hold only for a conserved angular momentum (which can have definite values at the same time as the energy). Strictly speaking, only the total angular momentum **J** of the system meets this condition. All these remarks apply without modification to formulae (27.11) and (27.13) for the matrix elements of arbitrary vector quantities.

The operators of the orbital angular momentum and the spin, since they act on functions of entirely different variables, of course commute with each other. Since, moreover, the spin does not, in non-relativistic theory, interact with the orbital motion of the particles (see §60 for a more detailed discussion), all the formulae derived in §31 are applicable to the addition of the angular momenta **L** and **S**.

§54. Spinors

Let $\psi(x, y, z; \sigma)$ be the wave function of a particle with spin σ; σ denotes the z-component of the spin, and takes values from $-s$ to $+s$. We shall call the functions $\psi(\sigma)$ with various values of σ the "components" of the wave function. We impose on the choice of these "components" the condition that the integral $\int |\psi(\sigma)|^2 \, dV$ determines the probability that the z-component of the spin of the particle is equal to σ. The probability that the particle is in an element of volume dV in space is $dV \sum_{\sigma=-s}^{s} |\psi(\sigma)|^2$. If the particle is in a state with a definite σ-value σ_0, only the component $\psi(\sigma)$ with $\sigma = \sigma_0$ is not zero, i.e. the wave function is of the form

$$\psi(x, y, z; \sigma) = \psi(x, y, z)\delta_{\sigma\sigma_0}.$$

In §§54–57 we shall not be interested in the dependence of the wave function on the co-ordinates. For example, in speaking of the behaviour of the function $\psi(\sigma)$ when the system of co-ordinates is rotated, we can suppose that the particle is at the origin, so that its co-ordinates remain unchanged by such a rotation, and the results obtained will characterise the behaviour of the function $\psi(\sigma)$ with regard to the spin variable σ.

Let us effect an infinitely small rotation through an angle $\delta\phi$ about the z-axis. The operator of such a rotation can be expressed in terms of the angular momentum operator (in this case the spin operator), in the form $1+i\delta\phi \, . \, \hat{s}_z$. Hence, as a result of the rotation, the functions $\psi(\sigma)$ become

$\psi(\sigma)+\delta\psi(\sigma)$, where $\delta\psi(\sigma) = i\delta\phi \cdot \hat{s}_z\psi(\sigma)$. But $\hat{s}_z\psi(\sigma) = \sigma\psi(\sigma)$, so that $\delta\psi(\sigma) = i\sigma\psi(\sigma)\delta\phi$. By a rotation through a finite angle ϕ the functions $\psi(\sigma)$ are therefore transformed into

$$\psi'(\sigma) = e^{i\sigma\phi}\psi(\sigma). \tag{54.1}$$

In particular, by a rotation through an angle 2π, they are multiplied by a factor $e^{2\pi i\sigma}$, which is the same for all σ and is $(-1)^{2s}$ (2σ is always of the same parity as $2s$). Thus we see that, when the system of co-ordinates is completely rotated about an axis, the wave functions of a particle of integral spin return to their original values, while those of a particle of half-integral spin change sign.

The variable σ differs from the ordinary variables (the co-ordinates) by being discrete. The most general form of a linear operator acting on functions of a discrete variable σ is evidently

$$(\hat{f}\psi)(\sigma) = \sum_{\sigma'} f_{\sigma\sigma'}\psi(\sigma'),$$

where the $f_{\sigma\sigma'}$ are constants. It is easy to see that the quantities $f_{\sigma\sigma'}$ are the same as the matrix elements of the operator $\hat{f}$, defined in the usual manner. For the "eigenfunction" of the operator $\hat{s}_z$ corresponding to the value $s_z = \sigma_0$ is $\psi(\sigma) = \delta_{\sigma\sigma_0}$. For this function we have

$$\hat{f}\delta_{\sigma\sigma_0} = \sum_{\sigma'} f_{\sigma\sigma'}\delta_{\sigma'\sigma_0} = f_{\sigma\sigma_0}.$$

The right-hand side of this equation can be rewritten in the form $\sum_{\sigma'} f_{\sigma'\sigma_0}\delta_{\sigma\sigma'}$, and then

$$\hat{f}\delta_{\sigma\sigma_0} = \sum_{\sigma'} f_{\sigma'\sigma_0}\delta_{\sigma\sigma'}.$$

This equation, however, agrees with the usual definition of the matrix of the operator $\hat{f}$ with respect to the eigenfunctions of the operator $\hat{s}_z$.

Thus the operators acting on functions of σ can be represented in the form of $(2s+1)$-rowed matrices. In particular, we have for the operators of the spin components themselves

$$(\hat{s}_x\psi)(\sigma) = \sum_{\sigma'} (s_x)_{\sigma\sigma'}\psi(\sigma'), \tag{54.2}$$

and similarly† for $\hat{s}_y$, $\hat{s}_z$. According to what has been said above, the matrices s_x, s_y, s_z are identical with the matrices L_x, L_y, L_z obtained in §25, where the letters L and M need only be replaced by s and σ. Thus the non-vanishing matrix elements of the spin operators are

$$\left.\begin{aligned}
(s_x)_{\sigma,\sigma-1} &= (s_x)_{\sigma-1,\sigma} = \tfrac{1}{2}\sqrt{[(s+\sigma)(s-\sigma+1)]}, \\
(s_y)_{\sigma,\sigma-1} &= -(s_y)_{\sigma-1,\sigma} = -\tfrac{1}{2}i\sqrt{[(s+\sigma)(s-\sigma+1)]}, \\
(s_z)_{\sigma\sigma} &= \sigma.
\end{aligned}\right\} \tag{54.2a}$$

---

† Attention is drawn to the fact that the sequence of suffixes in the matrix elements on the right-hand side of equation (54.2) is the reverse of the usual sequence (in (11.11)).

In the important case of a spin of $\frac{1}{2}$ ($s = \frac{1}{2}$, $\sigma = \pm\frac{1}{2}$), these matrices have two rows, and are of the form

$$(s_x) = \tfrac{1}{2}\begin{bmatrix} 0 & 1 \\ 1 & 0 \end{bmatrix}, \quad (s_y) = \tfrac{1}{2}\begin{bmatrix} 0 & -i \\ i & 0 \end{bmatrix}, \quad (s_z) = \tfrac{1}{2}\begin{bmatrix} 1 & 0 \\ 0 & -1 \end{bmatrix}. \tag{54.3}$$

These are called *Pauli matrices.*

By direct multiplication of the Pauli matrices, it is easy to verify that the relations

$$2\hat{s}_y\hat{s}_z = i\hat{s}_x, \quad 2\hat{s}_z\hat{s}_x = i\hat{s}_y, \quad 2\hat{s}_x\hat{s}_y = i\hat{s}_z \tag{54.4}$$

hold. Combining these with the usual commutation rules for the operators $\hat{s}_x$, $\hat{s}_y$, $\hat{s}_z$, we find that

$$\hat{s}_x\hat{s}_y+\hat{s}_y\hat{s}_x = 0 \quad \hat{s}_x\hat{s}_z+\hat{s}_z\hat{s}_x = 0, \quad \hat{s}_y\hat{s}_z+\hat{s}_z\hat{s}_y = 0, \tag{54.4a}$$

i.e. the Pauli matrices anticommute with one another.†

When the co-ordinate system is rotated, the set of functions $\psi(\sigma)$ corresponding to a spin s are transformed into linear combinations of one another in a definite manner; for an infinitely small rotation, the transformation in question is determined by the formulae (54.2). From a purely mathematical point of view, this means that we have found a classification of the possible types of transformation of quantities when the co-ordinate system is rotated. It can be shown that, if there are n different quantities which are transformed into linear combinations of one another (and the number of these quantities cannot be reduced by taking any linear combinations of them), we can assert that they are transformed as the "components" of a wave function corresponding to a spin of $s = \frac{1}{2}(n-1)$. Any set of quantities transformed linearly into one another when the co-ordinate system is rotated can be reduced (by a suitable linear transformation) to one or more systems of such functions.

Let us consider more closely the "spin" properties of wave functions. When the spin is zero, the wave function has only one component, $\psi(0)$. When the spin operators act upon it, the result is zero:

$$\hat{s}_x\psi = \hat{s}_y\psi = \hat{s}_z\psi = 0.$$

Since the spin operators are related to the rotation operators, this means that the wave function of a particle with spin zero is invariant under rotation of the co-ordinate system, i.e. it is a scalar.

The wave functions of particles with spin $\frac{1}{2}$ have two components, $\psi(\frac{1}{2})$ and $\psi(-\frac{1}{2})$. For convenience in later generalisations, we shall call these components ψ^1 and ψ^2 respectively (with upper indices 1 and 2). In any rotation of

† We may also notice the following easily verified relations:

$$\hat{\mathbf{s}}^2 = \tfrac{3}{4}, \quad (\hat{\mathbf{s}}\cdot\mathbf{a})(\hat{\mathbf{s}}\cdot\mathbf{b}) = \tfrac{1}{4}(\mathbf{a}\cdot\mathbf{b})+\tfrac{1}{2}i\hat{\mathbf{s}}\cdot(\mathbf{a}\times\mathbf{b}),$$

where **a** and **b** are any vectors.

the co-ordinate system, ψ^1 and ψ^2 undergo a linear transformation:

$$\psi^{1\prime} = \alpha\psi^1+\beta\psi^2, \quad \psi^{2\prime} = \gamma\psi^1+\delta\psi^2. \tag{54.5}$$

The coefficients† α, β, γ, δ are in general complex functions of the angles of rotation. They are connected by a relation which we derive by considering the bilinear form

$$\psi^1\phi^2-\psi^2\phi^1, \tag{54.6}$$

where (ψ^1, ψ^2) and (ϕ^1, ϕ^2) are two wave functions transformed according to (54.5). A simple calculation gives

$$\psi^{1\prime}\phi^{2\prime}-\psi^{2\prime}\phi^{1\prime} = (\alpha\delta-\beta\gamma)(\psi^1\phi^2-\psi^2\phi^1),$$

i.e. the quantity (54.6) is transformed into itself when the co-ordinate system is rotated. If, however, there is only one function which is transformed into itself, it can be regarded as corresponding to zero spin, and therefore must be a scalar, i.e. must remain unchanged when the co-ordinate system is rotated in any manner. Hence we have

$$\alpha\delta-\beta\gamma = 1. \tag{54.7}$$

This is the required relation.

The linear transformations (54.5) which leave the bilinear form (54.6) invariant are called *binary transformations*. A quantity having two components which undergoes a binary transformation when the co-ordinate system is rotated is called a *spinor*. Thus the wave function of a particle with spin $\frac{1}{2}$ is a spinor.

It is convenient to put the algebra of spinors in a form analogous to that of tensor algebra. This is done by introducing a vector space of two dimensions, in which the metric is defined by an antisymmetrical "metric tensor":

$$\begin{bmatrix} g_{11} & g_{12} \\ g_{21} & g_{22} \end{bmatrix} = \begin{bmatrix} 0 & 1 \\ -1 & 0 \end{bmatrix}. \tag{54.8}$$

The vectors in this space are spinors. Besides the contravariant components ψ^1, ψ^2 of the spinor, we may introduce the covariant components in accordance with the usual formulae of tensor algebra:

$$\psi_\lambda = \sum_{\mu=1}^{2} g_{\lambda\mu}\psi^\mu,$$

so that

$$\psi_1 = \psi^2, \qquad \psi_2 = -\psi^1. \tag{54.9}$$

The binary transformations for the covariant components of a spinor are

† Called the *Cayley-Klein parameters*.

obviously of the form

$$\psi_1' = \delta\psi_1 - \gamma\psi_2, \quad \psi_2' = -\beta\psi_1 + \alpha\psi_2. \tag{54.10}$$

The converse transformation from covariant to contravariant components can be written in the form

$$\psi^\lambda = \sum_\mu g^{\mu\lambda}\psi_\mu, \tag{54.11}$$

where the contravariant "metric tensor" $g^{\lambda\mu}$ has the components

$$\begin{bmatrix} g^{11} & g^{12} \\ g^{21} & g^{22} \end{bmatrix} = \begin{bmatrix} 0 & 1 \\ -1 & 0 \end{bmatrix}, \tag{54.12}$$

which are the same as the components $g_{\lambda\mu}$.

The invariant combination (54.6) can be written as a "scalar product"

$$\psi^\lambda\phi_\lambda = \psi^1\phi_1 + \psi^2\phi_2 = \psi^1\phi^2 - \psi^2\phi^1 = g_{\lambda\mu}\psi^\lambda\phi^\mu; \tag{54.13}$$

here, and in what follows, summation is implied over repeated (*dummy*) indices, as in tensor algebra. We may note the following rule which has to be borne in mind in spinor algebra. We have

$$\psi^\lambda\phi_\lambda = \psi^1\phi_1 + \psi^2\phi_2 = -\psi_2\phi^2 - \psi_1\phi^1 = -\psi_\lambda\phi^\lambda.$$

Thus

$$\psi^\lambda\phi_\lambda = -\psi_\lambda\phi^\lambda. \tag{54.14}$$

Hence it is evident that the scalar product of any spinor with itself is zero:

$$\psi^\lambda\psi_\lambda = 0. \tag{54.15}$$

The expression

$$|\psi^1|^2 + |\psi^2|^2 = \psi^1\psi^{1*} + \psi^2\psi^{2*},$$

which gives the probability of finding the particle at a given point in space, must clearly be a scalar. Comparing it with the scalar (54.13), we see that the components ψ^{1*}, ψ^{2*} of the wave function which is the complex conjugate of ψ^1, ψ^2 are transformed as covariant components of a spinor, i.e. as $\psi^2, -\psi^1$ respectively:

$$\psi^{1*\prime} = \delta\psi^{1*} - \gamma\psi^{2*}, \quad \psi^{2*\prime} = -\beta\psi^{1*} + \alpha\psi^{2*}.$$

On the other hand, by taking the complex conjugate equations to (54.5)

$$\psi^{1*\prime} = \alpha^*\psi^{1*} + \beta^*\psi^{2*}, \quad \psi^{2*\prime} = \gamma^*\psi^{1*} + \delta^*\psi^{2*}$$

and comparing them with the above, we find that the coefficients α, β, γ, δ are related also by

$$\alpha = \delta^*, \qquad \beta = -\gamma^*. \tag{54.16}$$

By virtue of the relations (54.7), (54.16), the four complex quantities

α, β, γ, δ actually contain only three independent real parameters, corresponding to the three angles which define a rotation of a three-dimensional system of co-ordinates.†

The fact that ψ^{1*}, ψ^{2*} are transformed as ψ^2, $-\psi^1$ is closely related to the symmetry with respect to a change in the sign of the time. As was remarked in §16, in quantum mechanics a change in the sign of the time corresponds to a replacement of the wave function by its complex conjugate. When the sign of the time is changed, however, so is that of the angular momentum. Hence the functions which are the complex conjugates of the components ψ^1, ψ^2 corresponding to projections of the spin $\sigma = \frac{1}{2}$ and $\sigma = -\frac{1}{2}$ must be equivalent in their properties to the components corresponding respectively to projections of the spin $\sigma = -\frac{1}{2}$ and $\sigma = \frac{1}{2}$.

§55. Spinors of higher rank

Analogously to the transition from vectors to tensors in ordinary tensor algebra, we can introduce the idea of spinors of higher rank. Thus, a quantity $\psi^{\lambda\mu}$, having four components which are transformed as the product $\psi^\lambda \phi^\mu$ of the components of two spinors of rank one, is called a spinor of rank two. Besides the contravariant components $\psi^{\lambda\mu}$ we can consider the covariant components $\psi_{\lambda\mu}$ and the mixed components $\psi_\lambda{}^\mu$ which are transformed as the products $\psi_\lambda\phi_\mu$ and $\psi_\lambda\phi^\mu$ respectively. The transition from one set of components to another is effected by means of a "metric tensor" $g_{\lambda\mu}$, in accordance with the usual formulae

$$\psi_\lambda{}^\mu = g_{\lambda\nu}\psi^{\nu\mu}, \qquad \psi_{\lambda\mu} = g_{\lambda\nu}g_{\mu\rho}\cdot\psi^{\nu\rho}$$

Thus $\psi_{12} = -\psi_1{}^1 = -\psi^{21}$, $\quad \psi_{11} = \psi_1{}^2 = \psi^{22}$, and so on. Spinors of any rank are similarly defined. The quantities $g_{\lambda\mu}$ themselves form an antisymmetrical spinor of rank two. It is easy to see that the values of its components remain unchanged under binary transformations.

It is easily verified that the product $g_{\lambda\nu}g^{\mu\nu}$ is, as it should be, a *unit spinor* of rank two, i.e. a spinor with components $\delta_1^1 = \delta_2^2 = 1$, $\delta_1^2 = \delta_2^1 = 0$. Thus

$$g_{\lambda\nu}g^{\mu\nu} = \delta_\lambda{}^\mu. \tag{55.1}$$

As in ordinary tensor algebra, there are two fundamental operations in spinor algebra: multiplication, and contraction with respect to a pair of indices. The *multiplication* of two spinors gives a spinor of higher rank; thus, from two spinors of ranks two and three, $\psi_{\lambda\mu}$ and $\phi^{\nu\rho\sigma}$, we can form a spinor of rank five, $\psi_{\lambda\mu}\phi^{\nu\rho\sigma}$. *Contraction* with respect to a pair of indices (i.e. summation of the components over corresponding values of one covariant and one contravariant index) decreases the rank of a spinor by two. Thus, a

† We notice that, by a suitable choice of the z-axis, one of the two components of a spinor can always be made zero. For, equating (say) $\psi^{1'}$ in (54.5) to zero, we obtain one complex equation, or two real ones. On the other hand, we have at our disposal two parameters (angles) which determine the direction of the z-axis, and by which these equations can always be satisfied. Physically, this means that, for a particle of spin $\frac{1}{2}$, there is always a direction in space along which the projection of the spin has a definite value.

contraction of the spinor $\psi_{\lambda\mu}{}^{\nu\rho\sigma}$ with respect to the indices μ and ν gives the spinor $\psi_{\lambda\mu}{}^{\mu\rho\sigma}$ of rank three; the contraction of the spinor $\psi_{\lambda}{}^{\mu}$ gives the scalar $\psi_{\lambda}{}^{\lambda}$. Here there is a rule similar to that expressed by formula (54.14): if we interchange the upper and lower indices with respect to which the contraction is effected, the sign is changed (i.e. $\psi_{\lambda}{}^{\lambda} = -\psi^{\lambda}{}_{\lambda}$). Hence, in particular, it follows that, if a spinor is symmetrical with respect to any two of its indices, the result of a contraction with respect to these indices is zero. Thus, for a symmetrical spinor of rank two, we have $\psi_{\lambda}{}^{\lambda} = 0$.

A spinor of rank n symmetrical with respect to all its indices is called a *symmetrical spinor*. From an asymmetrical spinor we can construct a symmetrical one by the process of *symmetrisation*, i.e. summation of the components obtained by all possible interchanges of the indices. From what has been said above, it is impossible to construct (by contraction) a spinor of lower rank from the components of a symmetrical spinor.

Only a spinor of rank two can be antisymmetrical with respect to all its indices. For, since each index can take only two values, at least two out of three or more indices must have the same value, and therefore the components of the spinor are zero identically. Any antisymmetrical spinor of rank two is a scalar multiple of the unit spinor $g_{\lambda\mu}$. We may notice here the following relation:

$$g_{\lambda\mu}\psi_{\nu}+g_{\mu\nu}\psi_{\lambda}+g_{\nu\lambda}\psi_{\mu} = 0 \tag{55.2}$$

(where ψ_{λ} is any spinor), which follows from the above; this rule is simply a consequence of the fact that the expression on the left is (as we may easily verify) an antisymmetrical spinor of rank three.

The spinor which is the product of a spinor $\psi_{\lambda\mu}$ with itself, on contraction with respect to one pair of indices, becomes antisymmetrical with respect to the other pair:

$$\psi_{\lambda\nu}\psi_{\mu}{}^{\nu} = -\psi_{\lambda}{}^{\nu}\psi_{\mu\nu}.$$

Hence, from what was said above, this spinor must be a scalar multiple of the spinor $g_{\lambda\mu}$. Defining the scalar factor so that contraction with respect to the second pair of indices gives the correct result, we find

$$\psi_{\lambda\nu}\psi_{\mu}{}^{\nu} = -\tfrac{1}{2}\psi_{\rho\sigma}\psi^{\rho\sigma}g_{\lambda\mu}. \tag{55.3}$$

The components of the spinor $\psi_{\lambda\mu\ldots}{}^{*}$ which is the complex conjugate of $\psi_{\lambda\mu\ldots}$ are transformed as the components of the contravariant spinor $\psi^{\lambda\mu\ldots}$, and conversely. In particular, the sum of the squared moduli of the components of any spinor is consequently invariant.

§56. The wave functions of particles with arbitrary spin

Having developed a formal algebra for spinors of any rank, we can now turn to our immediate problem, to study the wave functions of particles with arbitrary spin.

This subject is conveniently approached by considering an assembly of particles with spin $\frac{1}{2}$. The greatest possible value of the z-component of the total spin is $\frac{1}{2}n$, which is obtained when $s_z = \frac{1}{2}$ for every particle (i.e. all the spins are directed the same way, along the z-axis). In this case we can evidently say that the total spin S of the system is also $\frac{1}{2}n$.

All the components of the wave function $\psi(\sigma_1, \sigma_2, \dots, \sigma_n)$ of the system of particles are then zero, except for $\psi(\frac{1}{2}, \frac{1}{2}, \dots, \frac{1}{2})$. If we write the wave function as a product of n spinors $\psi^\lambda \phi^\mu \dots$, each of which refers to one of the particles, only the component with $\lambda, \mu, \dots = 1$ in each spinor is not zero. Thus only the product $\psi^1 \phi^1 \dots$ is not zero. The set of all these products, however, is a spinor of rank n which is symmetrical with respect to all its indices. If we transform the co-ordinate system (so that the spins are not directed along the z-axis), we obtain a spinor of rank n, general in form except that it is symmetrical as before.

The "spin" properties of wave functions, being essentially their properties with respect to rotations of the co-ordinate system, are evidently identical for a particle with spin s and for a system of $n = 2s$ particles each with spin $\frac{1}{2}$ directed so that the total spin of the system is s. Hence we conclude that the wave function of a particle with spin s is a symmetrical spinor of rank $n = 2s$.

It is easy to see that the number of independent components of a symmetrical spinor of rank $2s$ is equal to $2s+1$, as it should be. For all those components are the same whose indices include $2s$ ones and 0 twos; so are all those with $2s-1$ ones and 1 two, and so on up to 0 ones and $2s$ twos.

Thus we can say that any set of functions which are transformed into linear combinations of one another when the co-ordinate system is rotated can be reduced to one or more symmetrical spinors.†

Thus an arbitrary spinor $\psi_{\lambda\mu\nu\dots}$ of rank n can be reduced to symmetrical spinors of ranks $n, n-2, n-4, \dots$. In practice, such a reduction can be made as follows. By symmetrising the spinor $\psi_{\lambda\mu\nu\dots}$ with respect to all its indices, we form a symmetrical spinor of the same rank n. Next, by contracting the original spinor $\psi_{\lambda\mu\nu\dots}$ with respect to various pairs of indices, we obtain spinors of rank $n-2$, of the form $\psi^\lambda{}_{\lambda\nu\dots}$, which, in turn, we symmetrise, so that symmetrical spinors of rank $n-2$ are obtained. By symmetrising the spinors obtained by contracting $\psi_{\lambda\mu\dots}$ with respect to two pairs of indices, we obtain symmetrical spinors of rank $n-4$, and so on.

Let us consider, in particular, a spinor of rank $2(s_1+s_2)$ which is the product of two symmetrical spinors of rank $2s_1$ and $2s_2$:

$$\underbrace{\psi_{\lambda\mu\dots}}_{2s_1} \underbrace{\phi_{\rho\sigma\dots}}_{2s_2}$$

(for definiteness, suppose $s_1 \geqslant s_2$). Such a spinor can be contracted only with respect to pairs of indices of which one belongs to ψ and the other to ϕ (other-

† In other words, the symmetrical spinors form what are called irreducible representations of the rotation group (see §95).

wise we should obtain zero identically). The greatest number of pairs of indices with respect to which we can simultaneously contract is evidently $2s_2$. Hence it is clear that the spinor considered can be expanded in terms of symmetrical spinors of rank $2(s_1+s_2)$, $2(s_1+s_2-1)$, ..., $2(s_1-s_2)$. Physically, this result is equivalent to the already familiar rule of addition for angular momenta (§30), which states that a system composed of two particles with spins s_1 and s_2 can have a total spin† of s_1+s_2, s_1+s_2-1, ..., s_1-s_2.

We have still to establish the relation between the components of a symmetrical spinor of rank $2s$ and the $2s+1$ functions $\psi(\sigma)$, where $\sigma = s, s-1, \ldots, -s$. The component

$$\psi^{\overbrace{11\ldots1}^{s+\sigma}\overbrace{22\ldots2}^{s-\sigma}},$$

in whose indices 1 occurs $s+\sigma$ times and 2 $s-\sigma$ times, corresponds to a value σ of the projection of the spin on the z-axis. For, if we again consider a system of $n = 2s$ particles with spin $\frac{1}{2}$, instead of one particle with spin s, the product $\underbrace{\psi^1\phi^1\ldots}_{s+\sigma}\underbrace{\chi^2\rho^2\ldots}_{s-\sigma}$ corresponds to the above component; this product belongs to a state in which $s+\sigma$ particles have a projection of the spin equal to $\frac{1}{2}$, and $s-\sigma$ a projection of $-\frac{1}{2}$, so that the total projection is $\frac{1}{2}(s+\sigma)-\frac{1}{2}(s-\sigma) = \sigma$. Finally, the proportionality coefficient between the above component of the spinor and $\psi(\sigma)$ is chosen so that the equation

$$\sum_{\sigma=-s}^{s} |\psi(\sigma)|^2 = \sum_{\lambda,\mu,\ldots=1}^{2} |\psi^{\lambda\mu\ldots}|^2 \tag{56.1}$$

holds; this sum is a scalar, as it should be, since it determines the probability of finding the particle at a given point in space. In the sum on the right-hand side, the components with $(s+\sigma)$ indices 1 occur

$$\frac{(2s)!}{(s+\sigma)!\,(s-\sigma)!}$$

times. Hence it is clear that the relation between the functions $\psi(\sigma)$ and the components of the spinor is given by the formula

$$\psi(\sigma) = \sqrt{\left[\frac{(2s)!}{(s+\sigma)!\,(s-\sigma)!}\right]}\,\psi^{\overbrace{11\ldots1}^{s+\sigma}\overbrace{22\ldots2}^{s-\sigma}}. \tag{56.2}$$

The relation (56.2) ensures the fulfilment not only of the condition (56.1),

† To avoid misunderstanding, it is useful to make the following remark. The wave function of a system of several particles is always a spinor of rank equal to twice the sum Σs_a of the spins of the particles composing the system (not in general the same as the total spin S of the system). In some cases, however, this spinor may be equivalent to one of lower rank. Thus, for example, the wave function of a system of two particles with spin $\frac{1}{2}$ is a spinor of rank two; if the total spin of the system $S = 0$, this spinor is antisymmetrical, and hence can be reduced to a scalar. In general, the symmetry properties of the spinor are determined by the total spin of the system: if the total spin has a given value S, the spinor is symmetrical with respect to $2S$ indices and antisymmetrical with respect to pairs of the remainder.

but also, as we easily see, of the more general condition

$$\psi^{\lambda\mu\ldots}\phi_{\lambda\mu\ldots} = \sum_{\sigma}(-1)^{s-\sigma}\psi(\sigma)\phi(-\sigma), \tag{56.3}$$

where $\psi^{\lambda\mu\ldots}$ and $\phi_{\lambda\mu\ldots}$ are two different spinors of the same rank, while $\psi(\sigma), \phi(\sigma)$ are functions derived from these spinors by formula (56.2); the factor $(-1)^{s-\sigma}$ is due to the fact that, when all the indices of the spinor components are raised, the sign changes as many times as there are twos among the indices.

The matrices (54.2) determine the result of the action of the spin operator on the wave functions $\psi(\sigma)$. It is not difficult to find how these operators act on a wave function written in the form of a spinor of rank $2s$. For a spin $\frac{1}{2}$, the functions $\psi(\frac{1}{2}), \psi(-\frac{1}{2})$ are the same as the components ψ^1, ψ^2 of the spinor. According to (54.2) and (54.3), the result of the spin operators' acting on them will be

$$\begin{aligned}(\hat{s}_x\psi)^1 &= \tfrac{1}{2}\psi^2, \quad (\hat{s}_y\psi)^1 = -\tfrac{1}{2}i\psi^2, \quad (\hat{s}_z\psi)^1 = \tfrac{1}{2}\psi^1,\\ (\hat{s}_x\psi)^2 &= \tfrac{1}{2}\psi^1, \quad (\hat{s}_y\psi)^2 = \tfrac{1}{2}i\psi^1, \quad (\hat{s}_z\psi)^2 = -\tfrac{1}{2}\psi^2.\end{aligned} \tag{56.4}$$

To pass to the general case of arbitrary spin, we again consider a system of $2s$ particles with spin $\frac{1}{2}$, and write its wave function as a product of $2s$ spinors. The spin operator of the system is the sum of the spin operators of each particle, acting only on the corresponding spinor, the result of this action being given by formulae (54.2). Next, returning to arbitrary symmetrical spinors, i.e. to the wave functions of a particle with spin s, we obtain

$$\left.\begin{aligned}(\hat{s}_x\psi)^{\overbrace{11\ldots}^{s+\sigma}\overbrace{22\ldots}^{s-\sigma}} &= \tfrac{1}{2}(s+\sigma)\,\psi^{\overbrace{11\ldots}^{s+\sigma-1}\overbrace{22\ldots}^{s-\sigma+1}}+\tfrac{1}{2}(s-\sigma)\psi^{\overbrace{11\ldots}^{s+\sigma+1}\overbrace{22\ldots}^{s-\sigma-1}},\\ (\hat{s}_y\psi)^{\overbrace{11\ldots}^{s+\sigma}\overbrace{22\ldots}^{s-\sigma}} &= -\tfrac{1}{2}i(s+\sigma)\psi^{\overbrace{11\ldots}^{s+\sigma-1}\overbrace{22\ldots}^{s-\sigma+1}}+\tfrac{1}{2}i(s-\sigma)\psi^{\overbrace{11\ldots}^{s+\sigma+1}\overbrace{22\ldots}^{s-\sigma-1}},\\ (\hat{s}_z\psi)^{\overbrace{11\ldots}^{s+\sigma}\overbrace{22\ldots}^{s-\sigma}} &= \sigma\psi^{\overbrace{11\ldots}^{s+\sigma}\overbrace{22\ldots}^{s-\sigma}}.\end{aligned}\right\} \tag{56.5}$$

We notice that, by starting from these formulae and the relations (56.2), we could derive the expressions (54.2a) for the matrix elements of the spin operator acting on the functions $\psi(\sigma)$.

§57. The relation between spinors and vectors

Previously we have described the states of a particle with an integral orbital angular momentum l by spherical harmonics $Y_{lm}(m = l, l-1, \ldots, -l)$. It is clear that there must exist a definite relation between the laws of the transformation of these spherical harmonics into one another when the co-ordinate system is rotated, and the law of transformation of the components of a spinor of even rank $2l$. To find this relation, we write the angular part of the wave function of some particle, in an arbitrary state with angular momentum l, as a sum:

$$\Psi = \sum_m a_m Y_{lm}(\theta, \phi).$$

After a rotation of the co-ordinate system, this function takes the form

$$\Psi = \sum_m a'_m Y_{lm}(\theta', \phi');$$

θ' and ϕ' are angles in the new system of co-ordinates, and the coefficients a'_m are definite linear functions of the old coefficients a_m. From the physical point of view, the coefficients a_m are the probability amplitudes for the various values m of the z-component of the angular momentum. In this sense they correspond to the "components" $\psi(m)$ of the spin wave function (with $s = l$, $\sigma = m$); their law of transformation is thereby established.

The value of Ψ at a given point in space cannot, of course, be altered as a result of transforming the co-ordinates; hence it follows that the transformation of the functions Y_{lm}, when the co-ordinate system is rotated, must be such that the sum $\Sigma\, a_m Y_{lm}$ is a scalar. Comparing with the scalar (56.3), and recalling that the quantities a_m are transformed as some $\psi(m)$, we see that the above requirement is met if the functions Y_{lm} are, in their law of transformation, the "components" of some spin function $\phi(m)$, according to the formula

$$Y_{lm} = (-1)^{l-m}\phi(-m).$$

Since the factor $(-1)^l$ on the right-hand side of the equation is common to all Y_{lm}, it can be included in $\phi(-m)$; noticing also that, for integral m, we have $(-1)^{-m} = (-1)^m$, and changing the notation, we can write the relation between the spherical harmonics of integral order s and the components $\psi(\sigma)$ of the spin wave function in the form

$$Y_{s\sigma} = (-1)^\sigma \psi(-\sigma) \tag{57.1}$$

(where s is integral and $\sigma = s, s-1, \ldots, -s$).

The case $s = 1$ is of particular importance. The three spherical harmonics $Y_{1\sigma}$ are

$$Y_{10} = \sqrt{\frac{3}{4\pi}}\cos\theta = \sqrt{\frac{3}{4\pi}}\, n_z,$$

$$Y_{1,\pm1} = \mp\sqrt{\frac{3}{8\pi}}\sin\theta\, e^{\pm i\phi} = \mp\sqrt{\frac{3}{8\pi}}(n_x \pm i n_y),$$

where $\mathbf{n}$ is a unit vector along the radius vector. Comparing with (57.1), we see that the components of some vector $\mathbf{a}$ can be brought into correspondence with the components $\psi(\sigma)$ by the formulae

$$\psi(0) = a_z, \quad \psi(1)\sqrt{2} = -a_x + i a_y, \quad \psi(-1)\sqrt{2} = a_x + i a_y. \tag{57.2}$$

Introducing, in place of the components $\psi(\sigma)$, the components of a symmetrical spinor $\psi^{\lambda\mu}$ of rank two, according to formula (56.2):

$$\psi(1) = \psi^{11}, \quad \psi(-1) = \psi^{22}, \quad \psi(0) = \psi^{12}\sqrt{2},$$

we can write similar formulae for the correspondence between the components of such a spinor and those of a vector:

$$\begin{aligned} \psi^{12}\sqrt{2} &= a_z, \quad \psi^{11}\sqrt{2} = -a_x+ia_y, \quad \psi^{22}\sqrt{2} = a_x+ia_y; \\ a_z &= \psi^{12}\sqrt{2}, \quad a_x = (\psi^{22}-\psi^{11})/\sqrt{2}, \quad a_y = -i(\psi^{11}+\psi^{22})/\sqrt{2}. \end{aligned} \tag{57.3}$$

It is easily verified that, with this definition, the scalar $\psi_{\lambda\mu}\psi^{\lambda\mu}$ is the same, apart from the sign, as the scalar $\mathbf{a}^2$:

$$\mathbf{a}^2 = -\psi_{\lambda\mu}\psi^{\lambda\mu}. \tag{57.4}$$

In general, to any integral spin there corresponds a symmetrical spinor of even rank. This spinor reduces to an ordinary symmetrical tensor of half the rank, by contraction of which with respect to any pair of indices we obtain zero. This follows from the fact the numbers of independent components of the spinor and of the tensor are the same, as may easily be seen. The relation between the components of the spinor and of the tensor can be found by means of formulae (57.3), if we consider a spinor of the rank concerned as the product of several spinors of rank two, and the tensor as a product of vectors.

Finally, let us determine the relation between the angles of rotation of the co-ordinate system and the coefficients α, β, γ, δ of the binary transformation. This is done by noticing that, on the one hand, the cosines of the angles between the original and final axes of co-ordinates are the coefficients in the formulae for the transformation of the components of a vector:

$$a'_i = \sum_{k=1}^{3} \alpha_{ik} a_k, \tag{57.5}$$

and, on the other hand, this same transformation can be performed by means of a binary transformation, using formulae (57.3). Thus, for instance, we have

$$\begin{aligned} a'_z = \psi^{12\prime} &= \alpha\gamma\psi^{11}+\beta\delta\psi^{22}+(\alpha\delta+\beta\gamma)\psi^{12} \\ &= (-\alpha\gamma+\beta\delta)a_x+i(\alpha\gamma+\beta\delta)a_y+(\alpha\delta+\beta\gamma)a_z, \end{aligned}$$

so that

$$\alpha_{zx} = -\alpha\gamma+\beta\delta, \quad \alpha_{zy} = i(\alpha\gamma+\beta\delta), \quad \alpha_{zz} = \alpha\delta+\beta\gamma.$$

We can similarly determine the remaining α_{ik}, and thus obtain the following scheme of transformation coefficients:

$$(\alpha_{ik}) = \begin{bmatrix} \frac{1}{2}(\alpha^2-\beta^2-\gamma^2+\delta^2) & \frac{1}{2}i(-\alpha^2-\beta^2+\gamma^2+\delta^2) & (-\alpha\beta+\gamma\delta) \\ \frac{1}{2}i(\alpha^2-\beta^2+\gamma^2-\delta^2) & \frac{1}{2}(\alpha^2+\beta^2+\gamma^2+\delta^2) & -i(\alpha\beta+\gamma\delta) \\ (-\alpha\gamma+\beta\delta) & i(\alpha\gamma+\beta\delta) & \alpha\delta+\beta\gamma \end{bmatrix}. \tag{57.6}$$

The inverse expressions for the coefficients α, β, γ, δ in terms of the angles of rotation of the co-ordinate system can be found by using the Eulerian angles to define the rotation of the system. The matrix† of the coefficients α, β, γ, δ for a rotation through an angle ψ about the z-axis (denoted by $\omega(\psi)$), according to formula (54.1) with $\sigma = \pm\frac{1}{2}$, is of the form

$$\begin{bmatrix} \alpha & \beta \\ \gamma & \delta \end{bmatrix} \equiv \omega(\psi) = \begin{bmatrix} e^{\frac{1}{2}i\psi} & 0 \\ 0 & e^{-\frac{1}{2}i\psi} \end{bmatrix}.$$

The matrix $\Omega(\theta)$ expressing a rotation through an angle θ about the x-axis is easily calculated from formulae (57.6), in which the only α_{ik} which are not zero are $\alpha_{xx} = 1$, $\alpha_{yy} = \alpha_{zz} = \cos\theta$, $\alpha_{yz} = -\alpha_{zy} = \sin\theta$:

$$\Omega(\theta) = \begin{bmatrix} \cos\frac{1}{2}\theta & i\sin\frac{1}{2}\theta \\ i\sin\frac{1}{2}\theta & \cos\frac{1}{2}\theta \end{bmatrix}.$$

A rotation specified by the Eulerian angles ϕ, θ, ψ (Fig. 22; ON is the line of intersection of the xy and $x'y'$ planes) is carried out in three stages: a rotation

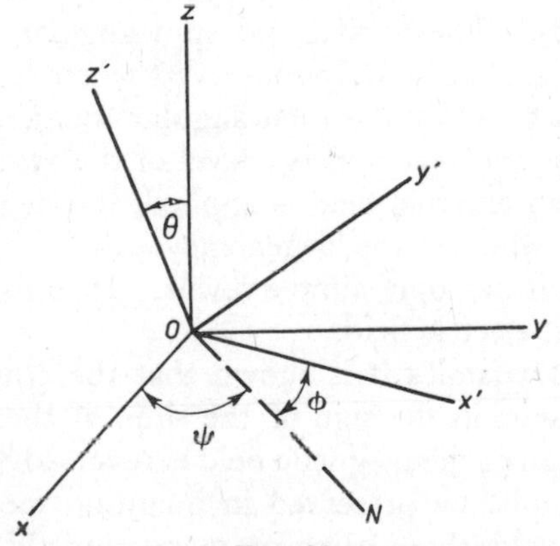

FIG. 22

through an angle ψ about the z-axis, one through an angle θ about the new position of the x-axis, and finally one through an angle ϕ about the final direction of the z-axis. Accordingly, the matrix of the complete transformation is equal to the product $\omega(\phi)\Omega(\theta)\omega(\psi)$. By direct multiplication of the matrices, we finally obtain

$$\begin{bmatrix} \alpha & \beta \\ \gamma & \delta \end{bmatrix} = \begin{bmatrix} \cos\frac{1}{2}\theta \,.\, e^{\frac{1}{2}i(\phi+\psi)} & i\sin\frac{1}{2}\theta \,.\, e^{\frac{1}{2}i(\phi-\psi)} \\ i\sin\frac{1}{2}\theta \,.\, e^{-\frac{1}{2}i(\phi-\psi)} & \cos\frac{1}{2}\theta \,.\, e^{-\frac{1}{2}i(\phi+\psi)} \end{bmatrix}. \tag{57.7}$$

PROBLEM

Determine the relation between the components of a symmetrical spinor of rank four and those of a symmetrical tensor of rank two (giving zero on contraction).

† The term *matrix* is here understood in the sense usual in the theory of linear transformations.

SOLUTION. Bearing in mind that the components of a tensor are transformed as products of the components of a vector, we find

$$a_{xx} = \tfrac{1}{2}(\psi^{1111}+\psi^{2222}-2\psi^{1122}), \quad a_{xy} = \tfrac{1}{2}i(\psi^{1111}-\psi^{2222}),$$
$$a_{yy} = -\tfrac{1}{2}(\psi^{1111}+\psi^{2222}+2\psi^{1122}), \quad a_{xz} = (\psi^{1222}-\psi^{1112}),$$
$$a_{zz} = 2\psi^{1122}, \quad a_{yz} = -i(\psi^{1222}+\psi^{1112}).$$

The relation between the components of the tensor and quantities transformed as the "components" $\psi(\sigma)$ of the wave function (with spin $s = 2$) is given by the formulae (we have used (56.2) to find the relation between $\psi(\sigma)$ and the components of the spinor):

$$a_{xx} = \tfrac{1}{2}[\psi(2)+\psi(-2)-\sqrt{\tfrac{2}{3}}\psi(0)], \quad a_{xy} = \tfrac{1}{2}i[\psi(2)-\psi(-2)],$$
$$a_{yy} = -\tfrac{1}{2}[\psi(2)+\psi(-2)+\sqrt{\tfrac{2}{3}}\psi(0)], \quad a_{xz} = \tfrac{1}{2}[\psi(-1)-\psi(1)],$$
$$a_{zz} = \sqrt{\tfrac{2}{3}}\psi(0), \quad a_{yz} = -\tfrac{1}{2}i[\psi(-1)+\psi(1)].$$

§58. Kramers' theorem

Let us consider a system of arbitrarily interacting particles (not necessarily all of the same kind). The orbital and spin angular momenta of such a system are not in general separately conserved when relativistic interactions are taken into account. Only the total angular momentum $\mathbf{J}$ is conserved. If there is no external field, each energy level of the system has $(2J+1)$-fold degeneracy. When an external field is applied, the degeneracy is removed. The question arises whether the degeneracy can be removed completely, i.e. so that the system has only simple levels. It is found that this is not always possible for an electric field.

In classical electrodynamics it is shown that the equations are invariant with respect to a change in the sign of the time, if the electric field is left unchanged and the sign of the magnetic field is reversed.† This fundamental property of motion must be preserved in quantum mechanics. Hence, in any external electric field (there being no magnetic field), there is symmetry with respect to a change in the sign of the time. This symmetry is expressed by the fact that, if ψ is the wave function of a stationary state, the complex conjugate function ψ^* also describes a possible state, with the same energy (§16).

The wave functions of the stationary states of the system are spinors $\psi^{\lambda\mu\cdots}$, whose rank n is twice the sum of the spins s_a of all the particles in the system ($n = 2\sum s_a$); this sum may not be equal to the total spin S of the system.

According to what was said above, we can assert that, in any electric field, the spinors $\psi^{\lambda\mu\cdots}$ and $\psi^{\lambda\mu\cdots *}$ must correspond to states with the same energy. If a level is non-degenerate, it is necessary that these states should be identical, i.e. the spinors $\psi^{\lambda\mu\cdots}$ and $\psi^{\lambda\mu\cdots *}$ must be essentially the same. Since the complex conjugate spinor $\psi^{\lambda\mu\cdots *}$ is a quantity which is transformed as the

† See, for example, *The Classical Theory of Fields*, §3-3, Addison-Wesley Press, Cambridge (Mass.) 1951.

covariant spinor $\psi_{\lambda\mu\dots}$, we can write the necessary condition for non-degeneracy in the form

$$\psi^{\lambda\mu\dots *} = C\psi_{\lambda\mu\dots}, \tag{58.1}$$

where C is a constant.

Taking the complex conjugate of both sides of this equation, we obtain

$$\psi^{\lambda\mu\dots} = C^*\psi_{\lambda\mu\dots}{}^*.$$

We lower the indices on the left-hand side of the equation and correspondingly raise them on the right. This means that we multiply both sides of the equation by $g_{\alpha\lambda}g_{\beta\mu}\dots$ and sum over the indices $\lambda, \mu, \dots$; on the right-hand side we must use the fact that

$$g_{\alpha\lambda}g_{\beta\mu}\dots = (-1)^n g^{\lambda\alpha}g^{\mu\beta}\dots$$

(we recall that $g_{\lambda\mu} = -g^{\mu\lambda}$). As a result we have

$$\psi_{\lambda\mu\dots} = C^*(-1)^n\psi^{\lambda\mu\dots *}.$$

Substituting $\psi^{\lambda\mu\dots *}$ from (58.1), we find

$$\psi_{\lambda\mu\dots} = (-1)^n CC^*\psi_{\lambda\mu\dots}.$$

This equation must clearly be satisfied identically, i.e. we must have $(-1)^n CC^* = 1$. Since, however, $|C|^2$ is always positive, it is clear that this is possible only for even n (i.e. for integral values of the sum $\Sigma\, s_a$). For odd n (half-integral values of $\Sigma\, s_a$) the condition (58.1) cannot be fulfilled.†

Thus we reach the result that an electric field can completely remove the degeneracy only for a system with an integral value of the sum of the spins of the particles. For a system with a half-integral value of this sum, in an arbitrary electric field, all the levels must be doubly degenerate, and complex conjugate spinors correspond to two different states with the same energy‡ (Kramers 1930).

† When the sum $\Sigma\, s_a$ is integral (or half-integral), all possible values of the total spin S of the system are also integral (or half-integral).

‡ If the electric field possesses a high (cubic) symmetry, fourfold degeneracy may occur (see §96, including the Problem).

CHAPTER IX

IDENTITY OF PARTICLES

§59. The principle of indistinguishability of similar particles

IN classical mechanics, identical particles (electrons, say) do not lose their "individuality", despite the identity of their physical properties. For we can imagine the particles at some instant to be "numbered", and follow the subsequent motion of each of these in its path; then at any instant the particles can be identified.

In quantum mechanics the situation is entirely different, as follows at once from the uncertainty principle. We have already mentioned several times that, by virtue of the uncertainty principle, the concept of the path of an electron ceases to have any meaning. If the position of an electron is exactly known at a given instant, its co-ordinates have no definite values even at an infinitely close subsequent instant. Hence, by localising and numbering the electrons at some instant, we make no progress towards identifying them at subsequent instants; if we localise one of the electrons, at some other instant, at some point in space, we cannot say which of the electrons has arrived at this point.

Thus, in quantum mechanics, there is in principle no possibility of separately following each of a number of similar particles and thereby distinguishing them. We may say that, in quantum mechanics, identical particles entirely lose their "individuality". The identity of the particles with respect to their physical properties is here very far-reaching: it results in the complete indistinguishability of the particles.

This principle of the *indistinguishability of similar particles*, as it is called, plays a fundamental part in the quantum-mechanical investigation of systems composed of identical particles. Let us start by considering a system of only two particles. Because of the identity of the particles, the states of the system obtained from each other by merely interchanging the two particles must be completely equivalent physically. This means that, as a result of this interchange, the wave function of the system can change only by an unimportant phase factor. Let $\psi(\xi_1, \xi_2)$ be the wave function of the system, ξ_1 and ξ_2 conventionally denoting the assemblies of the three co-ordinates and the spin projection for each particle. Then we must have

$$\psi(\xi_1, \xi_2) = e^{i\alpha}\psi(\xi_2, \xi_1),$$

where α is some real constant. By repeating the interchange, we return to the original state, while the function ψ is multiplied by $e^{2i\alpha}$. Hence it follows that $e^{2i\alpha} = 1$, or $e^{i\alpha} = \pm 1$. Thus

$$\psi(\xi_1, \xi_2) = \pm\psi(\xi_2, \xi_1).$$

We thus reach the result that there are only two possibilities: the wave function is either *symmetrical* (i.e. it is unchanged when the particles are interchanged) or *antisymmetrical* (i.e. it changes sign when this interchange is made). It is obvious that the wave functions of all the states of a given system must have the same symmetry; otherwise, the wave function of a state which was a superposition of states of different symmetry would be neither symmetrical nor antisymmetrical.

This result can be immediately generalised to systems consisting of any number of identical particles. For it is clear from the identity of the particles that, if any pair of them has the property of being described by, say, symmetrical wave functions, any other pair of such particles has the same property. Hence the wave function of identical particles must either be unchanged when any pair of particles are interchanged (and hence when the particles are permuted in any manner), or change sign when any pair are interchanged. In the first case we speak of a *symmetrical* wave function, and in the second case of an *antisymmetrical* one.

The property of being described by symmetrical or antisymmetrical wave functions depends on the nature of the particles. Particles described by antisymmetrical functions are said to obey *Fermi-Dirac statistics* (or *Fermi statistics*, for short), while those which are described by symmetrical functions are said to obey *Bose-Einstein statistics* (or *Bose statistics*, for short).† The majority of the elementary particles—electrons, positrons, protons, neutrons—obey Fermi statistics.

The statistics of complex particles is determined by the parity of the number of elementary Fermi particles entering into their composition. For an interchange of two identical complex particles is equivalent to the simultaneous interchange of several pairs of identical elementary particles. The interchange of Bose particles does not change the wave function, while the interchange of Fermi particles changes its sign. Hence complex particles containing an odd number of elementary Fermi particles obey Fermi statistics, while those containing an even number obey Bose statistics. Thus atomic nuclei of odd atomic weight (i.e. containing an odd number of neutrons and protons) obey Fermi statistics, and those of even atomic weight obey Bose statistics.

Experiment shows that the statistics obeyed by particles of a given kind is in one-to-one correspondence with their spin. There is, in fact, a general rule, according to which particles of half-integral spin obey Fermi statistics, while those of integral spin obey Bose statistics.‡ The above discussion of complex particles is in accordance with this general rule, since a complex

---

† This unfortunate terminology refers to the statistics which describes a perfect gas composed of particles with antisymmetrical and symmetrical wave functions respectively. In actual fact we are concerned here not only with a different statistics, but essentially with a different mechanics. Fermi statistics was proposed by FERMI for electrons in 1926, and its relation to quantum mechanics was elucidated by DIRAC (1926). Bose statistics was proposed by BOSE for light quanta, and generalised by EINSTEIN (1924).

‡ Theoretical reasons for this rule become apparent in relativistic quantum theory.

particle has an integral or a half-integral spin according as the number of particles with half-integral spin entering into its composition is even or odd.

Let us consider a system composed of N identical particles, whose mutual interaction can be neglected. Let $\psi_1, \psi_2, \ldots$ be the wave functions of the various stationary states which each of the particles separately may occupy.† The state of the system as a whole can be defined by giving the numbers of the states which the individual particles occupy. The question arises how the wave function Ψ of the whole system should be constructed from the functions $\psi_1, \psi_2, \ldots$.

Let $p_1, p_2, \ldots, p_N$ be the numbers of the states occupied by the individual particles (some of these numbers may be the same). If the particles obey Bose statistics, the wave function $\Psi(\xi_1, \xi_2, \ldots, \xi_N)$ is given by a sum of products of the form

$$\psi_{p_1}(\xi_1)\psi_{p_2}(\xi_2)\ldots\psi_{p_N}(\xi_N),$$

with all possible permutations of the different suffixes $p_1, p_2, \ldots$; this sum clearly possesses the required symmetry property. Thus, for example, for a system of two particles

$$\Psi(\xi_1, \xi_2) = [\psi_{p_1}(\xi_1)\psi_{p_2}(\xi_2)+\psi_{p_1}(\xi_2)\psi_{p_2}(\xi_1)]/\sqrt{2}; \tag{59.1}$$

we suppose that $p_1 \neq p_2$. The factor $1/\sqrt{2}$ is introduced for normalisation purposes; all the functions $\psi_1, \psi_2, \ldots$ are orthogonal and are supposed normalised.

If the particles obey Fermi statistics, the wave function Ψ is an antisymmetrical combination of these products. It can be written in the form of a determinant

$$\Psi = \frac{1}{\sqrt{N!}}\begin{vmatrix} \psi_{p_1}(\xi_1) & \psi_{p_1}(\xi_2) & \ldots & \psi_{p_1}(\xi_N) \\ \psi_{p_2}(\xi_1) & \psi_{p_2}(\xi_2) & \ldots & \psi_{p_2}(\xi_N) \\ \ldots & \ldots & \ldots & \ldots \\ \psi_{p_N}(\xi_1) & \psi_{p_N}(\xi_2) & \ldots & \psi_{p_N}(\xi_N) \end{vmatrix}. \tag{59.2}$$

Here an interchange of two particles corresponds to an interchange of two columns of the determinant, as a result of which the latter, as is well known, changes sign. For a system composed of two particles we have

$$\Psi = [\psi_{p_1}(\xi_1)\psi_{p_2}(\xi_2)-\psi_{p_1}(\xi_2)\psi_{p_2}(\xi_1)]/\sqrt{2}. \tag{59.3}$$

The following very important result is a consequence of the expression (59.2). If among the numbers $p_1, p_2, \ldots$ any two are the same, two rows of the

† If there is a strong interaction between the particles we cannot, of course, speak of such states.

determinant are the same, and it therefore vanishes identically. It will be different from zero only when all the numbers $p_1, p_2, \ldots$ are different. Thus, in a system consisting of identical particles obeying Fermi statistics, no two (or more) particles can be in the same state at the same time. This is called *Pauli's principle* (1925).

§60. Exchange interaction

The fact that SCHRÖDINGER's equation does not take account of the spin of particles does not invalidate this equation or the results obtained by means of it. This is because the electrical interaction of the particles does not depend on their spins.† Mathematically, this means that the Hamiltonian of a system of electrically interacting particles (in the absence of a magnetic field) does not contain the spin operators, and hence, when it is applied to the wave function, it has no effect on the spin variables. Hence SCHRÖDINGER's equation is actually satisfied by each component of the wave function; in other words, the wave function $\psi(\mathbf{r}_1, \sigma_1; \mathbf{r}_2, \sigma_2; \ldots)$ of the system of particles can be written in the form of a product

$$\chi(\sigma_1, \sigma_2, \ldots)\phi(\mathbf{r}_1, \mathbf{r}_2, \ldots)$$

of a function ϕ of the co-ordinates of the particles only and a function χ of the spins. We call the former a *co-ordinate* or *orbital* wave function, and the latter a *spin* wave function. SCHRÖDINGER's equation essentially determines only the co-ordinate function ϕ, the function χ remaining arbitrary. In any instance where we are not interested in the actual spin of the particles, we can therefore use SCHRÖDINGER's equation and regard as the wave function the co-ordinate function alone, as we have done hitherto.

However, despite the fact that the electrical interaction of the particles is independent of their spin, there is a peculiar dependence of the energy of the system on its total spin, arising ultimately from the principle of indistinguishability of similar particles.

Let us consider a system consisting of only two identical particles. By solving SCHRÖDINGER's equation we find a series of energy levels, to each of which there corresponds a definite co-ordinate wave function $\phi(\mathbf{r}_1, \mathbf{r}_2)$. These functions must be either symmetrical or antisymmetrical. For, by virtue of the identity of the particles, the Hamiltonian (and therefore the SCHRÖDINGER's equation) of the system is invariant with respect to interchange of the particles. If the energy levels are not degenerate, the function $\phi(\mathbf{r}_1, \mathbf{r}_2)$ can change only by a constant factor when the co-ordinates $\mathbf{r}_1$ and $\mathbf{r}_2$ are interchanged; repeating this interchange, we see that this factor can only be‡ ± 1. However, it must be borne in mind that the functions ϕ corresponding to different energy

† This is true only so long as we consider the non-relativistic approximation. When relativistic effects are taken into account, the interaction of charged particles does depend on their spin.

‡ When there is degeneracy we can always choose linear combinations of the functions belonging to a given level, such that this condition is again satisfied.

levels need not have the same symmetry; they may include both symmetrical and antisymmetrical functions.

Let us first suppose that the particles have zero spin. The spin factor for such particles is absent altogether, and the wave function reduces to a single co-ordinate function $\phi(\mathbf{r}_1, \mathbf{r}_2)$, which must be symmetrical (since particles with zero spin obey Bose statistics). Thus not all the energy levels obtained by a formal solution of SCHRÖDINGER's equation can actually exist; those to which antisymmetrical functions ϕ correspond are not possible for the system under consideration.

The interchange of two similar particles is equivalent to the operation of inversion of the co-ordinate system (the origin being taken to bisect the line joining the two particles). On the other hand, the result of inversion is to multiply the wave function ϕ by $(-1)^l$, where l is the orbital angular momentum of the relative motion of the two particles (see §28). By comparing these considerations with those given above, we conclude that a system of two identical particles with zero spin can have only an even orbital angular momentum.

Next, let us suppose that the system consists of two particles with spin $\frac{1}{2}$ (say, electrons). Then the complete wave function of the system (i.e. the product of the function $\phi(\mathbf{r}_1, \mathbf{r}_2)$ and the spin function $\chi(\sigma_1, \sigma_2)$) must certainly be antisymmetrical with respect to an interchange of the two electrons. Hence, if the co-ordinate function is symmetrical, the spin function must be antisymmetrical, and *vice versa*. We shall write the spin function in spinor form, i.e. as a spinor $\chi^{\lambda\mu}$ of rank two, each of whose indices corresponds to the spin of one of the electrons. A symmetrical spinor ($\chi^{\lambda\mu} = \chi^{\mu\lambda}$) corresponds to a function symmetrical with respect to the spins of the two particles, and an antisymmetrical spinor ($\chi^{\lambda\mu} = -\chi^{\mu\lambda}$) to an antisymmetrical function. We know, however, that a symmetrical spinor of rank two describes a system with total spin unity, while an antisymmetrical spinor reduces to a scalar, corresponding to zero spin.

Thus we reach the following conclusion. The energy levels to which there correspond symmetrical solutions $\phi(\mathbf{r}_1, \mathbf{r}_2)$ of SCHRÖDINGER's equation can actually occur when the total spin of the system is zero, i.e. when the spins of the two electrons are "antiparallel", giving a sum of zero. The values of the energy belonging to antisymmetrical functions $\phi(\mathbf{r}_1, \mathbf{r}_2)$, on the other hand, require a value of unity for the total spin, i.e. the spins of the two electrons must be "parallel". Conversely, we see that, if the value of the total spin of the system is given, not all the energy values obtained by solving SCHRÖDINGER's equation are possible, but only some of them.

In other words, the possible values of the energy of a system of electrons depend on their total spin. For this reason we can speak of a peculiar interaction of the particles which results in this dependence. This is called *exchange interaction*. It is a purely quantum effect, which entirely vanishes (like the spin itself) in the passage to the limit of classical mechanics.

The following situation is characteristic of the case of a system of two electrons which we have discussed. To each energy level there corresponds one definite value of the spin, 0 or 1. This one-valued correspondence between the spin values and the energy levels is preserved, as we shall see below (§61) in systems containing any number of electrons. It does not hold, however, for systems composed of particles whose spin exceeds $\frac{1}{2}$.

Let us consider a system of two particles, each with arbitrary spin s. Its spin wave function is a spinor of rank $4s$:

$$\chi^{\overbrace{\lambda\mu\ldots}^{2s}\;\overbrace{\rho\sigma\ldots}^{2s}},$$

half ($2s$) of whose indices correspond to the spin of one particle, and the other half to that of the other particle. The spinor is symmetrical with respect to the indices in each group. An interchange of the two particles corresponds to an interchange of all the indices λ, μ, ... of the first group with the indices ρ, σ, ... of the second group. In order to obtain the spin function of a state of the system with total spin S, we must contract this spinor with respect to $2s-S$ pairs of indices (each pair containing one index from λ, μ, ... and one from ρ, σ, ...), and symmetrise it with respect to the remainder; as a result we obtain a symmetrical spinor of rank $2S$. However, the contraction of a spinor with respect to a pair of indices means, as we know, the construction of a combination antisymmetrical with respect to these indices. Hence, when the particles are interchanged, the spin wave function is multiplied by $(-1)^{2s-S}$.

On the other hand, the complete wave function of a system of two particles must be multiplied by $(-1)^{2s}$ when they are interchanged (i.e. by $+1$ for integral s and by -1 for half-integral s). Hence it follows that the symmetry of the co-ordinate wave function with respect to an interchange of the particles is given by the factor $(-1)^S$, which depends only on S. Thus we reach the result that the co-ordinate wave function of a system of two identical particles is symmetrical when the total spin is even, and antisymmetrical when it is odd.

Recalling what was said above concerning the relation between interchange of the particles and inversion of the co-ordinate system, we conclude also that, when the spin S is even (odd), the system can have only an even (odd) orbital angular momentum.

We see that here also a certain dependence is revealed between the possible values of the energy of the system and the total spin, but this dependence is not necessarily one-valued. The energy levels to which there correspond symmetrical (antisymmetrical) co-ordinate wave functions can occur for any even (odd) value of S.

Let us calculate how many different states of the system there are with even and odd S. The quantity S takes $2s+1$ values: $2s$, $2s-1$, ..., 0. For any given S there are $2S+1$ states differing in the value of the z-component of the spin ($(2s+1)^2$ different states altogether). Let s be integral. Then, among the $2s+1$ values of S, $s+1$ are even and s odd. The total number of states with even S is equal to the sum

$$\sum_{S=0,2,\ldots,2s}(2S+1) = (2s+1)(s+1);$$

the remaining $s(2s+1)$ states have odd S. Similarly, we find that, when s is half-integral, there are $s(2s+1)$ states with even values of S and $(s+1)(2s+1)$ with odd values.

§61. Symmetry with respect to interchange

By considering a system composed of only two particles, we have been able to show that its co-ordinate wave functions $\phi(\mathbf{r}_1, \mathbf{r}_2)$ for the stationary states must be either symmetrical or antisymmetrical. In the general case of a system of an arbitrary number of particles, the solutions of SCHRÖDINGER's equation (the co-ordinate wave functions) need not necessarily be either symmetrical or antisymmetrical with respect to the interchange of any pair of particles, as the complete wave functions (which include the spin factor) must be. This is because an interchange of only the co-ordinates of two particles does not correspond to a physical interchange of them. The physical identity of the particles here leads only to the fact that the Hamiltonian of the system is invariant with respect to the interchange of the particles, and hence, if some function is a solution of SCHRÖDINGER's equation, the functions obtained from it by various interchanges of the variables will also be solutions.

Let us first of all make some remarks regarding interchanges in general. In a system of N particles, $N!$ different permutations in all are possible. If we imagine all the particles to be numbered, each permutation can be represented by a definite sequence of the numbers 1, 2, 3, ... Every such sequence can be obtained from the natural sequence 1, 2, 3, ... by successive interchanges of pairs of particles. The permutation is called *even* or *odd*, according as it is brought about by an even or odd number of such interchanges. We denote by $\hat{P}$ the operators of permutations of N particles, and introduce a quantity δ_P which is $+1$ if $\hat{P}$ is an even permutation and -1 if it is odd. If ϕ is a function symmetrical with respect to all the particles, we have

$$\hat{P}\phi = \phi,$$

while, if ϕ is antisymmetrical with respect to all the particles, then

$$\hat{P}\phi = \delta_P\phi.$$

From an arbitrary function $\phi(\mathbf{r}_1, \mathbf{r}_2, \ldots, \mathbf{r}_N)$, we can form a symmetrical function by the operation of *symmetrisation*, which can be written

$$\phi_{\text{sym}} = \text{constant} \times \sum_P \hat{P}\phi, \tag{61.1}$$

where the summation extends over all possible permutations. The formation of an antisymmetrical function (an operation sometimes called *alternation*) can be written as

$$\phi_{\text{ant}} = \text{constant} \times \sum_P \delta_P \hat{P}\phi. \tag{61.2}$$

Let us return to considering the behaviour, with respect to permutations, of the wave functions ϕ of a system of identical particles.† The fact that the Hamiltonian $\hat{H}$ of the system is symmetrical with respect to all the particles means, mathematically, that $\hat{H}$ commutes with all the permutation operators $\hat{P}$. These operators, however, do not commute with one another, and so they cannot be simultaneously brought into diagonal form. This means that the wave functions ϕ cannot be so chosen that each of them is either symmetrical or antisymmetrical with respect to all interchanges separately.‡

Let us try to determine the possible types of symmetry of the functions $\phi(\mathbf{r}_1, \mathbf{r}_2, \ldots, \mathbf{r}_N)$ of N variables (or of sets of several such functions) with respect to permutations of the variables. The symmetry must be such that it "cannot be increased", i.e. such that any additional operation of symmetrisation or alternation, on being applied to these functions, would reduce them either to linear combinations of themselves or to zero identically.

We already know two operations which give functions with the greatest possible symmetry: symmetrisation with respect to all the variables, and alternation with respect to all the variables. These operations can be generalised as follows.

We divide the set of all the N variables $\mathbf{r}_1, \mathbf{r}_2, \ldots, \mathbf{r}_N$ (or, what is the same thing, the suffixes $1, 2, 3, \ldots, N$) into several sets, containing $N_1, N_2, \ldots$ elements (variables); $N_1+N_2+\ldots = N$. This division can be conveniently shown by a diagram (known as a *Young diagram*) in which each of the numbers $N_1, N_2, \ldots$ is represented by a line of several cells (thus, Fig. 23 gives a diagram of the divisions $6+4+4+3+3+1+1$ and $7+5+5+3+1+1$ for

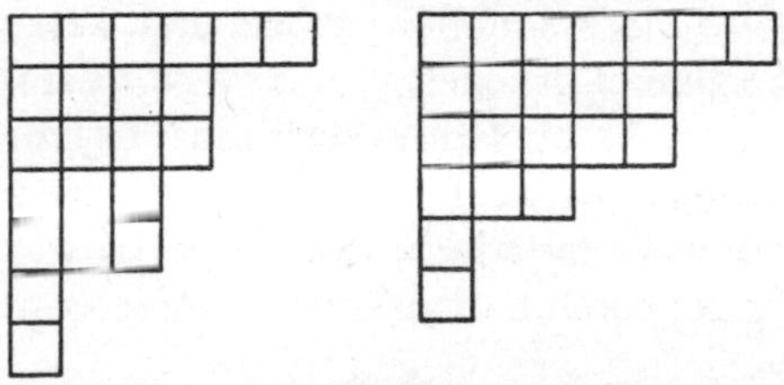

FIG. 23

$N = 22$); one of the numbers $1, 2, 3, \ldots$ is to be placed in each square. If we place the lines in order of decreasing length (as in Fig. 23), the diagram contains not only successive horizontal rows, but also vertical columns.

† From the mathematical point of view, the problem is to find irreducible representations of the group of permutations of N elements.

‡ Except for a system of only two particles, where there is a single interchange operator, which can be brought into diagonal form simultaneously with $\hat{H}$.

Let us symmetrise an arbitrary function $\phi(\mathbf{r}_1, \mathbf{r}_2, \dots, \mathbf{r}_N)$ with respect to the variables in each row. The alternation operation can then be performed only with respect to the variables in different rows; alternation with respect to a pair of variables in the same row clearly gives zero identically.

Having chosen one variable from each row, we can, without loss of generality, regard them as being in the first cells in each row (after symmetrisation, the order of the variables among the cells in each row is immaterial); let us alternate with respect to these variables. Having then deleted the first column, we alternate with respect to variables chosen one from each row in the thus "curtailed" diagram; these variables can again be regarded as being in the first cells of the "curtailed" rows. Continuing this process, we finally have the function first symmetrised with respect to the variables in each row and then alternated with respect to the variables in each column.†

Having distributed the N variables in various ways among the rows of a Young diagram (the distribution among the cells in each row is immaterial), we thus obtain a series of functions, which are transformed linearly into one another when the variables are permuted in any manner.‡ However, it must be emphasised that not all these functions are linearly independent; the number of independent functions is in general less than the number of possible distributions of the variables among the rows of the diagram. We shall not pause here, however, to discuss this more closely.‖

Thus any Young diagram determines some type of symmetry of functions with respect to permutations. By constructing all the possible Young diagrams (for a given N), we find all possible types of symmetry. This amounts to dividing the number N in all possible ways into a sum of smaller terms, including the number N itself; thus for $N = 4$ the possible partitions¶ are 4, $3+1$, $2+2$, $2+1+1$, $1+1+1+1$.

To each energy level of the system we can make correspond a Young diagram which determines the permutational symmetry of the appropriate solutions of SCHRÖDINGER's equation; in general, several different functions correspond to each value of the energy, and these are transformed linearly into each other by permutations.†† However, it must be emphasised that this does not signify any additional physical degeneracy of the energy levels. All these different co-ordinate wave functions, multiplied by the spin functions, enter into a single definite combination—the complete wave function—which

† After alternation, the function in general ceases to be symmetrical with respect to the variables in each row. The symmetry is preserved only with respect to the variables in the cells of the first row which project beyond the other rows.

‡ It would be possible to perform the symmetrisation and alternation in the reverse order: to alternate with respect to the variables in each column, and then to symmetrise with respect to those in the rows. This, however, would give effectively the same thing, since the functions obtained by the two methods are linear combinations of one another.

‖ The mathematical theory of representations of permutation groups (as applied to quantum mechanics) may be found in H. WEYL's book, *The Theory of Groups and Quantum Mechanics*, Methuen, London 1931, Chapter V.

¶ In the theory of permutation groups, these partitions are sometimes called *partitio numerorum*.

†† The existence of this "permutational degeneracy" is related to the fact that the permutation operators commuting with the Hamiltonian do not in general commute with one another (see the middle of §10).

satisfies (according to the number of particles) the condition of symmetry or antisymmetry.

Among the various types of symmetry there are always (for any given N) two to each of which only one function corresponds. One of these corresponds to a function symmetrical with respect to all the variables, and the other to one which is similarly antisymmetrical; in the first case, the Young diagram consists of a single row of N cells, and in the second case of a single column.

Let us now consider the spin wave functions $\chi(\sigma_1, \sigma_2, \dots, \sigma_N)$. Their kinds of symmetry with respect to permutations of the particles are given by the same Young diagrams, with the z-components of the spins of the particles taking the part of variables. There arises the question of what diagram must correspond to the spin function for a given diagram of the co-ordinate function. Let us first suppose that the spin of the particles is integral. Then the complete wave function ψ must be symmetrical with respect to all the particles. For this to be so, the symmetry of the spin and co-ordinate functions must be given by the same Young diagram, and the complete wave function ψ is expressed as definite bilinear combinations of the two; we shall not here pause to examine more closely the problem of constructing these combinations.

Next, suppose the spin of the particles to be half-integral. Then the complete wave function must be antisymmetrical with respect to all the particles. It can be shown that, for this to be so, the Young diagrams for the co-ordinate and spin functions must be obtained from each other by interchanging rows and columns (as in the two diagrams shown in Fig. 23).

Let us consider in more detail the important case of particles with spin $\frac{1}{2}$ (electrons, for instance). Each of the spin variables $\sigma_1, \sigma_2, \dots$ here takes only the two values $\pm\frac{1}{2}$. Since a function antisymmetrical with respect to any two variables vanishes when these variables take the same value, it is clear that the function χ can be alternated only with respect to pairs of variables; if we alternate with respect to even three variables, two of them must always take the same value, so that we have zero identically.

Thus, for a system of electrons, the Young diagrams for the spin functions can contain columns of only one or two cells (i.e. only one or two rows); in the Young diagrams for the co-ordinate functions, the same is true of the number of columns. The number of possible types of permutational symmetry for a system of N electrons is therefore equal to the number of possible partitions of the number N into a sum of ones and twos. When N is even, this number is $\frac{1}{2}N+1$ (partitions with $0, 1, \dots, \frac{1}{2}N$ twos), while if N is odd it is $\frac{1}{2}(N+1)$ (partitions with $0, 1, \dots, \frac{1}{2}(N-1)$ twos). Thus, for instance, Fig. 24 shows the possible Young diagrams (co-ordinate and spin) for $N = 4$.

It is easy to see that each of these types of symmetry (i.e. each of the Young diagrams) corresponds to a definite total spin S of the system of electrons. We shall consider the spin functions in spinor form, i.e. as spinors $\chi^{\lambda\mu\dots}$ of rank N, whose indices (each of which corresponds to the spin of an individual particle) will be the variables that are arranged in the cells of the Young diagrams. Let us examine the Young diagram consisting of two rows with N_1 and N_2 cells ($N_1+N_2 = N$, and $N_1 \geqslant N_2$). In each of the first N_2 columns there are two cells, and the spinor must be antisymmetrical with respect to the corresponding pairs of indices. With respect to the indices in the last $n = N_1-N_2$ cells in the first row, however, it must be symmetrical.

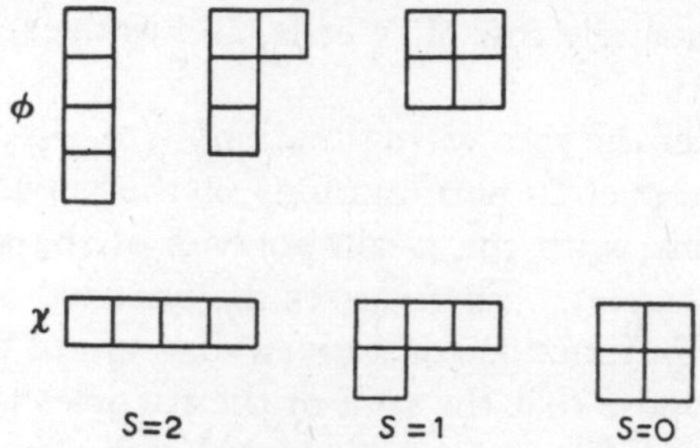

FIG. 24

As we know, such a spinor of rank N reduces to a symmetrical spinor of rank n, to which there corresponds a total spin $S = \frac{1}{2}n$. Returning to the Young diagrams for the co-ordinate functions, we can say that the diagram with n rows each of one cell corresponds to a total spin $S = \frac{1}{2}n$. For even n, the total spin can take integral values from 0 to $\frac{1}{2}n$, while for odd n it can take half-integral values from $\frac{1}{2}$ to $\frac{1}{2}n$, as it should.

We emphasise that this one-to-one correspondence between the Young diagrams and the total spin holds only for systems of particles with spin $\frac{1}{2}$; we have seen this, for a system of two particles, in the previous section.†

PROBLEM

Determine the number of energy levels with different values of the total spin S, for a system of N particles of spin $\frac{1}{2}$.

SOLUTION. A given value of the projection of the total spin of the system, $M_S = \Sigma\, \sigma$, can be obtained in

$$f(M_S) = N!/(\tfrac{1}{2}N+M_S)!\,(\tfrac{1}{2}N-M_S)!$$

ways; this is the number of combinations of N elements $\frac{1}{2}N+M_S$ at a time, since we put $\sigma = \frac{1}{2}$ for $\frac{1}{2}N+M_S$ particles and $\sigma = -\frac{1}{2}$ for the remainder. To each energy level with a

† In the third footnote to §18, we have remarked that, for a system of several identical particles, we cannot assert that the wave function of the stationary state of lowest energy is without nodes. We shall now amplify this statement and elucidate its origin.

The wave function (that is, the co-ordinate function), if it has no nodes, must certainly be symmetrical with respect to all the particles; for, if it were antisymmetrical with respect to the interchange of any pair of particles 1, 2, it would vanish for $\mathbf{r}_1 = \mathbf{r}_2$. If, however, the system consists of three or more electrons, no completely symmetrical co-ordinate wave function is possible: the Young diagram of the co-ordinate function cannot have rows with more than two cells.

Thus, although the solution of SCHRÖDINGER's equation which corresponds to the lowest eigenvalue is without nodes (by the theorem of the variational calculus), this solution may be physically inadmissible; the smallest eigenvalue of SCHRÖDINGER's equation will not then correspond to the normal state of the system, and the wave function of this state will in general have nodes.

For particles with a half-integral spin s, this situation occurs in systems with more than $2s+1$ particles. For systems of particles obeying Bose statistics, a completely symmetrical co-ordinate wave function is always possible.

given S, there correspond $2S+1$ states with values $M_S = S, S-1, \ldots, -S$ of the projected spin. Hence it is easy to see that the number of different energy levels with a given value of S is

$$n(S) = f(S)-f(S+1) = N!(2S+1)/(\tfrac{1}{2}N+S+1)!(\tfrac{1}{2}N-S)!$$

The total number of different energy levels is

$$n = \sum_S n(S) = f(0) = N!/[(\tfrac{1}{2}N)!]^2$$

for even N, and

$$n = f(\tfrac{1}{2}) = N!/(\tfrac{1}{2}N+\tfrac{1}{2})!(\tfrac{1}{2}N-\tfrac{1}{2})!$$

for odd N.

§62. Second quantisation. The case of Bose statistics

In the quantum-mechanical investigation of systems composed of a very large number of identical particles, interacting in any manner, there is a particularly useful method of considering the problem, known as *second quantisation*. This method is necessary in relativistic theory also, where we have to deal with systems in which the number of particles is itself variable.† Let us first consider systems of particles obeying Bose statistics.

We denote by $\psi_1(\xi)$, $\psi_2(\xi)$, ... some complete set of orthogonal and normalised wave functions. These may, for instance, correspond to the stationary states of a single particle in some external field. We emphasise that the choice of this field is arbitrary; it need not be the same as the actual field acting on the particles in the physical system considered. As in §59, ξ denotes the assembly of the co-ordinates and spin projection σ of a particle.

Let us consider, in a purely formal manner, a system of N non-interacting particles, in the field selected. Then every particle is in one of the states $\psi_1, \psi_2, \ldots$. Let N_i be the number of particles in the state ψ_i; it may, of course, be zero (and clearly $\sum N_i = N$). If the numbers $N_1, N_2, \ldots$ are given, the state of the system as a whole is determined; we shall indicate these numbers by suffixes to the wave function $\Psi_{N_1N_2\ldots}$ of the system. Let us seek to construct a mathematical formalism in which the *occupation numbers* $N_1, N_2, \ldots$ of the states (and not the co-ordinates of the particles) play the part of independent variables.

The function $\Psi_{N_1N_2\ldots}$ is a symmetrised (the particles obeying Bose statistics) sum of products of the functions ψ_i. Let us write it in the form

$$\Psi_{N_1N_2\ldots} = \sqrt{(N_1!N_2!\ldots/N!)}\sum \psi_{p_1}(\xi_1)\psi_{p_2}(\xi_2)\ldots\psi_{p_N}(\xi_N). \qquad (62.1)$$

Here $p_1, p_2, \ldots, p_N$ are the ordinal numbers of the states in which the individual particles are, and the sum is taken over all permutations of those suffixes $p_1, p_2, \ldots, p_N$ which are different. The numbers N_i show how many of the

† The method of second quantisation was developed by P. A. M. Dirac (1927) for particles obeying Bose statistics, and later extended to Fermi particles by E. Wigner and P. Jordan (1928).

suffixes $p_1, p_2, \ldots, p_N$ have the value i. The total number of terms in the sum (62.1) is evidently

$$N!/N_1!\,N_2!\ldots.$$

The constant factor in (62.1) is chosen so that the function is normalised; by virtue of the orthogonality of the functions ψ_i, on integrating† the square $|\Psi_{N_1N_2\ldots}|^2$ with respect to $\xi_1, \xi_2, \ldots, \xi_N$ all the terms vanish except the squared modulus of each term in the sum.

Next, let $\hat{f}^{(1)}_a$ be the operator of some physical quantity pertaining to the ath particle, i.e. acting only on functions of ξ_a. We introduce the operator

$$\hat{F}^{(1)} = \sum_a \hat{f}^{(1)}_a, \tag{62.2}$$

which is symmetrical with respect to all the particles (the summation being over all particles), and determine its matrix elements with respect to the wave functions (62.1). First of all, it is easy to see that the matrix elements will be different from zero only for transitions which leave the numbers $N_1, N_2, \ldots$ unchanged (diagonal elements) and for transitions where one of these numbers is increased, and another decreased, by unity. For, since each of the operators $\hat{f}^{(1)}_a$ acts only on one function in the product $\psi_{p_1}(\xi_1)\psi_{p_2}(\xi_2)\ldots\psi_{p_N}(\xi_N)$, its matrix elements can be different from zero only for transitions whereby the state of a single particle is changed; this, however, means that the number of particles in one state is diminished by unity, while the number in another state is correspondingly increased. The calculation of these matrix elements is in principle very simple; it is easier to do it oneself than to follow an account of it. Hence we shall give only the result of this calculation. The non-diagonal elements are

$$F^{(1)}{}^{N_i,N_k-1}_{N_i-1,N_k} = f^{(1)}_{ik}\sqrt{(N_iN_k)}. \tag{62.3}$$

We shall indicate only those suffixes with respect to which the matrix element is non-diagonal, omitting the remainder for brevity. Here $f^{(1)}_{ik}$ is the matrix element

$$f^{(1)}_{ik} = \int \psi_i^*(\xi)\hat{f}^{(1)}\psi_k(\xi)\,\mathrm{d}\xi. \tag{62.4}$$

It must be borne in mind that the operators $\hat{f}^{(1)}_a$ differ only in the naming of the variables on which they act, and hence the integrals $f^{(1)}_{ik}$ are independent of a. The diagonal matrix elements of $F^{(1)}$ are the mean values of the quantity $F^{(1)}$ in the states $\Psi_{N_1N_2\ldots}$; we denote them by $\overline{F^{(1)}}$. Calculation gives

$$\overline{F^{(1)}} = \sum_i f^{(1)}_{ii}N_i. \tag{62.5}$$

† By integration over ξ we conventionally understand integration over the co-ordinates and summation over σ.

We now introduce the operators $\hat{A}_i$, which play a leading part in the method of second quantisation; they act, not on functions of the co-ordinates, but on the variables $N_1, N_2, \ldots$, and are defined as follows. When acting on the function $\Psi_{N_1 N_2 \ldots}$, the operator $\hat{A}_i$ decreases the suffix N_i by unity, and at the same time it multiplies the wave function by $\sqrt{N_i}$:

$$\hat{A}_i \Psi_{N_1 N_2 \ldots N_i \ldots} = \sqrt{N_i} \Psi_{N_1 N_2 \ldots, N_i - 1, \ldots}. \tag{62.6}$$

We can say that the operator $\hat{A}_i$ diminishes by one the number of particles in the ith state. It can be represented in the form of a matrix whose only non-zero element is

$$(A_i)^{N_i - 1}_{N_i} = \sqrt{N_i}. \tag{62.7}$$

The operator $\hat{A}_i^+$ which is the Hermitian conjugate of $\hat{A}_i$ is, by definition (see §3), represented by a matrix with an element

$$(A_i^+)^{N_i}_{N_i - 1} = [(A_i)^{N_i - 1}_{N_i}]^*,$$

i.e.

$$(A_i^+)^{N_i}_{N_i - 1} = \sqrt{N_i}. \tag{62.8}$$

This means that, when acting on the function $\Psi_{N_1 N_2 \ldots}$, it increases the suffix N_i by unity:

$$\hat{A}_i^+ \Psi_{N_1 N_2 \ldots N_i \ldots} = \sqrt{(N_i + 1)} \Psi_{N_1 N_2 \ldots, N_i + 1, \ldots}. \tag{62.9}$$

In other words, the operator $\hat{A}_i^+$ increases by one the number of particles in the ith state.

The product of operators $\hat{A}_i^+ \hat{A}_i$, acting on the wave function, evidently multiplies it by a constant simply, leaving unchanged all the variables $N_1, N_2, \ldots$: the operator $\hat{A}_i$ diminishes N_i by unity, and $\hat{A}_i^+$ then restores it to its original value. Direct multiplication of the matrices (62.7) and (62.8) shows that $\hat{A}_i^+ \hat{A}_i$ is represented, as we should expect, by a diagonal matrix whose diagonal elements are N_i. We can write

$$\hat{A}_i^+ \hat{A}_i = N_i. \tag{62.10}$$

Similarly, we find that

$$\hat{A}_i \hat{A}_i^+ = N_i + 1. \tag{62.11}$$

Hence the commutation rule for the operators $\hat{A}_i$ and $\hat{A}_i^+$ is

$$\hat{A}_i \hat{A}_i^+ - \hat{A}_i^+ \hat{A}_i = 1. \tag{62.12}$$

The operators $\hat{A}_i$ and $\hat{A}_k$ (or $\hat{A}_i$ and $\hat{A}_k^+$) with i and k different act on different variables (N_i and N_k), and of course commute:

$$\hat{A}_i \hat{A}_k - \hat{A}_k \hat{A}_i = 0 \qquad (i \neq k). \tag{62.13}$$

From the above properties of the operators $\hat{A}_i$, $\hat{A}_i^+$ it is easy to see that the operator

$$\hat{F}^{(1)} = \sum_{i,k} f^{(1)}_{ik}\hat{A}_i^+\hat{A}_k \tag{62.14}$$

is the same as the operator (62.2). For all the matrix elements calculated from (62.7), (62.8) are the same as the elements (62.3), (62.5). This is a very important result. In formula (62.14), the quantities $f^{(1)}_{ik}$ are simply numbers. Thus we have been able to express an ordinary operator (of the form (62.2)), acting on functions of the co-ordinates, in the form of an operator acting on functions of new variables, the occupation numbers† N_i.

The result which we have obtained is easily generalised to operators of other forms. Let

$$\hat{F}^{(2)} = \sum_{a>b} \hat{f}^{(2)}_{ab}, \tag{62.15}$$

where $\hat{f}^{(2)}_{ab}$ is the operator of a physical quantity pertaining to two particles at once, and hence acts on functions of ξ_a and ξ_b. Similar calculations show that this operator can be expressed in terms of the operators $\hat{A}_i$, $\hat{A}_i^+$ by

$$\hat{F}^{(2)} = \tfrac{1}{2}\sum_{i,k,l,m} (f^{(2)})^{ik}_{lm}\hat{A}_i^+\hat{A}_k^+\hat{A}_m\hat{A}_l, \tag{62.16}$$

where

$$(f^{(2)})^{ik}_{lm} = \iint \psi_i^*(\xi_1)\psi_k^*(\xi_2)\hat{f}^{(2)}\psi_l(\xi_1)\psi_m(\xi_2)\, d\xi_1 d\xi_2.$$

The matrices calculated for (62.15) and (62.16) are the same. The generalisation of these formulae to operators of any other form symmetrical with respect to all the particles (of the form $\hat{F}^{(3)} = \sum \hat{f}^{(3)}_{abc}$ etc.) is obvious.

Finally, it remains to express, in terms of the operators $\hat{A}_i$, the Hamiltonian $\hat{H}$ of the physical system of N identical interacting particles that is actually being considered. The operator $\hat{H}$ is, of course, symmetrical with respect to all the particles. In the non-relativistic approximation,‡ it is independent of the spins of the particles, and can be represented in a general form as follows:

$$\hat{H} = \sum_a \hat{H}^{(1)}_a + \sum_{a>b} U^{(2)}(\mathbf{r}_a,\mathbf{r}_b) + \sum_{a>b>c} U^{(3)}(\mathbf{r}_a,\mathbf{r}_b,\mathbf{r}_c) + \dots. \tag{62.17}$$

Here $\hat{H}^{(1)}_a$ is the part of the Hamiltonian which depends on the co-ordinates of the ath particle only:

$$\hat{H}^{(1)}_a = -(\hbar^2/2\mu)\Delta_a + U^{(1)}(\mathbf{r}_a), \tag{62.18}$$

† Formula (62.14) bears a similarity to the expression (11.1)

$$\bar{f} = \sum f_{ik}a_i^* a_k$$

for the mean value of a quantity f, expressed in terms of the coefficients a_i in the expansion of the wave function of a given state in terms of the wave functions of the stationary states. This is the reason for calling this method the *second quantisation method*.

‡ In the absence of a magnetic field.

where $U^{(1)}(\mathbf{r}_a)$ is the potential energy of a single particle in the external field. The remaining terms in (62.17) correspond to the mutual interaction energy of the particles; for convenience, the terms depending on the co-ordinates of two, three, etc. particles have been separated.

This representation of the Hamiltonian enables us to apply formulae (62.14), (62.16) and their analogues directly. Thus

$$\hat{H} = \sum_{i,k} H^{(1)}{}_{ik}\hat{A}_i{}^+\hat{A}_k + \tfrac{1}{2}\sum_{i,k,l,m} (U^{(2)})^{ik}_{lm}\hat{A}_i{}^+\hat{A}_k{}^+\hat{A}_m\hat{A}_l + \dots . \qquad (62.19)$$

This gives the required expression for the Hamiltonian in the form of an operator acting on functions of the occupation numbers.

For a system of non-interacting particles, only the first term in the expression (62.19) remains:

$$\hat{H} = \sum_{i,k} H^{(1)}{}_{ik}\hat{A}_i{}^+\hat{A}_k.$$

If the functions ψ_i are taken to be the eigenfunctions of the Hamiltonian $\hat{H}^{(1)}$ of an individual particle, the matrix $H^{(1)}{}_{ik}$ is diagonal, and its diagonal elements are the eigenvalues ϵ_i of the energy of the particle. Thus

$$\hat{H} = \sum_i \epsilon_i\hat{A}_i{}^+\hat{A}_i;$$

replacing the operator $\hat{A}_i{}^+\hat{A}_i$ by its eigenvalues (62.10), we have for the energy levels of the system the expression

$$E = \sum_i \epsilon_i N_i,$$

a trivial result which could have been foreseen.

The formalism which we have developed can be put in a somewhat more compact form by introducing the operators†

$$\hat{\Phi}(\xi) = \sum_i \psi_i(\xi)\hat{A}_i, \quad \hat{\Phi}^+(\xi) = \sum_i \psi_i{}^*(\xi)\hat{A}_i{}^+, \qquad (62.20)$$

where the variables ξ are regarded as parameters. By what has been said above concerning the operators $\hat{A}_i$, $\hat{A}_i{}^+$, it is clear that the operator $\hat{\Phi}$ decreases the total number of particles in the system by one, while $\hat{\Phi}^+$ increases it by one.

It is easy to see that the operator $\hat{\Phi}^+(\xi_0)$ creates a particle at the point ξ_0. For the result of the action of the operator $\hat{A}_i{}^+$ is to create a particle in a state with wave function $\psi_i(\xi)$. Hence it follows that the result of the action of the

† Attention is drawn to the analogy between these expressions and the expansion

$$\Psi = \sum a_i \Psi_i$$

of the wave function in terms of the eigenfunctions of an operator (cf. the third footnote to this section).

operator $\hat{\Phi}^+(\xi_0)$ is to create a particle in a state with wave function $\Sigma\,\psi_i^*(\xi)\psi_i(\xi_0)$, or (by the general formula (5.9)) with wave function† $\delta(\xi-\xi_0)$, which corresponds to a particle with definite values of the co-ordinates (and spin).

The commutation rules for $\hat{\Phi}$ and $\hat{\Phi}^+$ are obtained at once from those for $\hat{A}_i$, $\hat{A}_i^+$. It is evident that

$$\hat{\Phi}(\xi)\hat{\Phi}(\xi')-\hat{\Phi}(\xi')\hat{\Phi}(\xi) = 0; \tag{62.21}$$

we also have

$$\hat{\Phi}(\xi)\hat{\Phi}^+(\xi')-\hat{\Phi}^+(\xi')\hat{\Phi}(\xi) = \sum_i \psi_i(\xi)\psi_i^*(\xi'),$$

or

$$\hat{\Phi}(\xi)\hat{\Phi}^+(\xi')-\hat{\Phi}^+(\xi')\hat{\Phi}(\xi) = \delta(\xi-\xi'). \tag{62.22}$$

The expression (62.14) for the operator (62.2) can be written, using these new operators, in the form

$$\hat{F}^{(1)} = \int \hat{\Phi}^+(\xi)f^{(1)}\hat{\Phi}(\xi)\,\mathrm{d}\xi, \tag{62.23}$$

where it is understood that the operator $f^{(1)}$ acts on functions of the parameters ξ in $\hat{\Phi}(\xi)$. For, substituting (62.20), we have

$$\hat{F}^{(1)} = \sum_{i,k} \int \psi_i^*(\xi)f^{(1)}\psi_k(\xi)\,\mathrm{d}\xi\,.\hat{A}_i^+\hat{A}_k = \sum_{i,k} f^{(1)}{}_{ik}\hat{A}_i^+\hat{A}_k,$$

which is the same as (62.14). Similarly, we have instead of (62.16)

$$\hat{F}^{(2)} = \tfrac{1}{2}\iint \hat{\Phi}^+(\xi)\hat{\Phi}^+(\xi')f^{(2)}\hat{\Phi}(\xi')\hat{\Phi}(\xi)\,\mathrm{d}\xi\mathrm{d}\xi'. \tag{62.24}$$

In particular, to a physical quantity $f(\xi)$ that is simply a function of ξ, there corresponds the operator (62.23), which in this case can be written in the form

$$\int f(\xi)\hat{\Phi}^+(\xi)\hat{\Phi}(\xi)\,\mathrm{d}\xi.$$

Hence it is clear that $\hat{\Phi}^+(\xi)\hat{\Phi}(\xi)\,\mathrm{d}\xi$ is the operator of the number of particles in the range $\mathrm{d}\xi$.

When expressed by means of the operators $\hat{\Phi}$, $\hat{\Phi}^+$, the operator $\hat{H}$ takes

† $\delta(\xi-\xi_0)$ conventionally denotes the product

$$\delta(x-x_0)\delta(y-y_0)\delta(z-z_0)\delta_{\sigma\sigma_0}.$$

the form

$$\hat{H} = \int \{(\hbar^2/2\mu)\nabla\hat{\Phi}^+(\xi)\nabla\hat{\Phi}(\xi) + U^{(1)}(\xi)\hat{\Phi}^+\hat{\Phi}\}\,d\xi +$$
$$+\tfrac{1}{2}\iint \hat{\Phi}^+(\xi)\hat{\Phi}^+(\xi')U^{(2)}(\xi,\xi')\hat{\Phi}(\xi')\hat{\Phi}(\xi)\,d\xi d\xi' + \dots . \tag{62.25}$$

We have used here the expression (62.18) for $\hat{H}^{(1)}$, and have integrated by parts (with respect to the co-ordinates) the term containing the Laplacian.

We can clarify the formula (62.25) by noticing the following point. Suppose that we have a system of particles, each of which is described (at a given instant) by the same wave function $\psi(\xi)$, which we suppose normalised so that $\int |\psi|^2\, d\xi = N$. Then it is immediately evident that, if we replace the operator $\hat{\Phi}$ in the expression (62.25) by the function ψ, this expression becomes the mean energy of the system in the state considered. This gives the following rule for deriving the Hamiltonian in the second quantisation formalism. The expression for the mean energy is written in terms of the wave function of an individual particle (normalised as stated above), and this function is then replaced by the operator $\hat{\Phi}$, the Hermitian conjugate operators $\hat{\Phi}^+$ being written to the left of the operators $\hat{\Phi}$.

§63. Second quantisation. The case of Fermi statistics

The basic theory of the method of second quantisation remains wholly unchanged for systems of identical particles obeying Fermi statistics, but the actual formulae for the matrix elements of quantities and for the operators $\hat{A}_i$ are naturally different.

The wave function $\Psi_{N_1 N_2 \dots}$ now has the form (59.2):

$$\Psi_{N_1 N_2 \dots} = \frac{1}{\sqrt{N!}} \begin{vmatrix} \psi_{p_1}(\xi_1) & \psi_{p_1}(\xi_2) & \dots & \psi_{p_1}(\xi_N) \\ \psi_{p_2}(\xi_1) & \psi_{p_2}(\xi_2) & \dots & \psi_{p_2}(\xi_N) \\ \dots & \dots & \dots & \dots \\ \psi_{p_N}(\xi_1) & \psi_{p_N}(\xi_2) & \dots & \psi_{p_N}(\xi_N) \end{vmatrix}. \tag{63.1}$$

Because of the antisymmetry of this function, the question of its sign arises first of all. This question did not arise in the case of Bose statistics, since, because of the symmetry of the wave function, its sign, once chosen, was preserved under all permutations of the particles. In order to make definite the sign of the function (63.1), we shall agree to choose it as follows. We number successively, once and for all, all the states ψ_i. We then complete the rows of the determinant (63.1) so that always

$$p_1 < p_2 < p_3 < \dots < p_N, \tag{63.2}$$

whilst in the successive columns we have functions of the different variables in the order $\xi_1, \xi_2, \ldots, \xi_N$. No two of the numbers $p_1, p_2, \ldots$ can be equal, since otherwise the determinant would vanish. In other words, the occupation numbers N_i can take only the values 0 and 1.

Let us again consider an operator of the form (62.2), $\hat{F}^{(1)} = \Sigma f^{(1)}{}_a$. As in §62, its matrix elements will be non-zero only for transitions where all the occupation numbers remain unchanged and for those where one occupation number (N_i) is diminished by unity (becoming zero instead of one) and another (N_k) is increased by unity (becoming one instead of zero). We easily find that, for $i < k$,

$$(F^{(1)})^{1_i 0_k}_{0_i 1_k} = f^{(1)}{}_{ik}(-1)^{\Sigma(i+1,\, k-1)},$$

$$\text{where} \quad \Sigma(i+1, k-1) \equiv \sum_{l=i+1}^{k-1} N_l; \tag{63.3}$$

by 0_i, 1_i we signify $N_i = 0$, $N_i = 1$. The factor -1 appears to a power equal to the sum of the occupation numbers of all the states between the ith and the kth.† For the diagonal elements we obtain our previous formula (62.5):

$$\overline{F^{(1)}} = \sum_i f^{(1)}{}_{ii} N_i. \tag{63.4}$$

In order to represent the operator $\hat{F}^{(1)}$ in the form (62.14), the operators $\hat{A}_i$ must be defined as matrices whose elements are

$$(A_i)^{0_i}_{1_i} = (A_i{}^+)^{1_i}_{0_i} = (-1)^{\Sigma(1,\, i-1)}; \tag{63.5}$$

the factor -1 is raised to a power equal to the sum of the occupation numbers of all states up to but excluding the ith. On multiplying these matrices, we find, for $k > i$,

$$(A_i{}^+ A_k)^{1_i 0_k}_{0_i 1_k} = (A_i{}^+)^{1_i 0_k}_{0_i 0_k} (A_k)^{0_i 0_k}_{0_i 1_k} = (-1)^{\Sigma(1,\, i-1)}(-1)^{\Sigma(1,\, i-1)+\Sigma(i+1,\, k-1)},$$

or

$$(A_i{}^+ A_k)^{1_i 0_k}_{0_i 1_k} = (-1)^{\Sigma(i+1,\, k-1)}. \tag{63.6}$$

If $i = k$, the matrix of $\hat{A}_i{}^+ \hat{A}_i$ is diagonal, and its elements are unity for $N_i = 1$, and zero for $N_i = 0$; this can be written

$$\hat{A}_i{}^+ \hat{A}_i = N_i. \tag{63.7}$$

On substituting these expressions in (62.14), we in fact obtain (63.3), (63.4).

Multiplying $\hat{A}_i{}^+$, $\hat{A}_k$ in the opposite order, we have

$$(A_k A_i{}^+)^{1_i 0_k}_{0_i 1_k} = (A_k)^{1_i 0_k}_{1_i 1_k} (A_i{}^+)^{1_i 1_k}_{0_i 1_k} = (-1)^{\Sigma(1,\, i-1)+1+\Sigma(i+1,\, k-1)+\Sigma(1,\, i-1)},$$

† For $i > k$ the exponent is $\Sigma(k+1, i-1)$, but for $i = k \pm 1$ these sums are to be put equal to zero.

or

$$(A_k A_i^+)_{0_i 1_k}^{1_i 0_k} = -(-1)^{\Sigma(i+1,\, k-1)}. \tag{63.8}$$

Comparing (63.8) with (63.6), we see that these quantities have opposite signs, i.e. we can write

$$\hat{A}_i^+ \hat{A}_k + \hat{A}_k \hat{A}_i^+ = 0 \qquad (i \neq k).$$

For the diagonal matrix $\hat{A}_i \hat{A}_i^+$, we find

$$\hat{A}_i \hat{A}_i^+ = 1 - N_i. \tag{63.9}$$

Adding this to (63.7), we obtain

$$\hat{A}_i \hat{A}_i^+ + \hat{A}_i^+ \hat{A}_i = 1.$$

Both the above equations can be written in the form

$$\hat{A}_i \hat{A}_k^+ + \hat{A}_k^+ \hat{A}_i = \delta_{ik}. \tag{63.10}$$

On carrying out similar calculations, we find for the products $\hat{A}_i \hat{A}_k$ the relations

$$\hat{A}_i \hat{A}_k + \hat{A}_k \hat{A}_i = 0, \tag{63.11}$$

and in particular $\hat{A}_i \hat{A}_i = 0$.

Thus we see that the operators $\hat{A}_i$ and $\hat{A}_k$ (or $\hat{A}_k^+$) for $i \neq k$ anticommute, whereas in the case of Bose statistics they commuted with one another. This difference is perfectly natural. In the case of Bose statistics, the operators $\hat{A}_i$ and $\hat{A}_k$ were completely independent; each of the operators $\hat{A}_i$ acted only on a single variable N_i, and the result of this action did not depend on the values of the other occupation numbers. In the case of Fermi statistics, however, the result of the action of the operator $\hat{A}_i$ depends not only on the number N_i itself, but also on the occupation numbers of all the preceding states, as we see from the definition (63.5). Hence the action of the various operators $\hat{A}_i$, $\hat{A}_k$ cannot be considered independent.

The properties of the operators $\hat{A}_i$, $\hat{A}_i^+$ having been thus defined, all the remaining formulae (62.14)–(62.19) remain valid. The formulae (62.23)–(62.25), which express the operators of physical quantities in terms of the operators $\hat{\Phi}(\xi)$, $\hat{\Phi}^+(\xi)$ defined by (62.20), also hold good†. The commutation rules (62.21), (62.22), however, are now obviously replaced by

$$\begin{aligned} \hat{\Phi}^+(\xi')\hat{\Phi}(\xi) + \hat{\Phi}(\xi)\hat{\Phi}^+(\xi') &= \delta(\xi - \xi'), \\ \hat{\Phi}(\xi')\hat{\Phi}(\xi) + \hat{\Phi}(\xi)\hat{\Phi}(\xi') &= 0. \end{aligned} \tag{63.12}$$

† The sequence of the factors $\hat{A}_i^+$, $\hat{A}_k^+$ and $\hat{A}_l$, $\hat{A}_m$ in (62.19) was of no importance in the case of Bose statistics, since these operators were commutable. However, it is important in the case of Fermi statistics, and the sequence of factors in (62.16) is such as to be correct for both cases. The same applies to formula (62.24).

CHAPTER X

THE ATOM

§64. Atomic energy levels

In the non-relativistic approximation, the stationary states of the atom are determined by SCHRÖDINGER's equation for the system of electrons, which move in the Coulomb field of the nucleus and interact electrically with one another; the spin operators of the electrons do not appear in this equation. As we know, for a system of particles in a centrally symmetric external field the total orbital angular momentum L and the parity of the state are conserved. Hence each stationary state of the atom will be characterised by a definite value of the orbital angular momentum L and by its parity. Moreover, the co-ordinate wave functions of the stationary states of a system of identical particles have a certain permutational symmetry. We have seen in §61 that, for a system of electrons, a definite value of the total spin of the system corresponds to each type of permutational symmetry (i.e. to each Young diagram). Hence every stationary state of the atom is characterised also by the total spin S of the electrons.

The converse, however, is of course not true; if L, S and the parity are given, the energy of the state is not uniquely determined.

The energy level having given values of S and L is degenerate to a degree equal to the number of different possible directions in space of the vectors $\mathbf{S}$ and $\mathbf{L}$. The degree of the degeneracy from the directions of L and S is respectively $2L+1$ and $2S+1$. Consequently, the total degree of the degeneracy of a level with given L and S is equal to the product $(2L+1)(2S+1)$.

In fact, however, there is always some relativistic electromagnetic interaction of the electrons, which depends on their spins. It has the result that the energy of the atom depends not only on the absolute values of the orbital angular momentum and spin vectors, but also on their relative positions. Strictly speaking, when the relativistic terms in the Hamiltonian operator are taken into account, it no longer commutes with the operators $\hat{\mathbf{L}}$ and $\hat{\mathbf{S}}$, i.e. the orbital angular momentum and the spin are not separately conserved. Only the total angular momentum $\mathbf{J} = \mathbf{L}+\mathbf{S}$ is conserved. The conservation of the total angular momentum is an exact law which follows at once from the isotropy of space relative to a closed system. For this reason the energy levels must be characterised by the values J of the total angular momentum.

However, if the relativistic effects are comparatively small (as happens in many cases), they can be allowed for as a perturbation. Under the action of this perturbation, a level with given L and S, having $(2L+1)(2S+1)$-fold degeneracy, is "split" into a number of distinct (though close) levels, which differ in the value of the total angular momentum J. These levels are determined (in the first approximation) by the appropriate secular equation (§39), while their wave functions (in the zero approximation) are definite linear combinations of the wave functions of the initial degenerate level with the given L and S. In this approximation we can therefore, as before, regard the absolute values of the orbital angular momentum and spin (but not their directions) as being conserved, and characterise the levels by the values of L and S also.

Thus, as a result of the relativistic effects, a level with given values of L and S is split into a number of levels with different values of J. This splitting is called the *fine structure* (or the *multiplet splitting*) of the level. As we know, J takes values from $L+S$ to $|L-S|$; hence a level with given L and S is split into $2S+1$ (if $L > S$) or $2L+1$ (if $L < S$) distinct levels. Each of these is still degenerate with respect to the directions of the vector $\mathbf{J}$; the degree of this degeneracy is $2J+1$. It is easily verified that the sum of the numbers $2J+1$ for all possible values of J is equal to $(2L+1)(2S+1)$, as it should be.

There is a generally accepted notation to denote the atomic energy levels (or, as they are called, the *spectral terms* of the atoms). The states with different values of the total orbital angular momentum L are denoted by capital Latin letters, as follows:

$$\begin{array}{cccccccccccccc} L = & 0 & 1 & 2 & 3 & 4 & 5 & 6 & 7 & 8 & 9 & 10 & \ldots \\ & S & P & D & F & G & H & I & K & L & M & N & \ldots \end{array}$$

Above and to the left of this letter is placed the number $2S+1$, called the *multiplicity* of the term (though it must be borne in mind that this number gives the number of fine-structure components of the level only when $L \geqslant S$). Below and to the right of the letter is placed the value of the total angular momentum J. Thus the symbols $^2P_{1/2}$, $^2P_{3/2}$ denote levels with $L = 1$, $S = \frac{1}{2}$, $J = \frac{1}{2}$ and $\frac{3}{2}$.

§65. Electron states in the atom

An atom with more than one electron is a complex system of mutually interacting electrons moving in the field of the nucleus. For such a system we can, strictly speaking, consider only states of the system as a whole. Nevertheless, it is found that we can, with fair accuracy, introduce the idea of the states of each individual electron in the atom, as being the stationary states of the motion of each electron in some effective centrally symmetric field due to the nucleus and to all the other electrons. These fields are in general different for different electrons in the atom, and they must all be defined simultaneously, since each of them depends on the states of all the other electrons. Such a field is said to be *self-consistent* (see §68).

Since the self-consistent field is centrally symmetric, each state of the electron is characterised by a definite value of its orbital angular momentum l. The states of an individual electron with a given l are numbered (in order of increasing energy) by the *principal quantum number* n, which takes the values $n = l+1, l+2, \ldots$; this choice of the order of numbering is made in accordance with what is usual for the hydrogen atom. However, it must be noticed that the sequence of levels of increasing energy for various l in complex atoms is in general different from that found in the hydrogen atom. In the latter, the energy is independent of l, so that the states with larger values of n always have higher energies. In complex atoms, on the other hand, the level with $n = 5$, $l = 0$, for example, is found to lie below that with $n = 4$, $l = 2$ (this is discussed in more detail in §70).

The states of individual electrons with different values of l are customarily denoted by the small Latin letters corresponding to the capitals used for the states of the whole atom:

$$\begin{matrix} l = 0 & 1 & 2 & 3 & 4 & 5 & 6 & 7 & \dots \\ s & p & d & f & g & h & i & k & \dots \end{matrix}$$

The values of the principal quantum number are usually denoted by a figure placed in front of the letter: thus $4d$ denotes the state with $n = 4$, $l = 2$. A complete description of the atom demands that, besides the values of the total L, S and J, the states of all the electrons should also be enumerated. Thus the symbol $1s\,2p\,{}^3P_0$ denotes a state of the helium atom in which $L = 1$, $S = 1$, $J = 0$ and the two electrons are in the $1s$ and $2p$ states. If several electrons are in states with the same l and n, this is usually shown for brevity by means of an index: thus $3p^2$ denotes two electrons in the $3p$ state. The distribution of the electrons in the atom among states with different l and n is called the *electron configuration*.

For given values of n and l, the electron can have different values of the projections of the orbital angular momentum (m) and of the spin (σ) on the z-axis. For a given l, the number m takes $2l+1$ values; the number σ is restricted to only two values, $\pm\frac{1}{2}$. Hence there are altogether $2(2l+1)$ different states with the same n and l; these states are said to be *equivalent*. According to Pauli's principle there can be only one electron in each such state. Thus at most $2(2l+1)$ electrons in an atom can simultaneously have the same n and l. An assembly of electrons occupying all the states with the given n and l is called a *closed shell* of the type concerned.

The difference in energy between atomic levels having different L and S but the same electron configuration† is due to the electrostatic interaction of the electrons. These energy differences are usually small, and several times less than the distances between the levels of different configurations. The following empirical principle (*Hund's rule*) is known concerning the relative position of levels with the same configuration but different L and S:

The term with the greatest possible value of S (for the given electron configuration) and the greatest possible value of L (for this S) has the lowest energy.‡

† We here ignore the fine structure of each multiplet level.

‡ The requirement that S should be as large as possible can be explained as follows. Let us consider, for example, a system of two electrons. Here we can have $S = 0$ or $S = 1$; the spin 1 corresponds to an antisymmetrical co-ordinate wave function $\phi(\mathbf{r}_1, \mathbf{r}_2)$. For $\mathbf{r}_1 = \mathbf{r}_2$, this function vanishes; in other words, in the state with $S = 1$ the probability of finding the two electrons close together is small. This means that their electrostatic repulsion is comparatively small, and hence the energy is less. Similarly, for a system of several electrons, the "most antisymmetrical" co-ordinate wave function corresponds to the greatest spin.

We shall show how the possible atomic terms can be found for a given electron configuration. If the electrons are not equivalent, the possible values of L and S are determined immediately from the rule for the addition of angular momenta. Thus, for instance, with the configurations np, $n'p$ (n, n' being different) the total angular momentum L can take the values 2, 1, 0, and the total spin $S = 0, 1$; combining these, we obtain the terms $^{1,3}S$, $^{1,3}P$, $^{1,3}D$.

If we are concerned with equivalent electrons, however, restrictions imposed by PAULI's principle make their appearance. Let us consider, for example, a configuration of three equivalent p electrons. For $l = 1$ (the p state), the projection m of the orbital angular momentum can take the values $m = 1, 0, -1$, so that there are six possible states, with the following values of m and σ:

$$(a)\ 1, \tfrac{1}{2} \quad (b)\ 0, \tfrac{1}{2} \quad (c)\ -1, \tfrac{1}{2}$$
$$(a')\ 1, -\tfrac{1}{2} \quad (b')\ 0, -\tfrac{1}{2} \quad (c')\ -1, -\tfrac{1}{2}.$$

The three electrons can be one in each of any three of these states. As a result we obtain states of the atom with the following values of the projections $M_L = \Sigma m$, $M_S = \Sigma \sigma$ of the total orbital angular momentum and spin:

$$(a+a'+b)\ 2, \tfrac{1}{2} \quad (a+a'+c)\ 1, \tfrac{1}{2} \quad (a+b+c)\ 0, \tfrac{3}{2}$$
$$(a+b+b')\ 1, \tfrac{1}{2} \quad (a+b+c')\ 0, \tfrac{1}{2}$$
$$(a+b'+c)\ 0, \tfrac{1}{2}$$
$$(a'+b+c)\ 0, \tfrac{1}{2}.$$

The states with M_L or M_S negative need not be written out, since they give nothing different. The presence of a state with $M_L = 2$, $M_S = \frac{1}{2}$ shows that there must be a ^2D term, and to this term there must correspond one state $(1, \frac{1}{2})$ and one $(0, \frac{1}{2})$. Next, there remains one state with $(1, \frac{1}{2})$, so that there must be a ^2P term; one of the states $(0, \frac{1}{2})$ corresponds to this. Finally, there remain the states $(0, \frac{3}{2})$ and $(0, \frac{1}{2})$, corresponding to a ^4S term. Thus, for a configuration of three equivalent p electrons, the only possibilities are one term of each of the types ^2D, ^2P, ^4S.

Table 1 gives the possible terms for various configurations of equivalent p and d electrons. The figures below the letters of the terms show the number of terms of the type concerned that exist for the given configuration, if this number is more than one. For the configuration with the greatest possible number of equivalent electrons (s^2, p^6, d^{10}, ...), the term is always ^1S. Like terms always correspond to configurations which differ in that one of them has as many electrons as the other lacks to form a closed shell. This is an evident result of the fact that the absence of an electron from the shell can be regarded as a "hole", whose state is defined by the same quantum numbers as the state of the missing electron.

TABLE 1

Possible terms for configurations of equivalent electrons

p, p^5	^2P		
p^2, p^4	^1SD	^3P	
p^3	^2PD	^4S	
d, d^9	^2D		
d^2, d^8	^1SDG	^3PF	
d^3, d^7	$^2P\underset{2}{D}FGH$	^4PF	
d^4, d^6	$^1\underset{2}{S}\underset{2}{D}F\underset{2}{G}I$	$^3\underset{2}{P}D\underset{2}{F}GH$	^5D
d^5	$^2SP\underset{3}{D}\underset{2}{F}\underset{2}{G}HI$	^4PDFG	^6S

§66. **Hydrogen-like energy levels**

The only atom for which SCHRÖDINGER's equation can be exactly solved is the simplest of all atoms, that of hydrogen. The energy levels of the hydrogen atom, and of the ions He^+, Li^{++}, ... which each have only one electron, are given by BOHR's formula

$$E = -\frac{\mu Z^2 e^4}{2\hbar^2(1+\mu/M)} \cdot \frac{1}{n^2}. \tag{66.1}$$

Here Ze is the charge on the nucleus, M its mass, and μ the mass of the electron. We notice that the dependence on the mass of the nucleus is only very slight.

The formula (66.1) does not take account of any relativistic effects.† In this approximation there is an additional (*accidental*) degeneracy, peculiar to the hydrogen atom, of which we have already spoken in §36; for a given principal quantum number n, the energy is independent of the orbital angular momentum l.

Other atoms have states whose properties recall those of hydrogen. We refer to highly excited states, in which one of the electrons has a large principal quantum number, and so is mostly at large distances from the nucleus. The motion of such an electron can be regarded, to a certain approximation, as motion in the Coulomb field of the rest of the atom, whose effective charge is unity. The values of the energy levels thus obtained are, however, too inexact; it is necessary to apply to them a correction to take account of the deviation of the field from the pure Coulomb field at small distances. The nature of this correction is easily ascertained from the following considerations.

Since the states with large quantum numbers are quasi-classical, the energy levels can be determined from BOHR's quantisation rule (52.3). The deviation from the Coulomb field near the nucleus can be formally allowed for by an alteration in the boundary condition imposed on the wave function at

† See §67 for certain properties of the fine structure of the energy levels in the hydrogen atom.

$r = 0$. This brings about a change in the constant γ, in equation (52.3), from the value which it would have in a pure Coulomb field. Since this equation is otherwise unchanged, we can conclude that we obtain for the energy levels an expression which differs from that for hydrogen in that the principal quantum number n is replaced by $n+\Delta_l$, where Δ_l is some constant (known as *Rydberg's correction*):

$$E = -\frac{\mu e^4}{2\hbar^2}\frac{1}{(n+\Delta_l)^2}. \tag{66.2}$$

Rydberg's correction is (by definition) independent of n, but it is of course a function of the azimuthal quantum number l of the excited electron (which we add as a suffix to Δ), and of the angular momenta L and S of the whole atom. For given L and S, Δ_l decreases as l increases. The greater l, the less time the electron spends near the nucleus, and hence the energy levels must approach more and more closely those of hydrogen as l increases.

§67. Fine structure of the levels

A detailed study of relativistic interactions will not be given here. We shall, however, state some results. It is found that the relativistic terms in the Hamiltonian of a system of particles fall into two classes. One of these contains terms linear with respect to the spin operators of the particles, while the other includes quadratic terms. The former correspond to the interaction between the orbital motion of the particles and their spin (this interaction is called *spin-orbit* interaction), while the latter correspond to the interaction between the spins of the particles (*spin-spin* interaction). Both interactions are of the same order (the second) with respect to the ratio of the velocity of the particles to that of light; in practice, the spin-orbit interaction considerably exceeds the spin-spin interaction in heavy atoms.

The spin-orbit interaction operator is of the form

$$\hat{V}_{sl} = \sum_a \hat{\mathbf{A}}_a \cdot \hat{\mathbf{s}}_a \tag{67.1}$$

(the summation being over all the electrons in the atom), where $\hat{\mathbf{s}}_a$ are the spin operators of the electron, and $\hat{\mathbf{A}}_a$ are some "orbital" operators, i.e. operators acting on functions of the co-ordinates. Regarding this interaction as a perturbation, we should, in order to calculate the energy, average the operator corresponding to this interaction with respect to the unperturbed state. The averaging is done in two steps. First of all, we average over electron states with given absolute values L and S of the total orbital angular momentum and spin, but not with given directions of these. After this averaging $\hat{V}_{sl}$ is still, of course, an operator, which we denote by† $\hat{V}_{SL}$. From considerations of

† This averaging signifies essentially the construction of a matrix with elements

$$\int \psi_{nM'_L M'_S}{}^* \hat{V}_{sl} \psi_{nM_L M_S} \,\mathrm{d}q$$

with all possible M_L, M'_L and M_S, M'_S and diagonal with respect to all the other quantum numbers (the assembly of which we denote by n).

symmetry it is evident that the mean values of $\hat{\mathbf{s}}_a$ must be "directed" along $\hat{\mathbf{S}}$, which is the only spin "vector" characterising the atom as a whole (it must be recalled that, in the zero approximation, the wave functions are products of a spin part and a co-ordinate part). Similarly, the mean values of $\hat{\mathbf{A}}_a$ must be "directed" along $\hat{\mathbf{L}}$. Thus the operator $\hat{V}_{SL}$ is of the form

$$\hat{V}_{SL} = A\,\hat{\mathbf{S}}.\hat{\mathbf{L}}, \tag{67.2}$$

where A is a constant characterising a given (unsplit) term, i.e. depending on S and L but not on the total angular momentum J of the atom.

To calculate the energy of the splitting of a degenerate level (with given S and L), we must solve the secular equation formed from the matrix elements of the operator $\hat{V}_{SL}$. In this case, however, we already know the correct functions in the zero approximation, in which the matrix of V_{SL} is diagonal. For these are the wave functions of states with definite values of the total angular momentum J. The averaging with respect to such a state involves replacing the operator $\hat{\mathbf{S}}.\hat{\mathbf{L}}$ by its eigenvalues, which, according to the general formula (30.2), are

$$\mathbf{L}.\mathbf{S} = \tfrac{1}{2}[J(J+1)-L(L+1)-S(S+1)].$$

Since the values of L and S are the same for all the components of a multiplet, and we are interested only in their relative position, we can write the energy of the multiplet splitting in the form

$$\tfrac{1}{2}AJ(J+1). \tag{67.3}$$

The intervals between adjacent components (with numbers J and $J-1$) are consequently

$$\Delta E_{J,J-1} = AJ. \tag{67.4}$$

This formula gives what is called *Landé's interval rule* (1923).

The constant A can be either positive or negative. For $A > 0$ the lowest component of the multiplet level is the one with the smallest possible J, i.e. $J = |L-S|$; such multiplets are said to be *normal*. If $A < 0$, on the other hand, the lowest level of the multiplet is that with $J = L+S$; these multiplets are said to be *inverted*. The following empirical rule to determine the value of J holds for normal states of atoms. If the electron configuration is such that the incomplete shell contains not more than half the greatest possible number of electrons for that shell, then $J = |L-S|$. If, however, the shell is more than half full, $J = L+S$.

For the averaged spin-spin interaction operator we should obtain, analogously to formula (67.2), an expression quadratic in $\hat{\mathbf{S}}$. The expressions $\hat{\mathbf{S}}^2$ and $(\hat{\mathbf{S}}.\hat{\mathbf{L}})^2$ are quadratic in $\hat{\mathbf{S}}$. The former has eigenvalues independent of J, and therefore does not give any splitting of the term. Hence it can be omitted, and we can write

$$\hat{V}_{SS} = B(\hat{\mathbf{S}}.\hat{\mathbf{L}})^2, \tag{67.5}$$

where B is a constant. The eigenvalues of this operator contain terms independent of J, terms proportional to $J(J+1)$, and finally a term proportional to $J^2(J+1)^2$. The first of these do not give any splitting and hence are without interest; the second can be included in the expression (67.3), which simply means a change in the constant A. Finally, the last term gives an energy

$$\tfrac{1}{4}BJ^2(J+1)^2. \tag{67.6}$$

The scheme for the construction of the atomic levels discussed in §§64–65 is based on the supposition that the orbital angular momenta of the electrons combine to give the total orbital angular momentum L of the atom, and their spins to give the total spin S. As has already been mentioned, this supposition is legitimate only when the relativistic effects are small; more exactly, the intervals in the fine structure must be small compared with the differences between levels with different L and S. This approximation is called the *Russell-Saunders case*, and we speak also of *LS coupling*.

In practice, however, this approximation has a limited range of applicability. The levels of the light atoms are arranged in accordance with the *LS* model, but as the atomic number increases the relativistic interactions in the atom become stronger, and the Russell-Saunders approximation becomes inapplicable.† It must also be noticed that this approximation is, in particular, inapplicable to highly excited levels, in which the atom contains an electron which is in a state with large n, and which is therefore mainly at large distances from the nucleus (see §66). The electrostatic interaction of this electron with the motion of the other electrons is comparatively weak, but the relativistic interaction in the rest of the atom is not diminished.

In the opposite limiting case the relativistic interaction is large compared with the electrostatic (or, more precisely, compared with that part of it which governs the dependence of the energy on L and S). In this case we cannot speak of the orbital angular momentum and spin separately, since they are not conserved. The individual electrons are characterised by their total angular momenta j, which combine to give the total angular momentum J of the atom. This scheme of arrangement of the atomic levels is called *jj coupling*. In practice, this coupling is not found in the pure state, but various types of coupling intermediate between LS and jj are observed among the levels of very heavy atoms.‡

A peculiar type of coupling is observed in certain highly excited states. Here the rest of the atom may be in a Russell-Saunders state, i.e. may be characterised by the values of L and S, while its coupling with the highly excited electron is of the jj type; this is again due to the weakness of the electrostatic interaction for this electron.

---

† Nevertheless, it must be mentioned that, although the quantitative formulae which describe this type of coupling become inapplicable, the method of classifying levels according to this scheme may itself remain meaningful for heavier atoms, especially for the lowest states (including the normal state).

‡ For further details regarding types of coupling and the quantitative aspect of the problem, see, for instance, E. U. CONDON and G. H. SHORTLEY, *The Theory of Atomic Spectra*, Cambridge University Press 1935.

The fine structure of the energy levels of the hydrogen atom has certain characteristic properties. It can be calculated exactly, but here we shall only mention that the result of the calculation shows that, for a given principal quantum number n, the energy depends only on the total angular momentum j of the electron. Thus the degeneracy of the levels is not completely removed; to a level with given n and j there correspond two states with orbital angular momenta $l = j \pm \frac{1}{2}$ (unless j has the value $n - \frac{1}{2}$, which is the greatest possible for a given n). Thus the level with $n = 3$ is split into three levels, of which the states $^2S_{1/2}$, $^2P_{1/2}$ correspond to one, $^2P_{3/2}$ and $^2D_{3/2}$ to another, and $^2D_{5/2}$ to the third.

Finally, we shall briefly consider what is called the *hyperfine structure* of the levels. This is due to the fact that the nucleus of the atom has a spin also (which we denote by i). The interaction of this spin with the electrons is extremely weak, however, and hence the splitting which it causes in the levels (the hyperfine structure) is very small. As a result of this splitting, a level with a given angular momentum J is split into a number of levels which differ in the values of the total angular momentum F of the atom (including the nucleus), which takes the values

$$F = J+i,\quad J+i-1,\quad \ldots,\quad |J-i|. \tag{67.7}$$

All that we have said regarding the spin-orbit interaction is equally applicable to the interaction of the nuclear spin with the orbital angular momentum of the electrons, provided that we replace L, S, J in the formulae by J, i, F respectively.

§68. The self-consistent field

SCHRÖDINGER's equation for atoms containing more than one electron cannot be directly solved in practice, even by numerical methods. Approximate methods of calculating the energies and wave functions of the stationary states of the atoms are therefore important. The most important of these methods is what is called the *self-consistent field method*. The idea of this method consists in regarding each electron in the atom as being in motion in the "self-consistent field" due to the nucleus together with all the other electrons.

As an example, let us consider the helium atom, restricting ourselves to those terms in which both the electrons are in s states (with or without the same n); the states of the whole atom will then be S states also. Let $\psi_1(r_1)$ and $\psi_2(r_2)$ be the wave functions of the electrons; in the s states they are functions only of the distances r_1, r_2 of the electrons from the nuclei. The wave function $\psi(r_1, r_2)$ of the atom as a whole is a symmetrised

$$\psi = \psi_1(r_1)\psi_2(r_2)+\psi_1(r_2)\psi_2(r_1) \tag{68.1}$$

or antisymmetrised

$$\psi = \psi_1(r_1)\psi_2(r_2)-\psi_1(r_2)\psi_2(r_1) \tag{68.2}$$

product of the two functions, according as we are concerned with states of total spin† $S = 0$ or $S = 1$. We shall consider the second of these. The functions ψ_1 and ψ_2 can then be regarded as orthogonal.‡

Let us try to determine the function of the form (68.2) which is the best approximation to the true wave function of the atom. To do so, it is natural to start from the variational principle, allowing only functions of the form (68.2) to be considered; this method was proposed and developed by V. A. Fok (1930).

As we know, Schrödinger's equation can be obtained from the variational principle

$$\iint \psi^* \hat{H} \psi \mathrm{d}V_1 \mathrm{d}V_2 = \text{minimum},$$

with the additional condition

$$\iint |\psi|^2 \mathrm{d}V_1 \mathrm{d}V_2 = 1$$

(the integration is extended over the co-ordinates of both electrons in the helium atom). The variation gives the equation

$$\iint \delta\psi^* (\hat{H} - E)\psi \, \mathrm{d}V_1 \mathrm{d}V_2 = 0, \tag{68.3}$$

and hence, with an arbitrary variation of the wave function ψ, we obtain the usual Schrödinger's equation. In the self-consistent field method, the expression (68.2) for ψ is substituted in (68.3), and the variation is effected with respect to the functions ψ_1 and ψ_2 separately. In other words, we seek an extremum of the integral with respect to functions ψ of the form (68.2); as a result we obtain, of course, an inexact eigenvalue of the energy and an inexact wave function, but the best of the functions that can be represented in this form.

The Hamiltonian for the helium atom is of the form

$$\hat{H} = \hat{H}_1 + \hat{H}_2 + e^2/r_{12}, \quad \hat{H}_1 = -(\hbar^2/2\mu)\Delta_1 - 2e^2/r_1, \tag{68.4}$$

where r_{12} is the distance between the electrons. Substituting (68.2) in (68.3), carrying out the variation, and equating to zero the coefficients of $\delta\psi_1$ and $\delta\psi_2$ in the integrand, we easily obtain the following equations:

$$\begin{aligned} &[(\hbar^2/2\mu)\Delta + 2e^2/r + E - H_{22} - G_{22}(r)]\psi_1(r) + [H_{12} + G_{12}(r)]\psi_2(r) = 0, \\ &[(\hbar^2/2\mu)\Delta + 2e^2/r + E - H_{11} - G_{11}(r)]\psi_2(r) + [H_{12} + G_{12}(r)]\psi_1(r) = 0, \end{aligned} \tag{68.5}$$

† The states of the helium atom with $S = 0$ are usually called *parahelium* states, and those with $S = 1$ *orthohelium* states.

‡ The wave functions $\psi_1, \psi_2, \ldots$ of the various states of the electron which are obtained by the self-consistent field method are not in general orthogonal, since they are solutions of different equations, not of the same equation. In (68.2), however, without altering the function ψ of the whole atom, we can replace ψ_2 by $\psi_2' = \psi_2 + \text{constant} \times \psi_1$; by an appropriate choice of the constant, we can always ensure that ψ_1 and ψ_2' are orthogonal.

where

$$G_{ab}(r_1) = e^2\int \psi_a(r_2)\psi_b(r_2)\,\mathrm{d}V_2/r_{12},$$

$$H_{ab} = \int \psi_a[-(\hbar^2/2\mu)\Delta - 2e^2/r]\psi_b\,\mathrm{d}V \quad (a, b = 1, 2). \tag{68.6}$$

These are the final equations resulting from the self-consistent field method; they can, of course, be solved only numerically.†

The equations are similarly derived in more complex cases. The wave function of the atom to be substituted in the integral in the variational principle is in the form of a linear combination of products of the wave functions of the individual electrons. This combination must be so chosen that, firstly, its permutational symmetry corresponds to the total spin S of the state of the atom considered and, secondly, it corresponds to the given value of the total orbital angular momentum L of the atom.‡

By using, in the variational principle, the wave function having the necessary permutational symmetry, we automatically take account of the exchange interaction of the electrons in the atom. Simpler equations (though leading to less accurate results) are obtained if we neglect the exchange interaction and also the dependence on L of the energy of the atom for a given electron configuration (D. R. HARTREE 1928). As an example, let us again consider the helium atom; we can then write the equations for the wave functions of the electrons immediately in the form of ordinary SCHRÖDINGER's equations:

$$[(\hbar^2/2\mu)\Delta_a + E_a - V_a(r_a)]\psi_a(r_a) = 0 \quad (a = 1, 2), \tag{68.7}$$

where V_a is the potential energy of one electron moving in the field of the nucleus and in that of the distributed charge of the other electron:

$$V_1(r_1) = -2e^2/r_1 + \int (e^2/r_{12})\psi_2^2(r_2)\,\mathrm{d}V_2, \tag{68.8}$$

and similarly for V_2. In order to find the energy E of the whole atom, we must notice that, in the sum E_1+E_2, the electrostatic interaction between the two electrons is counted twice, since it appears in the potential energy $V_1(r_1)$ of the first electron and in that—$V_2(r_2)$—of the second. Hence E is obtained from the sum E_1+E_2 by subtracting once the mean energy of this interaction; that is,

$$E = E_1 + E_2 - \iint (e^2/r_{12})\psi_1^2(r_1)\psi_2^2(r_2)\,\mathrm{d}V_1\mathrm{d}V_2. \tag{68.9}$$

To refine the results obtained by this simplified method, the exchange interaction and the dependence of the energy on L can afterwards be taken into account as perturbations.

---

† A comparison of the energy levels of light atoms, calculated by the self-consistent field method, with spectroscopic data enables us to estimate the accuracy of the method at about 5 per cent.

‡ The first requirement means that the product of the functions ψ_a must be symmetrised with respect to the appropriate Young diagram (§61). The question of how to choose the linear combination corresponding to a given value of L is dealt with in §97.

PROBLEM

Determine approximately the energy of the ground level of the helium atom, approximating the wave function by a product of two hydrogen functions with some effective charge on the nucleus.

SOLUTION. In the ground state of the helium atom, both electrons are in s states. Hence we seek the wave function as a product of two hydrogen functions with $l = 0$;

$$\psi = (Z_{\text{eff}}^3/\pi)e^{-Z_{\text{eff}}(r_1+r_2)}; \tag{1}$$

all quantities are measured in atomic units. Using this expression, we calculate the integral

$$\iint \psi \hat{H} \psi \,\mathrm{d}V_1 \mathrm{d}V_2 = Z_{\text{eff}}^2 - 27 Z_{\text{eff}}/8$$

$$(\hat{H} = -\tfrac{1}{2}\Delta_1 - \tfrac{1}{2}\Delta_2 - 2/r_1 - 2/r_2 + 1/r_{12}).$$

In accordance with the variational principle, we seek a minimum of this integral (as a function of the parameter Z_{eff}), and the minimum value is the required energy of the ground state. We find

$$Z_{\text{eff}} = 27/16 = 1{\cdot}695, \quad -E = (27/16)^2;$$

the value of Z_{eff} found experimentally is 1·810.

We may remark that the wave function obtained is the best, not only of all functions of the form (1), but also of all functions which depend only on the sum $r_1 + r_2$.

§69. The Thomas-Fermi equation

Numerical calculations of the charge distribution and field in the atom by the self-consistent field method are extremely cumbersome, especially for complex atoms. For these, however, there is another approximate method, whose value lies in its simplicity; its results are admittedly much less accurate than those of the self-consistent field method.

The basis of this method (E. FERMI, and L. THOMAS, 1927) is the fact that, in complex atoms with a large number of electrons, the majority of the electrons have comparatively large principal quantum numbers. In these conditions the quasi-classical approximation is applicable. Hence we can apply the concept of "cells in phase space" (§52) to the states of the individual electrons.

The volume of phase space corresponding to electrons which have momenta less than p and are in the volume element $\mathrm{d}V$ of physical space is $\frac{4}{3}\pi p^3 \,\mathrm{d}V$. The number of "cells", i.e. possible states, corresponding to this volume is† $4\pi p^3 \,\mathrm{d}V/3(2\pi)^3$, and in these states there cannot at any one time be more than

$$2\frac{4\pi p^3}{3(2\pi)^3}\,\mathrm{d}V = \frac{p^3}{3\pi^2}\,\mathrm{d}V$$

electrons (two electrons, with opposite spins, in each "cell"). In the normal state of the atom, the electrons in each volume element $\mathrm{d}V$ must occupy (in phase space) the cells corresponding to momenta from zero up to some maximum value p_0. Then the kinetic energy of the electrons will have its smallest

† In this section we use atomic units, putting $e = \mu = \hbar = 1$ (see the first footnote to §36).

possible value at every point. If we write the number of electrons in the volume $\mathrm{d}V$ as $n\mathrm{d}V$ (where n is the number of electrons per unit volume), we can say that the maximum value p_0 of the momenta of the electrons at every point is related to n by

$$p_0^3/3\pi^2 = n.$$

The greatest value of the kinetic energy of an electron at a point where the electron density is n is therefore

$$\tfrac{1}{2}p_0^2 = \tfrac{1}{2}(3\pi^2 n)^{2/3}. \tag{69.1}$$

Next, let $\phi(r)$ be the electrostatic potential, which we suppose zero at infinity. The total energy of the electron is $\frac{1}{2}p^2-\phi$. It is evident that the total energy of each electron must be negative, since otherwise the electron moves off to infinity. We denote the maximum value of the total energy of the electron at each point by $-\phi_0$, where ϕ_0 is a positive constant; if this quantity were not constant, the electrons would move from points with smaller ϕ_0 to those with greater ϕ_0. Thus we can write

$$\tfrac{1}{2}p_0^2 = \phi-\phi_0. \tag{69.2}$$

Equating the expressions (69.1) and (69.2), we obtain

$$n = [2(\phi-\phi_0)]^{3/2}/3\pi^2, \tag{69.3}$$

a relation between the electron density and the potential at every point in the atom.

For $\phi = \phi_0$ the density n vanishes; n must clearly be put equal to zero also in the whole of the region where $\phi < \phi_0$, and where the relation (69.2) would give a negative maximum kinetic energy. Thus the equation $\phi = \phi_0$ determines the boundary of the atom. There is, however, no field outside a centrally symmetric system of charges whose total charge is zero. Hence we must have $\phi = 0$ at the boundary of a neutral atom. It follows from this that, for a neutral atom, the constant ϕ_0 must be put equal to zero. On the other hand, ϕ_0 is not zero for an ion.

Below we shall consider a neutral atom, putting accordingly $\phi_0 = 0$. According to Poisson's electrostatic equation, we have $\Delta\phi = 4\pi n$; substituting (69.3) in this, we obtain the fundamental equation of the Thomas-Fermi method:

$$\Delta\phi = (8\sqrt{2}/3\pi)\phi^{3/2}. \tag{69.4}$$

The field distribution in the normal state of the atom is determined by the centrally symmetric solution of this equation that satisfies the following boundary conditions: for $r \to 0$ the field must become the Coulomb field of the nucleus, i.e. $\phi r \to Z$, while for $r \to \infty$ we must have $\phi r \to 0$. Introducing here, in place of the variable r, a new variable x according to the definitions

$$r = xbZ^{-1/3}, \quad b = \tfrac{1}{2}(\tfrac{3}{4}\pi)^{2/3} = 0{\cdot}885, \tag{69.5}$$

and, in place of ϕ, a new unknown function χ by †

$$\phi(r) = \frac{Z}{r}\chi\left(\frac{rZ^{1/3}}{b}\right) = \frac{Z^{4/3}}{b}\frac{\chi(x)}{x}, \tag{69.6}$$

we obtain the equation

$$x^{\frac{1}{2}}\, \mathrm{d}^2\chi/\mathrm{d}x^2 = \chi^{3/2}, \tag{69.7}$$

with the boundary conditions $\chi = 1$ for $x = 0$ and $\chi = 0$ for $x = \infty$. This equation contains no parameters, and thus defines a universal function $\chi(x)$. Table 2 gives values of this function obtained by numerical integration of equation (69.7).‡ The function $\chi(x)$ vanishes only at infinity.|| In other words, the atom has no boundaries in the Thomas-Fermi model, and formally extends to infinity.

The value of the derivative $\chi'(x)$ for $x = 0$ is $\chi'(0) = -1{\cdot}59$. Hence, as

TABLE 2

Values of the function $\chi(x)$

x	$\chi(x)$	x	$\chi(x)$	x	$\chi(x)$
0·000	1·000	0·584	0·569	3·960	0·110
0·010	0·985	0·625	0·552	4·375	0·0956
0·030	0·959	0·667	0·535	5·000	0·0788
0·060	0·924	0·709	0·518	6·042	0·0587
0·080	0·902	0·750	0·502	7·083	0·0450
0·100	0·882	0·792	0·488	8·125	0·0355
0·150	0·835	0·833	0·475	9·167	0·0287
0·200	0·793	0·875	0·461	10·000	0·0244
0·250	0·755	0·917	0·449	11·16	0·0198
0·292	0·727	0·958	0·436	12·01	0·0171
0·333	0·700	1·000	0·425	13·33	0·0139
0·375	0·675	1·250	0·364	15·01	0·0109
0·417	0·651	1·667	0·287	20·00	0·0058
0·458	0·627	2·083	0·234	24·00	0·0038
0·500	0·607	2·500	0·193	30·00	0·0022
0·542	0·582	3·125	0·150	36·92	0·0011

† In ordinary units,

$$\phi(r) = (Ze/r)\chi(rZ^{1/3}\mu e^2/0{\cdot}885\hbar^2).$$

‡ A more detailed table is given by V. BUSH and S. CALDWELL, *Physical Review* **38**, 1898, 1931.

|| The equation (69.7) has the exact solution $\chi(x) = 144x^{-3}$, which vanishes at infinity but does not satisfy the boundary condition at $x = 0$. It can be used as an asymptotic expression for the function $\chi(x)$ for large x. However, it must be borne in mind that this expression gives fairly exact values only for large x, whilst the Thomas-Fermi equation becomes inapplicable at large distances (see below).

$x \to 0$, the function $\chi(x)$ is of the form $\chi \cong 1-1{\cdot}59x$, and accordingly the potential $\phi(r)$ is

$$\phi(r) \cong Z/r - 1{\cdot}80 Z^{4/3}. \tag{69.8}$$

The first term is the potential of the field of the nucleus, while the second ($-1{\cdot}80\mu e^3 Z^{4/3}/\hbar^2$ in ordinary units) is the potential at the origin due to the electrons.

Substituting (69.6) in (69.3), we find for the electron density an expression of the form

$$n = Z^2 f(rZ^{1/3}/b), \tag{69.9}$$

where the function $f(x) = (32/9\pi^3)(\chi/x)^{3/2}$. We see that, in the Thomas-Fermi model, the charge density distribution in different atoms is similar, with $Z^{-1/3}$ as the characteristic length (in ordinary units $\hbar^2/\mu e^2 Z^{1/3}$, i.e. the Bohr radius divided by $Z^{1/3}$). If we measure distances in atomic units, the distances at which the electron density has its maximum value are the same for all Z. Hence we can say that the majority of the electrons in an atom of atomic number Z are at distances from the nucleus of the order of $Z^{-1/3}$. A numerical calculation shows that half the total electron charge in an atom lies inside a sphere of radius $1{\cdot}33Z^{-1/3}$.

Similar considerations show that the mean velocity of the electrons in the atom (taken, as an order of magnitude, as the square root of the energy) is of the order of $Z^{2/3}$.

The Thomas-Fermi equation becomes inapplicable both at very small and at very large distances from the nucleus. Its range of applicability for small r is restricted by the inequality (49.11); at smaller distances the quasi-classical approximation becomes invalid in the Coulomb field of the nucleus. Putting in (49.11) $\alpha = Z$, we find $1/Z$ as the lower limit of distance. The quasi-classical approximation becomes invalid for large r also in a complex atom. In fact, it is easy to see that, for $r \sim 1$, the de Broglie wavelength of the electron becomes of the same order of magnitude as the distance itself, so that the quasi-classical condition is undoubtedly violated. This can be seen by estimating the values of the terms in equations (69.2) and (69.4); indeed, the result is obvious without calculation, since equation (69.4) does not involve Z. Thus the applicability of the Thomas-Fermi equation is limited to distances large compared with $1/Z$ and small compared with unity. In complex atoms, however, the majority of the electrons in fact lie in this region.

By means of the Thomas-Fermi method we can calculate the total ionisation energy E, i.e. the energy needed to remove all the electrons from the neutral atom. To do this, we must calculate the electrostatic energy of the Thomas-Fermi distribution for the charges in the atom; the required total energy is half this electrostatic energy, since the mean kinetic energy in a system of particles interacting in accordance with Coulomb's law is (by the virial theorem) minus half the mean potential energy. The dependence of E on Z can be determined *a priori* from simple considerations: the electrostatic energy of Z electrons at a mean distance $Z^{-1/3}$ from a nucleus of charge Z, and moving in its field, is proportional to $Z \cdot Z/Z^{-1/3} = Z^{7/3}$. A numerical calculation gives the result $E = 20 \cdot 8 Z^{7/3}$ eV. The dependence on Z is in good agreement with the experimental data, though the empirical value of the coefficient is close to 16.

We have already mentioned that positive (non-zero) values of the constant ϕ_0 correspond to ionised atoms. If we define the function χ by $\phi - \phi_0 = Z\chi/r$, we obtain the same equation (69.7) for χ as previously. We must now, however, consider only solutions which vanish not at infinity as for the neutral atom, but for finite values x_0 of x. Such solutions exist for any x_0. At the point $x = x_0$, the charge density vanishes together with χ, but the potential remains finite. The value of x_0 is related to the degree of ionisation in the following manner. The total charge inside a sphere of radius r is, by Gauss's theorem, $-r^2 \partial\phi/\partial r = Z[\chi(x) - x\chi'(x)]$. The total charge z on the ion is obtained by putting $x = x_0$ in this; since $\chi(x_0) = 0$, we have

$$z = -Zx_0\chi'(x_0). \tag{69.10}$$

The thick line in Fig. 25 shows the curve of $\chi(x)$ for a neutral atom; below it are two curves for ions of different degrees of ionisation. The quantity z/Z is shown graphically by the length of the segment intercepted on the axis of ordinates by the tangent to the curve at $x = x_0$.

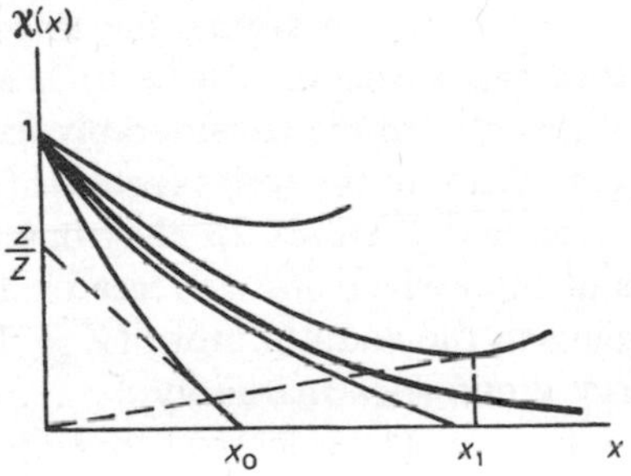

FIG. 25

Equation (69.7) also has solutions which are nowhere zero; these diverge at infinity. They can be regarded as corresponding to negative values of the constant ϕ_0. Fig. 25 also shows two such curves of $\chi(x)$; they lie above the curve for the neutral atom. At the point $x = x_1$, where

$$\chi(x_1) - x_1\chi'(x_1) = 0, \tag{69.11}$$

the total charge inside the sphere $x < x_1$ is zero (graphically, this point is evidently the one where the tangent to the curve passes through the origin). If we cut off the curve at this point, we can say that it defines $\chi(x)$ for a neutral atom at whose boundary the charge density remains non-zero. Physically, this corresponds to a "compressed" atom confined to some given finite volume.†

The Thomas-Fermi equation does not take account of the exchange interaction between electrons. The effects which this involves are of the next order of magnitude with respect to $Z^{-2/3}$. Hence an allowance for the exchange interaction in the Thomas-Fermi method requires a simultaneous consideration of both these effects and others of the same order of magnitude.‡

§70. The periodic system of D. I. Mendeleev

The elucidation of the nature of the periodic variation of properties, observed in the series of elements when they are placed in order of increasing atomic number, requires an examination of the peculiarities in the successive completion of the electron shells of atoms. The theory of the periodic system is due to N. Bohr (1922).

When we pass from one atom to the next, the charge is increased by unity and one electron is added to the envelope.‖ At first sight we might expect the binding energy of each of the successively added electrons to vary monotonically as the atomic number increases. The actual variation, however, is entirely different.

In the hydrogen atom there is only one electron, in the 1*s* state (we are speaking of the normal states of the atoms). In the atom of the next element, helium, another 1*s* electron is added; the binding energy of the 1*s* electrons in the helium atom is greater than in the hydrogen atom.¶ When we pass to the nucleus with $Z = 3$ (the lithium atom), the third electron enters the 2*s* state, since no more than two electrons can be in 1*s* states at the same time. The binding energy of this electron is considerably less than that of the electrons in the helium atom. Next, in the series from Be ($Z = 4$) to Ne ($Z = 10$), first one more 2*s* electron and then six 2*p* electrons are successively added. The binding energies of these electrons increase on the average. The next electron added, on going to the sodium atom ($Z = 11$), enters the 3*s* state, and the binding energy diminishes markedly.

This picture of the filling up of the electron envelope is characteristic of the whole sequence of elements. All the electron states can be divided into

† This approach may be useful in studying the equation of state of highly compressed matter.

‡ This has been done by A. S. Kompaneets and E. S. Pavlovskiĭ and by D. Kirzhnits (*JETP*, 32, 115, 1957), (*JETP*, 31, 927, 1956).

‖ We may recall that some atoms have the capacity of forming negative ions by uniting with an electron. The corresponding binding energy of the added electron is called the *affinity* of the electron for the atom. However, it must be borne in mind that by no means all atoms have this property. The reason is that the additional electron at large distances is attracted to the atom, not in accordance with Coulomb's law (energy $\sim 1/r$), but much less strongly ($\sim 1/r^4$). Hence, whereas Coulomb's law always gives an infinite number of levels, here the number of levels is invariably finite. In particular cases there may be no such levels at all; indeed, this situation occurs with the majority of atoms. An exception is formed by atoms of the halogens and of the oxygen group (with electron affinities of the order of 2 to 4 eV) and by the hydrogen atom (affinity 0·7 eV).

¶ The increase in the binding energy on going from hydrogen to helium is quite natural if we take into account the difference between the field in which the electron moves in the hydrogen atom and the field encountered by an electron added to the He^+ ion. At large distances these fields are approximately the same, but at small distances the field of the He^+ ion is stronger than that of the nucleus of the hydrogen atom, because of the twice as great charge on the nucleus of the helium atom.

successively occupied groups such that, as the states of each group are occupied in a series of elements, the binding energy increases on the average, but when the states of the next group begin to be occupied the binding energy decreases noticeably. The increase in the binding energy is due to the increase in the charge on the nucleus; if we consider the electrons in a single atom, however, it is found that the energy levels of the electrons in the states

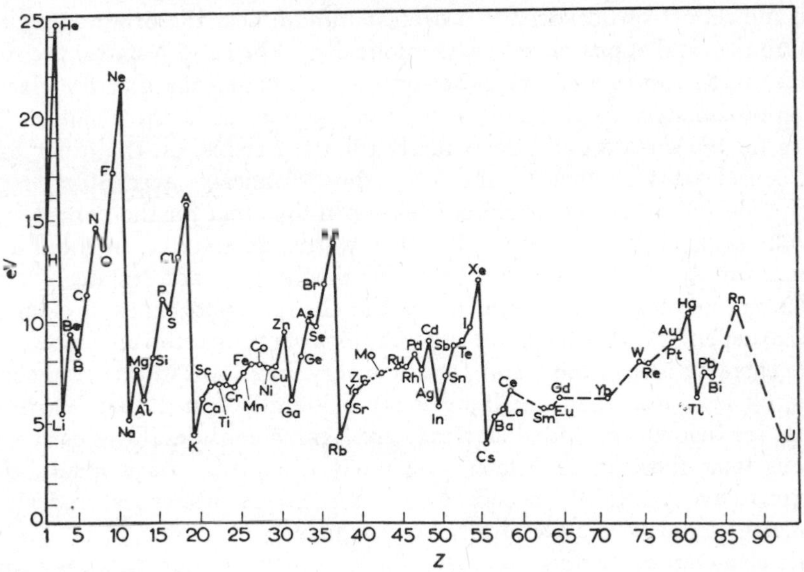

FIG. 26

of each group are close together, and are considerably removed from the energies of other groups. Fig. 26 shows those ionisation potentials of elements that are known from spectroscopic data; they give the binding energies of the electrons added as we pass from each element to the next.

The different states are distributed as follows into successively occupied groups:

$1s$	2 electrons	
$2s, 2p$	8 ,,	
$3s, 3p$	8 ,,	
$4s, 3d, 4p$	18 ,,	(70.1)
$5s, 4d, 5p$	18 ,,	
$6s, 4f, 5d, 6p$	32 ,,	
$7s, 6d, 5f$		

The first group is occupied in H and He; the occupation of the second and third groups corresponds to the first two (short) periods of the periodic system, containing 8 elements each. Next follow two long periods of 18 elements each, and a long period containing the rare-earth elements and 32 elements in all. The occupation of the final group of states is only begun by the existing elements.

To understand the variation of the properties of the elements as the states of each group are occupied, the following property of *s* and *p* states, which distinguishes them from *d* and *f* states, is important. The curves of the effective potential energy of the centrally symmetric field (composed of the electrostatic field and the centrifugal field) for an electron in a heavy atom have a rapid and almost vertical drop to a deep minimum near the origin; they then begin to rise, and approach zero asymptotically. For *s* and *p* states, the rising parts of these curves are very close together. This means that the electron is at approximately the same distance from the nucleus in these states. The curves for the *d* states, and particularly for the *f* states, on the other hand, pass considerably further to the left; the "classically accessible" region which they delimit ends considerably closer in than that for the *s* and *p* states with the same electron energy. In other words, an electron in the *d* and *f* states is mainly much closer to the nucleus than in the *s* and *p* states.

Many properties of atoms (including the chemical properties of elements; see §78) depend principally on the outer regions of the electron envelopes. The above characteristic of the *d* and *f* states is very important in this connection. Thus, for instance, when the 4*f* states are being filled (in the rare-earth elements; see below), the added electrons are located considerably closer to the nucleus than those in the states previously occupied. As a result, these electrons have practically no effect on the chemical properties, and all the rare-earth elements are chemically very similar.

The elements containing complete *d* and *f* shells (or not containing these shells at all) are called elements of the ***principal groups***; those in which the filling up of these states is actually in progress are called elements of the ***intermediate groups***. These groups of elements are conveniently considered separately.

Let us begin with the elements of the principal groups. Hydrogen and helium have the following normal states:

$$\mathrm{H}^1 : 1s\ {}^2S_{1/2} \qquad \mathrm{He}^2 : 1s^2\ {}^1S_0$$

(the index with the chemical symbol always signifies the atomic number). The electron configurations of the remaining elements of the principal groups are shown in Table 3.

In each atom, the shells shown on the right of the table in the same line and above are completely filled. The electron configuration in the shells that are being filled is shown at the top, while the principal quantum number of the electrons in these states is shown by the figure on the left of the table in the same line. The normal states of the whole atom are shown at the bottom. Thus, the aluminium atom has the electron configuration $1s^2\ 2s^2\ 2p^6\ 3s^2\ 3p\ {}^2P_{1/2}$.

The values of L and S in the normal state of the atom can be determined (the electron configuration being known) by means of Hund's rule (§65).

TABLE 3

Electron configurations of the atoms of elements in the principal groups

	s	s^2	s^2p	s^2p^2	s^2p^3	s^2p^4	s^2p^5	s^2p^6	
$n = 2$	Li^3	Be^4	B^5	C^6	N^7	O^8	F^9	Ne^{10}	$1s^2$
3	Na^{11}	Mg^{12}	Al^{13}	Si^{14}	P^{15}	S^{16}	Cl^{17}	A^{18}	$2s^2\, 2p^6$
4	K^{19}	Ca^{20}							$3s^2\, 3p^6$
4	Cu^{29}	Zn^{30}	Ga^{31}	Ge^{32}	As^{33}	Se^{34}	Br^{35}	Kr^{36}	$3d^{10}$
5	Rb^{37}	Sr^{38}							$4s^2\, 4p^6$
5	Ag^{47}	Cd^{48}	In^{49}	Sn^{50}	Sb^{51}	Te^{52}	I^{53}	Xe^{54}	$4d^{10}$
6	Cs^{55}	Ba^{56}							$5s^2\, 5p^6$
6	Au^{79}	Hg^{80}	Tl^{81}	Pb^{82}	Bi^{83}	Po^{84}	At^{85}	Rn^{86}	$4f^{14}\, 5d^{10}$
7	Fr^{87}	Ra^{88}							$6s^2\, 6p^6$
	${}^2S_{1/2}$	${}^1S_0$	${}^2P_{1/2}$	${}^3P_0$	${}^4S_{3/2}$	${}^3P_2$	${}^2P_{3/2}$	${}^1S_0$	

Here we must always consider only the unfilled shell, since the angular momenta of the electrons in the filled shells compensate one another. For example, let us consider the oxygen atom. The magnetic quantum number of a p electron can take three values, 0 and ± 1. Hence the set of four p electrons in the oxygen atom can have a total spin of not more than one (when the projections σ of the spins of the individual electrons are $\frac{1}{2}, \frac{1}{2}, \frac{1}{2}, -\frac{1}{2}$). The three electrons with $\sigma = \frac{1}{2}$ must have different m, i.e. -1, 0, $+1$. Suppose the fourth has the maximum value of m, i.e. 1. Then $M_L = \Sigma m = 1$; this means that the greatest possible value of L, for $S = 1$, is 1.

The value of J is determined by the rule given in §67. Thus, applying this rule to the filling-up of the p shell, we can say that, for the configurations p, p^2, p^3, we have $J = |L-S|$, whereas for the configurations p^4, p^5, p^6 we have $J = L+S$.

The atoms of the inert gases (He, Ne, A, Kr, Xe, Rn) occupy a special position in the table: the filling up of one of the groups of states listed in (70.1) is completed in each of them. Their electron configurations have unusual stability (their ionisation potentials are the greatest in their respective series). This causes the chemical inertness of these elements.

We see that the occupation of different states occurs very regularly in the series of elements of the principal groups: first the s states and then the p states are occupied for each principal quantum number n. The electron configurations of the ions of these elements are also regular (until electrons from the d and f shells are removed in the ionisation): each ion has the configuration corresponding to the preceding atom. Thus, the Mg^+ ion has the configuration of the sodium atom, and the Mg^{++} ion that of neon.

Let us now turn to the elements of the intermediate groups. The filling up of the $3d$, $4d$, and $5d$ shells takes place in groups of elements called respectively the *iron group*, the *palladium group* and the *platinum group*. Table 4 gives those electron configurations and terms of the atoms in these groups that are known from experimental spectroscopic data; dashes indicate that such data do not yet exist. As is seen from this table, the d shells are filled up with considerably less regularity than the s and p shells in the atoms

TABLE 4

Electron configurations of the atoms of elements in the iron, palladium and platinum groups

	Iron group							
	Sc^{21}	Ti^{22}	V^{23}	Cr^{24}	Mn^{25}	Fe^{26}	Co^{27}	Ni^{28}
A envelope +	$3d\,4s^2$	$3d^2\,4s^2$	$3d^3\,4s^2$	$3d^5\,4s$	$3d^5\,4s^2$	$3d^6\,4s^2$	$3d^7\,4s^2$	$3d^8\,4s^2$
	$^2D_{3/2}$	$^3F_2$	$^4F_{3/2}$	$^7S_3$	$^6S_{5/2}$	$^5D_4$	$^4F_{9/2}$	$^3F_4$
	Palladium group							
	Y^{39}	Zr^{40}	Nb^{41}	Mo^{42}	Tc^{43}	Ru^{44}	Rh^{45}	Pd^{46}
Kr envelope +	$4d\,5s^2$	$4d^2\,5s^2$	$4d^4\,5s$	$4d^5\,5s$	—	$4d^7\,5s$	$4d^8\,5s$	$4d^{10}$
	$^2D_{3/2}$	$^3F_2$	$^6D_{1/2}$	$^7S_3$	—	$^5F_5$	$^4F_{9/2}$	$^1S_0$
	Platinum group							
	La^{57}							
Xe envelope +	$5d\,6s^2$ $^2D_{3/2}$							
	Lu^{71}	Hf^{72}	Ta^{73}	W^{74}	Re^{75}	Os^{76}	Ir^{77}	Pt^{78}
Xe envelope $+4f^{14}+$	$5d\,6s^2$	$5d^2\,6s^2$	—	$5d^4\,6s^2$	$5d^5\,6s^2$	—	$5d^9$	$5d^9\,6s$
	$^2D_{3/2}$	$^3F_2$	—	$^5D_0$	$^6S_{5/2}$	—	$^2D_{5/2}$	$^3D_3$

of elements of the principal groups. Here a characteristic feature is the "competition" between the s and d states. It is seen in the fact that, instead of a regular sequence of configurations of the type $d^p\,s^2$ with increasing p, configurations of the type $d^{p+1}s$ or d^{p+2} are often found. Thus, in the iron group, the chromium atom has the configuration $3d^5\,4s$, and not $3d^4\,4s^2$; after nickel with 8 d electrons, there follows at once the copper atom with a completely filled d shell (and hence we place this element in the principal groups). This lack of regularity is observed in the terms of ions also: the electron configurations of the ions do not usually agree with those of the preceding atoms. For instance, the V^+ ion has the configuration $3d^4$ (and not $3d^2\,4s^2$ like titanium); the Fe^+ ion has $3d^6\,4s$ (instead of $3d^5\,4s^2$ as in manganese). We may remark that all ions found naturally in crystals and solutions contain only *d* (not *s* or *p*) electrons in their incomplete shells. Thus iron is found in crystals or solutions only as the ions Fe^{++} and Fe^{+++}, whose configurations are $3d^6$ and $3d^5$ respectively.

A similar situation occurs in the filling up of the $4f$ shell; this takes place in the series of elements known as the *rare earths* (Table 5).† The filling up of the $4f$ shell also occurs in a slightly irregular manner characterised by the "competition" between $4f$, $5d$ and $6s$ states. The ions of these elements that are found in Nature contain only *f* electrons (not *s*, *p* or *d* electrons) in their incomplete shells.

The last group of intermediate elements begins with actinium (Table 5a). In this group an electron shell is filled, similarly to what happens in the group of rare-earth elements. It is as yet uncertain at which element (Th, Pa or U) $5f$ electrons appear for the first time.

To conclude this section, let us examine an interesting application of the Thomas-Fermi method. We have seen that the electrons in the *p* shell first appear in the fifth element (boron), the *d* electrons for $Z = 21$ (scandium), and the *f* electrons for $Z = 58$ (cerium). These values of Z can be predicted by the Thomas-Fermi method, as follows.

An electron with orbital angular momentum l in a complex atom moves with an "effective potential energy"‡ of

$$U_l(r) = -\phi(r)+\tfrac{1}{2}(l+\tfrac{1}{2})^2/r^2.$$

The first term is the potential energy in an electric field described by the Thomas-Fermi potential $\phi(r)$. The second term is the centrifugal energy, in which we put $(l+\frac{1}{2})^2$ instead of $l(l+1)$, since the motion is quasi-classical. Since the total energy of the electron in the atom is negative, it is clear that, if (for given values of Z and l) $U_l(r) > 0$ for all r, there can be no electrons in the atom concerned with the given value of the angular momentum l. If we consider any definite value of l and vary Z, it is found that in fact $U_l(r) > 0$ everywhere when Z is sufficiently small. As Z is increased, a value is reached for which the curve of $U_l(r)$ touches the axis of abscissae, while for larger Z there is a region where $U_l(r) < 0$. Thus the value of Z at which electrons with the given l appear in the atom is determined by the condition that the curve of $U_l(r)$ touches the axis of abscissae, i.e. by the equations

$$U_l(r) = -\phi+\tfrac{1}{2}(l+\tfrac{1}{2})^2/r^2 = 0, \quad U_l'(r) = -\phi'(r)-(l+\tfrac{1}{2})^2/r^3 = 0.$$

Substituting here the expression (69.6) for the potential, we obtain the equations

$$\begin{aligned} Z^{2/3}\chi(x)/x &= (4/3\pi)^{2/3}(l+\tfrac{1}{2})^2/x^2, \\ Z^{2/3}[x\chi'(x)-\chi(x)]/x &= -2(4/3\pi)^{2/3}(l+\tfrac{1}{2})^2/x^2. \end{aligned} \tag{70.2}$$

† In books on chemistry, lutetium is also usually placed with the rare-earth elements. This, however, is incorrect, since the $4f$ shell is complete in lutetium; it must therefore be placed in the platinum group, as in Table 4.

‡ As in §69, we use atomic units.

TABLE 5

Electron configurations of the atoms of the rare-earth elements

	Ce^{58}	Pr^{59}	Nd^{60}	Pm^{61}	Sm^{62}	Eu^{63}	Gd^{64}	Tb^{65}	Dy^{66}	Ho^{67}	Er^{68}	Tu^{69}	Yb^{70}
Xe envelope +	—	—	$4f^4 6s^2$	—	$4f^6 6s^2$	$4f^7 6s^2$	$4f^7 5d 6s^2$	—	—	—	—	$4f^{13} 6s^2$	$4f^{14} 6s^2$
	—	—	$^5I_4$	—	$^7F_0$	$^8S_{7/2}$	$^9D_2$	—	—	—	—	$^2F_{7/2}$	$^1S_0$

TABLE 5a

Electron configurations of the atoms of elements in the actinium group

	Ac^{89}	Th^{90}	Pa^{91}	U^{92}	Np^{93}	Pu^{94}	Am^{95}	Cm^{96}	Bk^{97}	Cf^{98}
Rn envelope +	$6d\,7s^2$	—	—	$5f^3 6d\,7s^2$	—	—	$5f^7 7s^2$	$5f^7 6d\,7s^2$	—	—
	$^2D_{3/2}$	—	—	$^5L_6$	—	—	$^8S_{7/2}$	^9D	—	—

Dividing each side of the second equation by the corresponding side of the first, we find for x the equation

$$\chi'(x)/\chi(x) = -1/x,$$

and we then calculate Z from the first of equations (70.2). A numerical calculation gives

$$Z = 0\cdot155(2l+1)^3.$$

This formula determines the value of Z for which electrons with a given l first appear in the atom; the error is about 10 per cent.

Very accurate values are obtained by taking the coefficient as 0·17 instead of 0·155:

$$Z = 0\cdot17(2l+1)^3. \tag{70.3}$$

For $l = 1, 2, 3$ this formula gives respectively $Z = 4\cdot6, 21\cdot25, 58\cdot3$. Rounding these numbers to the nearest integer, we find the correct values 5, 21, 58. For $l = 4$, formula (70.3) gives $Z = 124$; this means that g electrons should first appear only in the 124th element.

§71. X-ray terms

The binding energy of the inner electrons† in the atom is so large that, if such an electron makes a transition into an outer unfilled shell, the excited atom is mechanically unstable with respect to ionisation, which is accompanied by the reconstruction of the electron envelope and the formation of a stable ion. However, because of the comparatively weak interaction between the electrons in the atom, the probability of such a transition is comparatively small, so that the lifetime τ of the excited state is long. Hence the "width" $\hbar/\tau$ of the level (see §44) is so small that it is reasonable to regard the energies of an atom with an excited inner electron as discrete energy levels of "quasi-stationary" states of the atom. These levels are called *X-ray terms.*‡

The X-ray terms are primarily classified according to the shell from which the electron is removed, or in which, as we say, a "hole" is formed. Which outer shell the electron enters has almost no effect on the energy of the atom, and hence is unimportant.

The total angular momentum of the set of electrons occupying any shell is zero. When one electron has been removed, the shell acquires some angular momentum j. For the (n, l) shell, the angular momentum j can obviously take the values $l\pm\frac{1}{2}$. Thus we obtain levels which might be denoted by $1s_{1/2}$, $2s_{1/2}$, $2p_{1/2}$, $2p_{3/2}$, ..., where the value of j is added as a suffix to the letter giving the position of the "hole". It is usual, however, to employ special symbols as follows:

$1s_{1/2}$	$2s_{1/2}$	$2p_{1/2}$	$2p_{3/2}$	$3s_{1/2}$	$3p_{1/2}$	$3p_{3/2}$	$3d_{3/2}$	$3d_{5/2}$	...
K	L_{I}	L_{II}	L_{III}	M_{I}	M_{II}	M_{III}	M_{IV}	M_{V}	...

The levels with $n = 4, 5, 6$ are similarly denoted by the letters N, O, P.

† By *inner electrons* we mean those in completed shells.

‡ The name is due to the fact that transitions between these levels cause the emission of X-rays by the atom.

Levels with the same n (denoted by the same capital letter) lie close together and at a distance from levels with a different n. The reason for this is that, owing to the relative nearness of the inner electrons to the nucleus, they are principally in the field of the nucleus, and hence their states are "hydrogen-like". In view of the well-known properties of the energy levels in hydrogen, it therefore follows that the X-ray terms depend, in the first approximation, only on n. If relativistic effects are taken into account, terms with different j are separated (cf. the discussion in §67 of the fine structure of the hydrogen levels), such as, for example, L_{I} and L_{II} from L_{III}, and M_{I} and M_{II} from M_{III} and M_{IV}. These pairs of levels are said to be *regular* (or *relativistic*) doublets. The separation of terms with different l and the same j (for instance L_{I} and L_{II}, M_{I} and M_{II}) is due to the deviation of the field in which the inner electrons move from the Coulomb field. These are said to be *irregular* (or *screening*) doublets.

§72. The Stark effect

If an atom is placed in an external electric field, its energy levels are altered; this phenomenon is known as the *Stark effect*.

In an atom placed in a homogeneous electric field, we have a system of electrons in an axially symmetric field (the field of the nucleus together with the external field). The total angular momentum of the atom is therefore, strictly speaking, no longer conserved; only the projection M_J of the total angular momentum $\mathbf{J}$ on the direction of the field is conserved. The states with different values of M_J have different energies, i.e. the electric field removes the degeneracy with respect to directions of the angular momentum. The removal is, however, incomplete: the states differing only in the sign of M_J are degenerate as before. For an atom in a homogeneous external electric field is symmetrical with respect to reflection in any plane passing through the axis of symmetry (i.e. the axis passing through the nucleus in the direction of the field; we shall later take this as the z-axis). Hence the states obtained from one another by such a reflection must have the same energy. On reflection in a plane passing through some axis, however, the angular momentum about this axis changes sign (the direction of a positive revolution about the axis becomes that of a negative one).

We shall suppose that the electric field is so weak that the additional energy due to it is small compared with the distances between neighbouring energy levels of the atom, including the fine-structure intervals. Then, in order to calculate the displacement of the levels in the electric field, we can use the perturbation theory developed in §§38 and 39. Here the perturbation operator is the energy of the system of electrons in the homogeneous field $\mathscr{E}$, and this is well known to be $-\mathbf{d} \cdot \mathscr{E} = -\mathscr{E} d_z$, where $\mathbf{d}$ is the dipole moment of the system. In the zero approximation, the energy levels are degenerate (with respect to directions of the total angular momentum); in the present case, however, this degeneracy is unimportant, and in applying perturbation theory we can proceed as if we were dealing with non-degenerate levels. This follows from the fact that, in the matrix of the quantity d_z (as in that of the z-component of any vector), only the elements for transitions without change of M_J are not zero (see §27), and hence states with different values of M_J behave independently when perturbation theory is applied.

The displacement of the energy levels is determined, in the first approximation, by the diagonal matrix elements of the perturbation. It is easy to see, however, that all the diagonal matrix elements of the dipole moment vanish identically. We have shown in §28 that the matrix of any polar vector (as **d** is) has non-zero elements only for transitions between states of different parity; hence the diagonal elements are always zero.

Thus the splitting of the levels in an electric field is a second-order effect, and is proportional to the square of the field.† The relation between the displacement of the levels and M_J is easily determined. The correction to the eigenvalues of the energy, in the second approximation, is given by formula (38.9); it is a sum of expressions each of which is proportional to the square of some matrix element of the perturbation. In this case we are concerned with the matrix elements of the z-component of a vector (d_z), whose dependence on M is completely determined by formulae (27.13), where we must put J for L and M_J for M. According to these formulae, the squares of the matrix elements are linear functions of M_J^2. The same is therefore true of the displacements of the energy levels. Numbering the unperturbed energy levels by a suffix n, we can write for the magnitudes of the displacements $\Delta E_n(M_J)$ of the levels into which a given unperturbed level is split

$$\Delta E_n = -\tfrac{1}{2}\mathscr{E}^2(a_n+b_n M_J^2), \tag{72.1}$$

where a_n and b_n are constants.

The polarisability of the atom in the electric field can also be expressed in terms of these constants. To do this, we make use of the following general formula. Let the Hamiltonian $\hat{H}$ of the system be a function of some parameter λ; its eigenvalues E_n are then functions of λ also. It can be shown that the mean value of the quantity represented by the operator $\partial\hat{H}/\partial\lambda$, in the state n (i.e. the diagonal matrix element $(\partial H/\partial\lambda)_{nn}$), is equal to the derivative, with respect to λ, of the corresponding eigenvalue‡ E_n:

$$(\partial H/\partial\lambda)_{nn} = \partial E_n/\partial\lambda. \tag{72.2}$$

† The hydrogen atom forms an exception; here the Stark effect is linear in the field (see the next section). The atoms of other elements, when in highly excited states (and therefore hydrogen-like; see §66), behave like hydrogen in sufficiently strong fields.

‡ To show this, we differentiate the equation $(\hat{H}-E)\psi_n = 0$ with respect to λ, and then multiply on the left by ψ_n^*:

$$\psi_n^*(\hat{H}-E_n)\,\partial\psi_n/\partial\lambda = \psi_n^*(\partial E_n/\partial\lambda-\partial\hat{H}/\partial\lambda)\psi_n.$$

Integrating with respect to q, we obtain zero on the left-hand side, since we have

$$\int \psi_n^*(\hat{H}-E_n)(\partial\psi_n/\partial\lambda)\,dq = \int (\partial\psi_n/\partial\lambda)(\hat{H}-E_n)\psi_n^*\,dq,$$

the operator $\hat{H}$ being Hermitian. The right-hand side gives the required equation (72.2).

In the case considered, the parameter λ is the electric field $\mathscr{E}$, and the derivative of the Hamiltonian $\hat{H} = \hat{H}_0 - \mathscr{E} d_z$ with respect to it is $-d_z$. Thus we have for the mean value of the dipole moment of the atom

$$\overline{d_z} = (a_n + b_n M_J{}^2)\mathscr{E}. \tag{72.3}$$

The coefficient of $\mathscr{E}$ is the polarisability of the atom.

PROBLEM

Determine the Stark splitting of the different components of a multiplet level as a function of J.

SOLUTION. The problem is conveniently solved by changing the order in which the perturbations are applied; we first consider the Stark splitting of the level in the absence of fine structure, and then bring in the spin-orbit interaction. Since the spin of the atom does not interact with the external electric field, the Stark splitting of a level with orbital angular momentum L is given by the formula

$$\Delta E = (\alpha + \beta M_L{}^2)\mathscr{E}^2,$$

i.e. it is of the same form as (72.1), except that M_J is replaced by M_L (we omit the suffixes to the constants). It can be regarded as an eigenvalue of the operator $(\alpha + \beta \hat{L}_z{}^2)\mathscr{E}^2$ or

$$\{\alpha\delta_{ik} + \tfrac{1}{2}\beta(\hat{L}_i\hat{L}_k + \hat{L}_k\hat{L}_i)\}\mathscr{E}_i\mathscr{E}_k; \tag{1}$$

summation over the suffixes i, k (values x, y, z) is understood.

When the spin-orbit interaction is introduced, the states of the atom must be characterised by the total angular momentum J. We average the operator (1) over the electron states with a given value J of the angular momentum (but not of its projection M_J).† Then $\overline{\hat{L}_i\hat{L}_k + \hat{L}_k\hat{L}_i}$ is still an operator, of the form

$$\overline{\hat{L}_i\hat{L}_k + \hat{L}_k\hat{L}_i} = c_1(\hat{J}_i\hat{J}_k + \hat{J}_k\hat{J}_i) + c_2\delta_{ik}; \tag{2}$$

this is the most general form of operator, symmetrical with respect to i and k, that can be constructed from the "vector" $\hat{\mathbf{J}}$, the only one which characterises the atom as a whole. The eigenvalues of the operator

$$\{(\alpha + \tfrac{1}{2}\beta c_2)\delta_{ik} + \tfrac{1}{2}\beta c_1(\hat{J}_i\hat{J}_k + \hat{J}_k\hat{J}_i)\}\mathscr{E}_i\mathscr{E}_k = \{(\alpha + \tfrac{1}{2}\beta c_2) + \beta c_1 \hat{J}_z{}^2\}\mathscr{E}^2$$

are

$$\Delta E = (\alpha + \tfrac{1}{2}\beta c_2 + \beta c_1 M_J{}^2)\mathscr{E}^2. \tag{3}$$

To determine the constants c_1, c_2 we multiply the equation (2) on the left by $\hat{J}_i$ and on the right by $\hat{J}_k$. Using the commutation rules for the components of the vectors $\hat{\mathbf{J}}$ and $\hat{\mathbf{L}}$ (and bearing in mind that the components of $\hat{\mathbf{S}}$ and $\hat{\mathbf{L}}$ commute), we obtain after some calculation the equation

$$2(\mathbf{J}\cdot\mathbf{L})^2 - \mathbf{J}\cdot\mathbf{L} = c_1[2J^2(J+1)^2 - J(J+1)] + c_2 J(J+1),$$

in which we have replaced the operators by their eigenvalues; by formula (30.3), the eigenvalue $\mathbf{J}\cdot\mathbf{L}$ is

$$\mathbf{J}\cdot\mathbf{L} = \tfrac{1}{2}[J(J+1) + L(L+1) - S(S+1)].$$

Another equation is obtained by putting $i = k$ in (2) and summing over i; this gives

$$2L(L+1) = 2c_1 J(J+1) + 3c_2.$$

† See §§67, 74 for a more detailed account of such averaging.

From these two equations we determine c_1 and c_2:

$$c_1 = \frac{3(\mathbf{J}.\mathbf{L})[2(\mathbf{J}.\mathbf{L})-1]-2J(J+1)L(L+1)}{J(J+1)(2J-1)(2J+3)},$$
$$c_2 = \frac{2L(L+1)[2J(J+1)-1]-2(\mathbf{J}.\mathbf{L})[2(\mathbf{J}.\mathbf{L})-1]}{(2J-1)(2J+3)}. \tag{4}$$

Formulae (3) and (4) give the solution of the problem proposed, since they determine the splitting as a function of J (but not, of course, of L and S, since the constants α and β also depend on these).

§73. The Stark effect in hydrogen

The levels of the hydrogen atom, unlike those of other atoms, undergo a splitting proportional to the field (the *linear Stark effect*) in a homogeneous electric field. This is due to the occurrence of an accidental degeneracy in the hydrogen terms, whereby states with different l (for a given principal quantum number n) have the same energy. The matrix elements of the dipole moment for transitions between these states are not zero, and hence the secular equation gives a non-zero displacement of the levels, even in the first approximation.

For purposes of calculation† it is convenient to choose the unperturbed wave functions so that the perturbation matrix is diagonal with respect to each group of mutually degenerate states. It is found that this is achieved by quantising the hydrogen atom in parabolic co-ordinates. The wave functions $\psi_{n_1n_2m}$ of the stationary states of the hydrogen atom in parabolic co-ordinates are given by formulae (37.15) and (37.16).

The perturbation operator‡ (the energy of an electron in the field $\mathscr{E}$) is $\mathscr{E}z = \frac{1}{2}\mathscr{E}(\xi-\eta)$; the field is directed along the positive z-axis, and the force on the electron along the negative z-axis. We are interested in the matrix elements for transitions $n_1n_2m \to n_1'n_2'm'$, for which the energy (i.e. the principal quantum number n) is unaltered. It is easy to see that, of these, only the diagonal matrix elements

$$\int |\psi_{n_1n_2m}|^2 \mathscr{E}z\,\mathrm{d}V = \tfrac{1}{8}\mathscr{E}\int_0^\infty\int_0^\infty\int_0^{2\pi}(\xi^2-\eta^2)|\psi_{n_1n_2m}|^2\,\mathrm{d}\phi\,\mathrm{d}\xi\,\mathrm{d}\eta$$

$$= \tfrac{1}{4}\mathscr{E}\int_0^\infty\int_0^\infty f_{n_1m}^2(\rho_1)f_{n_2m}^2(\rho_2)(\rho_1^2-\rho_2^2)\,\mathrm{d}\rho_1\mathrm{d}\rho_2 \tag{73.1}$$

are non-zero (we have made the substitution $\xi = n\rho_1$, $\eta = n\rho_2$). The matrix concerned is evidently diagonal with respect to the number m, while its diagonality with respect to the numbers n_1, n_2 follows from the orthogonality

† In the following calculations we do not take account of the fine structure of the hydrogen levels. Hence the field must be, though not strong (for perturbation theory to be applicable), yet such that the Stark splitting is large in comparison with the fine structure.

‡ In this section we use atomic units.

of the functions f_{n_1m} for different n_1 and the same n (see below). The integrations over ρ_1 and ρ_2 in (73.1) are separable; the integrals obtained are calculated in §f of the Mathematical Appendices (integral (f.6)). After a simple calculation, we find for the corrections to the energy levels in the first approximation

$$E^{(1)} = \tfrac{3}{2}\mathscr{E}n(n_1-n_2), \qquad (73.2)$$

or, in absolute units,

$$E^{(1)} = \tfrac{3}{2}n(n_1-n_2)e\mathscr{E}\hbar^2/\mu e^2.$$

The two extreme components of the split level correspond to $n_1 = n-1$, $n_2 = 0$ and $n_1 = 0$, $n_2 = n-1$. The distance between these two extreme levels is, by (73.2),

$$3\mathscr{E}n(n-1),$$

i.e. the total splitting of the level by the Stark effect is approximately proportional to n^2. It is natural that the splitting should increase with the principal quantum number: the further the electrons are from the nucleus, the greater the dipole moment of the atom.

The presence of the linear effect means that, in the unperturbed state, the atom has a dipole moment whose mean value is

$$\overline{d_z} = -\tfrac{3}{2}n(n_1-n_2). \qquad (73.3)$$

This is in accordance with the fact that, in a state determined by parabolic quantum numbers, the distribution of the charges in the atom is not symmetrical about the plane $z = 0$ (see §37). Thus, for $n_1 > n_2$, the electron is predominantly on the side of positive z, and hence the atom has a negative dipole moment (the charge on the electron being negative).

In the previous section we have shown that a homogeneous electric field cannot entirely remove degeneracy: there always remains a double degeneracy of states differing in the sign of the projection of the angular momentum on the direction of the field (in this case, states whose projected angular momenta are $\pm m$). However, we see from formula (73.2) that no such removal of the degeneracy occurs in the linear Stark effect in hydrogen: the displacement of the levels (for given n and n_1-n_2) is independent of m and n_2. A further removal of the degeneracy occurs in the second approximation; the calculation of this effect is the more interesting in that the linear Stark effect is altogether absent in states with $n_1 = n_2$.

To calculate the quadratic effect, it is not convenient to use ordinary perturbation theory, since it would be necessary to deal with infinite sums of complicated form. Instead we use the following slightly modified method.

Schrödinger's equation for the hydrogen atom in a homogeneous electric field is of the form

$$(\tfrac{1}{2}\Delta+E+1/r-\mathscr{E}z)\psi = 0.$$

Like the equation with $\mathscr{E} = 0$, it allows separation of the variables in parabolic co-ordinates. The same substitution (37.7) as was used in §37 gives the two equations

$$\left.\begin{aligned} \frac{d}{d\xi}\left(\xi\frac{df_1}{d\xi}\right)+\left(\tfrac{1}{2}E\xi-\tfrac{1}{4}\frac{m^2}{\xi}-\tfrac{1}{4}\mathscr{E}\xi^2\right)f_1 &= -\beta_1 f_1,\\ \frac{d}{d\eta}\left(\eta\frac{df_2}{d\eta}\right)+\left(\tfrac{1}{2}E\eta-\tfrac{1}{4}\frac{m^2}{\eta}+\tfrac{1}{4}\mathscr{E}\eta^2\right)f_2 &= -\beta_2 f_2,\\ \beta_1+\beta_2 &= 1, \end{aligned}\right\} \tag{73.4}$$

which differ from (37.8) by the presence of the terms in $\mathscr{E}$. We shall regard the energy E in these equations as a parameter which has a definite value, and the quantities β_1, β_2 as eigenvalues of corresponding operators; it is easy to see that these operators are self-conjugate. These quantities are determined, by solving the equations, as functions of E and $\mathscr{E}$, and then the condition $\beta_1+\beta_2 = 1$ gives the required relation between E and $\mathscr{E}$, or, in other words, the energy as a function of the external field.

For an approximate solution of equations (73.4), we regard the terms containing the field $\mathscr{E}$ as a small perturbation. In the zero approximation ($\mathscr{E} = 0$), the equations have the familiar solutions

$$\begin{aligned} f_1 &= \sqrt{\epsilon}\, f_{n_1 m}(\xi\epsilon),\\ f_2 &= \sqrt{\epsilon}\, f_{n_2 m}(\eta\epsilon), \end{aligned} \tag{73.5}$$

where the functions $f_{n_1 m}$ are the same as in (37.16), and instead of the energy we have introduced the parameter

$$\epsilon = \sqrt{(-2E)}. \tag{73.6}$$

The corresponding values of β_1, β_2 (from the equations (37.12), in which n must be replaced by $1/\epsilon$) are

$$\beta_1^{(0)} = (n_1+\tfrac{1}{2}|m|+\tfrac{1}{2})\epsilon, \quad \beta_2^{(0)} = (n_2+\tfrac{1}{2}|m|+\tfrac{1}{2})\epsilon. \tag{73.7}$$

The functions f_1 with different n_1 for a given ϵ are orthogonal, as are the eigenfunctions of any self-conjugate operator; we have already used this fact above in discussing the linear effect. In (73.5) these functions are normalised by the conditions

$$\int_0^\infty f_1^2\, d\xi = 1, \qquad \int_0^\infty f_2^2\, d\eta = 1.$$

The corrections to β_1 and β_2 in the first approximation are determined by the diagonal matrix elements of the perturbation:

$$\beta_1^{(1)} = \tfrac{1}{4}\mathscr{E}\int_0^\infty \xi^2 f_1^2 d\xi, \qquad \beta_2^{(1)} = -\tfrac{1}{4}\mathscr{E}\int_0^\infty \eta^2 f_2^2 d\eta.$$

Calculation gives

$$\beta_1^{(1)} = \tfrac{1}{4}\mathscr{E}(6n_1^2+6n_1|m|+m^2+6n_1+3|m|+2)/\epsilon^2.$$

The expression for $\beta_2^{(1)}$ is obtained by replacing n_1 by n_2 and changing the sign.

In the second approximation we have, by the general formulae of perturbation theory,

$$\beta_1^{(2)} = \frac{\mathscr{E}^2}{16} \sum_{n_1' \neq n_1} \frac{|(\xi^2)_{n_1 n_1'}|^2}{\beta_1^{(0)}(n_1)-\beta_1^{(0)}(n_1')}.$$

The integrals appearing in the matrix elements $(\xi^2)_{n_1 n_1'}$ are calculated in §*f* of the Mathematical Appendices. The only non-zero elements are

$$(\xi^2)_{n_1, n_1-1} = (\xi^2)_{n_1-1, n_1} = -2(2n_1+|m|)\sqrt{[n_1(n_1+|m|)]}/\epsilon^2,$$

$$(\xi^2)_{n_1, n_1-2} = (\xi^2)_{n_1-2, n_1} = \sqrt{[n_1(n_1-1)(n_1+|m|)(n_1+|m|-1)]}/\epsilon^2.$$

The differences occurring in the denominators are

$$\beta_1^{(0)}(n_1)-\beta_1^{(0)}(n_1') = \epsilon(n_1-n_1').$$

As a result of the calculations we have

$$\beta_1^{(2)} = -\mathscr{E}^2(|m|+2n_1+1)[4m^2+17(2|m|n_1+2n_1^2+|m|+2n_1)+18]/16\epsilon^5;$$

the expression for $\beta_2^{(2)}$ is obtained by replacing n_1 by n_2. Combining the expressions obtained and substituting in the relation $\beta_1+\beta_2 = 1$, we have the equation

$$\epsilon n-\mathscr{E}^2 n[17n^2+51(n_1-n_2)^2-9m^2+19]/16\epsilon^5+\tfrac{3}{2}\mathscr{E}n(n_1-n_2)/\epsilon^2 = 1.$$

Solving by successive approximations, we have in the second approximation for the energy $E = -\frac{1}{2}\epsilon^2$ the expression

$$E = -\frac{1}{2n^2}+\tfrac{3}{2}\mathscr{E}n(n_1-n_2)-\frac{\mathscr{E}^2}{16}n^4[17n^2-3(n_1-n_2)^2-9m^2+19]. \qquad (73.8)$$

The second term is the already familiar linear Stark effect, and the third is the required quadratic effect. We notice that this quantity is always negative, i.e. the terms are always displaced downwards by the quadratic effect. The mean value of the dipole moment is obtained by differentiating (73.8) with respect to the field; in the states with $n_1 = n_2$ it is

$$\overline{d_z} = \tfrac{1}{8}n^4(17n^2-9m^2+19)\mathscr{E}. \qquad (73.9)$$

Thus the polarisability of the hydrogen atom in the normal state ($n=1$, $m=0$) is 9/2 (in absolute units $9(\hbar^2/\mu e^2)^3/2$).

The absolute value of the energy of the hydrogen terms falls rapidly as the principal quantum number n increases, while the Stark splitting is increased. Hence it is of interest to examine the Stark effect for highly excited levels in fields so strong that the splitting they cause is comparable with the energy of the level itself, and perturbation theory is inapplicable.† This can be done by using the fact that states with large values of n are quasi-classical.

By the substitution

$$f_1 = \chi_1/\sqrt{\xi}, \qquad f_2 = \chi_2/\sqrt{\eta} \tag{73.10}$$

the equations (73.4) are brought into the form

$$\begin{aligned} \frac{d^2\chi_1}{d\xi^2}+\left(\tfrac{1}{2}E+\frac{\beta_1}{\xi}-\frac{m^2-1}{4\xi^2}-\tfrac{1}{4}\mathscr{E}\xi\right)\chi_1 &= 0, \\ \frac{d^2\chi_2}{d\eta^2}+\left(\tfrac{1}{2}E+\frac{\beta_2}{\eta}-\frac{m^2-1}{4\eta^2}+\tfrac{1}{4}\mathscr{E}\eta\right)\chi_2 &= 0. \end{aligned} \tag{73.11}$$

Each of these equations, however, is the same in form as the one-dimensional SCHRÖDINGER's equation, the part of the total energy of the particle being taken by $\tfrac{1}{4}E$, and that of the potential energy by the functions

$$\begin{aligned} U_1(\xi) &= -\frac{\beta_1}{2\xi}+\frac{m^2-1}{8\xi^2}+\tfrac{1}{8}\mathscr{E}\xi, \\ U_2(\eta) &= -\frac{\beta_2}{2\eta}+\frac{m^2-1}{8\eta^2}-\tfrac{1}{8}\mathscr{E}\eta \end{aligned} \tag{73.12}$$

respectively.

Figs. 27 and 28 respectively show the approximate form of these functions

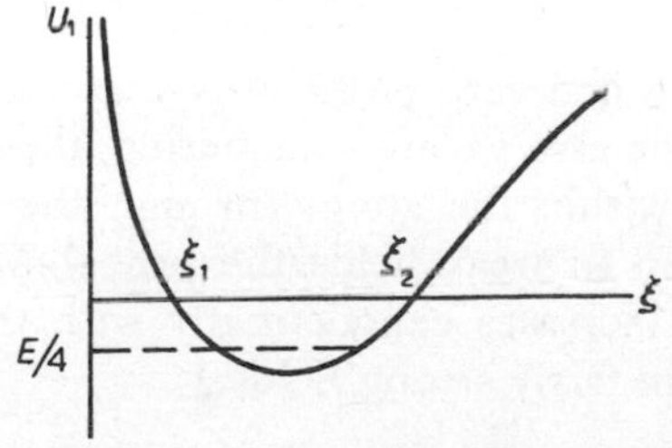

FIG. 27

† The applicability of perturbation theory to high levels requires the perturbation to be small only in comparison with the energy of the level itself (the binding energy of the electron), and not with the intervals between the levels. For in the quasi-classical case (which corresponds to highly excited states) the perturbation can be regarded as small if the force due to it is small in comparison with those acting on the particle in the unperturbed system; and this condition is equivalent to the one given above.

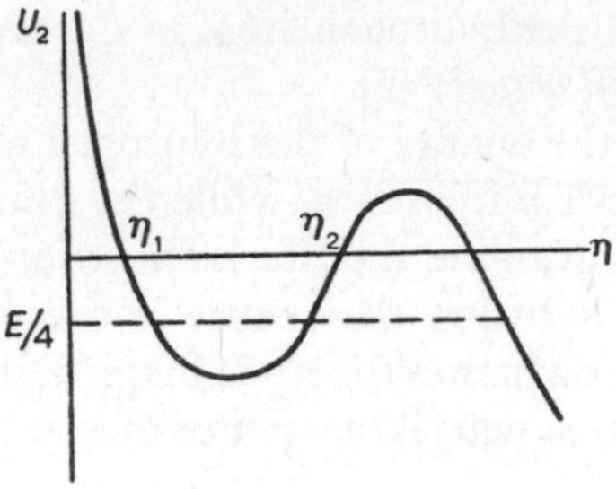

FIG. 28

(for $m > 1$). By BOHR's quantisation rule (48.1) we write

$$\int_{\xi_1}^{\xi_2} \sqrt{\{2[\tfrac{1}{4}E - U_1(\xi)]\}}\, d\xi = (n_1 + \tfrac{1}{2})\pi,$$

$$\int_{\eta_1}^{\eta_2} \sqrt{\{2[\tfrac{1}{4}E - U_2(\eta)]\}}\, d\eta = (n_2 + \tfrac{1}{2})\pi, \qquad (73.13)$$

where n_1, n_2 are integers.† These equations determine implicitly the dependence of the parameters β_1 and β_2 on E. Together with the equation $\beta_1 + \beta_2 = 1$, they therefore give the energies of the levels when displaced by the electric field. The integrals in equations (73.13) can be reduced to elliptic integrals; these equations can be solved only numerically.

The Stark effect in strong fields is complicated by another phenomenon, the ionisation of the atom by the electric field. The potential energy $\mathscr{E}z$ of an electron in the external field takes arbitrarily large negative values as $z \to -\infty$. Added to the potential energy of the electron within the atom, it has the effect that the region of possible motion for the electron (whose total energy E is negative) includes, besides the region inside the atom, the region of large distances from the nucleus in the direction of the anode. These two regions are separated by a potential barrier, whose width diminishes as the field increases. We know, however, that in quantum mechanics there is always a certain non-zero probability that a particle will penetrate a potential barrier. In the case we are considering, the emergence of the electron from the region within the atom, through the barrier, is simply the ionisation of the atom. In weak fields the probability of this ionisation is vanishingly small. It increases exponentially with the field, however, and becomes considerable in fairly strong fields.‡

† A detailed investigation shows that a more exact result is obtained by writing m^2 instead of $m^2 - 1$ in the expressions for U_1 and U_2. The integers n_1, n_2 are then equal to the parabolic quantum numbers.

‡ This phenomenon may serve to illustrate how a small perturbation may alter the nature of the energy spectrum. Even a weak field $\mathscr{E}$ is sufficient to create a potential barrier and produce a region, far from the nucleus, which is in principle accessible to the electron. As a result, the motion of the electron becomes, strictly speaking, infinite, and hence the energy spectrum becomes continuous instead of discrete. Nevertheless, the formal solution obtained by the methods of perturbation theory has a physical significance: it gives the energy levels of states which are not quite but "almost" stationary. An atom that is in such a state at some initial instant remains in it for a long period of time.

PROBLEM

Determine the probability of the ionisation of a hydrogen atom (in the ground state) in a strong electric field.

SOLUTION. In parabolic co-ordinates there is a potential barrier "along the η co-ordinate" (Fig. 28); the "extraction" of the electron from the atom in the direction $z \to -\infty$ corresponds to its passage into the region of large η. To determine the ionisation probability, it is necessary to investigate the form of the wave function for large η (and small ξ; we shall see below that small values of ξ are the important ones in the range which determines the total probability current for the emerging electron). The wave function of the electron in the normal state (in the absence of the field) is

$$\psi = e^{-\frac{1}{2}(\xi+\eta)}/\sqrt{\pi}. \tag{1}$$

When the field is present, the dependence of ψ on ξ in the region in which we are interested can be regarded as being the same as in (1), while to determine its dependence on η we have the equation

$$\frac{\partial^2\chi}{\partial\eta^2}+\left[-\tfrac{1}{4}+\frac{1}{2\eta}+\frac{1}{4\eta^2}+\tfrac{1}{4}\mathscr{E}\eta\right]\chi = 0, \tag{2}$$

where $\chi = \sqrt{\eta}\psi$ (equation (73.11) with $E = -\frac{1}{2}$, $m = 0$, $\beta_2 = \frac{1}{2}$). Let η_0 be some value of η ("within" the barrier) such that $1 \ll \eta_0 \ll 1/E$. For $\eta \gtrsim \eta_0$, the wave function is quasi-classical. Since, on the other hand, equation (2) has the form of the one-dimensional SCHRÖDINGER's equation, we can use formulae (50.4). Using the exact expression (1) for the wave function at the point $\eta = \eta_0$, we obtain in the region outside the barrier the expression

$$\chi = \frac{1}{\sqrt{\pi}}e^{-\frac{1}{2}(\xi+\eta_0)}\sqrt{\eta_0}\sqrt{\frac{|p_0|}{p}}\exp\Big[i\int_{\eta_0}^{\eta} p\,d\eta-\tfrac{1}{4}i\pi\Big],$$

where

$$p(\eta) = \sqrt{\left[-\tfrac{1}{4}+\frac{1}{2\eta}+\frac{1}{4\eta^2}+\tfrac{1}{4}\mathscr{E}\eta\right]}.$$

We shall be interested only in the square $|\chi|^2$. Hence the imaginary part of the exponent is unimportant. Denoting by η_1 the root of the equation $p(\eta) = 0$, we have

$$|\chi|^2 = \frac{\eta_0}{\pi}e^{-\xi}\frac{|p_0|}{p}\exp\Big[-2\int_{\eta_0}^{\eta_1}|p|\,d\eta-\eta_0\Big].$$

In the coefficient of the exponential we put

$$|p_0| \cong \tfrac{1}{2},\ p \cong \tfrac{1}{2}\sqrt{(\mathscr{E}\eta-1)};$$

in the exponent we must keep also the next term of the expansion:

$$|\chi|^2 = \frac{\eta_0}{\pi\sqrt{(\mathscr{E}\eta-1)}}e^{-\xi}\exp\left[-\int_{\eta_0}^{\eta_1}\sqrt{(1-\mathscr{E}\eta)}\,d\eta+\int_{\eta_0}^{\eta_1}\frac{d\eta}{\eta\sqrt{(1-\mathscr{E}\eta)}}-\eta_0\right],$$

where $\eta_1 \cong 1/\mathscr{E}$. Effecting the integration and neglecting η_0 compared with 1 wherever possible, we obtain

$$|\chi|^2 = \frac{4}{\pi\mathscr{E}}e^{-2/3\mathscr{E}}\frac{e^{-\xi}}{\sqrt{(\mathscr{E}\eta-1)}}. \tag{3}$$

The total probability current through a plane perpendicular to the z-axis (i.e. the required ionisation probability w) is

$$w = \int_0^\infty |\psi|^2 v_z 2\pi r \, dr.$$

For large η (and small ξ) we can put

$$dr = d\sqrt{(\xi\eta)} \cong \tfrac{1}{2}\sqrt{(\eta/\xi)}\, d\xi.$$

Substituting also for the velocity of the electron

$$v_z \cong \sqrt{[2(-\tfrac{1}{2}+\tfrac{1}{2}\mathscr{E}\eta)]} = \sqrt{(\mathscr{E}\eta-1)},$$

we have

$$w = \int_0^\infty |\chi|^2 \pi\sqrt{(\mathscr{E}\eta-1)}\, d\xi$$

$$= \frac{4}{\mathscr{E}} e^{-2/3\mathscr{E}} \int_0^\infty e^{-\xi}\, d\xi,$$

that is, finally,

$$w = (4/\mathscr{E})e^{-2/3\mathscr{E}}.$$

§74. The quadrupole moment of the atom

As we know from electrodynamics, the energy of a system in an inhomogeneous external electric field (which varies only slightly over the dimensions of the system) can be represented as a sum of what are called *dipole*, *quadrupole* etc. *energies*.† In quantum mechanics these energies must be regarded as operators. We have seen that the mean value of the dipole moment (and therefore the effect in the first approximation with respect to the dipole energy) vanishes for all atoms, except hydrogen in its excited states.‡ In an inhomogeneous field, however, there may be a quadrupole splitting which is linear with respect to the field.

The quadrupole energy is of the form

$$\frac{1}{6}\sum_{i,k=1}^{3} \frac{\partial^2\phi}{\partial x_i \partial x_k} D_{ik},$$

where ϕ is the potential of the electric field (the values of the derivatives are

† See, for example, *The Classical Theory of Fields*, §5–7, Addison-Wesley Press, Cambridge (Mass.) 1951.

‡ It is easy to see that the mean values of all 2^n-pole electric moments, where n is odd, vanish also.

understood to be taken at the position of the atom), and

$$D_{ik} = \Sigma\, e(3x_i x_k - \delta_{ik}\mathbf{r}^2)$$

is what is called the *quadrupole moment tensor*; the summation is taken over all the particles in the system, but we omit the suffix giving the numbers of the particles. The tensor D_{ik} is so defined that the sum of its diagonal terms is zero.

In quantum mechanics a certain operator corresponds to the quadrupole moment tensor, and the determination of the splitting energy requires an averaging of this operator with respect to the unperturbed state. The splitting is, as before, supposed small in comparison with the fine-structure intervals, so that the unperturbed states are those with given values of the total angular momentum J. The averaging is done in two stages (as in §67 for the spin-orbit interaction). We denote by $\hat{D}_{ik}$ the operator of the quadrupole moment, averaged over the electron states with a given value of the angular momentum J (but not of its projection M_J). The only vector which characterises the atom as a whole is the "vector" $\hat{\mathbf{J}}$. Hence the only tensor operator symmetrical with respect to i, k and such that the sum $\hat{D}_{ll}$ is zero is of the form

$$\hat{D}_{ik} = \frac{3D_0}{2J(2J-1)}(\hat{J}_i\hat{J}_k + \hat{J}_k\hat{J}_i - \tfrac{2}{3}\delta_{ik}\hat{\mathbf{J}}^2), \tag{74.1}$$

where D_0 is a constant, called simply the *quadrupole moment* of the atom.† The operators $\hat{J}_i$ must be supposed to be, like the known matrices of the angular momentum with the given value of J, not diagonal with respect to M_J; the operator $\hat{\mathbf{J}}^2$ can, of course, be simply replaced by its eigenvalue $J(J+1)$.

For $J = 0$ (so that $M_J = 0$ also), all the elements of these matrices are zero, so that the operators vanish identically. They also vanish identically for $J = \frac{1}{2}$. This is easily seen by direct multiplication of the Pauli matrices (54.3), which are the matrices of the components of any angular momentum equal to $\frac{1}{2}$.

The final averaging of the quadrupole energy depends on the actual form of the inhomogeneous field (see Problem).

PROBLEM

Determine the quadrupole splitting of the levels in an axially symmetric electric field.

SOLUTION. In a field symmetrical about the z-axis we have

$$\frac{\partial^2\phi}{\partial x^2} = \frac{\partial^2\phi}{\partial y^2} \equiv a, \quad \frac{\partial^2\phi}{\partial z^2} = -\left(\frac{\partial^2\phi}{\partial x^2} + \frac{\partial^2\phi}{\partial y^2}\right) = -2a,$$

† The constant D_0 is chosen so that $D_{zz} = D_0$ in the state with $J_z = J$.

while the remaining second derivatives are zero. The quadrupole energy operator is of the form

$$\frac{a}{6}(\hat{D}_{xx}+\hat{D}_{yy}-2\hat{D}_{zz}) = \frac{D_0 a}{2J(2J-1)}(\hat{J}_x^2+\hat{J}_y^2-2\hat{J}_z^2)$$

$$= \frac{D_0 a}{2J(2J-1)}(\hat{\mathbf{J}}^2-3\hat{J}_z^2).$$

Replacing the operators $\hat{\mathbf{J}}^2$ and $\hat{J}_z^2$ by their eigenvalues, we obtain for the displacement of the levels

$$\Delta E = a\frac{D_0}{2J(2J-1)}[J(J+1)-3M_J^2].$$

CHAPTER XI

THE DIATOMIC MOLECULE

§75. Electron terms in the diatomic molecule

In the theory of molecules an important part is played by the fact that the masses of atomic nuclei are very large compared with those of the electrons. Because of this difference in mass, the rates of motion of the nuclei in the molecule are small in comparison with the velocities of the electrons. This makes it possible to regard the motion of the electrons as being about fixed nuclei placed at given distances from one another. On determining the energy levels U_n for such a system, we find what are called the *electron terms* for the molecule. Unlike those for atoms, where the energy levels were certain numbers, the electron terms here are not numbers but functions of parameters, the distances between the nuclei in the molecule. The energy U_n includes also the electrostatic energy of the mutual interaction of the nuclei, so that U_n is essentially the total energy of the molecule for a given arrangement of the fixed nuclei.

We shall begin the study of molecules by taking the simplest type, the diatomic molecules, which permit the most complete theoretical investigation.

One of the chief principles in the classification of the atomic terms was the classification according to the values of the total orbital angular momentum L. In molecules, however, there is no law of conservation of the total orbital angular momentum of the electrons, since the electric field of several nuclei is not centrally symmetric.

In diatomic molecules, however, the field has axial symmetry about an axis passing through the two nuclei. Hence the projection of the orbital angular momentum on this axis is here conserved, and we can classify the electron terms of the molecules according to the values of this projection. The absolute value of the projected orbital angular momentum along the axis of the molecule is customarily denoted by the letter Λ; it takes the values 0, 1, 2, ... The terms with different values of Λ are denoted by the capital Greek letters corresponding to the Latin letters for the atomic terms with various L. Thus, for $\Lambda = 0, 1, 2$ we speak of Σ, Π and Δ terms respectively; higher values of Λ usually need not be considered.

Next, each electron state of the molecule is characterised by the total spin S of all the electrons in the molecule. If S is not zero, there is degeneracy of degree $2S+1$ with respect to the directions of the total spin.† The number $2S+1$ is, as in atoms, called the *multiplicity* of the term, and is written as an index before the letter for the term; thus $^3\Pi$ denotes a term with $\Lambda = 1$, $S = 1$.

† We here neglect the fine structure due to relativistic interactions (see §§80 and 81 below).

Besides rotations through any angle about the axis, the symmetry of the molecule allows also a reflection in any plane passing through the axis. If we effect such a reflection, the energy of the molecule is obviously unchanged. The state obtained from the reflection is, however, not completely identical with the initial state. For, on reflection in a plane passing through the axis of the molecule, the sign of the angular momentum about this axis is changed. Thus we conclude that all electron terms with non-zero values of Λ are doubly degenerate: to each value of the energy, there correspond two states which differ in the direction of the projection of the orbital angular momentum on the axis of the molecule. In the case where $\Lambda = 0$ the state of the molecule is not changed at all on reflection, so that the Σ terms are not degenerate. The wave function of a Σ term can only be multiplied by a constant as a result of the reflection. Since a double reflection in the same plane is an identity transformation, this constant is ± 1. Thus we must distinguish Σ terms whose wave functions are unaltered on reflection and those whose wave functions change sign. The former are denoted by Σ^+, and the latter by Σ^-.

If the molecule consists of two similar atoms, a new symmetry appears, and with it an additional characteristic of the electron terms. A diatomic molecule with identical nuclei has a centre of symmetry at the point bisecting the line joining the nuclei.† (We shall take this point as the origin.) Hence the Hamiltonian is invariant with respect to a simultaneous change of sign of the co-ordinates of all the electrons in the molecule (the co-ordinates of the nuclei remaining unchanged). Since the inversion operator also commutes with the orbital angular momentum operator (§28), we have the possibility of classifying terms with a given value of Λ according to their parity: the wave functions of *even* (g) states are unchanged when the co-ordinates of the electrons change sign, while those of *odd* (u) states change sign. The suffixes u, g indicating the parity are customarily written with the letter for the term: Π_u, Π_g, and so on.

Finally, we shall mention an empirical rule, according to which the normal electron state in the overwhelming majority of chemically stable diatomic molecules is completely symmetrical: the electron wave function is invariant with respect to all symmetry transformations in the molecule. As we shall show in §78, the total spin S is zero too, in the great majority of cases, in the normal state. In other words, the ground term of the molecule is ${}^1\Sigma^+$, and it is ${}^1\Sigma^+_g$ if the molecule consists of two similar atoms.‡

§76. The intersection of electron terms

The electron terms in a diatomic molecule are functions of a single parameter, the distance r between the nuclei. They can be represented graphically

† It has also a plane of symmetry perpendicularly bisecting the axis of the molecule. This element of symmetry need not be considered separately, however, since the existence of such a plane follows automatically from the existence of a centre of symmetry and of a plane of symmetry passing through the axis.

‡ Exceptions to these rules are formed by the molecules O_2 (whose normal term is ${}^3\Sigma^-_g$) and NO (normal term ${}^2\Pi$).

by plotting the energy as a function of r. It is of considerable interest to examine the intersection of the curves representing the different terms.

Let $U_1(r)$, $U_2(r)$ be two different electron terms. If they intersect at some point, then the functions U_1 and U_2 will have neighbouring values near this point. To decide whether such an intersection can occur, it is convenient to put the problem as follows. Let us consider a point r_0 where the functions $U_1(r)$, $U_2(r)$ have very close but not equal values (which we denote by E_1, E_2), and examine whether or not we can make U_1 and U_2 equal by displacing the point a short distance δr. The energies E_1 and E_2 are eigenvalues of the Hamiltonian $\hat{H}_0$ of the system of electrons in the field of the nuclei, which are at a distance r_0 from each other. If we add to the distance r_0 an increment δr, the Hamiltonian becomes $\hat{H}_0+\hat{V}$, where $\hat{V} = \delta r \,.\, \partial\hat{H}_0/\partial r$ is a small correction; the values of the functions U_1, U_2 at the point $r_0+\delta r$ can be regarded as eigenvalues of the new Hamiltonian. This point of view enables us to determine the values of the terms $U_1(r)$, $U_2(r)$ at the point $r_0+\delta r$ by means of perturbation theory, $\hat{V}$ being regarded as a perturbation to the operator $\hat{H}_0$.

The ordinary method of perturbation theory is here inapplicable, however, since the eigenvalues E_1, E_2 of the energy in the unperturbed problem are very close to each other, and their difference is in general small compared with the magnitude of the perturbation; the condition (38.8) is not fulfilled. Since, in the limit as the difference E_2-E_1 tends to zero, we have the case of degenerate eigenvalues, it is natural to attempt to apply to the case of close eigenvalues a method similar to that developed in §39.

Let ψ_1, ψ_2 be the eigenfunctions of the unperturbed operator $\hat{H}_0$ which correspond to the energies E_1, E_2. As an initial zero-order approximation we take, instead of ψ_1 and ψ_2 themselves, linear combinations of them of the form

$$\psi = c_1\psi_1+c_2\psi_2. \tag{76.1}$$

Substituting this expression in the perturbed equation

$$(\hat{H}_0+\hat{V})\psi = E\psi, \tag{76.2}$$

we obtain

$$c_1(E_1+\hat{V}-E)\psi_1+c_2(E_2+\hat{V}-E)\psi_2 = 0.$$

Multiplying this equation on the left by ψ_1^* and ψ_2^* in turn, and integrating, we have two algebraic equations:

$$\begin{aligned} c_1(E_1+V_{11}-E)+c_2V_{12} &= 0,\\ c_1V_{21}+c_2(E_2+V_{22}-E) &= 0, \end{aligned} \tag{76.3}$$

where $V_{ik} = \int \psi_i^*\hat{V}\psi_k \,\mathrm{d}q$. Since the operator $\hat{V}$ is Hermitian, the quantities V_{11} and V_{22} are real, while $V_{12} = V_{21}^*$. The compatibility condition for these equations is

$$\begin{vmatrix} E_1+V_{11}-E & V_{12} \\ V_{21} & E_2+V_{22}-E \end{vmatrix} = 0,$$

whence we obtain after some calculation

$$E = \tfrac{1}{2}(E_1+E_2+V_{11}+V_{22})\pm\sqrt{[\tfrac{1}{4}(E_1-E_2+V_{11}-V_{22})^2+|V_{12}|^2]}. \qquad (76.4)$$

This formula gives the required eigenvalues of the energy in the first approximation.

If the energy values of the two terms become equal at the point $r_0+\delta r$ (i.e. the terms intersect), this means that the two values of E given by formula (76.4) are the same. For this to happen, the expression under the radical in (76.4) must vanish. Since it is the sum of two squares, we obtain, as the condition for there to be points of intersection of the terms, the equations

$$E_1-E_2+V_{11}-V_{22} = 0, \quad V_{12} = 0. \qquad (76.5)$$

However, we have at our disposal only one arbitrary parameter giving the perturbation $\hat{V}$, namely the magnitude δr of the displacement. Hence the two equations (76.5) cannot in general be simultaneously satisfied (we suppose that the functions ψ_1, ψ_2 are chosen to be real, so that V_{12} also is real).

It may happen, however, that the matrix element V_{12} vanishes identically; there then remains only one equation (76.5), which can be satisfied by a suitable choice of δr. This happens in all cases where the two terms considered are of different symmetry. By *symmetry* we here understand all possible forms of symmetry: with respect to rotations about an axis, reflections in planes, inversion, and also with respect to interchanges of electrons. In the diatomic molecule this means that we may be dealing with terms of different Λ, different parity or multiplicity, or (for Σ terms) Σ^+ and Σ^- terms.

To prove this statement it is essential that the operator $\hat{V}$ (like the Hamiltonian itself) commutes with all the symmetry operators for the molecule: the operator of the angular momentum about an axis, the reflection and inversion operators, and the operators of interchanges of electrons. It has been shown in §§27 and 28 that, for a scalar quantity whose operator commutes with the angular momentum and inversion operators, only the matrix elements for transitions between states of the same angular momentum and parity are non-zero. This proof remains valid, in essentially the same form, for the general case of an arbitrary symmetry operator. We shall not pause to repeat it here, especially since in §94 we shall give another general proof, based on group theory.

Thus we reach the result that, in a diatomic molecule, only terms of different symmetry can intersect, while the intersection of terms of like symmetry is impossible (E. Wigner and J. von Neumann 1929). If, as a result of somx approximate calculation, we obtain two intersecting terms of the same symmetry, they are found to move apart on calculating the next approximation, as shown by the continuous lines in Fig. 29.

We emphasise that this result not only is true for the diatomic molecule, but is a general theorem of quantum mechanics; it holds for any case where the Hamiltonian contains some parameter and its eigenvalues are consequently functions of that parameter.

In a polyatomic molecule, the electron terms are functions of not one but several parameters, the distances between the various nuclei. Let s be the number of independent distances between the nuclei; in a molecule of $N(>2)$ atoms, this number is $s = 3N-6$ for an arbitrary arrangement of the nuclei. Each term $U_n(r_1, \ldots, r_s)$ is, from the geometrical point of view, a surface in a space of $s+1$ dimensions, and we can speak of the intersections of these

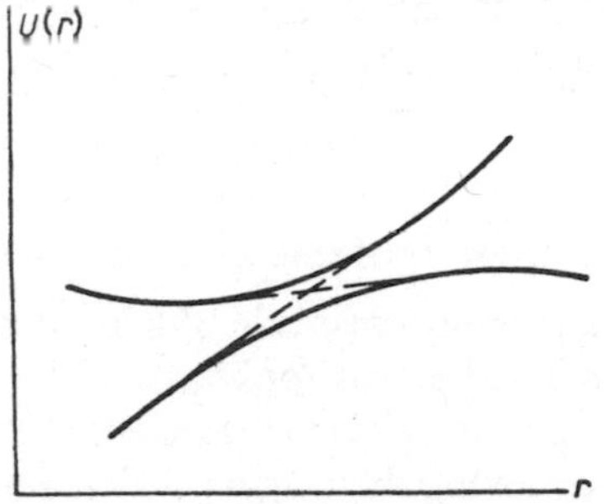

FIG. 29

surfaces in manifolds of varying numbers of dimensions, from 0 (intersection in a point) to $s-1$. The derivation given above is wholly valid, except that the perturbation $\hat{V}$ is here determined not by one but by s parameters, the displacements $\delta r_1, \ldots, \delta r_s$. Even with two parameters, the two equations (76.5) can in general be satisfied. Thus we conclude that, in polyatomic molecules, any two terms may intersect. If the terms are of like symmetry, the intersection is given by the two conditions (76.5), from which it follows that the number of dimensions of the manifold in which the intersection occurs is $s-2$. If the terms are of different symmetry, on the other hand, there remains only one condition, and the intersection takes place in a manifold of $s-1$ dimensions.

Thus for $s = 2$ the terms are represented by surfaces in a three-dimensional system of co-ordinates. The intersection of these surfaces occurs in lines ($s-1 = 1$) when the symmetry of the terms is different, and in points ($s-2 = 0$) when it is the same. It is easy to ascertain the form of the surfaces near the point of intersection in the latter case. The value of the energy near the points of intersection of the terms is given by formula (76.4). In this expression the matrix elements V_{11}, V_{22}, V_{12} are linear functions of the displacements δr_1, δr_2, and hence are linear functions of the distances r_1, r_2 themselves. Such an equation determines an elliptic cone, as we know from analytical geometry. Thus, near the points of intersection, the terms are represented by the surface of an arbitrarily situated double elliptic cone (Fig. 30).

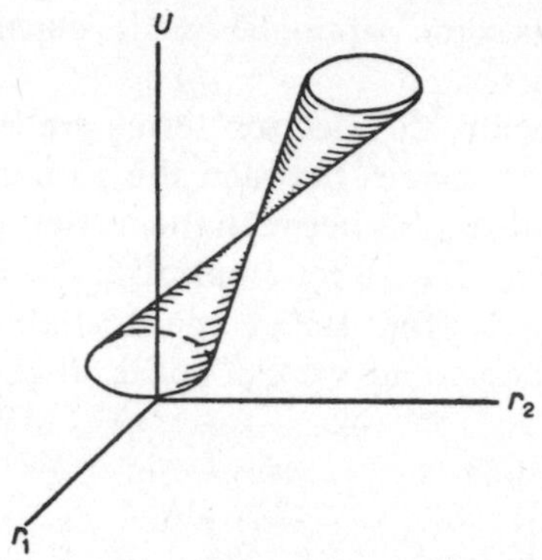

FIG. 30

§77. The relation between molecular and atomic terms

As we increase the distance between the nuclei in a diatomic molecule, we have in the limit two isolated atoms (or ions). The question thus arises of the correspondence between the electron terms of the molecule and the states of the atoms obtained by moving them apart. This relation is not one-to-one; if we bring together two atoms in given states, we may obtain a molecule in various electron states.

Let us first suppose that the molecule consists of two different atoms. Let the isolated atoms be in states with orbital angular momenta L_1, L_2 and spins S_1, S_2, and let $L_1 \geqslant L_2$. The projections of the angular momenta on the line joining the nuclei take the values $M_1 = -L_1, -L_1+1, \ldots, L_1$ and $M_2 = -L_2, -L_2+1, \ldots, L_2$. The absolute value of the sum M_1+M_2 determines the angular momentum Λ obtained on bringing the atoms together. On combining all possible values of M_1 and M_2, we find the following values for the numbers of times that we obtain the various values of $\Lambda = |M_1+M_2|$:

$\Lambda = L_1+L_2$	twice
L_1+L_2-1	four times
...	...
L_1-L_2	$2(2L_2+1)$ times
L_1-L_2-1	$2(2L_2+1)$ times
...	...
1	$2(2L_2+1)$ times
0	$2L_2+1$ times.

Remembering that all terms with $\Lambda \neq 0$ are doubly degenerate, while those with $\Lambda = 0$ are not degenerate, we find that there will be

$$\left.\begin{array}{rl} 1 \text{ term with } & \Lambda = L_1+L_2, \\ 2 \text{ terms with } & \Lambda = L_1+L_2-1, \\ \multicolumn{2}{c}{\cdots\cdots\cdots\cdots\cdots\cdots} \\ 2L_2+1 \text{ terms with } & \Lambda = L_1-L_2 \\ 2L_2+1 \text{ terms with } & \Lambda = L_1-L_2-1, \\ \multicolumn{2}{c}{\cdots\cdots\cdots\cdots\cdots\cdots} \\ 2L_2+1 \text{ terms with } & \Lambda = 0; \end{array}\right\} \tag{77.1}$$

in all, $(2L_2+1)(L_1+1)$ terms with values of Λ from 0 to L_1+L_2.

The spins S_1, S_2 of the two atoms combine to form the total spin of the molecule in accordance with the general rule for the addition of angular momenta, giving the following possible values of S:

$$S = S_1+S_2, \quad S_1+S_2-1, \quad \dots, \quad |S_1-S_2|. \tag{77.2}$$

On combining each of these values with each value of Λ in (77.1), we obtain the complete list of all possible terms in the molecule formed.

For Σ terms there is also the question of sign. This is easily resolved by noticing that the wave functions of the molecule can be written, as $r \to \infty$, in the form of products (or sums of products) of the wave functions of the two atoms. An angular momentum $\Lambda = 0$ can be obtained either by adding two non-zero angular momenta of the atoms such that $M_1 = -M_2$, or from $M_1 = M_2 = 0$. We denote the wave functions of the first and second atoms by $\psi^{(1)}{}_{M_1}$, $\psi^{(2)}{}_{M_2}$. For $M = |M_1| = |M_2| \neq 0$, we form the symmetrised and antisymmetrised products

$$\psi^+ = \psi^{(1)}{}_M\psi^{(2)}{}_{-M}+\psi^{(1)}{}_{-M}\psi^{(2)}{}_M,$$
$$\psi^- = \psi^{(1)}{}_M\psi^{(2)}{}_{-M}-\psi^{(1)}{}_{-M}\psi^{(2)}{}_M.$$

A reflection in a vertical plane (i.e. one passing through the axis of the molecule) changes the sign of the projection of the angular momentum on the axis, so that $\psi^{(1)}{}_M$, $\psi^{(2)}{}_M$ are changed into $\psi^{(1)}{}_{-M}$, $\psi^{(2)}{}_{-M}$ respectively, and *vice versa*. The function ψ^+ is thereby unchanged, while ψ^- changes sign; the former therefore corresponds to a Σ^+ term and the latter to a Σ^- term. Thus, for each value of M, we obtain one Σ^+ and one Σ^- term. Since M can take L_2 different values ($M = 1, \dots, L_2$), we have in all L_2 Σ^+ terms and L_2 Σ^- terms.

If, on the other hand, $M_1 = M_2 = 0$, the wave function of the molecule is of the form $\psi = \psi^{(1)}{}_0\psi^{(2)}{}_0$. In order to ascertain the behaviour of the function $\psi^{(1)}{}_0$ on reflection in a vertical plane, we take a co-ordinate system with its origin at the centre of the first atom, and the z-axis along the axis of the molecule, and we notice that a reflection in the vertical xz-plane is equivalent to an inversion with respect to the origin, followed by a rotation through 180°

about the y-axis. On inversion, the function $\psi^{(1)}{}_0$ is multiplied by I_1, where $I_1 = \pm 1$ is the parity of the given state of the first atom. Next, the result of applying to the wave function the operation of an infinitely small rotation (and therefore that of any finite rotation) is entirely determined by the total orbital angular momentum of the atom. Hence it is sufficient to consider the particular case of an atom having one electron, with orbital angular momentum l (and a z-component of the angular momentum $m = 0$); on putting L in place of l in the result, we obtain the required solution for any atom. The angular part of the wave function of an electron with $m = 0$ is, apart from a constant coefficient, $P_l(\cos\theta)$ (see (26.7)). A rotation through 180° about the y-axis is the transformation $x \to -x$, $y \to y$, $z \to -z$ or, in spherical co-ordinates, $r \to r$, $\theta \to \pi - \theta$, $\phi \to \pi - \phi$. Then $\cos\theta \to -\cos\theta$, and the function $P_l(\cos\theta)$ is multiplied by $(-1)^l$.

Thus we conclude that, as a result of reflection in a vertical plane, the function $\psi^{(1)}{}_0$ is multiplied by $(-1)^{L_1}I_1$. Similarly, $\psi^{(2)}{}_0$ is multiplied by $(-1)^{L_2}I_2$, so that the wave function $\psi = \psi^{(1)}{}_0\psi^{(2)}{}_0$ is multiplied by $(-1)^{L_1+L_2}I_1I_2$. The term is Σ^+ or Σ^- according as this factor is $+1$ or -1.

Summarising the results obtained, we find that, of the total number $2L_2+1$ of Σ terms (each of the appropriate multiplicity), L_2+1 terms are Σ^+ and L_2 are Σ^-, if $(-1)^{L_1+L_2}I_1I_2 = +1$, and *vice versa* if $(-1)^{L_1+L_2}I_1I_2 = -1$.

Let us now turn to a molecule consisting of similar atoms. The rules for the addition of the spins and orbital angular momenta of the atoms to form the total S and Λ for the molecule remain the same here as for a molecule composed of different atoms. The difference is that the terms may be even or odd. Here we must distinguish two cases, according as the combined atoms are in the same or different states.

If the atoms are in different states,† the total number of possible terms is doubled in comparison with the number when the atoms are different. For a reflection with respect to the origin (this being the point bisecting the axis of the molecule) results in an interchange of the states of the two atoms. Symmetrising or antisymmetrising the wave function of the molecule with respect to an interchange of the states of the atoms, we obtain two terms (with the same Λ and S), of which one is even and the other odd. Thus we have altogether the same number of even and odd terms.

If, on the other hand, both atoms are in the same state, the total number of states is the same as for a molecule with different atoms. An investigation which we shall not give here on account of its length‡ leads to the following results for the parity of these states. Let N_g, N_u be the numbers of even and odd terms with given values of Λ and S. Then

if Λ is odd, $N_g = N_u$;

if Λ is even and S is even ($S = 0, 2, 4, \dots$), $N_g = N_u+1$;

if Λ is even and S is odd ($S = 1, 3, 5, \dots$), $N_u = N_g+1$.

† In particular, we may be discussing the combination of a neutral and an ionised atom.

‡ It can be found in the original paper by E. Wigner and E. Witmer, *Zeitschrift für Physik* **51**, 859, 1928.

Finally, we must distinguish, among the Σ terms, between Σ^+ and Σ^-. Here,
if S is even, $N_g^+ = N_u^- + 1 = L+1$;
if S is odd, $N_u^+ = N_g^- + 1 = L+1$,
where $L_1 = L_2 \equiv L$. All the Σ^+ terms are of parity $(-1)^S$, and all Σ^- terms are of parity $(-1)^{S+1}$.

Besides the problem that we have examined of the relation between the molecular terms and those of the atoms obtained as $r \to \infty$, we may also propose the question of the relation between the molecular terms and those of the "composite atom" obtained as $r \to 0$, i.e. when both nuclei are brought to a single point (for example, between the terms of the H_2 molecule and those of the He atom). The following rules can be deduced without difficulty. From a term of the "composite" atom having spin S, orbital angular momentum L and parity I, we can obtain, on "moving the constituent atoms apart", molecular terms with spin S and angular momentum about the axis $\Lambda = 0, 1, \ldots, L$, with one term for each of these values of Λ. The parity of the molecular term is the same as the parity I of the atomic term (g for $I = +1$ and u for $I = -1$). The molecular term with $\Lambda = 0$ is a Σ^+ term if $(-1)^L I = +1$, and a Σ^- term if $(-1)^L I = -1$.

PROBLEMS

PROBLEM 1. Determine the possible terms for the molecules H_2, N_2, O_2, Cl_2 which can be obtained by combining atoms in the normal state.

SOLUTION. According to the rules given above, we find the following possible states:
H_2 molecule (atoms in the ^2S state):

$$^1\Sigma^+_g, \quad ^3\Sigma^+_u;$$

N_2 molecule (atoms in the ^4S state):

$$^1\Sigma^+_g, \quad ^3\Sigma^+_u, \quad ^5\Sigma^+_g, \quad ^7\Sigma^+_u;$$

Cl_2 molecule (atoms in the ^2P state):

$$2\,^1\Sigma^+_g, \quad ^1\Sigma^-_u, \quad ^1\Pi_g, \quad ^1\Pi_u, \quad ^1\Delta_g, \quad 2\,^3\Sigma^+_u, \quad ^3\Sigma^-_g, \quad ^3\Pi_g, \quad ^3\Pi_u, \quad ^3\Delta_u;$$

O_2 molecule (atoms in the ^3P state):

$$2\,^1\Sigma^+_g, \quad ^1\Sigma^-_u, \quad ^1\Pi_g, \quad ^1\Pi_u, \quad ^1\Delta_g, \quad 2\,^3\Sigma^+_u, \quad ^3\Sigma^-_g, \quad ^3\Pi_u, \quad ^3\Pi_g, \quad ^3\Delta_u,$$
$$2\,^5\Sigma^+_g, \quad ^5\Sigma^-_u, \quad ^5\Pi_g, \quad ^5\Pi_u, \quad ^5\Delta_g.$$

The figures in front of the symbols indicate the number of terms of the type concerned, if this number exceeds unity.

PROBLEM 2. The same as Problem 1, but for the molecules HCl, CO.

SOLUTION. When unlike atoms are combined, the parity of their states is important also. From formula (30.5) we find that the normal states of the H, O and C atoms are even, while that of the Cl atom is odd (see Table 3 for the electron configurations of these atoms). From the rules given above, we have
HCl molecule (atoms in the ^2S_g and ^2P_u states):

$$^{1,3}\Sigma^+, \quad ^{1,3}\Pi;$$

CO molecule (both atoms in the ^3P_g state):

$$2\,^{1,3,5}\Sigma^+, \quad ^{1,3,5}\Sigma^-, \quad 2\,^{1,3,5}\Pi, \quad ^{1,3,5}\Delta.$$

§78. Valency

The property of atoms of combining with one another to form molecules is described in chemistry by means of the concept of *valency*. To each atom we ascribe a definite valency, and when atoms combine their valencies must be mutually satisfied, i.e. to each valency bond of an atom there must correspond a valency bond of another atom. For example, in the methane molecule CH_4, the four valency bonds of the quadrivalent carbon atom are satisfied by the four univalent hydrogen atoms. In going on to give a physical interpretation of valency, we shall begin with the simplest example, the combination of two hydrogen atoms to form the molecule H_2.

Let us consider two hydrogen atoms in the ground state (^2S). When they approach, the resulting system may be in the molecular state $^1\Sigma^+_g$ or $^3\Sigma^+_u$. The singlet term corresponds to an antisymmetrical spin wave function, and the triplet term to a symmetrical function. The co-ordinate wave function, on the other hand, is symmetrical for the $^1\Sigma$ term and antisymmetrical for the $^3\Sigma$ term. It is evident that the ground term of the H_2 molecule can only be the $^1\Sigma$ term. For an antisymmetrical wave function $\phi(\mathbf{r}_1, \mathbf{r}_2)$ (where $\mathbf{r}_1$ and $\mathbf{r}_2$ are the radius vectors of the two electrons) always has nodes (since it vanishes for $\mathbf{r}_1 = \mathbf{r}_2$), and hence cannot belong to the lowest state of the system.

A numerical calculation shows that the electron term $^1\Sigma$ in fact has a deep minimum corresponding to the formation of a stable H_2 molecule. In the $^3\Sigma$ state, the energy $U(r)$ decreases monotonically as the distance between the nuclei increases, corresponding to the mutual repulsion of the two hydrogen atoms† (Fig. 31).

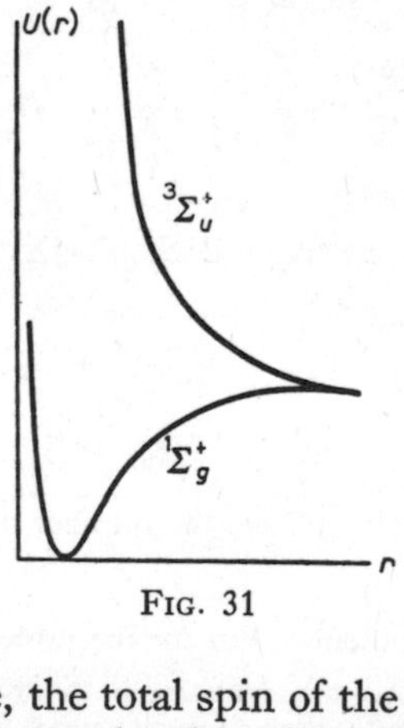

FIG. 31

Thus, in the ground state, the total spin of the hydrogen molecule is zero, $S = 0$. It is found that the molecules of practically all chemically stable compounds of elements of the principal groups have this property. Among inorganic molecules, exceptions are formed by the diatomic molecules O_2

† It must be mentioned that at large distances the function $U(r)$ begins to increase again, on account of the van der Waals attraction of the atoms. As a result, there is a minimum on the upper curve also. This minimum, however, lies at large distances r and is very shallow, and hence does not bring about the formation of stable molecules.

(ground state $^3\Sigma$) and NO (ground state $^2\Pi$) and the triatomic molecules NO_2, ClO_2 (total spin $S = \frac{1}{2}$). Elements of the intermediate groups have special properties which we shall discuss below, after studying the valency properties of the elements of the principal groups.

The property of atoms of combining with one another is thus related to their spin (W. Heitler and H. London 1927). The combination occurs in such a way that the spins of the atoms compensate one another. As a quantitative characteristic of the mutual combining powers of atoms, it is convenient to use an integer, twice the spin of the atom. This is equal to the chemical valency of the atom. Here it must be borne in mind that the same atom may have different valencies according to the state it is in.

Let us examine, from this point of view, the elements of the principal groups in the periodic system. The elements of the first group (the first column in Table 3, the group of alkali metals) have a spin $S = \frac{1}{2}$ in the normal state, and accordingly their valencies are unity. An excited state with a higher spin can be attained only by exciting an electron from a completed shell. Accordingly, these states are so high that the excited atom cannot form a stable molecule.†

The atoms of elements in the second group (the second column in Table 3, the group of alkaline-earth metals) have a spin $S = 0$ in the normal state. Hence these atoms cannot enter into chemical compounds in the normal state. However, comparatively close to the ground state there is an excited state having a configuration sp instead of s^2 in the incomplete shell, and a total spin $S = 1$. The valency of an atom in this state is 2, and this is the principal valency of the elements in the second group.

The elements of the third group have an electron configuration s^2p in the normal state, with a spin $S = \frac{1}{2}$. However, by exciting an electron from the completed s-shell, an excited state is obtained having a configuration sp^2 and a spin $S = 3/2$, and this state lies close to the normal one. Accordingly, the elements of this group are both univalent and tervalent. The first two elements in the group (boron, aluminium) behave only as tervalent elements. The tendency to exhibit a valency 1 increases with the atomic number, and thallium behaves equally as a univalent and as a tervalent element (for example, in the compounds TlCl and $TlCl_3$). This is due to the fact that, in the first few elements, the binding energy in the tervalent compounds is greater than for the univalent compounds, and this difference exceeds the excitation energy of the atom.

In the elements of the fourth group, the ground state has the configuration s^2p^2 with a spin of 1, and the adjacent excited state has a configuration sp^3 with a spin 2. The valencies 2 and 4 correspond to these states. As in the third group, the first two elements (carbon, silicon) exhibit mainly the higher valency (though the compound CO, for example, forms an exception), and the tendency to exhibit the lower valency increases with the atomic number.

† See the end of this section for the elements copper, silver and gold.

In the atoms of the elements of the fifth group, the ground state has the configuration s^2p^3 with a spin $S = 3/2$, so that the corresponding valency is three. An excited state of higher spin can be obtained only by the transition of one of the electrons into the shell with the next higher value of the principal quantum number. The nearest such state has the configuration s^2p^2s' and a spin $S = 5/2$ (by s' we conventionally denote here an s state of an electron with a principal quantum number one greater than in the state s). Although the excitation energy of this state is comparatively high, the excited atom can still form a stable compound. Accordingly, the elements of the fifth group behave as both tervalent and quinquevalent elements (thus, nitrogen is tervalent in NH_3 and quinquevalent in HNO_3).

In the sixth group of elements, the spin is 1 in the ground state (configuration s^2p^4), so that the atom is bivalent. The excitation of one of the p electrons leads to a state s^2p^3s' of spin 2, while the excitation of an s electron in addition gives a state $sp^3s'p'$ of spin 3. In both excited states the atom can enter into stable molecules, and accordingly exhibits valencies of 4 and 6. The first element of the sixth group (oxygen) shows only the valency 2, while the subsequent elements show higher valencies also (thus, sulphur in H_2S, SO_2, SO_3 is respectively bivalent, quadrivalent and sexivalent).

In the seventh group (the halogen group), the atoms are univalent in the ground state (configuration s^2p^5, spin $S = \frac{1}{2}$). They can, however, enter into stable compounds when they are in excited states having configurations s^2p^4s', $s^2p^3s'p'$, $sp^3s'p'^2$ with spins 3/2, 5/2, 7/2 and valencies 3, 5, 7 respectively. The first element in the group (fluorine) is always univalent, but the subsequent elements also exhibit the higher valencies (thus, chlorine in HCl, $HClO_2$, $HClO_3$, $HClO_4$ is respectively univalent, tervalent, quinquevalent and septivalent).

Finally, the atoms of the elements in the group of inert gases have completely filled shells in their ground states (so that the spin $S = 0$), and their excitation energies are very high. Accordingly, the valency is zero, and these elements are chemically inactive.†

The following general remark should be made concerning all these discussions. The assertion that an atom enters into a molecule with a valency pertaining to an excited state does not mean that, on moving the atoms apart to large distances, we necessarily obtain an excited atom. It means only that the distribution of the electron density in the molecule is such that, near the nucleus of the atom in question, it is close to that in the isolated and excited atom; but the limit to which the electron distribution tends as the distance between the nuclei is increased may correspond to non-excited atoms.

When atoms combine to form a molecule, the completed electron shells in

† This means that the interaction of an inert gas atom, in the normal state, with any other atom is repulsive in nature. The only exception is the interaction of an inert gas atom with an excited atom of the same gas. This is due to the doubling in the number of possible states obtained on bringing together two atoms, if these atoms are of the same element but in different states (see §77). The transition of the excitation from one atom to the other here replaces the exchange interaction which brings about the ordinary valency. The molecule He_2 is an example of such a molecule. The same type of binding occurs in molecular ions composed of two similar atoms (for instance, H_2^+).

the atoms are not much changed. The distribution of the electron density in the incomplete shells, on the other hand, may be considerably altered. In the most clearly defined cases of what is called *heteropolar binding*, all the valency electrons pass over from their own atoms to other atoms, so that we may say that the molecule consists of ions with charges equal (in units of *e*) to the valency. The elements of the first group are electropositive: in heteropolar compounds they lose electrons, forming positive ions. As we pass to the subsequent groups the electropositive character of the elements becomes gradually less marked and changes into electronegative character, which is present to the greatest extent in the elements of the seventh group. Regarding heteropolarity the same remark should be made as was made above concerning excited atoms in the molecule. If a molecule is heteropolar, this does not mean that, on moving the atoms apart, we necessarily obtain two ions. Thus, from the molecule KCl we should in fact obtain the ions K^+ and Cl^-, but the molecule NaCl gives in the limit the neutral atoms Na and Cl (since the affinity of chlorine for an electron is greater than the ionisation potential of potassium but less than that of sodium).

In the opposite limiting case of what is called *homopolar binding*, the atoms in the molecule remain neutral on the average. Homopolar molecules, unlike heteropolar ones, have no appreciable dipole moment. The difference between the heteropolar and homopolar types is purely quantitative, and any intermediate case may occur.

Let us now turn to the elements of the intermediate groups. Those of the palladium and platinum groups are very similar to the elements of the principal groups as regards their valency properties. The only difference is that, owing to the comparatively deep position of the *d* electrons inside the atom, they interact only slightly with the other atoms in the molecule. As a result, "unsaturated" compounds, whose molecules have non-zero spin (though in practice not exceeding $\frac{1}{2}$), are often found among the compounds of these elements. Each of the elements can exhibit various valencies, and these may differ by unity, and not only by two as with the elements of the principal groups (where the change in valency is due to the excitation of some electron whose spin is compensated, so that the spins of two electrons are simultaneously released).

The elements of the rare-earth group are characterised by the presence of an incomplete *f* shell. The *f* electrons lie much deeper than the *d* electrons, and therefore take no part in the valency. Thus the valency of the rare-earth elements is determined only by the *s* and *p* electrons in the incomplete shells.† However, it must be borne in mind that, when the atom is excited, *f* electrons may pass into *s* and *p* states, thereby increasing the valency by one. Hence the rare-earth elements too exhibit valencies differing by unity (in practice they are all tervalent and quadrivalent).

† The *d* electrons which are found in the incomplete shells of the atoms of some rare-earth elements are unimportant, since these atoms in practice always form compounds in excited states where there are no *d* electrons.

The elements of the uranium group occupy a unique position. Though the uranium atom in the normal state contains *f* electrons, in compounds it (like thorium) does not behave analogously to the rare-earth elements, but rather to those of the palladium and platinum groups. This shows that, when a chemical compound is formed, the *f* electrons in the uranium atom pass into other states. The elements neptunium and plutonium (and apparently americium and curium) are homologues of uranium in their chemical properties, and this shows that in their atoms the excess electrons over those present in uranium are in *f* states.

The elements of the iron group occupy, as regards their valency properties, a position intermediate between the rare-earth elements and those of the palladium and platinum groups. In their atoms, the *d* electrons lie comparatively deep, and in many compounds take no part in the valency bonds. In these compounds, therefore, the elements of the iron group behave like rare-earth elements. Such compounds include those of ionic type (for instance $FeCl_2$, $FeCl_3$), in which the metal atom enters as a simple cation. Like the rare-earth elements, the elements of the iron group can show very various valencies in these compounds.

Another type of compound of the iron-group elements is formed by what are called *complex compounds*. These are characterised by the fact that the atom of the intermediate element enters into the molecule not as a simple ion, bu as part of a complex ion (for instance the ion MnO_4^- in $KMnO_4$, or the ion $Fe(CN)_6^{4-}$ in $K_4Fe(CN)_6$). In these complex ions, the atoms are closer together than in simple ionic compounds, and in them the *d* electrons take part in the valency bond. Accordingly, the elements of the iron group behave in complex compounds like those of the palladium and platinum groups.

Finally, it must be mentioned that the elements copper, silver and gold, which in §70 we placed among the principal groups, behave as intermediate elements in some of their compounds. These elements can exhibit valencies of more than one, on account of a transition of an electron from a *d* shell to a *p* shell of nearly the same energy (for example, from 3*d* to 4*p* in copper). In such compounds the atoms have an incomplete *d* shell, and hence behave as intermediate elements: copper like the elements of the iron group, and silver and gold like those of the palladium and platinum groups.

PROBLEM

Determine the electron terms of the molecular ion H_2^+ obtained when a hydrogen atom in the normal state combines with an H^+ ion, using the approximation of starting from the unperturbed wave functions of the hydrogen atom.

SOLUTION. The electron wave function for the H_2^+ ion is obtained by symmetrising (or antisymmetrising) with respect to the two nuclei the wave function of the normal state of the hydrogen atom,†

$$\psi = \pi^{-\frac{1}{2}}e^{-r}:$$

$$\psi_g = \psi(r_1)+\psi(r_2), \quad \psi_u = \psi(r_1)-\psi(r_2)$$

† We use atomic units.

(ψ_g and ψ_u are not normalised), where r_1 and r_2 are the distances of the electron from the two nuclei. The function ψ_g corresponds to the term $^2\Sigma^+{}_g$, and ψ_u to $^2\Sigma^+{}_u$.

The Hamiltonian of the molecule is of the form

$$\hat{H} = -\tfrac{1}{2}\Delta + \frac{1}{r} - \frac{1}{r_1} - \frac{1}{r_2},$$

where r is the given distance between the nuclei. In the first approximation of perturbation theory, the energy of the terms is given by the formula

$$U_g(r) = \int \psi_g \hat{H} \psi_g \, \mathrm{d}V \Big/ \int \psi_g^2 \, \mathrm{d}V,$$

and similarly for $U_u(r)$. In calculating this, it must be borne in mind that the wave function of the normal state of the hydrogen atom satisfies SCHRÖDINGER's equation

$$\tfrac{1}{2}\Delta\psi(r_1) + (-\tfrac{1}{2} + 1/r_1)\psi(r_1) = 0,$$

and similarly for $\psi(r_2)$. Hence we find

$$U_{g,u}(r) = -\tfrac{1}{2} + \frac{1}{r} - \frac{\int [\psi^2(r_1)/r_2] \, \mathrm{d}V \pm \int [\psi(r_1)\psi(r_2)/r_1] \, \mathrm{d}V}{1 \pm \int \psi(r_1)\psi(r_2) \, \mathrm{d}V},$$

where the upper and lower signs refer to U_g and U_u respectively. The calculation of the first integral in the numerator is elementary, while the other integrals are easily found in terms of elliptic co-ordinates. As a result we obtain

$$U_{g,u} = -\tfrac{1}{2} + \frac{(1+1/r)e^{-2r} \pm (1/r - \frac{2}{3}r)e^{-r}}{1 \pm (1 + r + \frac{1}{3}r^2)e^{-r}}.$$

The term $U_g(r)$ corresponds to a stable molecule, while the term $U_u(r)$ is purely repulsive in character.

§79. Vibrational and rotational structures of singlet terms in the diatomic molecule

As has been pointed out at the beginning of this chapter, the great difference in the masses of the nuclei and the electrons makes it possible to divide the problem of determining the energy levels of a molecule into two parts. We first determine the energy levels of the system of electrons, for nuclei at rest, as functions of the distance between the nuclei (the electron terms). We can then consider the motion of the nuclei for a given electron state; this amounts to regarding the nuclei as particles interacting with one another in accordance with the law $U_n(r)$, where U_n is the corresponding electron term. The motion of the molecule is composed of its gradual displacement as a whole, together with the motion of the nuclei about their centre of mass. The gradual motion is, of course, without interest, and we can regard the centre of mass as fixed.

For convenience of discussion, let us first consider the electron terms in which the total spin S of the molecule is zero (the singlet terms). The problem of the relative motion of two particles (the nuclei) which interact according to the law $U(r)$ reduces, as we know, to that of the motion of a single particle of mass M (the reduced mass of the two particles) in a centrally symmetric field $U(r)$. By $U(r)$ we mean the energy of the electron term considered. The problem of motion in a centrally symmetric field $U(r)$, however, reduces in turn to that of a one-dimensional motion in a field where the effective energy is equal to the sum of $U(r)$ and the centrifugal energy.

We denote by $\mathbf{K}$ the total angular momentum of the molecule, composed of the orbital angular momentum $\mathbf{L}$ of the electrons and the angular momentum of the nuclei. Then the operator of the centrifugal energy of the nuclei is

$$B(r)(\hat{\mathbf{K}}-\hat{\mathbf{L}})^2,$$

where we have introduced the notation

$$B(r) = \hbar^2/2Mr^2 \tag{79.1}$$

for a convenient simplification of the formulae in the theory of diatomic molecules. Averaging this quantity (for a given r), we obtain the centrifugal energy as a function of r, which must appear in the effective potential energy $U_K(r)$. Thus

$$U_K(r) = U(r)+B(r)\overline{(\mathbf{K}-\mathbf{L})^2},$$

where the line denotes the average mentioned. Expanding the square and recalling that the square $\mathbf{K}^2$ of a conserved total angular momentum has the definite value $K(K+1)$ (where K is integral), we can rewrite this expression in the form

$$U_K(r) = U(r)+B(r)K(K+1)+B(r)(\overline{\mathbf{L}^2}-2\overline{\mathbf{L}}\cdot\mathbf{K}); \tag{79.2}$$

we omit the line over the quantity $\mathbf{K}$, since it is conserved.

In a state with a definite value of $L_z = \Lambda$, the mean values of the other two components of the orbital angular momentum are zero, $\bar{L}_x = \bar{L}_y = 0$; this follows at once from the fact that, in a representation in which $\hat{L}_z$ is diagonal, the diagonal matrix elements of the operators $\hat{L}_x$ and $\hat{L}_y$ are zero (see §25). Hence the mean value of the vector $\mathbf{L}$ is directed along the z-axis and we can write

$$\bar{\mathbf{L}} = \mathbf{n}\Lambda,$$

where $\mathbf{n}$ is a unit vector along the axis of the molecule. Next, in classical mechanics the angular momentum of a system of two particles (the nuclei) is directed perpendicular to the line joining them; in quantum mechanics the same is true for the angular momentum operator. Hence we can write $(\hat{\mathbf{K}}-\hat{\mathbf{L}})\cdot\mathbf{n} = 0$, and $\hat{\mathbf{K}}\cdot\mathbf{n} = \hat{\mathbf{L}}\cdot\mathbf{n}$. Hence, for the eigenvalues,

$$\mathbf{K}\cdot\mathbf{n} = \mathbf{L}\cdot\mathbf{n} = \Lambda. \tag{79.3}$$

Thus the projection of the total angular momentum $\mathbf{K}$ on the axis of the molecule is also Λ. Hence it follows that, in a state with a given value of Λ, the quantum number K can take only values from Λ upwards:

$$K \geqslant \Lambda. \tag{79.4}$$

Finally, substituting in (79.2) $\mathbf{L} \cdot \mathbf{K} = \Lambda \mathbf{n} \cdot \mathbf{K} = \Lambda^2$, we obtain

$$U_K(r) = U(r) + B(r)K(K+1) + B(r)(\overline{\mathbf{L}^2} - 2\Lambda^2). \tag{79.5}$$

The last term on the right-hand side is some function of r, depending only on the electron state, and not on the quantum number K. This function can be included in the energy $U(r)$, and (79.5) then takes the form

$$U_K(r) = U(r) + B(r)K(K+1). \tag{79.6}$$

On solving the one-dimensional SCHRÖDINGER's equation with this potential energy, we obtain a series of energy levels. We arbitrarily number these levels (for each given K) in order of increasing energy, using a number $v = 0, 1, 2, \ldots$, $v = 0$ corresponds to the lowest level. Thus the motion of the nuclei causes a splitting of each electron term into a series of levels characterised by the values of the two quantum numbers K and v.

The number of these levels (for a given electron term) may be either finite or infinite. If the electron state is such that, as $r \to \infty$, the molecule becomes two isolated neutral atoms, then as $r \to \infty$ the potential energy $U(r)$ (and therefore $U_K(r)$) tends to a constant limiting value $U(\infty)$ (the sum of the energies of the two isolated atoms) more rapidly than $1/r$ tends to zero (see §86). The number of levels in such a field is finite (see §16), though in actual molecules it is very large. The levels are so distributed that, for any given value of K, there is a definite number of levels (with different values of v), while the number of levels with the same K diminishes as K increases, until a value of K is reached for which there are no levels at all.

If, on the other hand, as $r \to \infty$ the molecule disintegrates into two ions, at large distances $U(r) - U(\infty)$ becomes the energy of the attraction of the ions according to Coulomb's law ($\sim 1/r$). In such a field there is an infinite number of levels, which become closer and closer as we approach the limiting value $U(\infty)$. We may remark that, for the majority of molecules, the previous case is found in the normal state; only a comparatively small number of molecules become pairs of ions when their nuclei are moved apart.

The dependence of the energy levels on the quantum numbers cannot be completely calculated in a general form. Such a calculation is possible only for low excited levels which lie not too far above the ground level.† Small values of the quantum numbers K and v correspond to these levels. It is with such levels that we are in fact most often concerned in the study of molecular spectra, and hence they are of particular interest.

The motion of the nuclei in slightly excited states can be regarded as small vibrations about the equilibrium position. Accordingly we can expand $U(r)$ in a series of powers of $\xi = r - r_e$, where r_e is the value of r for which $U(r)$

† We refer always to levels belonging to the same electron term.

has a minimum. Since $U'(r_e) = 0$, we have as far as terms of the second order

$$U(r) = U_e + \tfrac{1}{2}M\omega_e^2\xi^2,$$

where $U_e = U(r_e)$, and ω_e is the frequency of the vibrations.†

In the second term in (79.6)—the centrifugal energy—it is sufficient to put $r = r_e$, since it already contains the small quantity $K(K+1)$. Thus we have

$$U_K(r) = U_e + B_e K(K+1) + \tfrac{1}{2}M\omega_e^2\xi^2, \tag{79.7}$$

where $B_e = \hbar^2/2Mr_e^2 = \hbar^2/2I$ is what is called the ***rotational constant*** ($I = Mr_e^2$ is the moment of inertia of the molecule).

The first two terms in (79.7) are just constants, while the third corresponds to a one-dimensional harmonic oscillator. Hence we can at once write down the required energy levels:

$$E = U_e + B_e K(K+1) + \hbar\omega_e(v+\tfrac{1}{2}). \tag{79.8}$$

Thus, in the approximation considered, the energy levels are composed of three independent parts:

$$E = E_{el} + E_r + E_v. \tag{79.9}$$

Here $E_{el} = U_e$ is the electron energy (including the energy of the Coulomb interaction of the nuclei for $r = r_e$),

$$E_r = B_e K(K+1) \tag{79.10}$$

is the rotational energy from the rotation of the molecule,‡ and

$$E_v = \hbar\omega_e(v+\tfrac{1}{2}) \tag{79.11}$$

is the energy of the vibrations of the nuclei within the molecule. The number v denumerates, by definition, the levels with a given K in order of increasing energy; it is called the *vibrational quantum number*.

For a given form of the potential energy curve $U(r)$, the frequency ω_e is inversely proportional to $\sqrt{M}$. Hence the intervals ΔE_v between the vibrational levels are proportional to $1/\sqrt{M}$. The intervals ΔE_r between the rotational levels contain in the denominator the moment of inertia I, and are therefore proportional to $1/M$. The intervals ΔE_{el} between the electron levels, however, are independent of M, like the levels themselves. Since μ/M (μ being the electron mass) is a small parameter in the theory of diatomic molecules, we see that

$$\Delta E_{el} \gg \Delta E_v \gg \Delta E_r.$$

Thus the distribution of the energy levels of the molecule is rather unusual.

† We here use the international notation customary in the theory of diatomic molecules.

‡ A rotating system of two rigidly connected particles is often called a *rotator*. Formula (79.10) gives the quantum-mechanical energy levels for a rotator. The wave functions of the stationary states of a rotator evidently correspond to the case $\Lambda = 0$ and are ordinary spherical harmonic functions (see the Problem at the end of this section).

The vibrational motion of the nuclei splits the electron terms into levels lying comparatively close together. These levels, in turn, exhibit a fine splitting due to the rotational motion of the molecule.

In subsequent approximations, the separation of the energy into independent vibrational and rotational parts is impossible; rotational-vibrational terms appear, which contain both K and v. On calculating the successive approximations, we should obtain the levels E as an expansion in powers of the quantum numbers K and v.

We shall calculate here the next approximation after (79.8). To do this, we must continue the expansion of $U(r)$ in powers of ξ up to terms of the fourth order (cf. the problem of an anharmonic oscillator in §38). Similarly, the expansion of the centrifugal energy is extended as far as the terms in ξ^2. We then obtain

$$U_K(r) = U_e + \tfrac{1}{2}M\omega_e^2\xi^2 + (\hbar^2/2Mr_e^2)K(K+1) -$$
$$-a\xi^3 + b\xi^4 - (\hbar^2/Mr_e^3)K(K+1)\xi + (3\hbar^2/2Mr_e^4)K(K+1)\xi^2. \qquad (79.12)$$

Let us now calculate the correction to the eigenvalues (79.8), using perturbation theory and regarding the last four terms in (79.12) as the perturbation operator. Here it is sufficient, for the terms in ξ^2 and ξ^4, to take the first approximation of perturbation theory, but for those in ξ and ξ^3 we must calculate the second approximation, since the diagonal matrix elements of ξ and ξ^3 vanish identically. All the matrix elements needed for the calculation are derived in §21 and in §38, Problem 3. As a result, we obtain an expression which is usually written in the form

$$E = E_{el} + \hbar\omega_e(v+\tfrac{1}{2}) - x_e\hbar\omega_e(v+\tfrac{1}{2})^2 + B_vK(K+1) - D_eK^2(K+1)^2, \qquad (79.13)$$

where

$$B_v = B_e - \alpha_e(v+\tfrac{1}{2}) = B_0 - \alpha_e v. \qquad (79.14)$$

The constants x_e, B_e, α_e, D_e are related to the constants appearing in (79.12) by

$$B_e = \hbar^2/2I, \qquad D_e = 4B_0^3/\hbar^2\omega_e^2,$$

$$\alpha_e = \frac{6B_e^2}{\hbar\omega_e}\left(\frac{a\hbar}{M\omega_e^2}\sqrt{\frac{2}{MB_e}} - 1\right), \qquad x_e = \frac{3}{2\hbar\omega_e}\left(\frac{\hbar}{M\omega_e}\right)^2\left[\frac{5}{2}\frac{a^2}{M\omega_e^2} - b\right]. \qquad (79.15)$$

The terms independent of v and K are included in E_{el}.

PROBLEM

Determine the angular part of the wave function for a diatomic molecule with zero spin (F. Reiche 1926).

Solution. The required functions are just the eigenfunctions of the total angular momentum $\mathbf{K}$ of the molecule. The operator of the total angular momentum is the sum

$$\hat{\mathbf{K}} = \mathbf{r}\times\hat{\mathbf{p}} + \sum_a \mathbf{r}_a \times \hat{\mathbf{p}}_a,$$

where $\mathbf{p}$ is the linear momentum of the relative motion of the nuclei, $\mathbf{r}$ the radius vector between them, $\mathbf{r}_a$ and $\mathbf{p}_a$ the radius vectors and linear momenta of the electrons (relative to the centre of mass of the molecule). Introducing the polar angle θ and the azimuthal angle ϕ of the axis of the molecule relative to a fixed system of co-ordinates x, y, z, we have for the components of the operator $\hat{\mathbf{K}}$ expressions similar to (24.12), so that

$$\left.\begin{aligned} \hat{K}_x+i\hat{K}_y &= e^{i\phi}\left(\frac{\partial'}{\partial\theta}+i\cot\theta\frac{\partial'}{\partial\phi}\right)+(\hat{L}_x+i\hat{L}_y),\\ \hat{K}_x-i\hat{K}_y &= e^{-i\phi}\left(-\frac{\partial'}{\partial\theta}+i\cot\theta\frac{\partial'}{\partial\phi}\right)+(\hat{L}_x-i\hat{L}_y),\\ \hat{K}_z &= -i\frac{\partial'}{\partial\phi}+\hat{L}_z, \end{aligned}\right\} \tag{1}$$

where

$$\hat{L}_x = -i\sum_a\left(y_a\frac{\partial}{\partial z_a}-z_a\frac{\partial}{\partial y_a}\right), \ldots$$

are the operators of the angular momenta of the electrons; the primes on $\partial/\partial\theta$ and $\partial/\partial\phi$ signify that the differentiation is to be performed for constant x_a, y_a, z_a.

Besides the fixed system of co-ordinates x, y, z, we introduce a moving system ξ, η, ζ, with the same origin, the ζ-axis directed along the axis of the molecule, and the ξ-axis lying in the xy-plane. The co-ordinates ξ_a, η_a, ζ_a of the electrons in this system are related to the co-ordinates x_a, y_a, z_a by

$$\begin{aligned} \xi_a &= -x_a\sin\phi+y_a\cos\phi,\\ \eta_a &= -x_a\cos\theta\cos\phi-y_a\cos\theta\sin\phi+z_a\sin\theta,\\ \zeta_a &= x_a\sin\theta\cos\phi+y_a\sin\theta\sin\phi+z_a\cos\theta. \end{aligned}$$

Using these formulae, we can transform the derivatives:

$$\begin{aligned} \frac{\partial}{\partial z_a} &= \sin\theta\frac{\partial}{\partial\eta_a}+\cos\theta\frac{\partial}{\partial\zeta_a}, \text{ etc.,}\\ \frac{\partial'}{\partial\theta} &= \frac{\partial}{\partial\theta}+\sum_a\left(\frac{\partial'\xi_a}{\partial\theta}\frac{\partial}{\partial\xi_a}+\frac{\partial'\eta_a}{\partial\theta}\frac{\partial}{\partial\eta_a}+\frac{\partial'\zeta_a}{\partial\theta}\frac{\partial}{\partial\zeta_a}\right)\\ &= \frac{\partial}{\partial\theta}+\sum_a\left(\zeta_a\frac{\partial}{\partial\eta_a}-\eta_a\frac{\partial}{\partial\zeta_a}\right), \text{ etc.,} \end{aligned}$$

where $\partial/\partial\theta$ and $\partial/\partial\phi$ (unprimed) denote differentiation for constant ξ_a, η_a, ζ_a. As a result, we have for the operators of the components of the total angular momentum relative to the fixed system the expressions

$$\left.\begin{aligned} \hat{K}_x+i\hat{K}_y &= e^{i\phi}\left(\frac{\partial}{\partial\theta}+i\cot\theta\frac{\partial}{\partial\phi}\right)+\frac{e^{i\phi}}{\sin\theta}\hat{L}_\zeta,\\ \hat{K}_x-i\hat{K}_y &= e^{-i\phi}\left(-\frac{\partial}{\partial\theta}+i\cot\theta\frac{\partial}{\partial\phi}\right)+\frac{e^{-i\phi}}{\sin\theta}\hat{L}_\zeta,\\ \hat{K}_z &= -i\,\partial/\partial\phi, \end{aligned}\right\} \tag{2}$$

where

$$\hat{L}_\zeta = -i\sum_a \left(\xi_a \frac{\partial}{\partial \eta_a} - \eta_a \frac{\partial}{\partial \xi_a}\right)$$

is the operator of the angular momentum of the electrons about the axis of the molecule.

Let

$$\psi_{n\Lambda KM_K} = \phi_{n\Lambda K}(\xi_a, \eta_a, \zeta_a; r)\rho_{n\Lambda K}(r)\Theta_{\Lambda KM_K}(\theta)e^{iM_K\phi} \quad (3)$$

be the wave function of a state with definite values of the absolute value K and z-component M_K of the total angular momentum of the molecule, and a definite value Λ of the ζ-component of the electron angular momentum; n denotes the assembly of the remaining quantum numbers which determine the state of the molecule. $\phi_{n\Lambda K}$ is the electron wave-function, depending on r as a parameter, $\rho_{n\Lambda K}$ is the "radial part" of the nuclear wave function, $\Theta_{\Lambda KM_K}$ is the required function of the angle θ, and the dependence of ψ on the angle ϕ is obvious. When the operators $\hat{K}_z$, $\hat{L}_\zeta$ act on the function (3), we can replace them by their eigenvalues M_K, Λ, so that

$$\hat{K}_x + i\hat{K}_y = e^{i\phi}\left(\frac{\partial}{\partial\theta} - M_K \cot\theta\right) + \frac{e^{i\phi}}{\sin\theta}\Lambda,$$

$$\hat{K}_x - i\hat{K}_y = e^{-i\phi}\left(-\frac{\partial}{\partial\theta} - M_K \cot\theta\right) + \frac{e^{-i\phi}}{\sin\theta}\Lambda.$$

The subsequent argument exactly follows that at the end of §26. When the operator $\hat{K}_x + i\hat{K}_y$ acts on the function $\psi_{n\Lambda KK}$ (with $M_K = K$), the result is zero; hence we have the equation

$$\left(\frac{\partial}{\partial\theta} - K\cot\theta + \frac{\Lambda}{\sin\theta}\right)\Theta_{\Lambda KK} = 0,$$

whose solution is

$$\Theta_{\Lambda KK} = \text{constant}\times(1-\cos\theta)^{\frac{1}{2}(K-\Lambda)}(1+\cos\theta)^{\frac{1}{2}(K+\Lambda)};$$

we shall not determine the normalisation factor. The remaining functions are then calculated from the formula

$$\sqrt{\frac{(2K)!(K-M_K)!}{(K+M_K)!}}\,\Theta_{\Lambda KM_K} = (\hat{K}_x - i\hat{K}_y)^{K-M_K}\Theta_{\Lambda KK},$$

and as a result we obtain

$$\Theta_{\Lambda KM_K} = \text{constant}\times\frac{(1-\cos\theta)^{\frac{1}{2}(\Lambda-M_K)}}{(1+\cos\theta)^{\frac{1}{2}(\Lambda+M_K)}}\times$$

$$\times\left[\left(\frac{\partial}{\partial\cos\theta}\right)^{K-M_K}(1-\cos\theta)^{K-\Lambda}(1+\cos\theta)^{K+\Lambda}\right].$$

For $\Lambda = 0$ these functions become ordinary spherical harmonic functions, as they should.

$$\Theta_{0KM_K} = \text{constant}\times P_K^{M_K}(\cos\theta),$$

and are the wave functions of a rotator (eigenfunctions of the free angular momentum **K**).

§80. Multiplet terms. Case *a*

Let us now turn to the question of the classification of molecular levels with non-zero spin S. In the zero-order approximation, when relativistic effects are entirely neglected, the energy of the molecule, like that of any system of particles, is independent of the direction of the spin (the spin is "free"), and this results in a $(2S+1)$-fold degeneracy of the levels. When relativistic effects are taken into account, however, the degenerate levels are split, and the energy consequently becomes a function of the projection of the spin on the axis of the molecule. We shall refer to relativistic interactions in molecules as the *spin-axis interaction.* The chief part in this is played (as in the case of atoms) by the interaction of the spins with the orbital motion of the electrons.†

The nature and classification of molecular levels depend markedly on the relative parts played by the interaction of the spin with the orbital motion, on the one hand, and the rotation of the molecule, on the other. The part played by the latter is characterised by the distances between adjacent rotational levels. Accordingly, we have to consider two limiting cases. In one, the energy of the spin-axis interaction is large compared with the energy differences between the rotational levels, while in the other it is small. The first case is usually called *case* (or coupling type) *a*, following HUND, and the second is called *case b*.

Case *a* is the one most often found. An exception is formed by the Σ terms, where case *b* chiefly occurs, since the effect of the spin-axis interaction is very small for these terms‡ (see below). For other terms, case *b* is sometimes found in the lightest molecules, since the spin-axis interaction is here comparatively weak, while the distances between the rotational levels are large (the moment of inertia being small).

Of course, cases intermediate between *a* and *b* are also possible. It must also be borne in mind that the same electron state may pass continuously from case *a* to case *b* as the rotational quantum number changes. This is due to the fact that the distances between adjacent rotational levels increase with the rotational quantum number, and hence, when this is large, the distances may become large compared with the energy of the spin-axis coupling (case *b*), even if case *a* is found for the lower rotational levels.

In case *a*, the classification of the levels is in principle little different from that of the terms with zero spin. We first consider the electron terms for nuclei at rest, i.e. we neglect rotation entirely; besides the projection Λ of the orbital angular momentum of the electrons, we must now take into account the projection of the total spin on the axis of the molecule. This projection is denoted by|| Σ; it takes the values $S, S-1, \dots, -S$. We arbitrarily regard

† Besides the spin-orbit and spin-spin interactions there is also an interaction of the spin and orbital motion of the electrons with the rotation of the molecule. This part of the interaction is very small, however, and it is usually of no interest.

‡ A special case is the normal electron term of the molecule O_2 (the term $^3\Sigma$). For this we have a type of coupling intermediate between *a* and *b* (see §81, Problem 3).

|| Not to be confused with the symbol for terms with $\Lambda = 0$.

Σ as positive when the projection of the spin is in the same direction as that of the orbital angular momentum about the axis (we recall that Λ denotes the absolute value of the latter). The quantities Λ and Σ combine to give the total angular momentum of the electrons about the axis of the molecule:

$$\Omega = \Lambda + \Sigma; \tag{80.1}$$

this takes the values $\Lambda+S, \Lambda+S-1, \ldots, \Lambda-S$. Thus the electron term with orbital angular momentum Λ is split into $2S+1$ terms with different values of Ω; this splitting, as with atomic terms, is called the *fine structure* or *multiplet splitting* of the electron levels. The value of Ω is usually indicated as a suffix to the symbol for the term: thus, for $\Lambda = 1$, $S = \frac{1}{2}$ we obtain the terms ${}^2\Pi_{1/2}$, ${}^2\Pi_{3/2}$.

When the motion of the nuclei is taken into account, vibrational and rotational structures appear in each of these terms. The various rotational levels are characterised by the values of the quantum number J, which gives the total angular momentum of the molecule, including the orbital and spin angular momenta of the electrons and the angular momentum of the rotation of the nuclei.† This number takes all integral values from $|\Omega|$ upwards:

$$J \geqslant |\Omega|, \tag{80.2}$$

which is an obvious generalisation of (79.4).

Let us now derive quantitative formulae to determine the molecular levels in case *a*. First of all, we consider the fine structure of an electron term. In discussing the fine structure of atomic terms in §67, we used formula (67.2), according to which the mean value of the spin-orbit interaction is proportional to the projection of the total spin of the atom on the orbital angular momentum vector. Similarly, the spin-axis interaction in a diatomic molecule (averaged over electron states for a given distance r between the nuclei) is proportional to the projection Σ of the total spin of the molecule on its axis, so that we can write the split electron term in the form

$$U(r) + A(r)\Sigma,$$

where $U(r)$ is the energy of the original (unsplit) term, and $A(r)$ is some function of r; this function depends on the original term (and in particular on Λ), but not on Σ. Since one usually uses the quantum number Ω and not Σ, it is more convenient to put $A\Omega$ in place of $A\Sigma$; these expressions differ by $A\Lambda$, which can be included in $U(r)$. Thus we have for an electron term the expression

$$U(r) + A(r)\Omega. \tag{80.3}$$

We may notice that the components of the split term are equidistant from one another: the distance between adjacent components (with values of Ω differing by unity) is $A(r)$, independent of Ω.

† The notation **K** is, as usual, reserved for the total angular momentum of the molecule without allowance for its spin. In case *a* there is no quantum number K, since the angular momentum **K** is not even approximately conserved.

It is easy to see from general considerations that the value of A for Σ terms is zero. To show this, we perform the operation of changing the sign of the time. The energy must then remain unchanged, but the state of the molecule changes in that the direction of the orbital and spin angular momenta about the axis is reversed. In the energy $A(r)\Sigma$, the sign of Σ is changed, and if the energy remains unchanged $A(r)$ must change sign. If $\Lambda \neq 0$, we can draw no conclusions regarding the value of $A(r)$, since this depends on the orbital angular momentum, which itself changes sign. If $\Lambda = 0$, however, we can say that $A(r)$ is certainly unchanged, and consequently it must vanish identically. Thus, for the Σ terms, the spin-orbit interaction causes no splitting in the approximation considered; splitting would occur only on taking account of the spin-spin interaction, and would be very small. This is the reason for the fact, already mentioned, that case *b* usually occurs for Σ terms.

When the multiplet splitting has been determined, we can take account of the rotation of the molecule as a perturbation, just as in the derivation given at the beginning of §79. The angular momentum of the rotation of the nuclei is obtained from the total angular momentum by subtracting the orbital angular momentum and spin of the electrons. Hence the operator of the centrifugal energy now has the form

$$B(r)(\hat{\mathbf{J}}-\hat{\mathbf{L}}-\hat{\mathbf{S}})^2.$$

Averaging this quantity with respect to the electron state and adding to (80.3), we obtain the required effective potential energy $U_J(r)$:

$$\begin{aligned} U_J(r) &= U(r)+A(r)\Omega+B(r)\overline{(\mathbf{J}-\mathbf{L}-\mathbf{S})^2} \\ &= U(r)+A(r)\Omega+B(r)[\mathbf{J}^2-2\mathbf{J}\cdot\overline{(\mathbf{L}+\mathbf{S})}+\overline{\mathbf{L}^2}+2\overline{\mathbf{L}\cdot\mathbf{S}}+\overline{\mathbf{S}^2}]. \end{aligned}$$

The eigenvalue of $\mathbf{J}^2$ is $J(J+1)$. Next, by the same argument as in §79, we have

$$\overline{\mathbf{L}} = \mathbf{n}\Lambda, \qquad \overline{\mathbf{S}} = \mathbf{n}\Sigma, \tag{80.4}$$

and also $(\hat{\mathbf{J}}-\hat{\mathbf{L}}-\hat{\mathbf{S}})\cdot\mathbf{n} = 0$, whence we have for the eigenvalues

$$\mathbf{J}\cdot\mathbf{n} = (\mathbf{L}+\mathbf{S})\cdot\mathbf{n} = \Lambda+\Sigma = \Omega. \tag{80.5}$$

Substituting these values, we find

$$U_J(r) = U(r)+A(r)\Omega+B(r)[J(J+1)-2\Omega^2+\overline{\mathbf{L}^2}+2\overline{\mathbf{L}\cdot\mathbf{S}}+\overline{\mathbf{S}^2}].$$

The averaging with respect to the electron state is effected by means of the wave functions of the zero-order† approximation. In this approximation, however, the magnitude of the spin is conserved, and hence $\mathbf{S}^2 = S(S+1)$. The wave function is the product of the spin and co-ordinate functions; hence

† That is, the zero-order approximation with respect to both the effect of the rotation of the molecule and the spin-axis interaction.

the averaging of the angular momenta **L** and **S** takes place independently, and we obtain

$$\overline{\mathbf{L}.\mathbf{S}} = \Lambda\mathbf{n}.\bar{\mathbf{S}} = \Lambda\Sigma.$$

Finally, the mean value of the squared orbital angular momentum $\mathbf{L}^2$ is independent of the spin, and is some function of r characterising the given (unsplit) electron term. All the terms which are functions of r but independent of J and Σ can be included in $U(r)$, while the term proportional to Σ (or, what is the same thing, to Ω) can be included in the expression $A(r)\Omega$. Thus we have for the effective potential energy the formula

$$U_J(r) = U(r)+A(r)\Omega+B(r)[J(J+1)-2\Omega^2]. \tag{80.6}$$

The energy levels of the molecule can be obtained from this by the same method as in §79 when using the formula (79.6). Expanding $U(r)$ and $A(r)$ in series of powers of ξ, and retaining the terms up to and including the second order in the expansion of $U(r)$, but only the terms of zero order in the second and third terms, we obtain the energy levels in the form

$$E = U_e+A_e\Omega+\hbar\omega_e(v+\tfrac{1}{2})+B_e[J(J+1)-2\Omega^2], \tag{80.7}$$

where $A_e = A(r_e)$ and B_e are constants characterising the given (unsplit) electron term. On continuing the expansion to higher terms, we obtain a series of terms in higher powers of the quantum numbers, but we shall not pause to write these out here.

§81. Multiplet terms. Case *b*

Let us now turn to case *b*. Here the effect of the rotation of the molecule predominates over the multiplet splitting. Hence we must first consider the effect of rotation, neglecting the spin-axis interaction, and then the latter must be taken into account as a perturbation.

In a molecule with "free" spin, not only the total angular momentum **J** but also the sum **K** of the orbital angular momentum of the electrons and the angular momentum of the nuclei are conserved; the latter is related to **J** by

$$\mathbf{J} = \mathbf{K}+\mathbf{S}. \tag{81.1}$$

The quantum number K distinguishes different states of a rotating molecule with free spin that are obtained from a given electron term. The effective potential energy $U_K(r)$ in a state with a given value of K is evidently determined by the same formula (79.6) as for terms with $S = 0$:

$$U_K(r) = U(r)+B(r)K(K+1), \tag{81.2}$$

where K takes the values Λ, $\Lambda+1$, ...

When the spin-axis interaction is included, there is a splitting of each term into $2S+1$ terms in general (or $2K+1$ if $K < S$), which differ in the value of the total angular momentum† J. According to the general rule for the addition of angular momenta, the number J takes (for a given K) values from $K+S$ to $|K-S|$:

$$|K-S| \leqslant J \leqslant K+S. \tag{81.3}$$

To calculate the energy of the splitting (in the first approximation of perturbation theory), we must determine the mean value of the operator of the spin-axis interaction energy for the state in the zero-order approximation (with respect to this interaction). In the case considered, this means averaging with respect to both the electron state and the rotation of the molecule (for a given r). The result of the first averaging is, as we know, an operator of the form $A(r)\mathbf{n}\,.\,\hat{\mathbf{S}}$, which is proportional to the projection $\mathbf{n}\,.\,\hat{\mathbf{S}}$ of the spin operator on the axis of the molecule. Next we average this operator with respect to the rotation of the molecule, taking the direction of the spin vector to be arbitrary; then $\overline{\mathbf{n}\,.\,\hat{\mathbf{S}}} = \bar{\mathbf{n}}\,.\,\hat{\mathbf{S}}$. The mean value $\bar{\mathbf{n}}$ is a vector which, from considerations of symmetry, must have the same direction as the "vector" $\hat{\mathbf{K}}$, the only vector which characterises the rotation of the molecule. Thus we can write

$$\bar{\mathbf{n}} = \text{constant} \times \hat{\mathbf{K}}.$$

The coefficient of proportionality is easily determined by multiplying both sides of this equation by $\hat{\mathbf{K}}$; noting that the eigenvalues of $\mathbf{n}\,.\,\mathbf{K}$ and $\mathbf{K}^2$ are respectively Λ (see (79.3)) and $K(K+1)$, we find the constant to be $\Lambda/K(K+1)$. Thus

$$\overline{\mathbf{n}\,.\,\hat{\mathbf{S}}} = \Lambda\hat{\mathbf{K}}\,.\,\hat{\mathbf{S}}/K(K+1).$$

Finally, the eigenvalue of the product $\mathbf{K}\,.\,\mathbf{S}$, according to the general formula (30.2), is

$$\mathbf{K}\,.\,\mathbf{S} = \tfrac{1}{2}[J(J+1)-K(K+1)-S(S+1)]. \tag{81.4}$$

As a result, we arrive at the following expression for the required mean value of the energy of the spin-axis interaction:

$$\begin{aligned} &A(r)\Lambda[J(J+1)-S(S+1)-K(K+1)]/2K(K+1) \\ &= A(r)\Lambda[(J-S)(J+S+1)]/2K(K+1)-\tfrac{1}{2}A(r)\Lambda. \end{aligned}$$

This expression must be added to the energy (81.2). The term $\frac{1}{2}A(r)\Lambda$, being independent of K and J, can be included in $U(r)$, so that we have finally for the effective potential energy the expression

$$U_K(r) = U(r)+B(r)K(K+1)+A(r)\Lambda(J-S)(J+S+1)/2K(K+1). \tag{81.5}$$

† In case b, the projection $\mathbf{n}\,.\,\mathbf{S}$ of the spin on the axis of the molecule does not have definite values, so that there is no quantum number Σ (or Ω).

An expansion in powers of $\xi = r - r_e$ gives, in the usual manner, an expression for the energy levels of the molecule in case *b*:

$$E = U_e + \hbar\omega_e(v+\tfrac{1}{2}) + B_e K(K+1) + A_e\Lambda(J-S)(J+S+1)/K(K+1). \qquad (81.6)$$

As has been pointed out in the previous section, the spin-orbit interaction for Σ terms does not give a multiplet splitting in the first approximation, and to determine the fine structure we must take into account the spin-spin interaction, whose operator is quadratic with respect to the spins of the electrons. We are at present interested not in this operator itself, but in the result of averaging it with respect to the electron state of the molecule, as was done for the operator of the spin-orbit interaction. It is evident from considerations of symmetry that the required averaged operator must be proportional to the squared projection of the total spin of the molecule on the axis, i.e. it can be written in the form

$$\alpha(r)\,(\hat{\mathbf{S}}\,.\,\mathbf{n})^2, \qquad (81.7)$$

where $\alpha(r)$ is again some function of the distance r, characterising the given electron state. Symmetry allows also a term proportional to $\hat{\mathbf{S}}^2$, but this is immaterial since the absolute value of the spin is just a constant. We shall not pause here to derive the lengthy general formula for the splitting due to the operator (81.7); in Problem 1 of this section we give the derivation of the formula for triplet Σ terms.

The doublet Σ terms form a special case. According to Kramers' theorem (§58), the double degeneracy in a system of particles with total spin $S = \frac{1}{2}$ certainly persists, even when the internal relativistic interactions in the system are fully allowed for. Hence the $^2\Sigma$ terms remain unsplit, even when we take account of both the spin-orbit and the spin-spin interaction, and in any approximation.

The splitting is obtained here only by taking into account the relativistic interaction of the spin with the rotation of the molecule; this effect is very small. The averaged operator of this interaction must evidently be of the form $\gamma\hat{\mathbf{K}}\,.\,\hat{\mathbf{S}}$, and its eigenvalues are determined by the formula (81.1), in which we must put $S = \frac{1}{2}$, $J = K \pm \frac{1}{2}$. As a result, we obtain for the $^2\Sigma$ terms the formula

$$E = U_e + \hbar\omega_e(v+\tfrac{1}{2}) + B_e K(K+1) \pm \tfrac{1}{2}\gamma(K+\tfrac{1}{2}); \qquad (81.8)$$

a constant $-\frac{1}{4}\gamma$ is included in U_e.

PROBLEMS

PROBLEM 1. Determine the multiplet splitting of a $^3\Sigma$ term in case *b* (KRAMERS 1929).

SOLUTION. The required splitting is determined by the operator (81.7), which must be averaged with respect to the rotation of the molecule. We write it in the form $\alpha_e n_i n_k S_i S_k$ (where the suffixes i, k take the values x, y, z); summation over repeated suffixes is understood, and $\alpha_e = \alpha(r_e)$. Since the vector **S** is conserved, only the products $n_i n_k$ need be averaged. From considerations of symmetry it is clear that we must have

$$\overline{n_i n_k} = a(\hat{K}_i\hat{K}_k + \hat{K}_k\hat{K}_i) + b\delta_{ik},$$

where a and b are some constants; this is the most general symmetrical tensor of rank two depending only on the vector $\hat{\mathbf{K}}$. To determine the constants a and b, we use the equations $n_i n_i = 1$, $\hat{K}_i n_i n_k = 0$ (since $\hat{\mathbf{K}}\cdot\mathbf{n} = \Lambda = 0$). The first gives

$$2aK(K+1)+3b = 1,$$

on replacing the square $\hat{\mathbf{K}}^2$ by its eigenvalue $K(K+1)$. From the second we find

$$a\hat{K}_i{}^2\hat{K}_k+a\hat{K}_i\hat{K}_k\hat{K}_i+b\hat{K}_k = 0.$$

In the second term, we interchange the operators $\hat{K}_i$ and $\hat{K}_k$, using the commutation rules for the components of angular momentum; this is most simply done by taking as the suffix k any definite value and rewriting the equation in components. Performing this operation and cancelling $\hat{K}_k$, we have

$$2aK(K+1)-a+b = 0.$$

From the two equations obtained, we find

$$a = -1/(2K+3)(2K-1);$$

the constant b is without interest, since the corresponding term in the splitting energy is $\alpha_e b\hat{S}_i{}^2 = \alpha_e bS(S+1)$, i.e. it is a constant, independent of J. Thus the required splitting is determined by the operator

$$\alpha_e a\hat{S}_i\hat{S}_k(\hat{K}_i\hat{K}_k+\hat{K}_k\hat{K}_i).$$

In the products $\hat{K}_i\hat{K}_k$, we change the order of factors by means of the commutation rule, and then replace $\hat{S}_i\hat{K}_i$ by the eigenvalue (81.4) of $\mathbf{K}\,.\,\mathbf{S}$; we thereby obtain the splitting energy in the form

$$\alpha_e a[2(\mathbf{K}\,.\,\mathbf{S})^2+\mathbf{K}\,.\,\mathbf{S}].$$

The values $J = K+1, K, K-1$ correspond to the three components of the triplet $^3\Sigma$ $(S = 1)$. Taking as zero the energy E_K of the component with $J = K$, we have for the energies of the levels with $J = K\pm 1$ the values

$$E_{K+1} = -\alpha_e\frac{K+1}{2K+3},\quad E_{K-1} = -\alpha_e\frac{K}{2K-1},\quad E_K = 0.$$

PROBLEM 2. Determine the energy of a doublet term for cases intermediate between a and b (HILL and VAN VLECK 1928).

SOLUTION. Since the rotational energy and the energy of the spin-axis interaction are supposed of the same order of magnitude, they must be considered together in perturbation theory, so that the perturbation operator is of the form†

$$\hat{V} = B_e\hat{\mathbf{K}}^2+A_e\mathbf{n}\,.\,\hat{\mathbf{S}}.$$

As wave functions in the zero-order approximation it is convenient to use those of states in which the angular momenta K and J have definite values (i.e. those of case b). Since $S = \frac{1}{2}$ for a doublet term, the quantum number K, for a given J, can take the values $K = J\pm\frac{1}{2}$. To construct the secular equation, we must calculate the matrix elements $V^{nSKJ}_{nSK'J}$ (n denoting the assembly of quantum numbers defining the electron term), where K, K' take the above values. The matrix of the operator $\hat{\mathbf{K}}^2$ is diagonal; the diagonal elements are $K(K+1)$. The matrix elements of $\mathbf{n}\,.\,\hat{\mathbf{S}}$ are calculated from the general formulae (31.6), in which we must put $\mathbf{A} = \mathbf{n}$, $\mathbf{B} = \mathbf{S}$, $L_1 = S = \frac{1}{2}$, $L_2 = K$, $L = J$. Thus we have from the first of these formulae

$$(\mathbf{n}\,.\,\mathbf{S})^{nS,J+\frac{1}{2},J}_{nS,J+\frac{1}{2},J} = -\tfrac{1}{2}(J+\tfrac{3}{2})n^{n,J+\frac{1}{2}}_{n,J+\frac{1}{2}}S^{nS}_{nS} = -\Lambda/(2J+1);$$

† The averaging with respect to vibrations must be done before that with respect to rotation. Hence, restricting ourselves to the first terms of the expansions in ξ, we have replaced the functions $B(r)$ and $A(r)$ by the values B_e and A_e, and the unperturbed energy levels are $E^{(0)} = U_e+\hbar\omega_e(v+\frac{1}{2})$.

the quantities $n_{nK'}^{nK}$ are determined by formulae (84.1), while the S_{nS}^{nS} are clearly just unity. On similarly calculating the remaining matrix elements, we obtain the secular equation

$$\begin{vmatrix} B_e(J+\frac{1}{2})(J+\frac{3}{2})-A_e\Lambda/(2J+1)-E^{(1)} & A_e\sqrt{[(J+\frac{1}{2})^2-\Lambda^2]}/(2J+1) \\ A_e\sqrt{[(J+\frac{1}{2})^2-\Lambda^2]}/(2J+1) & B_e(J+\frac{1}{2})(J-\frac{1}{2})+A_e\Lambda/(2J+1)-E^{(1)} \end{vmatrix} = 0.$$

Solving this equation and adding $E^{(1)}$ to the unperturbed energy, we have

$$E = U_e+\hbar\omega_e(v+\tfrac{1}{2})+B_eJ(J+1)\pm\sqrt{[B_e^2(J+\tfrac{1}{2})^2-A_eB_e\Lambda+\tfrac{1}{4}A_e^2]};$$

a constant $\frac{1}{4}B_e$ is included in U_e. The inequality $A_e \gg B_eJ$ corresponds to case *a*, and the opposite one to case *b*.

PROBLEM 3. Determine the intervals between the components of a triplet level $^3\Sigma$ in a case intermediate between *a* and *b*.

SOLUTION. As in Problem 2, the rotational energy and the energy of the spin-spin interaction are considered together in the perturbation theory. The perturbation operator is of the form

$$V = B_e\mathbf{K}^2+\alpha_e(\mathbf{n}\cdot\mathbf{S})^2.$$

As wave functions in the zero-order approximation we use those of case *b*. The matrix elements $(\mathbf{n}\cdot\mathbf{S})_{K'}^{K}$ (we omit all suffixes with respect to which the matrix is diagonal) are again calculated from (31.6) and (84.1), this time with $\Lambda = 0$, $S = 1$. The non-zero elements are of the form

$$(\mathbf{n}\cdot\mathbf{S})_{J-1}^{J} = \sqrt{[(J+1)/(2J+1)]},\quad (\mathbf{n}\cdot\mathbf{S})_{J+1}^{J} = \sqrt{[J/(2J+1)]}.$$

For a given J, the number K can take the values $K = J, J\pm1$. For the matrix elements V_K^K we find

$$V_J^J = B_eJ(J+1)+\alpha_e,\quad V_{J-1}^{J-1} = B_e(J-1)J+\alpha_e(J+1)/(2J+1),$$

$$V_{J+1}^{J+1} = B_e(J+1)(J+2)+\alpha_eJ/(2J+1),$$

$$V_{J+1}^{J-1} = V_{J-1}^{J+1} = \alpha_e\sqrt{[J(J+1)]}/(2J+1).$$

We see that there are no transitions between states with $K = J$ and those with $K = J\pm1$. Hence one of the levels is simply $E_1 = V_J^J$. The other two (E_2, E_3) are obtained by solving the quadratic secular equation formed from the matrix elements V_{J-1}^{J-1}, V_{J+1}^{J+1}, V_{J+1}^{J-1}. Since we are here interested only in the relative position of the components of the triplet, we subtract the constant α_e from all three energies E_1, E_2, E_3. As a result we obtain

$$E_1 = B_eJ(J+1),$$

$$E_{2,3} = B_e(J^2+J+1)-\tfrac{1}{2}\alpha_e\pm\sqrt{[B_e^2(2J+1)^2-\alpha_eB_e+\tfrac{1}{4}\alpha_e^2]}.$$

In case *b* (α small), by considering three levels with the same K and different J ($J = K$, $K\pm1$), we again obtain the formulae of Problem 1.

§82. Multiplet terms. Cases *c* and *d*

Besides cases of *a* and *b* coupling and those intermediate between them, there are also other types of coupling. These originate as follows. The occurrence of the quantum number Λ is due ultimately to the electric interaction of the two atoms in the molecule, which results in the axial symmetry of the problem of determining the electron terms (this interaction in the molecule is called the coupling between the orbital angular momentum and the axis). The distances between terms with different values of Λ give a measure of the magnitude of this interaction. Previously we have tacitly supposed this interaction so strong that these distances are large both compared with the intervals in the multiplet splitting and compared with those in the rotational structure of the terms. There are, however, opposite cases where the interaction of the orbital angular momentum with the axis is comparable with or even small compared with the other effects; in such cases, of course, we cannot in any approximation speak of a conservation of the projection of the orbital angular momentum on the axis, so that the number Λ is no longer meaningful.

If the coupling of the orbital angular momentum with the axis is small in comparison with the spin-orbit coupling, we say that we have case *c*. It is found in molecules which contain an atom of a rare-earth element. These atoms are characterised by the presence of *f* electrons with uncompensated angular momenta; their interaction with the axis of the molecule is weakened by the deep position of the *f* electrons in the atom. Cases intermediate between the *a* and *c* types of coupling are found in heavy molecules.

If the coupling of the orbital angular momentum with the axis is small compared with the intervals in the rotational structure, we say that we have case *d*. This case is found for high rotational levels (with large J) in some electron terms of the lightest molecules (H_2, He_2). These terms are characterised by the presence in the molecule of a highly excited electron, whose interaction with the remaining electrons (or, as we say, with the "skeleton" of the molecule) is so weak that its orbital angular momentum is not quantised along the axis of the molecule (whereas the "skeleton" has a definite angular momentum Λ_{skel} about the axis).

As the distance r between the nuclei increases, the interaction between the atoms is diminished, and finally becomes small compared with the spin-orbit interaction within the atoms. Hence, if we consider the electron terms for fairly large r, we shall have case *c*. This must be borne in mind when ascertaining the relation between the electron terms of the molecule and the states of the atoms obtained as $r \to \infty$. In §77 we have already discussed this relation, neglecting the spin-orbit interaction. When the fine structure of the terms is included, there arises also the question of the relation between the values J_1 and J_2 of the total angular momenta of the isolated atoms and the values of the quantum number Ω for the molecule. We shall give the results here, without reiterating arguments which are entirely similar to those of §77.

If the molecule consists of different atoms, the possible values of† $|\Omega|$ obtained on combining atoms with angular momenta J_1, J_2 ($J_1 \geqslant J_2$) are given by the same table (77.1), in which we must put J_1, J_2 in place of L_1, L_2,

† In adding the two total angular momenta J_1, J_2 of the atoms to form the resultant angular momentum Ω, the sign of Ω is clearly immaterial.

and $|\Omega|$ in place of Λ. The only difference is that, for half-integral J_1+J_2, the smallest value of $|\Omega|$ is not zero as shown in the table, but $\frac{1}{2}$. For integral J_1+J_2, on the other hand, there are $2J_2+1$ terms with $\Omega = 0$, for which (as for Σ terms when the fine structure is neglected) we have to decide the question of sign. If J_1 and J_2 are each half-integral, the number $2J_2+1$ is even, and there are equal numbers of terms, which we shall denote by 0^+ and 0^-. If J_1 and J_2 are both integral, however, then J_2+1 terms are 0^+ and J_2 are 0^- (if $(-1)^{J_1+J_2}I_1I_2 = 1$) or *vice versa* (if $(-1)^{J_1+J_2}I_1I_2 = -1$).

If the molecule consists of similar atoms in different states, the resulting molecular states are the same as in the case of different atoms, the only difference being that the total number of terms is doubled, with each term appearing once as an even and once as an odd term.

Finally, if the molecule consists of similar atoms in the same state (with angular momenta $J_1 = J_2 \equiv J$), the total number of states is the same as in the case of different atoms, while their distribution in parity is such that,

if J is integral and Ω is even, $N_g = N_u+1$;
if J is integral and Ω is odd, $N_g = N_u$;
if J is half-integral and Ω is even, $N_u = N_g$;
if J is half-integral and Ω is odd, $N_u = N_g+1$.

All the 0^+ terms are even and all the 0^- terms odd.

As the nuclei approach, a coupling of type *c* usually passes into one of type *a*†. Here the following interesting circumstance may arise. Those terms with $\Omega = 0$ which, as the nuclei approach, become a molecular term with $\Lambda \neq 0$ (and hence $\Sigma = -\Lambda$) are found to be doubly degenerate, since the same energy corresponds to the terms 0^+ and 0^- in case *a*‡. Thus it may happen that the same molecular energy corresponds to two different pairs of atomic states of the fine structure.

§83. Symmetry of molecular terms

In §75 we have already examined some symmetry properties of the terms of a diatomic molecule. These properties characterised the behaviour of the wave functions in transformations which leave the co-ordinates of the nuclei unaltered. Thus the symmetry of the molecule with respect to reflection in a plane passing through its axis brings about the difference between Σ^+ and Σ^- terms; the symmetry with respect to a change in sign of the co-ordinates‖ of all the electrons (for molecules composed of like atoms) gives rise to the classification of terms into even and odd. These symmetry properties characterise the electron terms, and are the same for all rotational levels belonging to the same electron term.

---

† The correspondence between the classification of terms of types *a* and *c* cannot be derived in a general form. Its derivation necessitates a consideration of the actual potential energy curves, taking into account the rule that levels of like symmetry cannot intersect (§76).

‡ We here neglect what is called *Λ-doubling* (see §85).

‖ The origin is supposed to be taken on the axis of the molecule, and half-way between the two nuclei if the molecule consists of like atoms.

The rotational levels are characterised by other symmetry properties, which are connected with transformations of the co-ordinates of both the electrons and the nuclei.

The Hamiltonian of the molecule, like that of any system of particles (see §28), is invariant with respect to a simultaneous change in sign of the co-ordinates of all the electrons and the nuclei. For this reason, all the terms for the molecule can be divided into *positive* (whose wave functions are unaltered when the sign of the co-ordinates of the electrons and nuclei is reversed) and *negative* (whose wave functions change sign under this transformation).†

For $\Lambda \neq 0$, each term is doubly degenerate, on account of the two possible directions of the angular momentum about the axis of the molecule. As a result of inversion, the angular momentum itself does not change sign, but the direction of the axis of the molecule is reversed (since the atoms change places), and hence the direction of the angular momentum Λ relative to the axis of the molecule is reversed. Hence two wave functions belonging to the same energy level are transformed into each other, and from them we can always form a linear combination that is invariant with respect to inversion and one that changes sign under this transformation. Thus we obtain for each term two states, of which one is positive and the other negative. In practice, every term with $\Lambda \neq 0$ is split, however (see §85), and so these two states correspond to different values of the energy.

The Σ terms require special consideration to determine their sign. First of all, it is clear that the spin bears no relation to the sign of the term: the inversion operation changes only the co-ordinates of the particles, leaving the spin part of the wave function unaltered. Hence all the components of the multiplet structure of any given term have the same sign. In other words, the sign of the term depends only on K, and not on J.‡

The wave function of the molecule is the product of the electron and nuclear wave functions. It has been shown in §79 that, in a Σ state, the motion of the nuclei is equivalent to that of a single particle, of orbital angular momentum K, in a centrally symmetric field $U(r)$. Hence we can say that, when the sign of the co-ordinates is changed, the nuclear wave function is multiplied by $(-1)^K$ (see (28.7)).

The electron wave function characterises the electron term, and to ascertain its behaviour under inversion we must consider it in a system of co-ordinates rigidly connected to the nuclei and rotating with them. Let x, y, z be a system of co-ordinates fixed in space, and ξ, η, ζ a rotating system of co-ordinates in which the molecule is fixed. The direction of the axes of ξ, η, ζ is defined so that the ζ-axis coincides with the axis of the molecule from (say) nucleus

---

† We retain the customary terminology. It is inconvenient, however, since in the case of an atom the behaviour of the terms with respect to the operation of inversion is referred to as *parity* and not *sign*.

The sign of which we are here speaking must not be confused with the + and − which are added as indices to Σ terms.

‡ We recall that case *b* usually holds for Σ terms, and so it is necessary to use the quantum numbers K and J.

1 to nucleus 2, and the relative position of the positive directions of the axes of ξ, η, ζ is the same as in the system x, y, z (i.e. if the system x, y, z is left-handed, the system ξ, η, ζ is so too). As a result of the inversion operation, the direction of the axes of x, y, z is reversed, and the system changes from left-handed to right-handed. The system ξ, η, ζ must also become right-handed, but the ζ-axis, being rigidly connected to the nuclei, retains its former direction. For this to be so, the direction of either one of the axes of ξ, η must be reversed. Thus the operation of inversion in the fixed system of co-ordinates is equivalent in the moving system to a reflection in a plane passing through the axis of the molecule. Under such a reflection, however, the electron wave function of a Σ^+ term is unaltered, while that of a Σ^- term changes sign.

Thus the sign of the rotational components of a Σ^+ term is determined by the factor $(-1)^K$; all the levels with even K are positive, while those with odd K are negative. For a Σ^- term, the sign of the rotational levels is determined by the factor $(-1)^{K+1}$; all levels with even K are negative, while those with odd K are positive.

If the molecule consists of similar atoms,† its Hamiltonian is also invariant with respect to an interchange of the co-ordinates of the two nuclei. A term is said to be *symmetric* with respect to the nuclei if its wave function is unaltered when they are interchanged, and *antisymmetric* if its wave function changes sign. The symmetry with respect to the nuclei is closely related to the parity and sign of the term. An interchange of the co-ordinates of the nuclei is equivalent to a change in sign of the co-ordinates of all the particles (electrons and nuclei), followed by a change in sign of the co-ordinates of the electrons only. Hence it follows that, if the term is even and positive (or odd and negative), it is symmetric with respect to the nuclei. If, on the other hand, it is even and negative (or odd and positive), then it is antisymmetric with respect to the nuclei.

At the end of §60 we have established a general theorem that the co-ordinate wave function of a system of two identical particles is symmetrical when the total spin of the system is even, and antisymmetrical when it is odd. If we apply this result to the two nuclei of a molecule composed of similar atoms, we find that the symmetry of a term is related to the parity of the total spin I obtained by adding the spins i of the two nuclei. The term is symmetric when I is even, and antisymmetric when I is odd.‡ In particular, if the nuclei have no spin ($i = 0$), I is zero also; hence the molecule has no antisymmetric terms. We see that the nuclear spin has an important indirect influence on the molecular terms, although its direct influence (the hyperfine structure of the terms) is quite unimportant and can always be neglected.

When the spin of the levels is taken into account, an additional degeneracy

† The two atoms must be not only of the same element, but also of the same isotope.

‡ Recalling the relation between the parity, sign and symmetry of terms, we conclude that, when the total spin I of the nuclei is even, the positive levels are even and the negative levels odd, and *vice versa* when I is odd.

of the levels results. Again in §60, we have calculated the number of states with even and odd values of I that are obtained on adding two spins i. Thus, when i is half-integral, the number of states with even I is $i(2i+1)$, and with odd I is $(i+1)(2i+1)$. From what was said above, we conclude that the ratio of the degrees g_s, g_a of the degeneracy† of symmetric and antisymmetric terms for terms with half-integral i is

$$g_s/g_a = i/(i+1). \tag{83.1}$$

For integral i, we similarly find that this ratio is

$$g_s/g_a = (i+1)/i. \tag{83.2}$$

We have seen that the sign of the rotational components of a Σ^+ term is determined by the number $(-1)^K$. Hence, for example, the rotational components of a $\Sigma^+{}_g$ term for even K are positive, and therefore symmetric, while for odd K they are negative and consequently antisymmetric. Bearing in mind the results obtained above, we conclude that the nuclear statistical weights of the rotational components of a $\Sigma^+{}_g$ level with successive values of K take alternate values, in the ratios (83.1) or (83.2). A wholly similar situation is found for $\Sigma^+{}_u$, $\Sigma^-{}_g$ and $\Sigma^-{}_u$ levels. In particular, for $i = 0$ the statistical weights of levels with even K for $\Sigma^+{}_u$ and $\Sigma^-{}_g$ terms, and of levels with odd K for $\Sigma^+{}_g$ and $\Sigma^-{}_u$ terms, are zero. In other words, in the electron states $\Sigma^+{}_u$, $\Sigma^-{}_g$ there are no rotational states with even K, and in $\Sigma^+{}_g$, $\Sigma^-{}_u$ states there are none with odd K.

Because of the extremely weak interaction of the nuclear spins with the electrons, the probability of a change in I is very small, even in collisions of molecules. Hence molecules differing in the parity of I, and accordingly having only symmetric or only antisymmetric terms, behave almost as different forms of matter. Such, for instance, are orthohydrogen and parahydrogen; in the molecule of the former, the spins $i = \frac{1}{2}$ of the two nuclei are parallel ($I = 1$), while in that of the latter they are antiparallel ($I = 0$).

§84. Matrix elements for the diatomic molecule

In calculating the matrices of various quantities in the diatomic molecule, let us begin with the matrix elements for transitions between states with zero spin.

Let $\mathbf{n}$ be a unit vector along the axis of the molecule. The vector $\mathbf{n}$, regarded as an operator, commutes with the operator of the energy of the electrons and with that of the vibrational energy, but not with the angular momentum $\mathbf{K}$ of the molecule. Hence the matrix of $\mathbf{n}$ is diagonal with respect to all the quantum numbers except K and M_K (where by M_K we denote the magnitude of the projection of the angular momentum $\mathbf{K}$ on a z-axis fixed

† The degree of degeneracy of a level is often referred to in this connection as its *statistical weight*. Formulae (83.1), (83.2) determine the ratio of the nuclear statistical weights of symmetric and antisymmetric levels.

in space). Omitting all suffixes but these two, we write the matrix elements in the form $(\mathbf{n})_{K'M'_K}^{KM_K}$. Their dependence on M_K is given directly by the general formulae (27.11), (27.13), in which L and M must be replaced by K and M_K, and the suffix n may be omitted. We denote the coefficients $A_{n'L'}^{nL}$ in these formulae by $n_{K'}^{K}$ for the present case, so that, for example,

$$(n_z)_{KM_K}^{KM_K} = M_K n_K^K.$$

To calculate the quantities $n_{K'}^{K}$, we start from the equations $\mathbf{n}\cdot\hat{\mathbf{K}} = \Lambda$, $\mathbf{n}^2 = 1$, written in the form

$$\tfrac{1}{2}(n_x+in_y)(\hat{K}_x-i\hat{K}_y)+\tfrac{1}{2}(n_x-in_y)(\hat{K}_x+i\hat{K}_y)+n_z\hat{K}_z = \Lambda,$$

$$(n_x+in_y)(n_x-in_y)+n_z^2 = 1,$$

and the commutation relation

$$n_z(n_x+in_y)-(n_x+in_y)n_z = 0.$$

Taking the diagonal matrix elements of these equations (the matrix elements of $\mathbf{K}$ being determined from the general formulae (25.13) with K, M_K in place of L, M), we obtain, after some calculations which we here omit, the following formulae for the quantities required (H. HÖNL and F. LONDON 1925):

$$n_K^K = \Lambda/K(K+1),\quad n_{K-1}^K = n_K^{K-1} = \frac{1}{K}\sqrt{\frac{(K-\Lambda)(K+\Lambda)}{(2K-1)(2K+1)}}. \tag{84.1}$$

For $\Lambda = 0$ these formulae give

$$n_K^K = 0,\quad n_{K-1}^K = n_K^{K-1} = 1/\sqrt{(4K^2-1)};$$

these correspond, as we should expect, to the matrix elements of a unit vector for motion in a centrally symmetric field (see (29.2)).

Next, let $\mathbf{A}$ be some vector physical quantity characterising the state of the molecule when the nuclei are fixed.† Let us first consider this quantity in the system of co-ordinates ξ, η, ζ, which rotates with the molecule (the ζ-axis coinciding with the axis of the molecule). The results of §27 cannot here be applied in their entirety, since the angular momentum of the molecule with respect to the system of co-ordinates ξ, η, ζ (i.e. the electron angular momentum $\mathbf{L}$) is not conserved; only its ζ-component Λ is conserved. The results concerning the selection rules for the quantum number Λ (M in §27) evidently remain fully valid, however. Thus the matrix elements of the vector $\mathbf{A}$ that are not zero are

$$(A_\zeta)_{n'\Lambda}^{n\Lambda},\quad (A_\xi+iA_\eta)_{n',\Lambda-1}^{n\Lambda},\quad (A_\xi-iA_\eta)_{n'\Lambda}^{n,\Lambda-1}; \tag{84.2}$$

we denote by n the assembly of quantum numbers for the electron term, with the exception of Λ.

† For example, the dipole moment or magnetic moment of the molecule.

If both the terms are Σ terms, we must also bear in mind the selection rule arising from the symmetry with respect to reflection in a plane passing through the axis of the molecule (the ζ-axis). Under such a reflection, the ζ-component of an ordinary (polar) vector is unchanged, while that of an axial vector changes sign. Hence we conclude that, for a polar vector, A_ζ has non-zero matrix elements only for the transitions $\Sigma^+ \to \Sigma^+$ and $\Sigma^- \to \Sigma^-$, while for an axial vector the elements are non-zero for the transitions $\Sigma^+ \to \Sigma^-$. We need not discuss the components A_ξ, A_η, since for these no transitions without change of Λ are possible.

If the molecule consists of similar atoms, there is also a selection rule regarding parity. The components of a (polar) vector change sign under inversion. Hence their matrix elements are non-zero only for transitions between states of different parity (the reverse is true for an axial vector). In particular, all the diagonal matrix elements of the components of a polar vector vanish identically.

The question arises how the matrix elements (84.2) are related to those of the same vector **A** in a fixed system of co-ordinates. In this system we can again use the general formulae (27.11), (27.13), which give the dependence of the matrix elements $(A)^{n\Lambda KM_K}_{n'\Lambda'K'M'_{K'}}$ on the quantum number M_K. The coefficients in these formulae are naturally denoted by $A^{n\Lambda K}_{n\Lambda'K'}$; we have to relate these to the quantities (84.2).

It is seen from (84.2) that there are matrix elements diagonal with respect to Λ only for the component along the axis of the molecule. Hence we can write the equation

$$(\mathbf{A})^{n\Lambda KM_K}_{n'\Lambda'K'M'_{K'}} = (A_\zeta \mathbf{n})^{n\Lambda KM_K}_{n'\Lambda K'M'_{K'}}.$$

In particular,

$$(A_z)^{n\Lambda KM_K}_{n'\Lambda K'M_{K'}} = (A_\zeta)^{n\Lambda}_{n'\Lambda}(n_z)^{KM_K}_{K'M_{K'}}.$$

Separating out the dependence on M_K, we hence have

$$A^{n\Lambda K}_{n'\Lambda K'} = n^K_{K'}(A_\zeta)^{n\Lambda}_{n'\Lambda}, \tag{84.3}$$

where the $n^K_{K'}$ are determined by formulae (84.1). Thus we have found some of the relations which we desire.

To find the remaining relations (for the components non-diagonal with respect to Λ), we notice that, since the quantity **A** refers to the molecule with fixed nuclei, the operators $\hat{A}_\xi$, $\hat{A}_\eta$, $\hat{A}_\zeta$ evidently commute with the vector **n**. The components of the vector **A** in the system x, y, z are linear combinations of the components in the system ξ, η, ζ, the coefficients in these combinations being functions of n_x, n_y, n_z. Hence $\hat{A}_x$, $\hat{A}_y$, $\hat{A}_z$ also commute with the vector **n**. In particular

$$\hat{A}_z n_z - n_z \hat{A}_z = 0.$$

Taking from this equation the matrix elements for the transitions Λ, $K \rightarrow \Lambda-1$, K' with $K' = K$, $K\pm1$, we obtain three equations, from which the dependence on K of the required quantities $A^{n\Lambda K}_{n',\Lambda-1,K'}$ can be found. The coefficients in the resulting formulae can be related to the quantities (84.2) by comparing the matrix elements of the scalar $\mathbf{A}^2$, these being calculated† in the two systems of co-ordinates x, y, z and ξ, η, ζ. As a result, we obtain the following final formulae:

$$\left.\begin{aligned} A^{n\Lambda K}_{n',\Lambda-1,K} &= (A_\xi+iA_\eta)^{n\Lambda}_{n',\Lambda-1}\sqrt{[(K+\Lambda)(K-\Lambda+1)]}/2K(K+1), \\ A^{n\Lambda K}_{n',\Lambda-1,K-1} &= -(A_\xi+iA_\eta)^{n\Lambda}_{n',\Lambda-1}\sqrt{[(K+\Lambda)(K+\Lambda-1)]}/2K\sqrt{[(2K+1)(2K-1)]}, \\ A^{n\Lambda,K-1}_{n',\Lambda-1,K} &= (A_\xi+iA_\eta)^{n\Lambda}_{n',\Lambda-1}\sqrt{[(K-\Lambda)(K-\Lambda+1)]}/2K\sqrt{[(2K+1)(2K-1)]}. \end{aligned}\right\} \tag{84.4}$$

The components with $\Lambda-1 \rightarrow \Lambda$ are the complex conjugates of those given.

Finally, we must find how the formulae we have obtained should be modified for transitions between states with non-zero spin. Here it is important to know whether the states belong to case *a* or to case *b*.

First, let the two states belong to case *a*. The unit vector $\mathbf{n}$ commutes with the spin vector $\mathbf{S}$, and hence its matrix is diagonal with respect to the quantum numbers S and Σ (or, what is the same thing, S and Ω, since $\Omega = \Lambda+\Sigma$, and this matrix is diagonal with respect to Λ also). The quantum numbers K and M_K do not exist, and instead we have the total angular momentum J and its projection M on the z-axis. Instead of the relation $\mathbf{n}\cdot\mathbf{K} = \Lambda$, which we used to derive (84.1), we now have $\mathbf{n}\cdot\mathbf{J} = \Omega$. Accordingly, we again obtain the same formulae (84.1), except that K and Λ must now be replaced by J and Ω respectively (we omit the diagonal suffix S).

The same is true for any orbital vector $\mathbf{A}$ (i.e. one which does not depend on the spin). Such a vector commutes with $\mathbf{S}$ also, and hence its matrix is diagonal with respect to S and Σ; if we use the quantum number Ω in place of Σ, it changes together with Λ in the non-zero matrix elements (i.e. if $\Lambda' = \Lambda\pm1$, then $\Omega' = \Omega\pm1$). The formulae (84.3) and (84.4) are unchanged except that we must add the suffixes Ω and Ω', and everywhere (except the suffixes) replace K and Λ by J and Ω. Thus, for instance,

$$A^{n\Lambda\Omega J}_{n'\Lambda\Omega J} = (A_\zeta)^{n\Lambda\Omega}_{n'\Lambda\Omega}n^J_J = (A_\zeta)^{n\Lambda\Omega}_{n'\Lambda\Omega}\frac{\Omega}{J(J+1)}.$$

If the vector $\mathbf{A}$ depends on the spin, however, the selection rules are different. The vector $\mathbf{S}$ commutes with the orbital angular momentum, and also with the Hamiltonian, and hence its matrix is diagonal with respect to n and Λ;

† The calculation is conveniently performed directly from the general formula (27.15), where we must put $\mathbf{B} = \mathbf{A}$, replace L by K, and take n as n, Λ.

we omit these suffixes. It is, however, not diagonal with respect to Σ (or Ω). The matrix elements of the components of **S** in the system ξ, η, ζ are determined by formulae (25.13), with S and Σ in place of L and M, and then the transition to the system x, y, z is effected by the formulae (84.3), (84.4), where we must everywhere (including the suffixes) replace K and Λ by J and Ω. Thus, for example,

$$S^{\Omega J}_{\Omega-1,J} = (S_\xi + iS_\eta)^{\Omega}_{\Omega-1}\sqrt{[(J+\Omega)(J-\Omega+1)]/2J(J+1)}$$

$$= \sqrt{[(S-\Sigma+1)(S+\Sigma)(J+\Omega)(J-\Omega+1)]/2J(J+1)}.$$

Now let both states belong to case b. The calculation of the matrix elements is here performed in two stages. First we consider the rotating molecule without taking into account the addition of the spin to the angular momentum **K**; the matrix elements are then determined by the same formulae (84.1)–(84.4). The vector **A** is supposed orbital, so that, like **n**, it commutes with **S**, and so the matrices are diagonal with respect to the quantum number S, which we omit from the suffixes. The angular momentum **K** is then added to **S** to form the total angular momentum **J**, and the transition to the new matrix elements is effected by the general formulae (31.5). The part of $\mathbf{L}_1$ in these formulae is here taken by **S**, that of $\mathbf{L}_2$ by **K**, and that of **L** by **J**, and we write n, Λ in place of n_2; we neglect the spin-axis interaction in calculating the matrix elements, so that the conditions of applicability of the formulae in §31 are fulfilled. Thus, for instance, we obtain for the elements diagonal with respect to Λ, K, J

$$A^{n\Lambda KJ}_{n'\Lambda KJ} = A^{n\Lambda K}_{n'\Lambda K}\frac{J(J+1)-S(S+1)+K(K+1)}{2J(J+1)}$$

$$= (A_\zeta)^{n\Lambda}_{n'\Lambda}\Lambda\frac{J(J+1)-S(S+1)+K(K+1)}{2J(J+1)K(K+1)}.$$

If one of the states belongs to case a and the other to case b, the calculation of the matrix elements for transitions between the states is more involved; we shall not here pause to consider this problem.†

PROBLEMS

PROBLEM 1. Determine the Stark splitting of the terms for a diatomic molecule having a constant dipole moment, in the case where the term belongs to case a.

SOLUTION. The energy of a dipole **d** in an electric field $\mathscr{E}$ is $-\mathbf{d}\cdot\mathscr{E}$. From considerations of symmetry, it is evident that the dipole moment of a diatomic molecule is directed along its axis; $\mathbf{d} = d\mathbf{n}$, where d is a constant. Taking the direction of the field as the z-axis, we obtain the perturbation operator in the form $-dn_z\mathscr{E}$.

Determining the diagonal matrix elements of n_z in accordance with the formulae derived

† See E. HILL and J. VAN VLECK, *Physical Review* 32, 250, 1928.

above, we find that in case *a* the splitting of the levels is given by the formula†

$$\Delta E_{M_J} = -\mathscr{E} d M_J \Omega / J(J+1).$$

PROBLEM 2. The same as Problem 1, but for the case where the term belongs to case *b* (and $\Lambda \neq 0$).

SOLUTION. By the same method we have

$$\Delta E_{M_J} = -\mathscr{E} d M_J \Lambda \frac{J(J+1)-S(S+1)+K(K+1)}{2K(K+1)J(J+1)}.$$

PROBLEM 3. The same as Problem 2, but for a ${}^1\Sigma$ term.

SOLUTION. For $\Lambda = 0$ the linear effect is absent, and we must go to the second approximation of perturbation theory. In the summation in the general formula (38.9), it is sufficient to retain only those terms which correspond to transitions between rotational components of the electron term concerned; for other terms the energy differences in the denominators are large. Thus we find

$$\Delta E_{M_K} = d^2 \mathscr{E}^2 \left\{ \frac{|(n_z)_{K-1,M_K}^{KM_K}|^2}{E_K - E_{K-1}} + \frac{|(n_z)_{K+1,M_K}^{KM_K}|^2}{E_K - E_{K+1}} \right\},$$

where $E_K = BK(K+1)$. A simple calculation gives

$$\Delta E_{M_K} = \frac{d^2 \mathscr{E}^2}{B} \frac{K(K+1)-3M_K^2}{2K(K+1)(2K-1)(2K+3)}.$$

§85. Λ-doubling

The double degeneracy of the terms with $\Lambda \neq 0$ (§75) is in fact only approximate. It occurs only so long as we neglect the effect of the rotation of the molecule on the electron state (and also the higher approximations with respect to the spin-orbit interaction), as we have done throughout the above theory. When the interaction between the electron state and the rotation is taken into account, a term with $\Lambda \neq 0$ is split into two levels close together. This phenomenon is called Λ-*doubling* (HILL and VAN VLECK, and KRONIG, 1928).

To consider this effect quantitatively, we again begin with the singlet terms ($S = 0$). We have calculated (in §79) the energy of the rotational levels in the first approximation of perturbation theory, determining the diagonal matrix elements (i.e. the mean value) of the operator

$$B(r)(\mathbf{K}-\mathbf{L})^2.$$

To calculate the subsequent approximations, we must consider the elements of this operator that are not diagonal with respect to Λ. The operators $\mathbf{K}^2$ and $\mathbf{L}^2$ are diagonal with respect to Λ, so that we need consider only the operator $-2B\mathbf{K}\cdot\mathbf{L}$.

† It may seem that there is here a contradiction of the general assertion that there is no linear Stark effect (§72). In fact, of course, there is no contradiction, since the presence of a linear Stark effect is here due to the double degeneracy of the levels with $\Omega \neq 0$; the formula obtained is therefore applicable provided that the energy of the Stark splitting is large compared with that of what is called the Λ-*doubling* (§85).

The calculation of the matrix elements of $\hat{\mathbf{K}}\,.\,\hat{\mathbf{L}}$ is conveniently effected by means of the general formula (27.15), in which we must put $\mathbf{A} = \mathbf{K}$, $\mathbf{B} = \mathbf{L}$; the parts of L and M are taken by K and M_K, while in place of n we must put n, Λ, where n denotes the assembly of quantum numbers (other than Λ) which determine the electron term. Since the matrix of the vector $\mathbf{K}$, which is conserved, is diagonal with respect to n, Λ, while that of the vector $\mathbf{L}$ contains non-diagonal elements only for transitions in which Λ changes by unity (cf. what was said in §84 concerning an arbitrary vector $\mathbf{A}$), we find

$$\begin{aligned}(\mathbf{K}\,.\,\mathbf{L})^{n\Lambda K M_K}_{n',\Lambda-1,KM_K} &= K(K+1)(K^{n\Lambda K}_{n\Lambda K})(L^{n\Lambda K}_{n',\Lambda-1,K}) \\ &= \tfrac{1}{2}(L_\xi + iL_\eta)^{n\Lambda}_{n',\Lambda-1}\sqrt{[(K+\Lambda)(K+1-\Lambda)]}; \qquad (85.1)\end{aligned}$$

the quantities $L^{n\Lambda K}_{n',\Lambda-1,K}$ are determined by formulae (84.4), while the $K^{n\Lambda K}_{n\Lambda K}$ are obviously unity. There are no non-zero matrix elements corresponding to any greater change in Λ.

The perturbing effect of the matrix elements with $\Lambda \to \Lambda-1$ can cause the appearance of an energy difference between states with $\pm\Lambda$ only in the 2Λth approximation of perturbation theory. Accordingly, the effect is proportional to $B^{2\Lambda}$, i.e. to $(\mu/M)^{2\Lambda}$, where M is the mass of the molecule and μ that of the electron. For $\Lambda > 1$, this quantity is so small that it is of no interest. Thus the Λ-doubling effect is of importance only for Π terms ($\Lambda = 1$), which are considered below.

For $\Lambda = 1$ we must go to the second approximation. The corrections to the eigenvalues of the energy can be determined from the general formula (38.9). In the denominators of the terms in the sum occurring in this equation we have energy differences, of the form $E_{n\Lambda K} - E_{n',\Lambda-1\,K}$. In these differences, the terms containing K cancel, since, for a given distance r between the nuclei, the rotational energy is the same quantity, $B(r)K(K+1)$, for all the terms. Hence the dependence on K of the required splitting ΔE is entirely determined by the squared matrix elements in the numerators. Among these are the squared elements for transitions in which Λ changes from 1 to 0 and from 0 to -1; these both give, by (85.1), the same dependence on K, and we find that the splitting of the $^1\Pi$ term is of the form

$$\Delta E = \text{constant} \times K(K+1), \qquad (85.2)$$

where the constant is of the order of magnitude of B^2/ϵ, ϵ being the order of magnitude of the differences between neighbouring electron terms.

Let us pass now to terms with non-zero spin ($^2\Pi$ and $^3\Pi$ terms; higher values of S are not found in practice). If the term belongs to case *b*, the multiplet splitting has no effect on the Λ-doubling of the rotational levels, which is determined as before by formula (85.2).

In case *a*, however, the effect of the spin is important. Here each electron term is characterised by the number Ω as well as Λ. If we simply replace

Λ by $-\Lambda$, then $\Omega = \Lambda + \Sigma$ is changed, so that we obtain an entirely different term. The levels with Λ, Ω and $-\Lambda$, $-\Omega$ are mutually degenerate. This degeneracy can here be removed not only by the effect, considered above, of the interaction between the orbital angular momentum and the rotation of the molecule, but also by the effect of the spin-orbit interaction. The conservation of the projection Ω of the total angular momentum on the axis of the molecule is (if the nuclei are fixed) an exact conservation law, and so cannot be destroyed by the spin-orbit interaction; the latter can, however, change Λ and Σ (i.e. there are matrix elements for the corresponding transitions) in such a way that Ω remains unchanged. This effect, alone or in combination with the orbit-rotation interaction (which alters Λ but not Σ), may cause Λ-doubling.

Let us first consider the $^2\Pi$ terms. For the $^2\Pi_{1/2}$ term ($\Lambda = 1$, $\Sigma = -\frac{1}{2}$, $\Omega = \frac{1}{2}$), the splitting is obtained on taking into account simultaneously the spin orbit and orbit-rotation interactions, each in the first approximation. For the former gives the transition $\Lambda = 1$, $\Sigma = -\frac{1}{2} \rightarrow \Lambda = 0$, $\Sigma = \frac{1}{2}$, and then the latter converts the state $\Lambda = 0$, $\Sigma = \frac{1}{2}$ into $\Lambda = -1$, $\Sigma = \frac{1}{2}$, which differs from the initial state by the signs of Λ and Ω being reversed. The matrix elements of the spin-orbit interaction are independent of the rotational quantum number J, while the dependence of those for the orbit-rotation interaction is determined by formula (85.1), in which (under the radical) we must replace K and Λ by J and Ω. Thus we have for the Λ-doubling of a $^2\Pi_{1/2}$ term the expression

$$\Delta E_{1/2} = \text{constant} \times (J + \tfrac{1}{2}), \tag{85.3}$$

where the constant is of the order of AB/ϵ. For a $^2\Pi_{3/2}$ term, on the other hand, the splitting can be found only in higher approximations, so that in practice $\Delta E_{3/2} = 0$.

Finally, let us consider $^3\Pi$ terms. For a $^3\Pi_0$ term ($\Lambda = 1$, $\Sigma = -1$), the splitting is obtained on taking into account the spin-orbit interaction in the second approximation (because of the transitions $\Lambda = 1$, $\Sigma = -1 \rightarrow \Lambda = 0$, $\Sigma = 0 \rightarrow \Lambda = -1$, $\Sigma = 1$). Accordingly, the Λ-doubling in this case is entirely independent of J:

$$\Delta E_0 = \text{constant} \sim A^2/\epsilon. \tag{85.4}$$

For a $^3\Pi_1$ term, $\Sigma = 0$, and so the spin has no effect on the splitting; hence we again have a formula like (85.2), but with K replaced by J:

$$\Delta E_1 = \text{constant} \times J(J+1). \tag{85.5}$$

For a $^3\Pi_2$ term, higher approximations are needed, so that we can suppose $\Delta E_2 = 0$.

One of the levels of the doublet resulting from Λ-doubling is always positive, and the other negative; we have already discussed this in §83. An investigation of the wave functions of the molecule enables us to establish the regularities of the alternation of positive and negative levels. Here we shall give only the results of the investigation.† It is found that if, for some value of J, the positive level is below the negative one, then in the doublet for $J+1$ the order is opposite, the positive level being above the negative one, and so on; the order varies alternately as the total angular momentum takes successive values. We are speaking here of case *a* terms; for case *b*, the same holds for successive values of the angular momentum K.

PROBLEM

Determine the Λ-splitting for a $^1\Delta$ term.

SOLUTION. Here the effect appears in the fourth approximation of perturbation theory. Its dependence on K is determined by the products of the four matrix elements (85.1) for transitions with change of $\Lambda: 2 \rightarrow 1, 1 \rightarrow 0, 0 \rightarrow -1, -1 \rightarrow -2$. This gives

$$\Delta E = \text{constant} \times (K-1)K(K+1)(K+2),$$

where the constant is of order of B^4/ϵ^3.

§86. The interaction of atoms at large distances

Let us consider two atoms in S states which are at a great distance from each other, and determine the energy of their interaction. In other words, we shall discuss the determination of the form of the electron terms $U_n(r)$ when the distance between the nuclei is large.

To solve this problem we apply perturbation theory, regarding the two isolated atoms as the unperturbed system, and the potential energy of their electrical interaction as the perturbation operator. As we know from electrostatics, the electrical interaction of two systems of charges at a large distance apart can be expanded in powers of $1/r$, and successive terms of this expansion correspond to the interaction of the total charges, dipole moments, quadrupole moments, etc., of the two systems. For neutral atoms, the total charges are zero. The expansion here begins with the dipole-dipole interaction ($\sim 1/r^3$); then follow the dipole-quadrupole terms ($\sim 1/r^4$), the quadrupole-quadrupole (and dipole-octupole) terms ($\sim 1/r^5$), and so on.

In the first approximation of perturbation theory, the required energy of the interaction of the atoms is determined as the diagonal matrix element of the perturbation operator, calculated with respect to the unperturbed wave functions of the system (expressed in terms of products of the unperturbed functions for the atoms). In S states, however, the diagonal matrix elements, i.e. the mean values of the dipole, quadrupole, etc. moments, are zero; this follows at once from considerations of symmetry, since the distribution of charges in an atom in the S state is spherically symmetrical on the average. Hence each of the terms of the expansion of the perturbation operator in powers of $1/r$ gives zero in the first approximation of perturbation theory.‡

---

† This may be found in E. WIGNER and E. WITMER, *Zeitschrift für Physik* **51**, 859, 1928.

‡ This, of course, does not imply that the mean value of the interaction energy of the atoms is precisely zero. It diminishes exponentially with distance, i.e. more rapidly than every finite power of $1/r$, and hence each term of the expansion vanishes.

In the second approximation it is sufficient to restrict ourselves to the dipole interaction in the perturbation operator, since this decreases least rapidly as r increases, i.e. to the term

$$V = [-\mathbf{d}_1 \cdot \mathbf{d}_2 + 3(\mathbf{d}_1 \cdot \mathbf{n})(\mathbf{d}_2 \cdot \mathbf{n})]/r^3,$$

where $\mathbf{n}$ is a unit vector in the direction joining the two atoms. Since the non-diagonal matrix elements of the dipole moment are in general different from zero, we obtain in the second approximation of perturbation theory a non-vanishing result which, being quadratic in V, is proportional to $1/r^6$. The correction in the second approximation to the lowest eigenvalue is, as we know, always negative (§38). Hence we obtain for the interaction energy of atoms in their normal states an expression of the form†

$$U(r) = -\text{constant}/r^6, \tag{86.1}$$

where the constant is positive (F. London 1928).

Thus two atoms in normal S states, at a great distance apart, attract each other with a force $(-dU/dr)$ which is inversely proportional to the seventh power of the distance. The attractive forces between atoms are usually called *van der Waals forces*.

If only one of the atoms is in the S state, the same result (86.1) is obtained for the interaction energy, since, for the first approximation to vanish, it is sufficient for the dipole (etc.) moment of only one atom to be zero. The constant in the numerator of (86.1) here depends, not only on the states of the two atoms, but also on their mutual orientation, i.e. on the value Ω of the projection of the angular momentum on the axis joining the atoms.

If both atoms have non-zero orbital and total angular momenta, however, the situation is changed. The mean value of the dipole moment is zero in every state of the atom‡. The mean values of the quadrupole moment in states with $L \neq 0$, $J \neq 0$ are not zero, however. Hence the quadrupole-quadrupole term in the perturbation operator gives a non-zero result even in the first approximation, and we find that the interaction energy of the atoms diminishes as the fifth, not the sixth, power of the distance:

$$U(r) = \text{constant}/r^5. \tag{86.2}$$

Here the constant may be either positive or negative, i.e. we may have either attraction or repulsion. As in the previous case, this constant depends not only on the states of the atoms, but also on the state of the molecule formed by the two atoms.

A special case is the interaction of two similar atoms in different states.

---

† For brevity, we here and later omit the unimportant constant term in $U(r)$, i.e. the value of $U(\infty)$, which is the sum of the energies of the two isolated atoms.

‡ For the dipole moment, as for any polar vector, only the matrix elements for transitions between states of different parity can be non-zero. The matrix elements for transitions between states of the same parity, including the diagonal elements, vanish identically (see §30).

The unperturbed system (the two isolated atoms) has here an additional degeneracy due to the possibility of interchanging the states of the atoms. Accordingly, the correction in the first approximation will be given by the secular equation, in which the non-diagonal matrix elements of the perturbation appear as well as the diagonal ones. If the states of the two atoms have different parities, and angular momenta L differing by ± 1 or 0 but not both zero (the same restriction being placed on J), then the non-diagonal matrix elements of the dipole moment for transitions between these states are in general not zero. Hence an effect in the first approximation is obtained from the dipole term in the perturbation operator. Thus the interaction energy of the atoms is here proportional to $1/r^3$:

$$U(r) = \text{constant}/r^3, \tag{86.3}$$

where the constant may have either sign.

It should be emphasised that the results (86.2) and (86.3) are valid only for the particular problem considered, that is, when not only the states of the two isolated atoms but also the state of the whole system are given. If we average over all states of the diatomic system (the state of each atom being given), the expressions (86.2) and (86.3) vanish, and we again have the interaction law (86.1). Such an averaging corresponds to a determination of the mean interaction of atoms in a gas.

§87. Pre-dissociation

A basic premise of the theory of diatomic molecules as given in this chapter is the assumption that the wave function of the molecule falls into the product of an electron wave function (depending on the distance between the nuclei as a parameter) and a wave function for the motion of the nuclei. This supposition amounts to neglecting, in the exact Hamiltonian of the molecule, certain small terms corresponding to the interaction of the nuclear and electron motions.

When these terms are taken into account and perturbation theory is applied, transitions between different electron states appear.† Physically, the transitions between states of which at least one belongs to the continuous spectrum are of particular importance.

Fig. 32 shows curves for the potential energy of two electron terms.‡ The energy E' (the lower dashed line in Fig. 32) is the energy of some vibrational level of a stable molecule in the electron state 2. In state 1, this energy lies in the range of the continuous spectrum. In other words, in passing from state 2 to state 1 the molecule automatically disintegrates; this phenomenon is called *pre-dissociation*.‖ As a result of pre-dissociation, the state of the discrete spectrum corresponding to curve 2 has in reality a finite lifetime. This

† As well as the splitting of the levels by Λ-doubling (§85).

‡ Strictly speaking, these curves must represent the effective potential energy U_J in some given rotational states of the molecule.

‖ Curve 1 may have no minimum at all if it corresponds only to purely repulsive forces between the atoms.

means that the discrete energy level is broadened, i.e. acquires a certain width (see the end of §44).

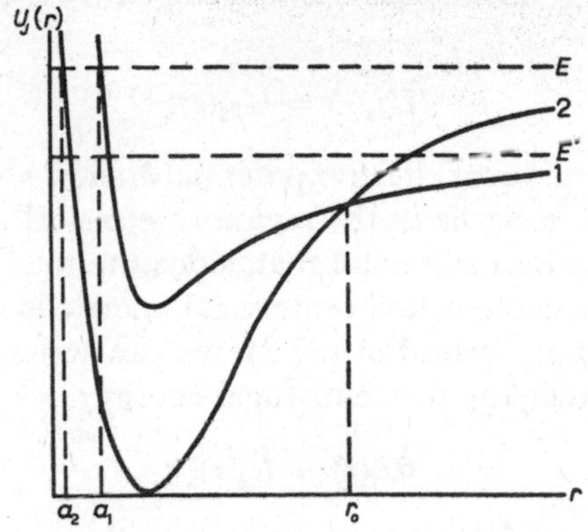

FIG. 32

If, on the other hand, the total energy E lies above the dissociation limit in both states (the upper dashed line in Fig. 32), the transition from one state to the other corresponds to what is called a *collision of the second kind.* Thus the transition $1 \to 2$ signifies the collision of two atoms, as a result of which the atoms are left in excited states, and separate with diminished kinetic energy (for $r \to \infty$, curve 1 passes below curve 2; the difference $U_2(\infty) - U_1(\infty)$ is the excitation energy of the atoms).

The transition probability is determined by the corresponding matrix elements of the terms neglected in the Hamiltonian. After integration over the electron co-ordinates and the rotational angles of the molecule, there remains an integral of the form

$$\int_0^\infty \chi_{\text{nuc},2}{}^* V \chi_{\text{nuc},1}\, dr, \tag{87.1}$$

where $V(r)$ is the matrix element of the perturbing energy with respect to the electron wave functions.† The nuclear wave functions $\chi_{\text{nuc},1} = r\psi_{\text{nuc},1}$ and $\chi_{\text{nuc},2} = r\psi_{\text{nuc},2}$ are solutions of SCHRÖDINGER's equation for one-dimensional motion in the fields $U_{J1}(r)$ and $U_{J2}(r)$. Because of the large masses of the nuclei, their motion is quasi-classical everywhere except in the neighbourhood of points where $E = U_J(r)$. Hence the results obtained in §51 are applicable to the integral (87.1). It follows from these results that the probability of a transition will be fairly high if equation (51.7) has a real root in the region where $E > U_{J1}, U_{J2}$. Then the real part of the exponent in (51.8) vanishes, so

† Strictly speaking, $V(r)$ is an operator acting on functions of the distance r between the nuclei. However, since the motion of the nuclei is quasi-classical, V can be regarded as simply some function of r.

that the matrix element, and therefore the transition probability, will not contain a small (exponentially decreasing) factor.

Since the energy of the molecule is unchanged by the transition, equation (51.7) reduces to

$$U_{J1}(r) = U_{J2}(r). \tag{87.2}$$

In other words, the curves of effective potential energy must intersect, and the point of intersection must lie in the region of classical motion (as shown in Fig. 32). It must be borne in mind that, since the total angular momentum of the molecule is conserved, the centrifugal energy is the same in the two states 1 and 2. Hence, instead of (87.2), we can write an equation for the potential energies excluding the centrifugal energy:

$$U_1(r) = U_2(r),$$

i.e. the position of the point of intersection is independent of the angular momentum.

The fact that the point determined by equation (87.2) plays a fundamental part in the integral (87.1) can be interpreted as follows. If the potential (and total) energies are the same, so are the linear momenta. Hence the condition (87.2) may also be written in the form

$$r_1 = r_2, \quad p_1 = p_2, \tag{87.3}$$

where p is the momentum of the relative radial motion of the nuclei, and the suffixes 1 and 2 refer to the two electron states. Thus we can say that the distance between the nuclei and their relative momentum remain unchanged at the instant when the transition occurs (this is called *Franck and Condon's principle*). Physically, this is due to the fact that the electron velocities are large compared with those of the nuclei, and "during an electron transition" the nuclei cannot noticeably change their position or velocity.

It is not difficult to establish the selection rules for the transitions in question. First of all, there are two obvious exact rules. The total angular momentum J and the sign of the term (positive or negative; see §83) cannot change in a transition. This follows at once from the fact that the conservation of the total angular momentum and of the behaviour of the wave function under inversion of the co-ordinate system are exact laws for any (closed) system of particles.

Next, the rule which forbids (for molecules composed of similar atoms) transitions between states of like parity is very nearly accurate. For the parity of the state is uniquely determined by the nuclear spin and the sign of the term. The conservation of the sign of the term is an exact law, however, while the nuclear spin is very nearly conserved by virtue of the weakness of its interaction with the electrons.

The requirement that there should be a point of intersection of the potential energy curves means that the terms must be of different symmetry (see §76).

Let us consider transitions occurring in the first approximation of perturbation theory; the probability of transitions which occur only in higher approximations is so small that there is no point in considering them. First of all, we notice that the terms in the Hamiltonian which lead to the transitions in question are just those which cause the Λ-doubling of the levels. Among these terms are, firstly, terms representing the spin-orbit interaction. They are the product of two axial vectors, of which one is of spin character (i.e. is composed of the operators of the electron spins), and the other is of co-ordinate character; we emphasise, however, that these vectors are not simply the vectors $\hat{\mathbf{S}}$ and $\hat{\mathbf{L}}$. Hence they have non-zero matrix elements for transitions in which S and Λ change by $\Delta S = 0, \pm 1$, $\Delta\Lambda = 0, \pm 1$. The case where ΔS and $\Delta\Lambda$ are both zero (and $\Lambda \neq 0$) must be omitted, since the symmetry of the term would then be unchanged in the transition. The transition between two Σ terms is possible if one of them is a Σ^+ term and the other a Σ^- term; an axial vector has non-zero matrix elements only for transitions between Σ^+ and Σ^- (see §84).

The term in the Hamiltonian which corresponds to the interaction between the rotation of the molecule and its orbital angular momentum is proportional to $\hat{\mathbf{J}}\cdot\hat{\mathbf{L}}$. Its matrix elements are non-zero for transitions with $\Delta\Lambda = \pm 1$ without change of spin (only the ζ-component of the vector, i.e. L_ζ, has elements with $\Delta\Lambda = 0$, but L_ζ is diagonal with respect to the electron states).

As well as the terms we have considered, there is also a perturbation due to the fact that the operator of the kinetic energy of the nuclei (i.e. the operator of differentiation with respect to the co-ordinates of the nuclei) acts, not only on the wave function of the nuclei, but also on the electron function, which depends on r as a parameter. The corresponding terms in the Hamiltonian are of the same symmetry as the unperturbed Hamiltonian. Hence they can lead only to transitions between electron terms of like symmetry, the probability of which is negligible in view of the non-intersection of these terms.

Let us go on to the actual calculation of the transition probability. For definiteness, we shall consider a collision of the second kind. According to the general formula (43.1), the required probability is given by the expression

$$w = \frac{2\pi}{\hbar}\left|\int \chi_{\text{nuc},2}{}^{*}V(r)\chi_{\text{nuc},1}\,\mathrm{d}r\right|^2, \tag{87.4}$$

where $V(r)$ is the perturbing energy; we have taken, as the quantity ν in (43.1), the energy E and integrated with respect to it. The final wave function $\chi_{\text{nuc},2}$ must be normalised by the delta function of energy. The quasi-classical function (47.5), thus normalised, is

$$\chi_{\text{nuc},2} = \sqrt{\frac{2}{\pi\hbar v_2}}\cos\left\{\frac{1}{\hbar}\int_{a_2}^{r} p_2\,\mathrm{d}r - \tfrac{1}{4}\pi\right\}. \tag{87.5}$$

the normalising factor is determined by the rule given at the end of §19. The wave function of the initial state can be written in the form

$$\chi_{\mathrm{nuc},1} = \frac{2}{\sqrt{v_1}} \cos\left\{\frac{1}{\hbar}\int_{a_1}^{r} p_1\,\mathrm{d}r - \tfrac{1}{4}\pi\right\}. \tag{87.6}$$

It is normalised so that the current density is unity in each of the travelling waves into which the stationary wave (87.6) can be resolved; v_1 and v_2 are the velocities of the relative radial motion of the nuclei. On substituting these functions in (87.4), we obtain the dimensionless transition probability w. It can be regarded as the transition probability for the nuclei to pass twice the point $r = r_0$ (the point of intersection of the levels). It must be borne in mind that the wave function (87.6) corresponds, in a certain sense, to a double passage through this point, since it contains both the incident and the reflected travelling waves.

The matrix element of $V(r)$, calculated with respect to the functions (87.5), (87.6), contains in the integrand a product of cosines, which can be written in terms of the cosines of the sum and difference of the arguments. On integrating near the point $r = r_0$ where the terms intersect, only the second cosine is important, so that

$$w = \frac{4}{\hbar^2}\left|\int \cos\left[\frac{1}{\hbar}\int_{a_1}^{r} p_1\,\mathrm{d}r - \frac{1}{\hbar}\int_{a_2}^{r} p_2\,\mathrm{d}r\right]\frac{V(r)\,\mathrm{d}r}{\sqrt{(v_1 v_2)}}\right|^2.$$

The integral rapidly converges as we move away from the point of intersection. Hence we can expand the argument of the cosine in powers of $\xi = r - r_0$ and integrate over ξ from $-\infty$ to $+\infty$ (replacing the slowly varying coefficient of the cosine by its value at $r = r_0$). Bearing in mind that, at the point of intersection, $p_1 = p_2$, we find

$$\int_{a_1}^{r} p_1\,\mathrm{d}r - \int_{a_2}^{r} p_2\,\mathrm{d}r \cong S_0 + \tfrac{1}{2}\left(\frac{\mathrm{d}p_1}{\mathrm{d}r_0} - \frac{\mathrm{d}p_2}{\mathrm{d}r_0}\right)\xi^2,$$

where S_0 is the value of the difference of the integrals at the point $r = r_0$. The derivative of the momentum can be expressed in terms of the force $F = -\mathrm{d}U/\mathrm{d}r$: differentiating the equation $p_1^2/2\mu + U_1 = p_2^2/2\mu + U_2$ (where μ is the reduced mass of the nuclei), we have $v_1\,\mathrm{d}p_1/\mathrm{d}r - v_2\,\mathrm{d}p_2/\mathrm{d}r = F_1 - F_2$. Thus

$$\int_{a_1}^{r} p_1\,\mathrm{d}r - \int_{a_2}^{r} p_2\,\mathrm{d}r \cong S_0 + \frac{F_1 - F_2}{2v}\xi^2,$$

where v is the common value of v_1 and v_2 at the point of intersection. The integration is effected by means of the well-known formula

$$\int_{-\infty}^{\infty} \cos(\alpha+\beta\xi^2)\,d\xi = \sqrt{\frac{\pi}{\beta}}\cos(\alpha+\tfrac{1}{4}\pi),$$

and as a result we have

$$w = \frac{8\pi V^2}{\hbar v|F_2-F_1|}\cos^2\left(\frac{S_0}{\hbar}+\tfrac{1}{4}\pi\right). \qquad (87.7)$$

The quantity $S_0/\hbar$ is large and varies rapidly with the energy E. Hence, on averaging over even a small interval of energy, the squared cosine can be replaced by its mean value. As a result we obtain the formula†

$$w = 4\pi V^2/\hbar v|F_2-F_1|. \qquad (87.8)$$

All the quantities on the right-hand side of the equation are taken at the point of intersection of the potential-energy curves.

In the application to pre-dissociation, we are interested in the probability of the disintegration of the molecule in unit time. In this time, the nuclei in their vibrations pass $2(\omega/2\pi)$ times through the point $r = r_0$ (where ω is the circular frequency of the vibrations). Hence the required pre-dissociation probability is obtained by multiplying w (the probability for a double passage) by $\omega/2\pi$, i.e. it is

$$2V^2\omega/\hbar v|F_2-F_1|. \qquad (87.9)$$

The following remark must be made concerning these calculations. In speaking of the intersection of terms, we have had in mind the eigenvalues of the "unperturbed" Hamiltonian $\hat{H}_0$ of the electron motion in the molecule; in this, the terms $\hat{V}$ which lead to the transitions concerned are not taken into account. If we include these terms in the Hamiltonian, the intersection of the terms becomes impossible, and the curves move apart slightly, as shown in Fig. 33. This follows from the results of §76 when regarded from a slightly different point of view.

Let $U_{J1}(r)$ and $U_{J2}(r)$ be two eigenvalues of the operator $\hat{H}_0$ (in which r is regarded as a parameter). In the region near the point r_0 where the curves $U_{J1}(r)$ and $U_{J2}(r)$ intersect, to determine the eigenvalues $U(r)$ of the perturbed operator $\hat{H}_0+\hat{V}$ we must use the method given in §76, as a result of which we obtain the formula

$$U(r) = \tfrac{1}{2}(U_{J1}+U_{J2}+V_{11}+V_{22})\pm\sqrt{[\tfrac{1}{4}(U_{J1}-U_{J2}+V_{11}-V_{22}) +|V_{12}|^2]}; \qquad (87.10)$$

the matrix elements V_{11}, V_{22}, V_{12}, like U_{J1} and U_{J2}, are functions of r. The interval between the two levels is now

$$\Delta U = \sqrt{[(U_{J1}-U_{J2}+V_{11}-V_{22})^2+4|V_{12}|^2]}. \qquad (87.11)$$

† Derived by L. Landau (1932).

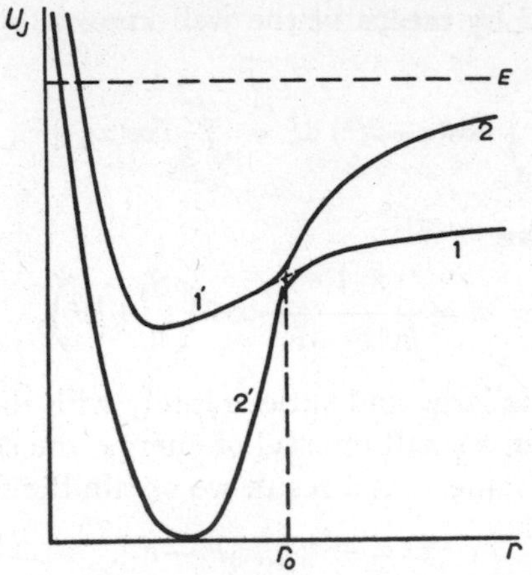

FIG. 33

Hence it is clear that, if there are transitions between the two states (i.e. the matrix element V_{12} is not zero), the intersection of the levels disappears. The least distance between the curves is now

$$\Delta = 2|V_{12}|.$$

The formulae obtained above for the transition probability are applicable only so long as the "divergence" of the curves is fairly small. If the latter becomes considerable, the transition probability cannot be calculated by ordinary perturbation theory.

To examine this problem, we use the following method. Let ψ_1, ψ_2 be the wave functions of the electron states corresponding to the "unperturbed" terms U_{J1} and U_{J2}, i.e. these functions are solutions of the equations

$$\hat{H}_0\psi_1 = U_{J1}\psi_1, \quad \hat{H}_0\psi_2 = U_{J2}\psi_2.$$

Let us seek the solution of the perturbed wave equation

$$i\hbar\, \partial\Psi/\partial t = (\hat{H}_0+\hat{V})\Psi$$

in the form

$$\Psi = b_1(t)\psi_1+b_2(t)\psi_2. \tag{87.12}$$

Substituting this expression in the wave equation, multiplying the latter firstly by ψ_1 and secondly by ψ_2, and integrating, we obtain two equations for the functions $b_1(t)$ and $b_2(t)$:

$$i\hbar \mathrm{d}b_1/\mathrm{d}t = U_{J1}b_1+Vb_2, \quad i\hbar \mathrm{d}b_2/\mathrm{d}t = U_{J2}b_2+Vb_1; \tag{87.13}$$

we here include V_{11}, V_{22} in U_{J1}, U_{J2}, and denote V_{12} by $V(r)$ simply, in agreement with the notation in the preceding formulae. We consider the motion of the nuclei quasi-classically. Accordingly, the variables r and t are related by $\mathrm{d}r/\mathrm{d}t = v$, where v is the classical velocity of the nuclei.

Near the point r_0 where the curves of $U_{J1}(r)$ and $U_{J2}(r)$ intersect (shown by the dashed line in Fig. 33), we can expand U_{J1} and U_{J2} as series of powers of $\xi = r - r_0$, writing

$$U_{J1} = U_J - F_{J1}\xi, \qquad U_{J2} = U_J - F_{J2}\xi, \tag{87.14}$$

where U_J is the common value of U_{J1} and U_{J2} at the point $r = r_0$, and we have introduced the notation $F_J = -(\partial U_J/\partial r)_{r_0}$. Introducing also new unknowns a_1, a_2 in place of b_1, b_2 by means of

$$b_1 = a_1 e^{-(i/\hbar)U_J t}, \qquad b_2 = a_2 e^{-(i/\hbar)U_J t}, \tag{87.15}$$

and replacing the differentiation with respect to t by one with respect to ξ ($\mathrm{d}/\mathrm{d}t = v\,\mathrm{d}/\mathrm{d}\xi$), we obtain from equations (87.13)

$$i\hbar v\, \mathrm{d}a_1/\mathrm{d}\xi = -F_{J1}\xi a_1 + Va_2, \quad i\hbar v\, \mathrm{d}a_2/\mathrm{d}\xi = -F_{J2}\xi a_2 + Va_1, \tag{87.16}$$

where v and V may be taken with sufficient accuracy to have their values at the point of intersection.

If we solve equations (87.16) with the boundary condition $a_1 = 1$, $a_2 = 0$ as $\xi \to +\infty$, then $|a_1(-\infty)|^2$ determines the probability that, as the nuclei pass through the point $\xi = 0$, the molecule remains in the electron state ψ_1, indicating a transition from the curve 12′ to the curve 21′ (see Fig. 33). Similarly, $|a_2(-\infty)|^2 = 1 - |a_1(-\infty)|^2$ is the probability of a transition to the electron state ψ_2, i.e. the probability that the molecule remains on the curve 12′. The transition from curve 1 to curve 2 (as $\xi \to +\infty$) in a double passage through the point of intersection can be effected in two ways: either by $1 \to 1' \to 2$ (as the nuclei approach, the transition from curve 12′ to curve 21′ occurs, and as they recede the molecule remains on the curve 21′), or by $1 \to 2' \to 2$. Hence the required probability for such a transition is

$$w = 2|a_1(-\infty)|^2\{1 - |a_1(-\infty)|^2\}.$$

We shall not pause here to explain the manner of solution of equations (87.16) (they reduce to a single equation of the second order, which can be solved by Laplace's method), but give only the final result†:

$$|a_1(-\infty)|^2 = e^{-2\pi V^2/\hbar v|F_2 - F_1|}$$

(the difference $F_{J2} - F_{J1}$ is replaced by the equal difference $F_2 - F_1$). Thus

$$w = 2e^{-2\pi V^2/\hbar v|F_2 - F_1|}\{1 - e^{-2\pi V^2/\hbar v|F_2 - F_1|}\}. \tag{87.17}$$

We see that the probability of the transition in question is small in two limiting cases, when V is fairly small and fairly large. For $V^2 \ll \hbar v|F_2 - F_1|$, formula (87.17) becomes (87.8).

Finally, let us consider the phenomenon, akin to pre-dissociation, of what are called *perturbations* in the spectra of diatomic molecules. If two discrete

† The details of the calculation may be found in the original paper by C. Zener (*Proceedings of the Royal Society* A 137, 696, 1932).

molecular levels E_1 and E_2 corresponding to two intersecting electron terms are close together, the possibility of a transition between the two electron states results in a displacement of the levels. According to the general formula (76.4) of perturbation theory, we have for the displaced levels the expression

$$\tfrac{1}{2}(E_1+E_2)\pm\sqrt{[\tfrac{1}{4}(E_1-E_2)^2+|V_{12,\mathrm{nuc}}|^2]}, \tag{87.18}$$

where $V_{12,\mathrm{nuc}}$ is the matrix element (87.1) of the perturbation for the transition between the molecular states 1 and 2; the matrix elements $V_{11,\mathrm{nuc}}$ and $V_{22,\mathrm{nuc}}$ must, of course, be included in E_1 and E_2. From this formula we see that the two levels are moved apart, being displaced in opposite directions (the higher level is raised and the other lowered). The amount of the displacement is the greater, the smaller the difference $|E_1-E_2|$.

The matrix element $V_{12,\mathrm{nuc}}$ is calculated in exactly the same way as for determining the probability of a collision of the second kind. The only difference is that the wave functions $\chi_{\mathrm{nuc},1}$ and $\chi_{\mathrm{nuc},2}$ belong to the discrete spectrum, and hence must be normalised to unity. According to (48.2) we have for these functions

$$\chi_{\mathrm{nuc},1} = \sqrt{\frac{2\omega_1}{\pi v_1}}\cos\left\{\frac{1}{\hbar}\int_{a_1}^{r} p_1\,\mathrm{d}r-\tfrac{1}{4}\pi\right\},$$

$$\chi_{\mathrm{nuc},2} = \sqrt{\frac{2\omega_2}{\pi v_2}}\cos\left\{\frac{1}{\hbar}\int_{a_2}^{r} p_2\,\mathrm{d}r-\tfrac{1}{4}\pi\right\}.$$

A comparison with formulae (87.4) to (87.6) shows that the matrix element $V_{12,\mathrm{nuc}}$ here considered is related to the transition probability w for a double passage through the point of intersection by

$$|V_{12,\mathrm{nuc}}|^2 = w(\hbar\omega_1/2\pi)(\hbar\omega_2/2\pi). \tag{87.19}$$

PROBLEMS

PROBLEM 1. Determine the total effective cross-section for collisions of the second kind, as a function of the kinetic energy E of the colliding atoms, for transitions pertaining to the spin-orbit interaction.

SOLUTION. On account of the quasi-classical motion of the nuclei, we can introduce the concept of the *impact parameter* ρ (the distance at which the nuclei would pass if there were no interaction between them) and define the effective cross-sections $\mathrm{d}\sigma$ as the product of the "target area" $2\pi\rho\,\mathrm{d}\rho$ and the transition probability $w(\rho)$ per collision.† The total effective cross-section σ is obtained by integrating with respect to ρ.

For spin-orbit interaction, the matrix element $V(r)$ is independent of the angular momentum M of the colliding atoms. We write the velocity v at the point $r = r_0$, where the curves intersect, in the form

$$v = \sqrt{[(2/\mu)(E-U-M^2/2\mu r_0^2)]}.$$

† Cf. *Mechanics*, §21, Moscow 1940.

Here U is the common value of U_1 and U_2 at the point of intersection, μ is the reduced mass of the atoms, and the angular momentum $M = \mu\rho v_\infty$, where v_∞ is the relative velocity of the atoms at infinity. The zero of energy is chosen so that the interaction energy of the atoms in the initial state is zero at infinity; then $E = \frac{1}{2}\mu v_\infty^2$. Hence we can write

$$v = \sqrt{[(2/\mu)(E-U-\rho^2E/r_0^2)]}.$$

Substituting this expression in (87.8), we find

$$d\sigma = 2\pi\rho\, d\rho\,.\,w = \frac{8\pi^2V^2}{\hbar|F_2-F_1|}\frac{\rho d\rho}{\sqrt{[2(E-U-\rho^2E/r_0^2)/\mu]}}.$$

The integration with respect to ρ must be taken from zero up to the value for which the velocity v vanishes. As a result we have

$$\sigma = \frac{4\sqrt{(2\mu)}\pi^2V^2r_0^2}{\hbar|F_2-F_1|}\frac{\sqrt{(E-U)}}{E}.$$

PROBLEM 2. The same as Problem 1, but for transitions pertaining to the interaction between the rotation of the molecule and its orbital angular momentum.

SOLUTION. The matrix element V is of the form $V(r) = MD/\mu r^2$, where $D(r)$ is the matrix element of the electron orbital angular momentum. By the same method as in Problem 1 we obtain

$$\sigma = \frac{16\sqrt{2\pi^2D^2}}{3\hbar\sqrt{\mu}|F_2-F_1|}\frac{(E-U)^{3/2}}{E}.$$

PROBLEM 3. Determine the transition probability for energies E close to the value U_J of the potential energy at the point of intersection.

SOLUTION. For small values of $E-U_J$, formula (87.8) is inapplicable, since the velocity v of the nuclei cannot be regarded as constant near the point of intersection, and hence it cannot be taken outside the integral as it was in deriving (87.8).

Near the point of intersection we replace the curves of U_{J1}, U_{J2} by the straight lines (87.14). The wave functions $\chi_{\mathrm{nuc},1}$ and $\chi_{\mathrm{nuc},2}$ in this region are wave functions of one-dimensional motion in a homogeneous field (§22). The calculations are conveniently effected by means of wave functions in the momentum representation. The wave function normalised by the delta function of energy is of the form (see §22, Problem)

$$a_2 = \frac{1}{\sqrt{(2\pi\hbar|F_{J2}|)}}\exp\left\{\frac{i}{\hbar F_{J2}}[(E-U_J)p-p^3/6\mu]\right\},$$

while the wave function normalised to unit current density in the incident and reflected waves is obtained by multiplying by $\sqrt{(2\pi\hbar)}$:

$$a_1 = \frac{1}{\sqrt{|F_{J1}|}}\exp\left\{\frac{i}{\hbar F_{J1}}[(E-U_J)p-p^3/6\mu]\right\}.$$

On integrating, the perturbing energy (matrix element) V may again be taken outside the integral, replacing it by its value at the point of intersection;

$$w = \frac{2\pi}{\hbar}\left|V\int_{-\infty}^{\infty} a_1a_2^*\, dp\right|^2.$$

As a result we obtain

$$w = \frac{4\pi V^2(2\mu)^{2/3}}{\hbar^{4/3}(F_{J1}F_{J2})^{1/3}(F_{J2}-F_{J1})^{2/3}}\Phi\left[-(E-U_J)\left(\frac{2\mu}{\hbar^2}\right)^{1/3}\left(\frac{1}{F_{J2}}-\frac{1}{F_{J1}}\right)^{2/3}\right],$$

where $\Phi(\xi)$ is the Airy function (see §*b* of the Mathematical Appendices). For large $E-U_J$, this formula reduces to (87.8).

CHAPTER XII

THE THEORY OF SYMMETRY

§88. Symmetry transformations

THE classification of terms in the polyatomic molecule is fundamentally related to its symmetry, as in the diatomic molecule. Hence we shall begin by examining the types of symmetry which a molecule can have.

The symmetry of a body is determined by the assembly of all those rearrangements after which the body is unaltered; these rearrangements are called *symmetry transformations*. Any possible symmetry transformation can be represented as a combination of one or more of the three fundamental types of transformation. These three essentially different types are: the *rotation* of the body through a definite angle about some axis, the *reflection* of it in some plane, and the *parallel displacement* of the body over some distance. Of these, the last evidently is applicable only to an infinite medium (a crystal lattice). A body of finite dimensions (in particular, a molecule) can be symmetrical only with respect to rotations and reflections.

If the body is unaltered on rotation through an angle $2\pi/n$ about some axis, then that axis is said to be an *axis of symmetry of the* n*th order*. The number n can take any integral value: $n = 2, 3, \ldots$. The value $n = 1$ corresponds to a rotation through an angle of 2π or, what is the same thing, of 0, i.e. it corresponds to an identical transformation. We shall symbolically denote by C_n the operation of rotation through an angle $2\pi/n$ about a given axis. Repeating this operation two, three, ... times, we obtain rotations through angles $2(2\pi/n)$, $3(2\pi/n)$, ..., which also leave the body unaltered; these rotations may be denoted by $C_n^2, C_n^3, \ldots$. It is obvious that, if p divides n,

$$C_n^p = C_{n/p}. \tag{88.1}$$

In particular, performing the rotation n times, we return to the initial position, i.e. we effect an identical transformation. The latter is customarily denoted by E, so that we can write

$$C_n^n = E. \tag{88.2}$$

If the body is left unaltered by a reflection in some plane, this plane is said to be a *plane of symmetry*. We shall denote by the symbol σ the operation of reflection in a plane. It is evident that a double reflection in the same plane is the identical transformation:

$$\sigma^2 = E. \tag{88.3}$$

A simultaneous application of the two transformations (rotation and reflection) gives what are called the *rotary-reflection axes*. A body has a rotary-reflection axis of the nth order if it is left unaltered by a rotation through an angle $2\pi/n$ about this axis, followed by a reflection in a plane perpendicular to the axis (Fig. 34). It is easy to see that this is a new form

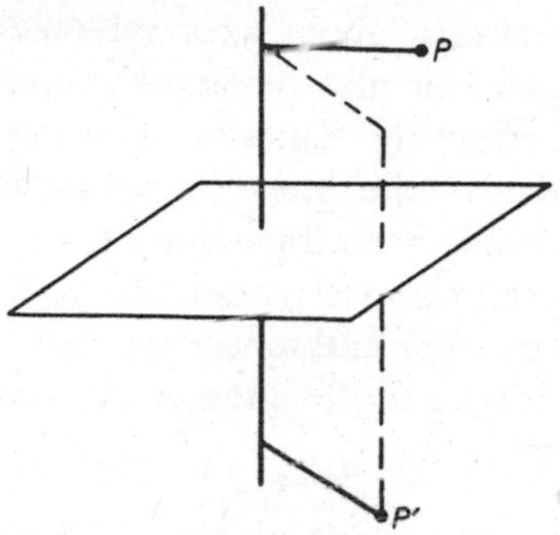

FIG. 34

of symmetry only when n is even. For, if n is odd, an n-fold repetition of the rotary-reflection transformation would be equivalent to a simple reflection in a plane perpendicular to the axis (since the angle of rotation is 2π, while an odd number of reflections in the same plane amounts to a simple reflection). Repeating this transformation a further n times, we have as a result that the rotary-reflection axis reduces to the simultaneous presence of an axis of symmetry of the nth order and an independent plane of symmetry perpendicular to this axis. If, however, n is even, an n-fold repetition of the rotary-reflection transformation returns the body to its initial position.

We denote the rotary-reflection transformation by the symbol S_n. Denoting by σ_h a reflection in a plane perpendicular to a given axis, we can put, by definition,

$$S_n = C_n\sigma_h = \sigma_h C_n; \tag{88.4}$$

the order in which the operations C_n and σ_h are performed clearly does not affect the result.

An important particular case is a rotary-reflection axis of the second order. It is easy to see that a rotation through an angle π, followed by a reflection in a plane perpendicular to the axis of rotation, is the inversion transformation, whereby a point P of the body is carried into another point P', lying on the continuation of the line which joins P to the intersection O of the axis and the plane, and such that the distances OP and OP' are the same. A body symmetrical with respect to this transformation is said to have a *centre of symmetry*. We shall denote the operation of inversion by I, so that we have

$$I \equiv S_2 = C_2\sigma_h. \tag{88.5}$$

It is also evident that $I\sigma_h = C_2$, $IC_2 = \sigma_h$; in other words, an axis of the second order, a plane of symmetry perpendicular to it and a centre of symmetry at their point of intersection are mutually dependent: if any two of these elements are present, the third is automatically present also.

We shall now give various purely geometrical properties of rotations and reflections which it is useful to bear in mind in studying the symmetry of bodies.

A product of two rotations about axes intersecting at some point is a rotation about some third axis also passing through that point. A product of two reflections in intersecting planes is equivalent to a rotation; the axis of this rotation is evidently the line of intersection of the planes, while the angle of rotation is easily seen, by a simple geometrical construction, to be twice the angle between the two planes. If we denote a rotation through an angle ϕ about an axis by $C(\phi)$, and reflections in two planes passing through that axis by the symbols† σ_v and σ'_v, the above statement can be written as

$$\sigma_v \sigma'_v = C(2\phi), \tag{88.6}$$

where ϕ is the angle between the two planes. It must be noted that the order in which the two reflections are performed is not immaterial. The transformation $\sigma_v \sigma'_v$ gives a rotation in the direction from the plane of σ'_v to that of σ_v; on interchanging the factors we have a rotation in the opposite direction. Multiplying equation (88.6) on the left by σ_v, we obtain

$$\sigma'_v = \sigma_v C(2\phi); \tag{88.7}$$

in other words, the operation of rotation, followed by reflection in a plane passing through the axis, is equivalent to a reflection in another plane intersecting the first at half the angle of rotation. In particular, it follows from this that an axis of symmetry of the second order and two mutually perpendicular planes of symmetry passing through it are mutually dependent; if two of them are present, so is the third.

We shall show that the product of rotations through an angle π about two axes intersecting at an angle ϕ (Oa and Ob in Fig. 35) is a rotation through

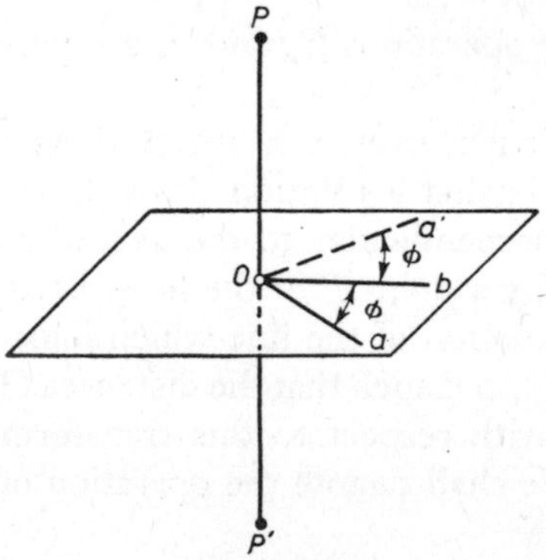

FIG. 35

† The suffix v customarily denotes a reflection in a plane passing through a given axis (a "vertical" plane), and the suffix h a reflection in a plane perpendicular to the axis (a "horizontal" plane).

an angle 2ϕ about an axis perpendicular to the first two (PP' in Fig. 35). For it is obvious that the resulting transformation is also a rotation; after the first rotation (about Oa) the point P is carried into P', and after the second (about Ob) it returns to its original position. This means that the line PP' remains fixed, and is therefore an axis of rotation. To determine the angle of rotation, it is sufficient to note that, in the first rotation, the axis Oa remains fixed, while after the second it takes the position Oa', which makes an angle 2ϕ with Oa. In the same way we can see that, when the order of the two transformations is reversed, we obtain a rotation in the opposite direction.

Although the result of two successive transformations in general depends on the order in which they are performed, in some cases the order of operations is immaterial: the transformations commute. This is so for the following transformations:

(1) Two rotations about the same axis.
(2) Two reflections in mutually perpendicular planes (equivalent to a rotation through π about their line of intersection).
(3) Two rotations through π about mutually perpendicular axes (equivalent to a rotation through π about the third perpendicular axis).
(4) A rotation and a reflection in a plane perpendicular to the axis of rotation.
(5) Any rotation or reflection and an inversion with respect to a point lying on the axis of rotation or in the plane of reflection; this follows from (1) and (4).

§89. Transformation groups

The set of all the symmetry transformations for a given body is called its *symmetry transformation group* (or simply its *symmetry group*). Hitherto we have spoken of these transformations as geometrical rearrangements of the body. However, in quantum-mechanical applications it is more convenient to regard symmetry transformations as transformations of the co-ordinates which leave the Hamiltonian of the system in question invariant. It is obvious that, if the system is left unaltered by some rotation or reflection, the corresponding transformation does not change its SCHRÖDINGER's equation. Thus we shall speak of a transformation group with respect to which a given SCHRÖDINGER's equation is invariant.†

† This point of view enables us to include in our considerations not only the rotation and reflection groups discussed here, but also other types of transformation which leave SCHRÖDINGER's equation unaltered. These include the interchange of the co-ordinates of identical particles forming part of the system considered (a molecule or atom). The set of all possible permutations of identical particles in a given system is called its *permutation group* (we have already met these permutations in §61). The general properties of groups given below apply to permutation groups also; we shall not pause to study this type of group in more detail here.

The following remark should be made concerning the notation which we use in this chapter. Symmetry transformations are essentially operators just like those which we consider all through the book (in particular, we have already considered the inversion operator in §28). They ought, therefore, to be denoted by letters with circumflexes. We do not do this, in view of the generally accepted notation, and because this omission cannot lead to misunderstandings in the present chapter. For the same reason we denote the identical transformation by the customary symbol E, and not by 1, which would correspond to the notation in the other chapters.

Symmetry groups are conveniently studied with the help of the general mathematical techniques of what is called *group theory*, the fundamentals of which we shall explain below. At first we shall consider groups, each of which contains a finite number of transformations (known as *finite groups*). Each of the transformations forming a group is said to be an *element* of the group.

Symmetry groups have the following important properties. Each group contains the identical transformation E (called the *unit element* of the group). The elements of a group can be "multiplied" by one another; by the *product* of two (or more) transformations we mean the result of applying them in succession. It is obvious that the product of any two elements of a group is also an element of that group. For the multiplication of elements we have the associative law $(AB)C = A(BC)$, where A, B, C are elements of a group. There is evidently no general commutative law; in general, $AB \neq BA$. For each element A of a group there is in the same group an *inverse* element A^{-1} (the *inverse transformation*), such that $AA^{-1} = E$. In some cases an element may be its own inverse; in particular, $E^{-1} = E$. It is evident that mutually inverse elements A and A^{-1} commute.

The element inverse to the product AB of two elements is

$$(AB)^{-1} = B^{-1}A^{-1},$$

and similarly for the product of a greater number of elements; this is easily seen by effecting the multiplication and using the associative law.

If all the elements of a group commute, the group is said to be *Abelian*. A particular case of Abelian groups is formed by what are called *cyclic* groups. By a cyclic group we mean a group, all of whose elements can be obtained by raising one of them to successive powers, i.e. a group consisting of the elements

$$A, A^2, A^3, \ldots, A^n = E,$$

where n is some integer.

Let $\boldsymbol{G}$ be some group.† If we can separate from it some set of elements $\boldsymbol{H}$ such that the latter is itself a group, then the group $\boldsymbol{H}$ is called a *sub-group* of the group $\boldsymbol{G}$. A given element of a group may appear in several of its sub-groups.

By taking any element A of a group and raising it to successive powers, we finally obtain the unit element (since the total number of elements in the group is finite). If n is the smallest number for which $A^n = E$, then n is called the *order* of the element A, and the set of elements $A, A^2, \ldots, A^n = E$ is called the *period* of A. The period is denoted by $\{A\}$; it is itself a group, i.e. it is a sub-group of the original group, and is cyclic.

In order to find whether a given set of elements of a group is a sub-group of it, it is sufficient to find whether, on multiplying any two of its elements, we obtain another element of the set. For in that case we have, together with

† We shall denote groups by bold italic letters.

each element A, all its powers, including A^{n-1} (where n is the order of A), which is the inverse of A (since $A^{n-1}A = A^n = E$); and there will obviously be a unit element.

The total number of elements in a group is called its *order*. It is easy to see that the order of a sub-group is a factor of the order of the whole group. To show this, let us consider a sub-group H of a group G, and let G_1 be some element of G which does not belong to H. Multiplying all the elements of H (on the right, say) by G_1, we obtain a set (or *complex*, as it is called) of elements, denoted by HG_1. All the elements of this complex clearly belong to the group G. However, none of them belongs to H; for, if for any two elements H_a, H_b belonging to H we had $H_aG_1 = H_b$, it would follow that $G_1 = H_a^{-1}H_b$, i.e. G_1 would also belong to the sub-group H, which is contrary to hypothesis. Similarly we can show that, if G_2 is an element of G not belonging to H or to HG_1, none of the elements of the complex HG_2 will belong to H or to HG_1. Continuing this process, we finally exhaust all the elements contained in the finite group G. Thus all the elements are divided among the complexes

$$H, HG_1, HG_2, \ldots, HG_m$$

(where m is some integer), each of which contains h elements, h being the order of the sub-group H. Hence it follows that the order g of the group G is $g = hm$, and this proves the theorem.

If the order of a group is a prime number, it follows at once from the above that the group has no sub-groups (except itself and E). The converse theorem is also valid: a group having no sub-groups is of prime order and in addition must be cyclic (since otherwise it would contain elements whose period would form a sub-group).

We shall now introduce the important concept of *conjugate* elements. Two elements A and B are said to be conjugate if

$$A = CBC^{-1},$$

where C is also an element of the group; multiplying this equation on the right by C and on the left by C^{-1}, we have the converse equation $B = C^{-1}AC$. An important property of conjugate elements is that, if A is conjugate to B, and B to C, then A is conjugate to C; for, if $B = P^{-1}AP$, $C = Q^{-1}BQ$ (P and Q being elements of the group), it follows that $C = (PQ)^{-1}A(PQ)$. For this reason we can speak of sets of conjugate elements of a group. Such sets are called *classes* of the group. Each class is completely determined by any one element A of it; for, given A, we obtain the whole class by forming the products GAG^{-1}, where G is successively every element of the group (of course, this may give each element of the class several times). Thus we can divide the whole group into classes; each element of the group can clearly appear in only one class. The unit element of the group is a class by itself, since for every element of the group $GEG^{-1} = E$. If the group is Abelian, each of its elements is a class by itself; since all the elements, by definition, commute, each element is conjugate only to itself. We emphasise that a class of a group (not being E) is not a sub-group of it; this is evident from the fact that it does not contain a unit element.

All the elements of a given class are of the same order. For, if n is the order of the element A (so that $A^n = E$), then for a conjugate element $B = CAC^{-1}$ we have $(CAC^{-1})^n = CA^nC^{-1} = E$.

Let $\boldsymbol{H}$ be a sub-group of $\boldsymbol{G}$, and G_1 an element of $\boldsymbol{G}$ not belonging to $\boldsymbol{H}$. It is easy to see that the set of elements $G_1 \boldsymbol{H} G_1^{-1}$ has all the properties of a group, i.e. it also is a sub-group of the group $\boldsymbol{G}$. The sub-groups $\boldsymbol{H}$ and $G_1 \boldsymbol{H} G_1^{-1}$ are said to be *conjugate*; each element of one is conjugate to one element of the other. By giving G_1 various values, we obtain a series of conjugate sub-groups, which may partly coincide. It may happen that all the sub-groups conjugate to $\boldsymbol{H}$ are $\boldsymbol{H}$ itself. In this case $\boldsymbol{H}$ is called a ***normal divisor*** of the group $\boldsymbol{G}$. Thus, for example, every sub-group of an Abelian group is clearly a normal divisor of it.

Let us consider a group $\boldsymbol{A}$ with n elements $A, A', A'', \ldots$, and a group $\boldsymbol{B}$ with m elements $B, B', B'', \ldots$, and suppose that all the elements of $\boldsymbol{A}$ (apart from the unit E) are different from those of $\boldsymbol{B}$ but commute with them. If we multiply every element of group $\boldsymbol{A}$ by every element of group $\boldsymbol{B}$, we obtain a set of nm elements, which also form a group. For, for any two elements of this set we have $AB \,.\, A'B' = AA' \,.\, BB' = A''B''$, i.e. another element of the set. The group of order nm thus obtained is denoted by $\boldsymbol{A} \times \boldsymbol{B}$, and is called the *direct product* of the groups $\boldsymbol{A}$ and $\boldsymbol{B}$.

Finally, we shall introduce the concept of the *isomorphism* of groups. Two groups $\boldsymbol{A}$ and $\boldsymbol{B}$ of the same order are said to be *isomorphous* if we can establish a one-to-one correspondence between their elements, such that, if the element B corresponds to the element A, and B' to A', then $B'' = BB'$ corresponds to $A'' = AA'$. Two such groups, considered in the abstract, clearly have identical properties, though the actual meaning of their elements may be different.

§90. Point groups

Transformations which appear in the symmetry group of a body of finite dimensions (in particular, a molecule) must be such that at least one point of the body remains fixed when any of these transformations is applied. In other words, all axes and planes of symmetry of a molecule must have at least one common point of intersection. For a successive rotation of the body about two non-intersecting axes or a reflection in two non-intersecting planes results in a translation of the body, which obviously cannot then be left unaltered. Symmetry groups having the above property are called *point groups*.

Before going on to construct the possible types of point group, we shall explain a simple geometrical procedure whereby the elements of a group may be easily divided into classes. Let Oa be some axis, and let the element A of the group be a rotation through a definite angle about this axis. Next, let G

be a transformation (rotation or reflection) in the same group, which on being applied to the same axis Oa carries it to the position Ob. We shall show that the element $B = GAG^{-1}$ then corresponds to a rotation about the axis Ob through the same angle as that of the rotation about Oa to which the element A corresponds. For, let us consider the effect of the transformation GAG^{-1} on the axis Ob itself. The transformation G^{-1} inverse to G carries the axis Ob to the position Oa, so that the subsequent rotation A leaves it in this position; finally, G carries it back to its initial position. Thus the axis Ob remains fixed, so that B is a rotation about this axis. Since A and B belong to the same class, their orders are the same; this means that they effect rotations through the same angle.

Thus we reach the result that two rotations through the same angle belong to the same class if there is, among the elements of the group, a transformation whereby one axis of rotation can be carried into the other. In exactly the same way we can show that two reflections in different planes belong to the same class if some transformation in the group carries one plane into the other. The axes or planes of symmetry whose directions can be carried into each other are said to be *equivalent*.

Some additional comments are necessary in the case where both rotations are about the same axis. The element inverse to the rotation C_n^k ($k = 1, 2, \ldots, n-1$) about an axis of symmetry of the nth order is the element $C_n^{-k} = C_n^{n-k}$, i.e. a rotation through an angle $(n-k)2\pi/n$ in the same direction or, what is the same thing, a rotation through an angle $2k\pi/n$ in the opposite direction. If, among the transformations in the group, there is a rotation through an angle π about a perpendicular axis (this rotation reverses the direction of the axis under consideration), then, by the general rule proved above, the rotations C_n^k and C_n^{-k} belong to the same class. A reflection σ_h in a plane perpendicular to the axis also reverses its direction; however, it must be borne in mind that the reflection also changes the direction of rotation. Hence the existence of σ_h does not render C_n^k and C_n^{-k} conjugate. A reflection σ_v in a plane passing through the axis, on the other hand, does not change the direction of the axis, but changes the direction of rotation, and therefore $C_n^{-k} = \sigma_v C_n^k \sigma_v$, so that C_n^k and C_n^{-k} belong to the same class if such a plane of symmetry exists. If rotations about an axis through the same angle in opposite directions are conjugate, we shall call it *bilateral*.

The determination of the classes of a point group is often facilitated by the following rule. Let G be some group not containing the inversion I, and C_i a group consisting of the two elements I and E. Then the direct product $G \times C_i$ is a group containing twice as many elements as G; half of them are the same as the elements of the group G, while the remainder are obtained by multiplying the latter by I. Since I commutes with any other transformation of a point group, it is clear that the group $G \times C_i$ contains twice as many classes as G; to each class A of the group G there correspond the two classes A and AI in the group $G \times C_i$. In particular, the inversion I always forms a class by itself.

Let us now go on to enumerate all possible point groups. We shall construct these by starting from the simplest ones and adding new elements of symmetry. We shall denote point groups by bold italic Latin letters with appropriate suffixes.

I. C_n *groups*

The simplest type of symmetry has a single axis of symmetry of the nth order. The group C_n is the group of rotations about an axis of the nth order. This group is evidently cyclic. Each of its n elements forms a class by itself. The group C_1 contains only the identical transformation E, and corresponds to the absence of any symmetry.

II. S_{2n} *groups*

The group S_{2n} is the group of rotary-reflections about a rotary-reflection axis of even order $2n$. It contains $2n$ elements and is evidently cyclic. In particular, the group S_2 contains only two elements, E and I; it is also denoted by C_i. We may note also that, if the order of a group is a number of the form $2n = 4p+2$, inversion is among its elements; it is clear that $(S_{4p+2})^{2p+1} = C_2 \sigma_h = I$. Such a group can be written as a direct product $S_{4p+2} = C_{2p+1} \times C_i$; it is also denoted by $C_{2p+1,i}$.

III. C_{nh} *groups*

These groups are obtained by adding to an axis of symmetry of the nth order a plane of symmetry perpendicular to it. The group C_{nh} contains $2n$ elements: n rotations of the group C_n and n rotary-reflection transformations $C_n{}^k \sigma_h$, $k = 1, 2, \dots, n$ (including the reflection $C_n{}^n \sigma_h = \sigma_h$). All the elements of the group commute, i.e. it is Abelian; the number of classes is the same as the number of elements. If n is even ($n = 2p$), the group contains a centre of symmetry (since $C_{2p}{}^p \sigma_h = C_2 \sigma_h = I$). The simplest group, C_{1h}, contains only two elements, E and σ_h; it is also denoted by C_s.

IV. C_{nv} *groups*

If we add to an axis of symmetry of the nth order a plane of symmetry passing through it, this automatically gives another $n-1$ planes intersecting along the axis at angles of π/n, as follows at once from the geometrical theorem† (88.7) stated in §88. The group C_{nv} thus obtained therefore contains $2n$ elements: n rotations about the axis of the nth order, and n reflections σ_v in vertical planes. Fig. 36 shows, as an example, the systems of axes and planes of symmetry for the groups C_{3v} and C_{4v}.

To determine the classes, we notice that, because of the presence of planes of symmetry passing through the axis, the latter is bilateral. The actual distribution of the elements among the classes depends on whether n is even or odd.

---

† It is easy to see that, in a finite group, there cannot be two planes of symmetry intersecting at an angle which is not a rational fraction of 2π. If there were two such planes, it would follow that there were an infinite number of other planes of symmetry, intersecting along the same line and obtained by reflecting one plane in the other *ad infinitum*. In other words, if there are two such planes, there must be complete axial symmetry.

If n is odd ($n = 2p+1$), successive rotations C_{2p+1} carry each of the planes successively into each of the other $2p$ planes, so that all the planes of symmetry are equivalent, and the reflections in them belong to a single class. Among rotations about the axis there are $2p$ operations apart from the identity, and these are conjugate in pairs, forming p classes each of two elements ($C_{2p}{}^{k}$ and $C_{2p}{}^{-k}$, $k = 1, 2, \ldots, p$); moreover, E forms an extra class. Thus there are $p+2$ classes altogether.

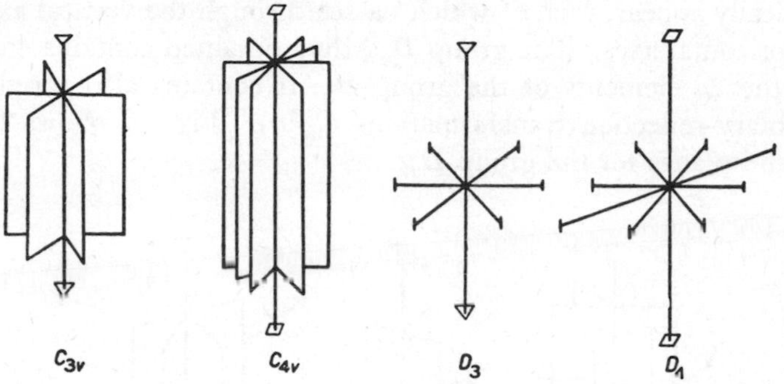

FIG. 36

If, on the other hand, n is even ($n = 2p$), only every alternate plane can be interchanged by successive rotations C_{2p}; two adjacent planes cannot be carried into each other. Thus there are two sets of p equivalent planes, and accordingly two classes of p elements (reflections) each. Of the rotations about the axis, $C_{2p}{}^{2p} = E$ and $C_{2p}{}^{p} = C_2$ each form a class by themselves, while the remaining $2p-2$ rotations are conjugate in pairs and give another $p-1$ classes, each of two elements. The group $C_{2p,v}$ thus has $p+3$ classes altogether.

V. D_n *groups*

If we add to an axis of symmetry of the nth order an axis of the second order perpendicular to it, this involves the appearance of a further $n-1$ such axes, so that there are altogether n horizontal axes of the second order, intersecting at angles π/n. The resulting group D_n contains $2n$ elements: n rotations about an axis of the nth order, and n rotations through an angle π about horizontal axes (we shall denote the latter by U_2, reserving the notation C_2 for a rotation through an angle π about a vertical axis). Fig. 36 shows, as an example, the systems of axes for the groups D_3 and D_4.

In an exactly similar manner to case IV, we may verify that the axis of the nth order is bilateral, while the horizontal axes of the second order are all equivalent if n is odd, or form two non-equivalent sets if n is even. Consequently, the group D_{2p} has the following $p+3$ classes: E, 2 classes each of p rotations U_2, the rotation C_2, and $p-1$ classes each of two rotations about the vertical axis. The group D_{2p+1}, on the other hand, has $p+2$ classes: E, $2p+1$ rotations U_2, and p classes each of two rotations about the vertical axis.

An important particular case is the group D_2. Its system of axes is composed of three mutually perpendicular axes of the second order. This group is also denoted by V.

VI. D_{nh} *groups*

If we add to the system of axes of a group D_n a horizontal plane of symmetry passing through the n axes of the second order, n vertical planes automatically appear, each of which passes through the vertical axis and one of the horizontal axes. The group D_{nh} thus obtained contains $4n$ elements; besides the $2n$ elements of the group D_n, it contains also n reflections σ_v and n rotary-reflection transformations $C_n{}^k\sigma_h$. Fig. 37 shows the system of axes and planes for the group D_{3h}.

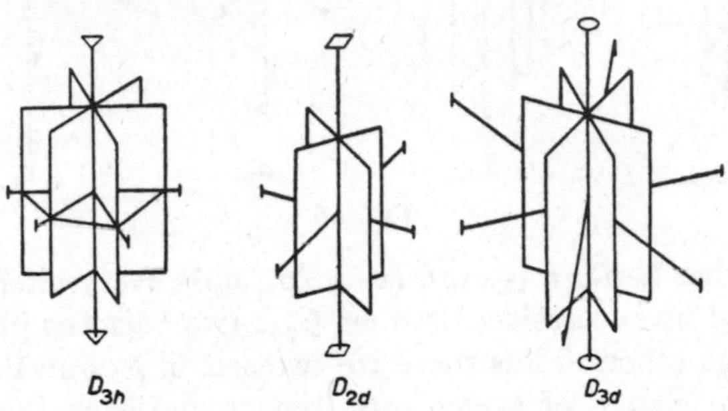

FIG. 37

The reflection σ_h commutes with all the other elements of the group; hence we can write D_{nh} as the direct product $D_{nh} = D_n \times C_s$, where C_s is the group consisting of the two elements E and σ_h. For even n the inversion operation is among the elements of the group, and we can also write $D_{2p,h} = D_{2p} \times C_i$.

Hence it follows that the number of classes in the group D_{nh} is twice the number in the group D_n. Half of them are the same as those of the group D_n (rotations about axes), while the remainder are obtained by multiplying these by σ_h. The reflections σ_v in vertical planes all belong to a single class (if n is odd) or form two classes (if n is even). The rotary-reflection transformations $\sigma_h C_n{}^k$ and $\sigma_h C_n{}^{-k}$ are conjugate in pairs.

VII. D_{nd} *groups*

There is another way of adding planes of symmetry to the system of axes of the group D_n. This is to draw vertical planes through the axis of the nth order, midway between each adjacent pair of horizontal axes of the second order. The adding of one such plane again involves the appearance of another $(n-1)$ planes. The system of axes and planes of symmetry thus obtained determines the group D_{nd}. Fig. 37 shows the axes and planes for the groups D_{2d} and D_{3d}.

The group D_{nd} contains $4n$ elements. To the $2n$ elements of the group D_n are added n reflections in the vertical planes (denoted by σ_d—the "diagonal" planes) and n transformations of the form $G = U_2\sigma_d$. In order to ascertain the nature of these latter, we notice that the rotation U_2 can, by (88.6), be written in the form $U_2 = \sigma_h\sigma_v$, where σ_v is a reflection in the vertical plane passing through the corresponding axis of the second order. Then $G = \sigma_h\sigma_v\sigma_d$ (the transformations σ_v, σ_h alone are not, of course, among the elements of the group). Since the planes of the reflections σ_v and σ_d intersect along an axis of the nth order, forming an angle $(2k+1)\pi/2n$, where $k = 0, \ldots, (n-1)$ (since here the angle between adjacent planes is $\pi/2n$), it follows that, by (88.6), we have $\sigma_v\sigma_d = C_{2n}^{2k+1}$. Thus we find that $G = \sigma_h C_{2n}^{2k+1} = S_{2n}^{2k+1}$, i.e. these elements are rotary-reflection transformations about the vertical axis, which is consequently not a simple axis of symmetry of the nth order, but a rotary-reflection axis of the $2n$th order.

The diagonal planes reflect two adjacent horizontal axes of the second order into each other; hence, in the groups under consideration, adjacent axes of the second order are equivalent (for both even and odd n). Similarly, all the axes of the second order are equivalent. The rotary-reflection transformations S_{2n}^{2k+1} and S_{2n}^{-2k-1} are conjugate in pairs.†

Applying these considerations to the group $D_{2p,d}$, we find that it contains the following $2p+3$ classes: E, the rotation C_2 about the axis of the nth order, $(p-1)$ classes each of two conjugate rotations about the same axis, one class of the $2p$ rotations U_2, one class of $2p$ reflections σ_d, and p classes each of two rotary-reflection transformations.

For odd n ($= 2p+1$), inversion is among the elements of the group; this is seen from the fact that, in this case, one of the horizontal axes is perpendicular to a vertical plane. Hence we can write $D_{2p+1,d} = D_{2p+1} \times C_i$, so that the group $D_{2p+1,d}$ contains $2p+4$ classes, which are obtained at once from the $p+2$ classes of the group D_{2p+1}.

VIII. *The group T (the tetrahedron group)*

The system of axes of this group is the system of axes of symmetry of a tetrahedron. It can be obtained by adding to the system of axes of the group V four oblique axes of the third order, rotations about which carry the three axes of the second order into one another. This system of axes is conveniently represented by showing the three axes of the second order as passing through the centres of opposite faces of a cube, and those of the third order as the spatial diagonals of the cube. Fig. 38 shows the position of these axes in a cube and in a tetrahedron (one axis of each type is shown).

The three axes of the second order are mutually equivalent. The axes of the third order are also equivalent, since they are carried into one another by

---

† For we have

$$\sigma_d S_{2n}^{2k+1}\sigma_d = \sigma_d\sigma_h C_{2n}^{2k+1}\sigma_d = \sigma_h\sigma_d C_{2n}^{2k+1}\sigma_d = \sigma_h C_{2n}^{-2k-1} = S_{2n}^{-2k-1}.$$

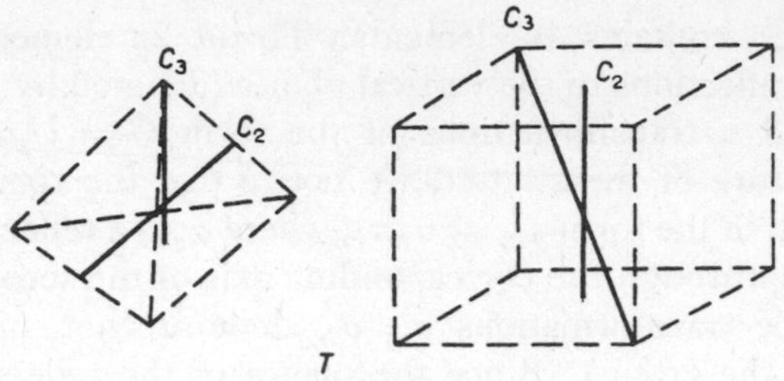

FIG. 38

the rotation C_2, but they are not bilateral axes. Hence it follows that the twelve elements in the group T are divided into four classes: E, the three rotations C_2, the four rotations C_3 and the four rotations C_3^2.

IX. *The group T_d*

This group contains all the symmetry transformations of the tetrahedron. Its system of axes can be obtained by adding to the axes of the group T planes of symmetry, each of which passes through one axis of the second order and

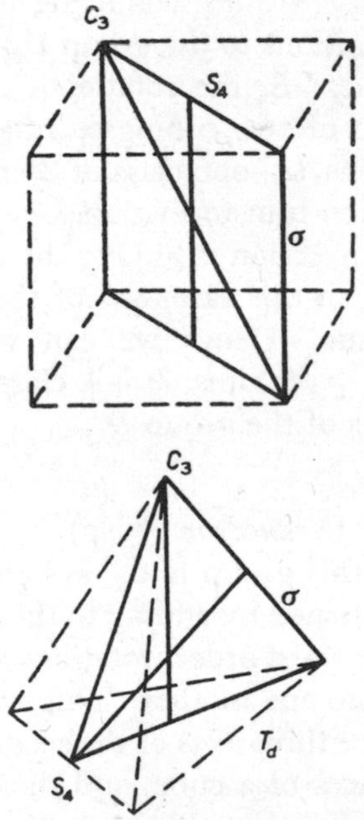

FIG. 39

two of the third order. The axes of the second order thereby become rotary-reflection axes of the fourth order (as in the case of the group D_{2d}). This system is conveniently represented by showing the three rotary-reflection axes as passing through the centres of opposite faces of a cube, the four axes of the third order as its spatial diagonals, and the six planes of symmetry as passing through each pair of opposite edges (Fig. 39 shows one of each kind of axis and one plane).

Since the planes of symmetry are vertical with respect to the axes of the third order, the latter are bilateral axes. All the axes and planes of a given kind are equivalent. Hence the 24 elements of this group are divided into the following five classes: E, eight rotations C_3 and C_3^2, six reflections in planes, six rotary-reflection transformations S_4 and S_4^3, and three rotations $C_2 = S_4^2$.

X. *The group* T_h

This group is obtained from T by adding a centre of symmetry: $T_h = T \times C_i$. As a result, three mutually perpendicular planes of symmetry appear, passing through each pair of axes of the second order, and the axes of the third order become rotary-reflection axes of the sixth order (Fig. 40 shows one of each kind of axis and one plane).

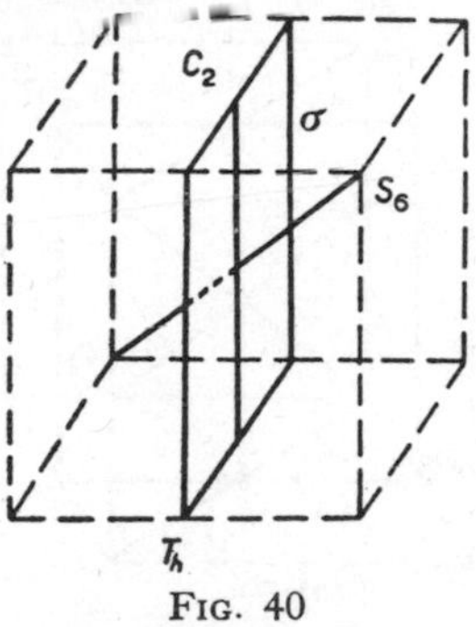

FIG. 40

The group contains 24 elements divided among eight classes, which are obtained at once from those of the group T.

XI. *The group O (the octahedron group)*

The system of axes of this group is the system of axes of symmetry of a cube: three axes of the fourth order pass through the centres of opposite

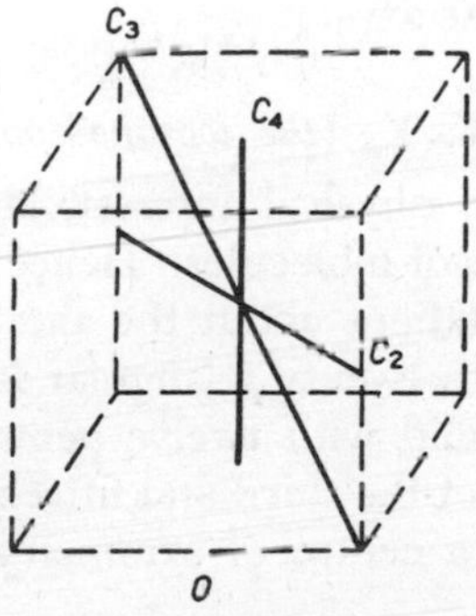

FIG. 41

faces, four axes of the third order through opposite corners, and six axes of the second order through the midpoints of opposite edges (Fig. 41).

It is easy to see that all the axes of a given order are equivalent, and each of them is bilateral. Hence the 24 elements are divided among the following five classes: E, eight rotations C_3 and C_3^2, six rotations C_4 and C_4^3, three rotations C_4^2 and six rotations C_2.

XII. *The group* O_h

This is the group of all symmetry transformations of the cube.† It is obtained by adding to the group O a centre of symmetry: $O_h = O \times C_i$. The axes of the third order in the group O are thereby converted into rotary-reflection axes of the sixth order (the spatial diagonals of the cube); in addition, another six planes of symmetry appear, passing through each pair of opposite edges, and three planes parallel to the faces of the cube (Fig. 42). The group contains 48 elements divided among ten classes, which

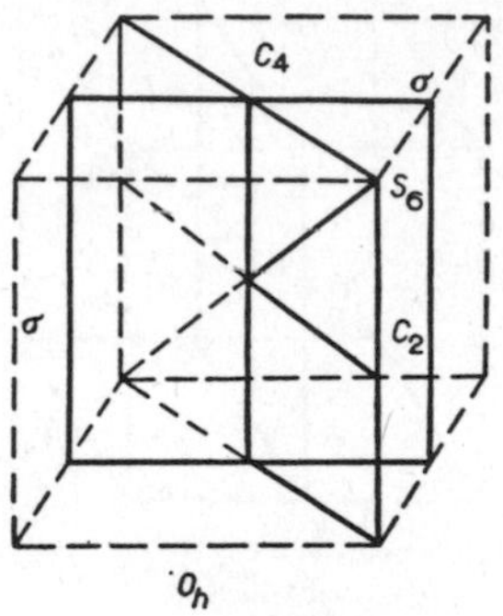

FIG. 42

can be at once obtained from those of the group O; five classes are the same as those of the group O, while the remainder are: I, eight rotary-reflection transformations S_6 and S_6^5, six rotary-reflection transformations $C_4\sigma_h$, $C_4^3\sigma_h$ about axes of the fourth order, three reflections σ_h in planes horizontal with respect to the axes of the fourth order, and six reflections σ_v in planes vertical with respect to these axes.

XIII, XIV. *The groups* Y, Y_h *(the icosahedron groups)*

These groups are of no physical interest, since they do not occur in Nature as symmetry groups of molecules. Hence we shall here only mention that Y is a group of 60 rotations about the axes of symmetry of the icosahedron (a regular solid with twenty triangular faces) or of the pentagonal dodecahedron (a regular solid with twelve pentagonal faces); there are six axes of the fifth order, ten of the third and fifteen of the second. The group Y_h is obtained by adding a centre of symmetry: $Y_h = Y \times C_i$, and is the

† The groups T, T_d, T_h, O, O_h are often called *cubic*.

complete group of symmetry transformations of the above-mentioned polyhedra.

This exhausts all possible types of point group containing a finite number of elements. In addition, we must consider what are called *continuous point groups*, which contain an infinite number of elements. This we shall do in §95.

§91. Representations of groups

Let us consider any symmetry group, and let ψ_1 be some one-valued function of the co-ordinates.† Under the transformation of the co-ordinate system which corresponds to an element G of the group, this function is changed into some other function. On performing in turn all the g transformations in the group (g being the order of the group), we in general obtain g different functions from ψ_1. For certain ψ_1, however, some of these functions may be linearly dependent. As a result we obtain some number $f\ (\leqslant g)$ of linearly independent functions $\psi_1, \psi_2, \ldots, \psi_f$, which are transformed into linear combinations of one another under the transformations belonging to the group in question. In other words, as a result of the transformation G, each of the functions ψ_i ($i = 1, 2, 3, \ldots, f$) is changed into a linear combination of the form

$$\sum_{k=1}^{f} G_{ki}\psi_k,$$

where the G_{ik} are constants depending on the transformation G. The array of these constants is called the *matrix* of the transformation.‡

In this connection it is convenient to regard the elements G of the group as operators acting on the functions ψ_i, so that we can write

$$\hat{G}\psi_i = \sum_k G_{ki}\psi_k; \tag{91.1}$$

the functions ψ_i can always be chosen so as to be orthogonal and normalised. Then the concept of the matrix of the transformation is the same as that of the matrix of the operator, in the form defined in §11:

$$G_{ik} = \int \psi_i{}^*\hat{G}\psi_k\, dq. \tag{91.2}$$

To the product of two elements G and H of the group there corresponds the matrix obtained from the matrices of G and H by the ordinary rule of matrix multiplication (11.12):

$$(GH)_{ik} = \sum_l G_{il}H_{lk}. \tag{91.3}$$

The set of matrices of all the elements in a group is called a *representation*

† In the configuration space of the physical system concerned.

‡ Since the functions ψ_i are one-valued, a definite matrix corresponds to each element of the group.

of the group. The functions $\psi_1, \ldots, \psi_f$ with respect to which these matrices are defined are called the *basis* of the representation. The number f of these functions gives what is called the *dimension* of the representation.

Let us consider the integral $\int |\psi|^2 \, dq$, where ψ is some function of the co-ordinates. Since the integral is taken over all space†, it is evident that its value is unchanged by any rotation or reflection of the co-ordinate system. Hence, for any symmetry transformation G, we can write

$$\int (\hat{G}^*\psi^*)(\hat{G}\psi) \, dq = \int \psi^*\psi \, dq.$$

Introducing the transposed operator $\tilde{\hat{G}}$, we have

$$\int (\hat{G}^*\psi^*)(\hat{G}\psi) \, dq = \int \psi\tilde{\hat{G}}\hat{G}^*\psi^* \, dq = \int \psi^*\psi \, dq,$$

whence, from the fact that ψ is arbitrary, it follows that $\tilde{\hat{G}}\hat{G}^* = 1$, or

$$\tilde{\hat{G}}^* \equiv \hat{G}^+ = \hat{G}^{-1}, \qquad (91.4)$$

i.e. the Hermitian conjugate operator is equal to the inverse operator (the operator $\hat{f}^{-1}$ inverse to $\hat{f}$ being understood to be that for which $\hat{f}\hat{f}^{-1} = 1$). The equation (91.4) is the general definition of what is called the *unitary property* of operators; operators having this property are said to be *unitary*.

If we define the matrix elements of the operator $\hat{G}$ with respect to an orthogonal and normalised system of functions, then, by (11.9), we have $G^+_{ik} = G^*_{ki}$. The equation (91.4), rewritten in matrix form, is then

$$\sum_l G^*_{il}G_{kl} = \delta_{ik}. \qquad (91.5)$$

Matrices satisfying these equations are said to be *unitary*.

Thus a representation of a symmetry group in terms of normalised and orthogonal base functions is unitary, i.e. the group is represented by unitary matrices.

Suppose that we perform on the system of functions $\psi_1, \ldots, \psi_f$ the linear transformation

$$\psi'_i = \sum_k S_{ki}\psi_k; \qquad (91.6)$$

this transformation can be conventionally written in the operator form

$$\psi'_i = \hat{S}\psi_i.$$

If we now take, as the basis of the representation, the functions ψ'_i, we obtain a new representation of the same dimension. Such representations, obtained from one another by a linear transformation of their base functions, are said to be *equivalent*; it is evident that they are not essentially different.

† It is vital to the proof that the integral of the essentially positive function $|\psi|^2$ should exist and be non-zero.

It is easy to find how the matrices of equivalent representations can be expressed in terms of one another.

To do this, we notice that, if the functions ψ'_i are expressed in terms of the functions ψ_i by (91.6), then conversely the ψ_i are expressed in terms of the ψ'_i by the equation

$$\psi_i = \sum_k S^{-1}{}_{ki}\psi'_k,$$

where $S^{-1}{}_{ki}$ are the matrix elements of the operator $\hat{S}^{-1}$ which is the inverse of $\hat{S}$. Applying the operator $\hat{G}$ to both sides of equation (91.6), we therefore have

$$\hat{G}\psi'_i = \sum_k S_{ki}\hat{G}\psi_k = \sum_{k,l} S_{ki}G_{lk}\psi_l = \sum_{k,l,m} S_{ki}G_{lk}S^{-1}{}_{ml}\psi'_m$$
$$= \sum_m (\hat{S}^{-1}\hat{G}\hat{S})_{mi}\psi'_m.$$

Thus the matrix of the operator $\hat{G}$ in the new representation is the matrix of the operator

$$\hat{G}' = \hat{S}^{-1}\hat{G}\hat{S} \tag{91.7}$$

in the old representation.

If the functions ψ_i are orthogonal and normalised, and we want the same to be true of the functions ψ'_i, the matrix S_{ik} of the transformation (91.6) must be unitary. For, if we substitute (91.6) in the condition $\int \psi'_i{}^*\psi'_k \mathrm{d}q = \delta_{ik}$, we obtain

$$\sum_{l,m} \int S_{li}{}^*\psi_l{}^*S_{mk}\psi_m \,\mathrm{d}q = \sum_{l,m} S_{li}{}^*S_{mk}\delta_{lm} = \sum_l S_{li}{}^*S_{lk} = \delta_{ik}.$$

An important property of a unitary transformation is that it leaves unaltered the sum of the squared moduli of the transformed functions. For

$$\sum_i |\psi'_i|^2 = \sum_{k,l,i} S_{ki}\psi_k S_{li}{}^*\psi_l{}^* = \sum_{k,l} \psi_k\psi_l{}^*\delta_{kl} = \sum_k |\psi_k|^2.$$

The sum of the diagonal elements of the matrix representing an element G of a group is called its *character*; we shall denote it by $\chi(G)$. It is a very important result that the characters of the matrices of equivalent representations are the same. For, by the rule of matrix multiplication, we have for the character of the matrix of the operator $\hat{G}'$ (91.7)

$$\chi(G') = \sum_i G'_{ii} = \sum_{i,k,l} S^{-1}{}_{ik}G_{kl}S_{li} = \sum_{k,l} G_{kl}\delta_{kl} = \sum_k G_{kk},$$

i.e.

$$\chi(G) = \chi(G') \tag{91.8}$$

(here we have used the fact that, by the definition of the inverse operator, we must have $\sum_i S_{li}S^{-1}_{ik} = \delta_{lk}$). This circumstance gives particular importance to the description of group representations by stating their characters: it enables us to distinguish at once the fundamentally different representations from those which are equivalent. Henceforward we shall regard as different representations only those which are not equivalent.

If we take S in (91.7) to be that element of the group which relates the conjugate elements G and G', we have the result that, in any given representation of a group, the characters of the matrices representing elements of the same class are the same.

The identical transformation corresponds to the unit element E of the group. Hence the matrix representing the latter is diagonal in every representation, and the diagonal elements are unity. The character $\chi(E)$ is consequently just the dimension of the representation:

$$\chi(E) = f. \tag{91.9}$$

Let us consider some representation of dimension f. It may happen that, as a result of a suitable linear transformation (91.6), the base functions divide into sets of $f_1, f_2, \ldots$ functions ($f_1+f_2+\ldots = f$), in such a way that, when any element of the group acts on them, the functions in each set are transformed only into combinations of themselves, and do not involve functions from other sets. In such a case the representation in question is said to be *reducible*.

If, on the other hand, the number of base functions that are transformed only into combinations of themselves cannot be reduced by any linear transformation of them, the representation which they give is said to be *irreducible*. Any reducible representation can, as we say, be *decomposed* into irreducible ones. This means that, by the appropriate linear transformation, the base functions divide into several sets, of which each is transformed by some irreducible representation when the elements of the group act on it. Here it may be found that several different sets transform by the same irreducible representation; in such a case this irreducible representation is said to be contained so many times in the reducible one.

Irreducible representations are an important characteristic of a group, and play a fundamental part in all quantum-mechanical applications of group theory. We shall give the chief properties of irreducible representations.

It may be shown that the number of different irreducible representations of a group is equal to the number r of classes in the group. We shall distinguish the characters of the various irreducible representations by indices; the characters of the matrices of the element G in the representations are $\chi^{(1)}(G), \chi^{(2)}(G), \ldots, \chi^{(r)}(G)$.

The matrix elements of irreducible representations satisfy a number of orthogonality relations.† First of all, for two different irreducible representations

† The proof of these relations may be found in books on group theory, for example E. WIGNER, *Gruppentheorie und ihre Anwendung auf die Quantenmechanik der Atomspektren*, Vieweg, Brunswick 1931; H. WEYL, *The Theory of Groups and Quantum Mechanics*, Methuen, London 1931.

the relations

$$\sum_G G^{(\alpha)}{}_{ik} G^{(\beta)}{}_{lm}{}^* = 0 \tag{91.10}$$

hold, where α and β ($\alpha \neq \beta$) refer to the two irreducible representations, and the summation is taken over all the elements of the group. For any irreducible representation the relations

$$\sum_G G^{(\alpha)}{}_{ik} G^{(\alpha)}{}_{lm}{}^* = \frac{g}{f_\alpha}\delta_{il}\delta_{km} \tag{91.11}$$

hold, i.e. only the sums of the squared moduli of the matrix elements are not zero:

$$\sum_G |G^{(\alpha)}{}_{ik}|^2 = g/f_\alpha.$$

The relations (91.10), (91.11) can be combined in the form

$$\sum_G G^{(\alpha)}{}_{ik} G^{(\beta)}{}_{lm}{}^* = \frac{g}{f_\alpha}\delta_{\alpha\beta}\delta_{il}\delta_{km}. \tag{91.12}$$

In particular, we can obtain from this an important orthogonality relation for the characters of the representations. Summing both sides of equation (91.12) over equal values of the suffixes i, k and l, m, we have

$$\sum_G \chi^{(\alpha)}(G)\chi^{(\beta)}(G)^* = g\delta_{\alpha\beta}. \tag{91.13}$$

For $\alpha = \beta$ we have

$$\sum_G |\chi^{(\alpha)}(G)|^2 = g,$$

i.e. the sum of the squared moduli of the characters of an irreducible representation is equal to the order of the group. We may notice that this relation can be used as a criterion of the irreducibility of a representation; for a reducible representation, this sum is always greater than g (it is ng, where n is the number of irreducible representations contained in the reducible one).

It also follows from (91.13) that the equality of the characters of two irreducible representations is not only a necessary but also a sufficient condition for them to be equivalent.

The relation (91.13) enables any reducible representation to be very easily decomposed into irreducible ones if the characters of both are known. Let $\chi(G)$ be the characters of some reducible representation of dimension f, and let the numbers $a^{(1)}, a^{(2)}, \ldots, a^{(r)}$ indicate how many times the corresponding irreducible representations are contained in it, so that

$$\sum_{\beta=1}^{r} a^{(\beta)} f_\beta = f, \tag{91.14}$$

where f_β are the dimensions of the irreducible representations. Then the characters $\chi(G)$ can be written

$$\chi(G) = \sum_{\beta=1}^{r} a^{(\beta)}\chi^{(\beta)}(G). \qquad (91.15)$$

Multiplying this equation by $\chi^{(\alpha)}(G)^*$ and summing over all G, we have by (91.13)

$$a^{(\alpha)} = \frac{1}{g}\sum_G \chi(G)\chi^{(\alpha)}(G)^*. \qquad (91.16)$$

Let us consider a representation of dimension $f = g$, given by the g functions $\hat{G}\psi$, ψ being some general function of the co-ordinates (so that all the g functions $\hat{G}\psi$ obtained from it are linearly independent); such a representation is said to be *regular*. It is clear that none of the matrices of this representation will contain any diagonal elements, with the exception of the matrix corresponding to the unit element; hence $\chi(G) = 0$ for $G \neq E$, while $\chi(E) = g$. Decomposing this representation into irreducible ones, we have for the numbers $a^{(\alpha)}$, by (91.16), the values $a^{(\alpha)} = (1/g)gf^{(\alpha)} = f^{(\alpha)}$, i.e. each irreducible representation is contained in the reducible one under consideration as many times as its dimension. Substituting this in (91.14), we find the relation

$$f_1^2 + f_2^2 + \dots + f_r^2 = g; \qquad (91.17)$$

the sum of the squared dimensions of the irreducible representations of a group is equal to its order.† Hence it follows, in particular, that for Abelian groups (where $r = g$) all the irreducible representations are of dimension one ($f_1 = f_2 = \dots = f_r = 1$).

We may also remark, without proof, that the dimensions of the irreducible representations of a group divide its order.

Among the irreducible representations of any group there is always a trivial one, given by a single base function invariant under all the transformations in the group. This one-dimensional representation is called the *unit* representation; in it, all the characters are unity.

Let us consider two different systems of functions $\psi_1^{(\alpha)}, \dots, \psi_{f_\alpha}^{(\alpha)}$ and $\psi_1^{(\beta)}, \dots, \psi_{f_\beta}^{(\beta)}$, which form two irreducible representations of a group. By forming the products $\psi_i^{(\alpha)}\psi_k^{(\beta)}$ we obtain a system of $f_\alpha f_\beta$ new functions, which can serve as the basis for a new representation of dimension $f_\alpha f_\beta$. This representation is called the *direct product* of the other two; it is irreducible only if f_α or f_β is unity. It is easy to see that the characters of the direct product are equal to the products of the characters of the two component representations. For, if

$$\hat{G}\psi_i^{(\alpha)} = \sum_l G_{li}^{(\alpha)}\psi_l^{(\alpha)}, \qquad \hat{G}\psi_k^{(\beta)} = \sum_m G_{mk}^{(\beta)}\psi_m^{(\beta)},$$

† It may be mentioned that, for point groups, equation (91.17) for given r and g can be satisfied in only one way by a set of integers $f_1, \dots, f_r$.

then

$$\hat{G}\psi_i^{(\alpha)}\psi_k^{(\beta)} = \sum_{l,m} G_{li}^{(\alpha)}G_{mk}^{(\beta)}\psi_l^{(\alpha)}\psi_m^{(\beta)};$$

hence we have for the characters, which we denote by $(\chi^{(\alpha)}\times\chi^{(\beta)})(G)$,

$$(\chi^{(\alpha)}\times\chi^{(\beta)})(G) = \sum_{i,k} G_{ii}^{(\alpha)}G_{kk}^{(\beta)} = \sum_i G_{ii}^{(\alpha)} \sum_k G_{kk}^{(\beta)},$$

i.e.

$$(\chi^{(\alpha)}\times\chi^{(\beta)})(G) = \chi^{(\alpha)}(G)\chi^{(\beta)}(G). \tag{91.18}$$

The two irreducible representations so multiplied may, in particular, be the same; in this case we have two different sets of functions $\psi_1, \dots, \psi_f$ and $\phi_1, \dots, \phi_f$ giving the same representation, while the direct product of the representation with itself is given by the f^2 functions $\psi_i\phi_k$, and has the characters

$$(\chi\times\chi)(G) = [\chi(G)]^2.$$

This reducible representation can be at once decomposed into two representations of smaller dimension (although these are, in general, themselves reducible). One of them is given by the $\frac{1}{2}f(f+1)$ functions $\psi_i\phi_k+\psi_k\phi_i$, the other by the $\frac{1}{2}f(f-1)$ functions $\psi_i\phi_k-\psi_k\phi_i$, $i \neq k$; it is evident that the functions in each of these sets are transformed only into combinations of themselves. The former is called the *symmetric product* of the representation with itself, and its characters are denoted by the symbol $[\chi^2](G)$; the latter is called the *antisymmetric product*, and its characters are denoted by $\{\chi^2\}(G)$. To determine the characters of the symmetric product, we write

$$\begin{aligned}\hat{G}(\psi_i\phi_k+\psi_k\phi_i) &= \sum_{l,m} G_{li}G_{mk}(\psi_l\phi_m+\psi_m\phi_l)\\ &= \tfrac{1}{2}\sum_{l,m}(G_{li}G_{mk}+G_{mi}G_{lk})(\psi_l\phi_m+\psi_m\phi_l).\end{aligned}$$

Hence we have for the character

$$[\chi^2](G) = \tfrac{1}{2}\sum_{i,k}(G_{ii}G_{kk}+G_{ik}G_{ki}).$$

But $\sum_i G_{ii} = \chi(G)$, and $\sum_{i,k} G_{ik}G_{ki} = \chi(G^2)$; thus we finally obtain the formula

$$[\chi^2](G) = \tfrac{1}{2}\{[\chi(G)]^2+\chi(G^2)\}, \tag{91.19}$$

which enables us to determine the characters of the symmetric product of a representation with itself from the characters of the representation. In an exactly similar manner, we find for the characters of the antisymmetric product the formula

$$\{\chi^2\}(G) = \tfrac{1}{2}\{[\chi(G)]^2-\chi(G^2)\}. \tag{91.20}$$

If the functions ψ_i and ϕ_i are the same, we can evidently construct from them only the symmetric product, formed by the squares ψ_i^2 and the products $\psi_i\psi_k$, $i \neq k$. In applications, symmetric products of higher orders are also encountered; their characters may be obtained in a similar manner.

For applications it is useful to know a formula which enables us to represent an arbitrary function ψ as a sum of functions transformed by the irreducible representations of the group, i.e. in the form

$$\psi = \sum_\alpha \sum_i \psi_i^{(\alpha)}, \tag{91.21}$$

where the functions $\psi_i^{(\alpha)}$ $(i = 1, 2, \ldots, f_\alpha)$ are transformed by the αth irreducible representation. The problem consists in determining the functions $\psi_i^{(\alpha)}$ from the function ψ, and is solved by the formula

$$\psi_i^{(\alpha)} = \frac{f_\alpha}{g} \sum_G G_{ii}^{(\alpha)*} \hat{G}\psi. \tag{91.22}$$

To prove this, it suffices to show that the expression on the right-hand side of the equation reduces to $\psi_i^{(\alpha)}$ identically if we put $\psi = \psi_i^{(\alpha)}$, and to zero if we put $\psi = \psi_k^{(\beta)}$ with $k \neq i$ or $\beta \neq \alpha$; both these results follow at once from the orthogonality relations (91.10,) (91.11), putting $\hat{G}\psi_k^{(\beta)} = \sum_l G_{lk}^{(\beta)}\psi_l^{(\beta)}$.

If we substitute (91.22) in (91.21) and effect the summation over i, we obtain a simpler expansion of the arbitrary function ψ into functions $\psi^{(\alpha)}$ belonging to the various irreducible representations, but not to any definite rows of these representations:

$$\psi = \sum_\alpha \psi^{(\alpha)}, \quad \psi^{(\alpha)} = \frac{f_\alpha}{g} \sum_G \chi^{(\alpha)}(G)^* \hat{G}\psi. \tag{91.23}$$

Finally, we shall make a few remarks regarding the irreducible representations of a group which is the direct product of two other groups (not to be confused with the direct product of two representations of the same group). If the functions $\psi_i^{(\alpha)}$ give an irreducible representation of the group $\boldsymbol{A}$, and the functions $\phi_k^{(\beta)}$ give one of the group $\boldsymbol{B}$, the products $\phi_k^{(\beta)}\psi_i^{(\alpha)}$ are the basis of an $f_\alpha f_\beta$-dimensional representation of the group $\boldsymbol{A}\times\boldsymbol{B}$, and this representation is irreducible. The characters of this representation are obtained by multiplying the corresponding characters of the original representations (cf. the derivation of formula (91.18)); to an element $C = AB$ of the group $\boldsymbol{A}\times\boldsymbol{B}$ there corresponds the character

$$\chi(C) = \chi^{(\alpha)}(A)\chi^{(\beta)}(B). \tag{91.24}$$

Multiplying together in this way all the irreducible representations of the groups $\boldsymbol{A}$ and $\boldsymbol{B}$, we obtain all the irreducible representations of the group $\boldsymbol{A}\times\boldsymbol{B}$.

§92. Irreducible representations of point groups

Let us pass now to the actual determination of the irreducible representations of those point groups which are of physical interest. The great majority of molecules have axes of symmetry only of the second, third, fourth or sixth order. Hence it is unnecessary to consider the icosahedron groups Y, Y_h; we shall examine the groups C_n, C_{nh}, C_{nv}, D_n, D_{nh} only for the values $n = 1, 2, 3, 4, 6$, and the groups S_{2n}, D_{nd} only for $n = 1, 2, 3$.

The simplest problem is to determine the irreducible representations for the cyclic groups. A cyclic group, like any Abelian group, has only one-dimensional representations. Let G be a *generating element* of the group (*i.e.* one which, on being raised to successive powers, gives all the elements of the group). Since $G^g = E$ (where g is the order of the group), it is clear that, when the operator $\hat{G}$ acts on a base function ψ, the latter can be multiplied only by $1^{1/g}$, i.e.†

$$\hat{G}\psi = e^{2\pi i k/g}\psi \qquad (k = 1, 2, \ldots, g).$$

The character tables obtained are given in Table 6.

Isomorphous groups evidently have the same irreducible representations, and are given together in the same table. The left-hand columns show the conventional names usually given to the representations.‡ Beside these letters are placed the letters x, y, z; these show the representations by which the co-ordinates themselves are transformed (with a view to later quantum-mechanical applications). The z-axis is always taken along the principal axis of symmetry. The letters ϵ and ω denote

$$\epsilon = e^{2\pi i/3}, \qquad \omega = e^{2\pi i/6} = -\omega^4.$$

Let us consider the group C_{2h} (and the isomorphous groups C_{2v} and D_2). This group is Abelian, so that all its irreducible representations are one-dimensional, and the characters can only be ± 1 (since the square of every element is E).

Next we consider the group C_{3v}. As compared with the group C_3, the reflections σ_v in vertical planes (all belonging to one class) are here added. A function invariant with respect to rotation about the axis (a base function

† For the point group C_n we can, for example, take as the functions ψ the functions $e^{ik\phi}$, $k = 1, 2, \ldots, n$, where ϕ is the angle of rotation about the axis, measured from some fixed direction.

‡ The one-dimensional representations are denoted by the letters A, B, the two-dimensional ones by E, and the three-dimensional ones by F; the notation E for a two-dimensional irreducible representation should not be confused with the unit element of a group. The base functions of A representations are symmetric, and those of B representations antisymmetric, with respect to rotations about a principal axis of the nth order. The functions of different symmetry with respect to a reflection σ_h are distinguished by the number of primes (one or two), while the suffixes g and u show the symmetry with respect to inversion.

The reason why two complex conjugate one-dimensional representations are shown as one two-dimensional one is explained in §93.

The numbers in front of the symbols for the elements of a group in the upper rows show the number of elements in the corresponding classes; see §90 for the distribution of the elements of point groups among classes.

of the representation A of the group C_3) may be either symmetric or antisymmetric with respect to the reflections σ_v. Functions multiplied by ϵ and ϵ^2 under the rotation C_3, on the other hand (base functions of the complex conjugate representations E), change into each other on reflection.†

TABLE 6

Characters of irreducible representations of point groups

C_1	E
A	1

C_i			E	I
	C_2		E	C_2
		C_s	E	σ
A_g	$A; z$	$A'; x, y$	1	1
$A_u; x, y, z$	$B; x, y$	$A''; z$	1	-1

C_3	E	C_3	C_3^2
$A; z$	1	1	1
$E; x\pm iy$	1	ε	ε^2
	1	ε^2	ε

C_{2h}			E	C_2	σ_h	I
	C_{2v}		E	C_2	σ_v	σ'_v
		$V \equiv D_2$	E	C_2^z	C_2^y	C_2^x
A_g	$A_1; z$	A	1	1	1	1
B_g	$B_2; y$	$B_3; x$	1	-1	-1	1
$A_u; z$	A_2	$B_1; z$	1	1	-1	-1
$B_u; x, y$	$B_1; x$	$B_2; y$	1	-1	1	-1

C_{3v}		E	$2C_3$	$3\sigma_v$
	D_3	E	$2C_3$	$3U_2$
$A_1; z$	A_1	1	1	1
A_2	$A_2; z$	1	1	-1
$E; x, y$	$E; x, y$	2	-1	0

C_4		E	C_4	C_2	C_4^3
	S_4	E	S_4	C_2	S_4^3
$A; z$	A	1	1	1	1
B	$B; z$	1	-1	1	-1
$E; x\pm iy$	$E; x\pm iy$	1	i	-1	$-i$
		1	$-i$	-1	i

C_6	E	C_6	C_3	C_2	C_3^2	C_6^5
$A; z$	1	1	1	1	1	1
B	1	-1	1	-1	1	-1
E_1	1	ω^2	$-\omega$	1	ω^2	$-\omega$
	1	$-\omega$	ω^2	1	$-\omega$	ω^2
$E_2; x\pm iy$	1	ω	ω^2	-1	$-\omega$	$-\omega^2$
	1	$-\omega^2$	$-\omega$	-1	ω^2	ω

† These functions may, for example, be taken as $\psi_1 = e^{i\phi}$, $\psi_2 = e^{-i\phi}$. On reflection in a vertical plane, ϕ changes sign.

TABLE 6—*continued*

C_{4v}			E	C_2	$2C_4$	$2\sigma_v$	$2\sigma'_v$
	D_4		E	C_2	$2C_4$	$2U_2$	$2U'_2$
		D_{2d}	E	C_2	$2S_4$	$2U_2$	$2\sigma_d$
$A_1; z$	A_1	A_1	1	1	1	1	1
A_2	$A_2; z$	A_2	1	1	1	−1	−1
B_1	B_1	B_1	1	1	−1	1	−1
B_2	B_2	$B_2; z$	1	1	−1	−1	1
$E; x, y$	$E; x, y$	$E; x, y$	2	−2	0	0	0

D_6			E	C_2	$2C_3$	$2C_6$	$3U_2$	$3U'_2$
	C_{6v}		E	C_2	$2C_3$	$2C_6$	$3\sigma_v$	$3\sigma'_v$
		D_{3h}	E	σ_h	$2C_3$	$2S_3$	$3U_2$	$3\sigma'_v$
A_1	$A_1; z$	A_1'	1	1	1	1	1	1
$A_2; z$	A_2	A_2'	1	1	1	1	−1	−1
B_1	B_2	A_1''	1	−1	1	−1	1	−1
B_2	B_1	$A_2''; z$	1	−1	1	−1	−1	1
E_2	E_2	$E'; x, y$	2	2	−1	−1	0	0
$E_1; x, y$	$E_1; x, y$	E''	2	−2	−1	1	0	0

T	E	$3C_2$	$4C_3$	$4C_3^2$
A	1	1	1	1
E	1	1	ε	ε^2
	1	1	ε^2	ε
$F; x, y, z$	3	−1	0	0

O		E	$8C_3$	$3C_2$	$6C_2$	$6C_4$
	T_d	E	$8C_3$	$3C_2$	$6\sigma_d$	$6S_4$
A_1	A_1	1	1	1	1	1
A_2	A_2	1	1	1	−1	−1
E	E	2	−1	2	0	0
F_2	$F_2; x, y, z$	3	0	−1	1	−1
$F_1; x, y, z$	F_1	3	0	−1	−1	1

It follows from these considerations that the group C_{3v} (and D_3, which is isomorphous with it) has two one-dimensional irreducible representations and one two-dimensional, with the characters shown in the table. The fact that we have indeed found all the irreducible representations may be seen from the result $1^2+1^2+2^2 = 6$, which is the order of the group.

Similar considerations give the characters of the representations of other groups of the same type (C_{4v}, C_{6v}).

The group T is obtained from the group V by adding rotations about four oblique axes of the third order. A function invariant with respect to transformations of the group V (a basis of the representation A) can be multiplied, under the rotation C_3, by 1, $e^{2\pi i/3}$ or $e^{2(2\pi i/3)}$. The base functions of the three one-dimensional representations B_1, B_2, B_3 of the group V change into one another under rotations about the axis of the third order (this is seen, for example, if we take as these functions the co-ordinates x, y, z themselves). Thus we obtain three one-dimensional irreducible representations and one three-dimensional ($1^2+1^2+1^2+3^2 = 12$).

Finally, let us consider the isomorphous groups O and T_d. The group T_d is obtained from the group T by adding reflections σ_d in planes each of which passes through two axes of the third order. A base function of the unit representation A of the group T may be symmetric or antisymmetric with respect to these reflections (which all belong to one class), and this gives two one-dimensional representations of the group T_d. Functions multiplied by ϵ or ϵ^2 under a rotation about an axis of the third order (the basis of the complex conjugate representations E of the group T) change into each other on reflection in a plane passing through this axis, so that one two-dimensional representation is obtained. Finally, of three base functions of the representation F of the group T, one is transformed into itself on reflection (and can either remain unaltered or change sign), while the other two change into each other. Thus we have altogether two one-dimensional representations, one two-dimensional and two three-dimensional.

The representations of the remaining point groups in which we are interested can be obtained immediately from those already given, if we notice that the remaining groups are direct products of those already considered with the group C_i (or C_s):

$$
\begin{array}{lll}
C_{3h} = C_3\times C_s & D_{2h} = D_2\times C_i & D_{3d} = D_3\times C_i \\
C_{4h} = C_4\times C_i & D_{4h} = D_4\times C_i & D_{6h} = D_6\times C_i \\
C_{6h} = C_6\times C_i & S_6 = C_3\times C_i & T_h = T\times C_i \\
 & & O_h = O\times C_i
\end{array}
$$

Each of these direct products has twice as many irreducible representations as the original group, half of them being symmetric and the other half antisymmetric with respect to inversion. The characters of these representations are obtained from those of the representations of the original group by multiplying by ± 1 (in accordance with the rule (91.24)). Thus, for instance, we have for the group $\boldsymbol{D}_{3d}$ the representations:

D_{3d}	E	$2C_3$	$3U_2$	I	$2S_6$	$3\sigma_d$
A_{1g}	1	1	1	1	1	1
A_{2g}	1	1	−1	1	1	−1
E_g	2	−1	0	2	−1	0
A_{1u}	1	1	1	−1	−1	−1
A_{2u}	1	1	−1	−1	−1	1
E_u	2	−1	0	−2	1	0

§93. Irreducible representations and the classification of terms

The quantum-mechanical applications of group theory are based on the fact that the SCHRÖDINGER's equation for a physical system (an atom or molecule) is invariant with respect to symmetry transformations of the system. It follows at once from this that, on applying the elements of a group to a function satisfying SCHRÖDINGER's equation for some value of the energy (an eigenvalue), we must again obtain solutions of the same equation for the same value of the energy. In other words, under a symmetry transformation the wave functions of the stationary states of the system belonging to a given energy level transform into linear combinations of one another, i.e. they give some representation of the group. An important fact is that this representation is irreducible. For functions which are invariably transformed into linear combinations of themselves under symmetry transformations must belong to the same energy level; the equality of the eigenvalues of the energy corresponding to several groups of functions (into which the basis of a reducible representation can be divided), which are not transformed into combinations of one another, would, however, be an utterly improbable coincidence (provided that there is no special reason for such equality; see below).

Thus, to each energy level of the system, there corresponds some irreducible representation of its symmetry group. The dimension of this representation determines the degree of degeneracy of the level concerned, i.e. the number of different states with the energy in question. The fixing of the irreducible representation determines all the symmetry properties of the given state, i.e. its behaviour with respect to the various symmetry transformations.

Irreducible representations of dimension greater than one are found only in groups containing non-commuting elements; Abelian groups have only one-dimensional irreducible representations. It is apposite to recall here that the relation between degeneracy and the presence of operators which do not commute with one another (but do commute with the Hamiltonian) has already been found above from considerations unrelated to group theory (§10).

The following important reservation should be made regarding all these statements. As has already been pointed out (§16), the symmetry (valid in the absence of a magnetic field) with respect to a change in the sign of the time has, in quantum mechanics, the result that complex conjugate wave functions must belong to the same eigenvalue of the energy. Hence it follows that, if some set of functions and the set of complex conjugate functions give different irreducible representations of a group, these two complex conjugate representations must be regarded, from the physical point of view, as forming together a single representation of twice the dimension. In the preceding section we had examples of such representations. Thus the group C_3 has only one-dimensional representations; however, two of these are complex conjugates, and correspond physically to doubly degenerate energy levels. (In the presence of a magnetic field there is no symmetry with respect to a change in the sign of the time, and hence complex conjugate representations correspond to different energy levels.)

Let us suppose that a physical system is subjected to the action of some perturbation (i.e. the system is placed in an external field). The question arises to what extent the perturbation can result in a splitting of the degenerate levels. The external field has itself a certain symmetry. If this symmetry is the same as or higher† than that of the unperturbed system, the symmetry of the perturbed Hamiltonian $\hat{H} = \hat{H}_0 + \hat{V}$ is the same as the symmetry of the unperturbed operator $\hat{H}_0$. It is clear that, in this case, no splitting of the degenerate levels occurs. If, however, the symmetry of the perturbation is lower than that of the unperturbed system, then the symmetry of the Hamiltonian $\hat{H}$ is the same as that of the perturbation $\hat{V}$. The wave functions which gave an irreducible representation of the symmetry group of the operator $\hat{H}_0$ will also give a representation of the symmetry group of the perturbed operator $\hat{H}$, but this representation may be reducible, and this means that the degenerate level is split.

The most important examples of this kind relate to the splitting of the energy levels of atoms in a crystal lattice. For example, we may consider the energy levels of the *d* and *f* shells of ions in a crystal lattice, which interact slightly with the surrounding atoms. The field acting on an ion due to the remaining atoms can then be regarded as a weak perturbation $\hat{V}$, and its symmetry is that of a point group. The unperturbed Hamiltonian $\hat{H}_0$, on the other hand, relates to a free atom, and its symmetry is that of the group of complete spherical symmetry (see §95). The Problem to §96 gives an instance of the determination of the splitting in such a case.

---

† If a symmetry group H is a sub-group of the group G, we say that H corresponds to a *lower symmetry* and G to a *higher symmetry*. It is evident that the symmetry of the sum of two expressions, one of which has the symmetry of G and the other that of H, is the lower symmetry, that of H.

§94. Selection rules for matrix elements

Group theory not only enables us to carry out a classification of the terms of any symmetrical physical system, but also gives us a simple method of finding the selection rules for the matrix elements of the various quantities which characterise the system.

This method is based on the following general theorem. Let $\psi_i^{(\alpha)}$ be one of the base functions of an irreducible (non-unit) representation of a symmetry group. Then the integral of this function over all space† vanishes identically:

$$\int \psi_i^{(\alpha)} \, dq = 0. \tag{94.1}$$

The proof is based on the evident fact that the integral over all space is invariant with respect to any transformation of the co-ordinate system, including any symmetry transformation. Hence

$$\int \psi_i^{(\alpha)} \, dq = \int \hat{G}\psi_i^{(\alpha)} \, dq = \int \sum_k G_{ki}^{(\alpha)} \psi_k^{(\alpha)} \, dq.$$

We sum this equation over all the elements of the group. The integral on the left is simply multiplied by g, the order of the group, and we have

$$g \int \psi_i^{(\alpha)} \, dq = \sum_k \int \psi_k^{(\alpha)} \sum_G G_{ki}^{(\alpha)} \, dq.$$

However, for any non-unit irreducible representation we have identically

$$\sum_G G_{ki}^{(\alpha)} = 0;$$

this is a particular case of the orthogonality relations (91.10), when one of the irreducible representations is the unit representation. This proves the theorem.

If ψ is a function belonging to some reducible representation of a group, the integral $\int \psi \, dq$ will be zero except when this representation contains the unit representation. This theorem is a direct consequence of the previous one.

Let f be the operator of some scalar physical quantity. By definition, it is invariant with respect to all symmetry transformations. Its matrix elements are the integrals

$$\int \psi_i^{(\alpha)*} f \psi_k^{(\beta)} \, dq, \tag{94.2}$$

where the indices α, β distinguish different terms of the system, and the suffixes i, k denumerate the wave functions of states belonging to the same degenerate term. We denote the irreducible representations of the symmetry

† That is, the configuration space of the physical system concerned.

group of the system concerned that are given by the functions $\psi_i^{(\alpha)}$ and $\psi_k^{(\beta)}$ by the symbols $D^{(\alpha)}$ and $D^{(\beta)}$. The products $\psi_i^{(\alpha)} \psi_k^{(\beta)}$ give the representation $D^{(\alpha)} \times D^{(\beta)}$; since the operator $\hat{f}$ itself is invariant with respect to all transformations, the whole expression in the integrand belongs to this representation. The direct product of two different irreducible representations, however, does not contain the unit representation, whilst the direct product of an irreducible representation with itself always contains the unit representation, and only once; the integrals (94.2) are a constant (independent of i and k)† times δ_{ik}. Thus we reach the conclusion that, for a scalar quantity, the matrix elements are non-zero only for transitions between states of the same type (i.e. belonging to the same irreducible representation). This is the most general form of a theorem of which we have already met several particular cases.

Let us next consider some vector physical quantity **A**. The three components A_x, A_y, A_z transform into linear combinations of themselves under symmetry transformations, like the components of any vector, and therefore give some representation of the symmetry group, which we shall denote by‡ D_A. The products $\psi_i^{(\alpha)} \hat{\mathbf{A}} \psi_k^{(\beta)}$ give the representation $D^{(\alpha)} \times D_A \times D^{(\beta)}$; the matrix elements are non-zero if this representation contains the unit representation. In practice, it is more convenient to decompose into irreducible parts the direct product $D^{(\alpha)} \times D_A$; this gives us immediately all the types $D^{(\beta)}$ of states for transitions into which (from a state of type $D^{(\alpha)}$) the matrix elements are not zero.

The diagonal matrix elements (unlike those for transitions between different states of the same type) require special consideration. In this case we have only one system of functions $\psi_i^{(\alpha)}$, not two different ones, and their products in pairs give the symmetric product $[D^{(\alpha)2}]$ of the representation $D^{(\alpha)}$ with itself, not the direct product $D^{(\alpha)} \times D^{(\alpha)}$. Hence the presence of diagonal matrix elements of a vector quantity means that the unit representation is present in the decomposition of the product $[D^{(\alpha)2}] \times D_A$, or, what is the same thing, that D_A is present in $[D^{(\alpha)2}]$||.

Similarly we can find the selection rules for the matrix elements of a tensor. Examples of the application of these rules are given in the following Problems.

PROBLEMS

PROBLEM 1. Find the selection rules for the matrix elements of a polar vector when symmetry $\boldsymbol{O}$ is present.

SOLUTION. The components of a vector are transformed by the irreducible representation F_1. The decompositions of the direct products of F_1 with the other representations of the

† The characters of the representation $D^{(\alpha)} \times D^{(\beta)}$ are equal to $\chi^{(\alpha)}(G)\, \chi^{(\beta)}(G)$. In order to find whether the unit representation is contained in this representation, we simply sum the characters over G (in accordance with (91.16)) and divide the result by the order g of the group. According to the orthogonality relations, we then have zero if $D^{(\alpha)}$ and $D^{(\beta)}$ are different, and unity if they are the same.

‡ In general D_A is different for polar and axial vectors.

|| We did not make this remark in considering the scalar quantity f, seeing that the symmetric product $[D^{(\alpha)2}]$, like the direct product $D^{(\alpha)} \times D^{(\alpha)}$, always contains the unit representation. Hence the diagonal matrix elements of a scalar quantity are, in general, different from zero.

group O are

$$F_1\times A_1 = F_1, \quad F_1\times A_2 = F_2, \quad F_1\times E = F_1+F_2,$$
$$F_1\times F_1 = A_1+E+F_1+F_2, \quad F_1\times F_2 = A_2+E+F_1+F_2. \tag{1}$$

Hence the non-zero non-diagonal matrix elements are those for the transitions

$$F_1\leftrightarrow A_1, E, F_1, F_2; \qquad F_2\leftrightarrow A_2, E, F_2.$$

The symmetric products of the irreducible representations of the group O are

$$[A_1^2] = [A_2^2] = A_1, \quad [E^2] = A_1+E, \quad [F_1^2] = [F_2^2] = A_1+E+F_2. \tag{2}$$

F_1 is contained in none of these; hence the diagonal matrix elements vanish.

PROBLEM 2. The same as Problem 1, but for symmetry D_{3d}.

SOLUTION. The z-component of the vector is transformed by the representation A_{2u}, the x and y components by E_u. We have

$$E_u\times A_{1g} = E_u\times A_{2g} = E_u, \quad E_u\times A_{1u} = E_u\times A_{2u} = E_g,$$
$$E_u\times E_u = A_{1g}+A_{2g}+E_g, \quad E_u\times E_g = A_{1u}+A_{2u}+E_u. \tag{1}$$

Hence the non-diagonal matrix elements of A_x, A_y are non-zero for the transitions $E_u \leftrightarrow A_{1g}$, A_{2g}, E_g; $E_g \leftrightarrow A_{1u}$, A_{2u}. In the same way we find the selection rules for the matrix elements of A_z: $A_{1g} \leftrightarrow A_{2u}$, $A_{2g} \leftrightarrow A_{1u}$, $E_g \leftrightarrow E_u$.

The symmetric products of the irreducible representations are

$$[A_{1g}^2] = [A_{1u}^2] = [A_{2g}^2] = [A_{2u}^2] = A_{1g},$$
$$[E_g^2] = [E_u^2] = E_g+A_{1g}. \tag{2}$$

These do not contain either A_{2u} or E_u; hence the diagonal matrix elements vanish for both A_z and A_x, A_y.

PROBLEM 3. Find the selection rules for the matrix elements of a symmetrical tensor A_{ik} of rank two (with $A_{xx}+A_{yy}+A_{zz} = 0$) when symmetry O is present.

SOLUTION. The components A_{xy}, A_{xz}, A_{yz} are transformed by F_2. Decomposing the direct products of F_2 with all the representations of the group O, we find the selection rules $F_1 \leftrightarrow A_2$, E, F_1, F_2; $F_2 \leftrightarrow A_1$, E, F_1, F_2. The diagonal matrix elements exist (as we see from (2), Problem 1) for the states F_1 and F_2.

The sums $A_{xx}+\varepsilon A_{yy}+\varepsilon^2 A_{zz}$, $A_{xx}+\varepsilon^2 A_{yy}+\varepsilon A_{zz}$ ($\varepsilon = e^{2\pi i/3}$) are transformed by the representation E. The selection rules for the non-diagonal elements are $E \leftrightarrow A_1, A_2, E$; $F_1 \leftrightarrow F_1, F_2$; $F_2 \leftrightarrow F_2$. The diagonal elements are non-zero for the states E, F_1, F_2.

PROBLEM 4. The same as Problem 3, but for symmetry D_{3d}.

SOLUTION. A_{zz} is transformed by A_{1g}, i.e. A_{zz} behaves as a scalar. The components $A_{xx}-A_{yy}$ and A_{xy} are transformed by E_g; the same is true of the components A_{xz}, A_{yz}. Decomposing the direct products of E_g with all the representations of the group D_{3d}, we find the selection rules for the non-diagonal matrix elements; $E_g \leftrightarrow A_{1g}$, A_{2g}, E_g; $E_u \leftrightarrow A_{1u}$, A_{2u}, E_u. The diagonal elements are not zero (as we see from (2), Problem 2) only for the states E_g and E_u.

§95. Continuous groups

As well as the point groups enumerated in §90, there exist also what are called *continuous point groups*, having an infinite number of elements. These are the groups of axial and spherical symmetry.

The simplest axial symmetry group is the group C_∞, which contains rotations $C(\phi)$ through any angle ϕ about the axis of symmetry; this is called the *two-dimensional rotation group*. It may be regarded as the limiting case of the groups $\boldsymbol{C}_n$ as $n \to \infty$. Similarly, as limiting cases of the groups $\boldsymbol{C}_{nh}$, $\boldsymbol{C}_{nv}$, $\boldsymbol{D}_n$, $\boldsymbol{D}_{nh}$ we obtain the continuous groups $\boldsymbol{C}_{\infty h}$, $\boldsymbol{C}_{\infty v}$, $\boldsymbol{D}_{\infty}$, $\boldsymbol{D}_{\infty h}$.

A molecule has axial symmetry only if it consists of atoms lying in a straight line. If it meets this condition, but is asymmetric about its midpoint, its point group will be the group $\boldsymbol{C}_{\infty v}$, which, besides rotations about the axis, contains also reflections σ_v in any plane passing through the axis. If, on the other hand, the molecule is symmetrical about its midpoint, its point group will be $\boldsymbol{D}_{\infty h} = \boldsymbol{C}_{\infty v} \times \boldsymbol{C}_i$. The groups $\boldsymbol{C}_{\infty}$, $\boldsymbol{C}_{\infty h}$, $\boldsymbol{D}_{\infty}$ cannot appear as the symmetry groups of a molecule.

The group of complete spherical symmetry contains rotations through any angle about any axis passing through the centre, and reflections in any plane passing through the centre; this group, which we shall denote by $\boldsymbol{K}_h$, is the symmetry group of a single atom. It contains as a sub-group the group $\boldsymbol{K}$ of all spatial rotations (called the *three-dimensional rotation group*, or simply the *rotation group*). The group $\boldsymbol{K}_h$ can be obtained from the group $\boldsymbol{K}$ by adding a centre of symmetry ($\boldsymbol{K}_h = \boldsymbol{K} \times \boldsymbol{C}_i$).

The elements of a continuous group may be distinguished by one or more parameters which take a continuous range of values. Thus, in the rotation group, the parameters might be the two angles determining the direction of the axis, and the angle of rotation about this axis.

The general properties of finite groups described in §89, and the concepts appertaining to them (sub-groups, conjugate elements, classes, etc.), can be at once generalised to continuous groups. Of course, the statements which directly concern the order of the group (for instance, that the order of a sub-group divides the order of the group) are no longer meaningful.

In the group $\boldsymbol{C}_{\infty v}$ all planes of symmetry are equivalent, so that all reflections σ_v form a single class with a continuous series of elements; the axis of symmetry is bilateral, so that there is a continuous series of classes, each containing two elements $C(\pm\phi)$. The classes of the group $\boldsymbol{D}_{\infty h}$ are obtained at once from those of the group $\boldsymbol{C}_{\infty v}$, since $\boldsymbol{D}_{\infty h} = \boldsymbol{C}_{\infty v} \times \boldsymbol{C}_i$.

In the rotation group $\boldsymbol{K}$, all axes are equivalent and bilateral; hence the classes of this group are rotations through an angle of fixed absolute magnitude $|\phi|$ about any axis. The classes of the group $\boldsymbol{K}_h$ are obtained at once from those of the group $\boldsymbol{K}$.

The concept of representations, reducible and irreducible, can also be immediately generalised to the case of continuous groups. Each irreducible representation contains a continuous series of matrices, but the number of base functions that are transformed into combinations of themselves (i.e. the dimension of the representation) is finite. These functions can always be chosen so that the representation is unitary. The number of different irreducible representations of a continuous group is infinite, but they form a discrete series, i.e. they can be denumerated. For the matrix elements and characters of these representations we have orthogonality relations which are a direct generalisation of the corresponding relations for finite groups.

Instead of (91.12) we now have

$$\int G_{ik}^{(\alpha)}G_{lm}^{(\beta)*}\,\mathrm{d}\tau_G = \frac{1}{f_\alpha}\delta_{\alpha\beta}\delta_{il}\delta_{km}\int \mathrm{d}\tau_G, \tag{95.1}$$

and for the characters, instead of (91.13),

$$\int \chi^{(\alpha)}(G)\chi^{(\beta)}(G)^*\,\mathrm{d}\tau_G = \delta_{\alpha\beta}\int \mathrm{d}\tau_G. \tag{95.2}$$

The integration in these formulae is what is called *invariant integration* over the group; the element of integration $\mathrm{d}\tau_G$ is expressed in terms of the parameters of the group and their differentials, in such a way that any transformation of the group acting on $\mathrm{d}\tau_G$ leaves it unchanged.† Thus, in the rotation group, we can take $\mathrm{d}\tau_G = \sin\theta\,\mathrm{d}\theta\,\mathrm{d}\psi\,\mathrm{d}\phi$, where θ, ψ, ϕ are Eulerian angles (see the end of §57) determining the rotation.

We have already found, in essence, the irreducible representations of the three-dimensional rotation group (without using the terminology of group theory), when determining the eigenvalues and eigenfunctions of the total angular momentum. For the angular momentum operator is fundamentally the operator of an infinitely small rotation, and its eigenvalues characterise the behaviour of the wave functions with respect to spatial rotations. To a value j of the angular momentum there correspond $2j+1$ different eigenfunctions, differing in the values of the z-component of the angular momentum and all belonging to one $(2j+1)$-fold degenerate energy level. Under rotations of the co-ordinate system, these functions are transformed into linear combinations of themselves, and thus give irreducible representations of the rotation group. Thus, from the group-theory point of view, the numbers j number the irreducible representations of the rotation group, and one $(2j+1)$-dimensional representation corresponds to each j. The number j takes integral and half-integral values, so that the dimension $2j+1$ of the representation takes all the integral values 1, 2, 3, ...

The base functions of these representations have been, in essence, investigated in Chapter VIII. The basis of a representation of given j is formed by the $2j+1$ independent components of a symmetrical spinor of rank $2j$.

It is easy to determine the characters of the irreducible representations of the rotation group. Since the characters of elements of the same class are the same, it suffices to consider rotations about a single axis, the z-axis. The behaviour of the wave functions under rotation about the z-axis is determined, as we know, by the value of the z-component of the angular momentum, i.e. by the value of m; the wave function of a state with a given m is simply multiplied by $e^{im\phi}$ on rotation through an angle ϕ about the z-axis. By giving

† These statements regarding the properties of irreducible representations of continuous groups are valid only if the integrals in (95.1) and (95.2) converge; in particular, the "volume of the group" $\int \mathrm{d}\tau_G$ must be finite. This condition is satisfied for continuous point groups. However, in relativistic quantum mechanics we meet with another continuous group (called the *Lorentz group*), which does not satisfy the above condition.

m all values from $-j$ to j, we obtain the transformation matrix of the $2j+1$ base functions; it is diagonal, with character

$$\chi^{(j)}(\phi) = \sum_{m=-j}^{j} e^{im\phi}.$$

Effecting the summation, we have

$$\chi^{(j)}(\phi) = \frac{e^{i(j+1)\phi}-e^{-ij\phi}}{e^{i\phi}-1} = \frac{\sin(j+\frac{1}{2})\phi}{\sin\frac{1}{2}\phi}. \qquad (95.3)$$

The irreducible representations of the rotation group which correspond to half-integral values of j are distinguished by important properties. We see from (95.3) that, for half-integral j,

$$\chi(\phi+2\pi) = -\chi(\phi),$$

while for integral j

$$\chi(\phi+2\pi) = \chi(\phi).$$

This means that, under a rotation through 2π, the base functions of the representation change sign (in accordance with the behaviour of spinors of odd rank). Since, however, a rotation through 2π is the same as the unit element of the group, we reach the result that representations with half-integral j are, as we say, *two-valued*; to each element of the group (a rotation through an angle ϕ, $0 \leqslant \phi \leqslant 2\pi$, about some axis) there correspond in such a representation not one but two matrices, with characters differing in sign.†

An isolated atom has, as we have already remarked, the symmetry $\boldsymbol{K}_h = \boldsymbol{K}\times\boldsymbol{C}_i$. Hence, from the group-theory point of view, there corresponds to each term of the atom some irreducible representation of the rotation group $\boldsymbol{K}$ (determining the value of the total angular momentum J of the atom) and an irreducible representation of the group $\boldsymbol{C}_i$ (determining the parity of the state).‡

Let us pause to consider briefly also the irreducible representations of the axial symmetry group $\boldsymbol{C}_{\infty v}$. This problem has, in essence, been solved when we ascertained the classification of the electron terms of a diatomic molecule having this symmetry $\boldsymbol{C}_{\infty v}$ (i.e. when the two atoms are different). To the

† It must be mentioned that "two-valued representations" of a group are not, properly speaking, representations in the true sense of the word, since they are not given by one-valued base functions.

‡ Moreover, the Hamiltonian of the atom is invariant with respect to interchanges of the electrons. In the non-relativistic approximation, the co-ordinate and spin wave functions are separable, and we can speak of representations of the permutation group that are given by the co-ordinate functions. If the irreducible representation of the permutation group is given, the total spin s of the atom is determined (§61). When the relativistic interactions are taken into account, however, the separation of the wave functions into co-ordinate and spin parts is not possible. The symmetry with respect to simultaneous interchange of the co-ordinates and spins of the particles does not characterise the term, since Pauli's principle admits only those total wave functions which are antisymmetric with respect to all the electrons. This is in accordance with the fact that, when the relativistic interactions are taken into account, the spin is not, strictly speaking, conserved; only the total angular momentum J is conserved.

terms 0^+ and 0^- (with $\Omega = 0$) there correspond two one-dimensional irreducible representations, while to the doubly degenerate terms with $\Omega \neq 0$ there corresponds an infinite series of two-dimensional representations. Under a rotation through an angle ϕ about the axis of symmetry, the wave functions of states having values $\pm\Omega$ of the angular momentum about the axis are multiplied by $e^{\pm i\Omega\phi}$, while on reflection in a vertical plane they change into each other. Hence the characters of the irreducible representations of the group $C_{\infty v}$ are

$C_{\infty v}$	E	$2C(\phi)$	$\infty\sigma_v$
A_1	1	1	1
A_2	1	1	-1
E_1	2	$2\cos\phi$	0
...	...	...	...
E_k	2	$2\cos k\phi$	0
...	...	...	...

The irreducible representations of the group $D_{\infty h} = C_{\infty v} \times C_i$ are obtained at once from those of the group $C_{\infty v}$ (and correspond to the classification of the terms of a diatomic molecule composed of like nuclei).

If we take half-integral values for Ω, the functions $e^{\pm i\Omega\phi}$ give two-valued irreducible representations of the group $C_{\infty v}$, corresponding to the terms of the molecule having half-integral spin.†

§96. Two-valued representations of finite point groups

To the states of a system with half-integral spin (and therefore half-integral total angular momentum) there correspond two-valued representations of the point symmetry group of the system. This is a general property of spinors, and therefore holds for both continuous and finite point groups. The necessity thus arises of finding the two-valued irreducible representations of finite point groups.

As we have already remarked, the two-valued representations are not really true representations of a group. In particular, the relations discussed in §91 do not apply to them, and where all irreducible representations were considered in these relations (for example, in the relation (91.17) for the sum of the squared dimensions of the irreducible representations), only the true one-valued representations were meant.

To find the two-valued representations, it is convenient to employ the

† Contrary to the result for the three-dimensional rotation group, it would here be possible, by a suitable choice of fractional values of Ω, to obtain not only one-valued and two-valued representations, but also those of three or more values. However, the physically possible eigenvalues of the angular momentum, which is the operator of an infinitely small rotation, are determined by the representations of the aforementioned three-dimensional rotational group. Hence the three (or more)-valued representations of the two-dimensional rotation group (and of any finite symmetry group), though mathematically determinate, are without physical significance.

following artifice (H. BETHE 1929). We introduce, in a purely formal manner, the concept of a new element of the group (denoted by Q); this is a rotation through an angle of 2π about an arbitrary axis, and is not the unit element, but gives the latter when applied twice: $Q^2 = E$. Accordingly, rotations C_n about the axes of symmetry of the nth order will give identical transformations only after being applied $2n$ times (and not n times):

$$C_n^{\ n} = Q, \qquad C_n^{\ 2n} = E. \tag{96.1}$$

The inversion I, being an element which commutes with all rotations, must give E as before on being applied twice. A twofold reflection in a plane, however, gives Q, not E:

$$\sigma^2 = Q, \qquad \sigma^4 = E; \tag{96.2}$$

this follows, since the reflection can be written in the form $\sigma_h = IC_2$. As a result we obtain a set of elements forming some fictitious point symmetry group, whose order is twice that of the original group; such groups we shall call *double* point groups. The two-valued representations of the actual point group will clearly be one-valued (i.e. true) representations of the corresponding double group, so that they can be found by the usual methods.

The number of classes in the double group is greater than in the original group (but not, in general, twice as great). The element Q commutes with all the other elements of the group,† and hence always forms a class by itself. If the axis of symmetry is bilateral, the elements $C_n^{\ k}$ and $C_n^{\ 2n-k} = QC_n^{\ n-k}$ are conjugate in the double group. Hence, when axes of the second order are present, the distribution of the elements among classes depends also on whether these axes are bilateral (in ordinary point groups this is unimportant, since C_2 is the same as the opposite rotation C_2^{-1}).

Thus, for instance, in the group T the axes of the second order are equivalent, and each of them is bilateral, while the axes of the third order are equivalent but not bilateral. Hence the 24 elements of the double group‡ T' are distributed in seven classes: E, Q, the class of three rotations C_2 and three C_2Q, and the classes $4C_3$, $4C_3^{\ 2}$, $4C_3Q$, $4C_3^{\ 2}Q$.

The irreducible representations of a double point group include, firstly, representations which are the same as those of the simple group (a unit matrix corresponding to both Q and E); secondly, the two-valued representations of the simple group, a negative unit matrix corresponding to Q. It is these latter representations in which we are now interested.

The double groups C_n' ($n = 1, 2, 3, 4, 6$) and S_4', like the corresponding simple groups, are cyclic.‖ All their irreducible representations are one-dimensional, and can be found without difficulty as shown at the beginning of §92.

---

† This is obvious for rotations and inversion; for a reflection in a plane, it follows since the reflection can be represented as the product of an inversion and a rotation.

‡ We distinguish the double groups by primes to the symbols for the ordinary groups.

‖ The groups $S_2' \equiv C_i'$, $S_6' \equiv C_{3i}'$, however, which contain the inversion I, are Abelian but not cyclic.

The irreducible representations of the groups D_n' (or C_{nv}', which are isomorphous with them) can be found by the same method as for the corresponding simple groups. These representations are given by functions of the form $e^{\pm ik\phi}$, where ϕ is the angle of rotation about an axis of the nth order, and k is given half-integral values (the integral values correspond to the ordinary one-valued representations). Rotations about horizontal axes of the second order change these functions into one another, while the rotation C_n multiplies them by $e^{\pm 2\pi ik/n}$.

It is a little less easy to find the representations of the double cubic groups. The 24 elements of the group T' are divided among seven classes. Hence there are altogether seven irreducible representations, of which four are the same as those of the simple group T. The sum of the squared dimensions of the remaining three representations must be 12, and hence we find that they are all two-dimensional. Since the elements C_2 and C_2Q belong to the same class, $\chi(C_2) = \chi(C_2Q) = -\chi(C_2)$, whence we conclude that $\chi(C_2) = 0$ in all three representations. Next, at least one of the three representations must be real, since complex representations can occur only in conjugate pairs. Let us consider this representation, and suppose that the matrix of the element C_3 is brought to diagonal form, with diagonal elements a_1, a_2. Since $C_3^3 = Q$, $a_1^3 = a_2^3 = -1$. In order that $\chi(C_3) = a_1+a_2$ may be real, we must take $a_1 = e^{\pi i/3}$, $a_2 = e^{-\pi i/3}$. Hence we find that $\chi(C_3) = 1$, $\chi(C_3^2) = a_1^2+a_2^2 = -1$. Thus one of the required representations is obtained. By comparing its direct products with the two complex conjugate one-dimensional representations of the group T, we find the other two representations.

By means of similar arguments, which we shall not pause to give here, we may find the representations of the group O'. Table 7 gives the characters of the representations of the double groups mentioned above. Only those representations are shown which correspond to two-valued representations of the ordinary groups.

The remaining point groups are isomorphous with those we have considered, or else are obtained by direct multiplication of the latter by the group C_i, so that their representations do not need to be specially calculated.

For the same reasons as for ordinary representations, two complex conjugate two-valued representations must be regarded, from the physical point of view, as one representation of twice the dimension. However, in some cases it is necessary to pair two-valued representations even when they have real characters. We have seen in §58 that, in systems with half-integral spin, complex conjugate wave functions must be linearly independent. Hence, if we have a two-valued one-dimensional representation† with real characters (given by some function ψ), then, although the complex conjugate function ψ^* is transformed by the same representation, we can nevertheless see that ψ and ψ^* are linearly independent. Since, on the other hand, the complex conjugate wave functions must belong to the same energy level, we see that in physical applications this representation must be doubled.

† Such representations are found in the group C_n' for odd n; the characters are $\chi(C_n^k) = (-1)^k$.

TABLE 7
Two-valued representations of point groups

D_2'	E	Q	$C_2^{(x)}$ $C_2^{(x)}Q$	$C_2^{(y)}$ $C_2^{(y)}Q$	$C_2^{(z)}$ $C_2^{(z)}Q$
E'	2	-2	0	0	0

D_3'	E	Q	C_3 C_3^2Q	C_3^2 C_3Q	$3U_2$	$3U_2Q$
E_1'	1	-1	-1	1	i	$-i$
	1	-1	-1	1	$-i$	i
E_2'	2	-2	1	-1	0	0

D_6'	E	Q	C_2 C_2Q	C_3 C_3^2Q	C_3^2 C_3Q	C_6 C_6^5Q	C_6^5 C_6Q	$3U_2$ $3U_2Q$	$3U'_2$ $3U'_2Q$
E_1'	2	-2	0	1	-1	$\sqrt{3}$	$-\sqrt{3}$	0	0
E_2'	2	-2	0	1	-1	$-\sqrt{3}$	$\sqrt{3}$	0	0
E_3'	2	-2	0	-2	2	0	0	0	0

D_4'	E	Q	C_2 C_2Q	C_4 C_4^3Q	C_4^3 C_4Q	$2U_2$ $2U_2Q$	$2U'_2$ $2U'_2Q$
E_1'	2	-2	0	$\sqrt{2}$	$-\sqrt{2}$	0	0
E_2'	2	-2	0	$-\sqrt{2}$	$\sqrt{2}$	0	0

T'	E	Q	$4C_3$	$4C_3^2$	$4C_3Q$	$4C_3^2Q$	$3C_2$ $3C_2Q$
E'	2	-2	1	-1	-1	1	0
G'	2	-2	ε	$-\varepsilon^2$	$-\varepsilon$	ε^2	0
	2	-2	ε^2	$-\varepsilon$	$-\varepsilon^2$	ε	0

O'	E	Q	$4C_3$ $4C_3^2Q$	$4C_3^2$ $4C_3Q$	$3C_4^2$ $3C_4^2Q$	$3C_4$ $3C_4^3Q$	$3C_4^3$ $3C_4Q$	$6C_2$ $6C_2Q$
E_1'	2	-2	1	-1	0	$\sqrt{2}$	$-\sqrt{2}$	0
E_2'	2	-2	1	-1	0	$-\sqrt{2}$	$\sqrt{2}$	0
G'	4	-4	-1	1	0	0	0	0

PROBLEM

Determine how the levels of an atom (with given values of the total angular momentum J) are split when it is placed in a field having the cubic symmetry† O.

SOLUTION. The wave functions of the states of an atom with angular momentum J and various values M_J give a $(2J+1)$-dimensional reducible representation of the group O, with characters determined by the formula (95.3). Decomposing this representation into irreducible parts (one-valued for integral J and two-valued for half-integral J), we at once find the required splitting (cf. §93). We shall list the irreducible parts of the representations corresponding to the first few values of J;

$J=0$	A_1
1/2	E_1'
1	F_1
3/2	G'
2	$E+F_2$
5/2	$E_2'+G'$
3	$A_2+F_1+F_2$
...	...

§97. Addition of angular momenta

The concept of irreducible representations of the rotation group enables us to give a new derivation of the rule of addition for angular momenta.

Let j_1, j_2 ($j_1 \geqslant j_2$) be the angular momenta of two particles (or systems), whose interaction we neglect. To their energy levels there correspond $(2j_1+1)$- and $(2j_2+1)$-dimensional representations of the rotation group, which we shall denote by the symbols D_{j_1} and D_{j_2}. The basis of these representations is formed by the wave functions of the two systems, which we denote by $\psi^{(1)}_{j_1m_1}$ ($m_1 = -j_1, -j_1+1, \ldots, j_1$) and $\psi^{(2)}_{j_2m_2}$ ($m_2 = -j_2, \ldots, j_2$) respectively.

If we regard the two particles together as one system, all its possible states (for given j_1, j_2) are described, in the approximation considered, by the wave functions $\psi^{(1)}_{j_1m_1}\psi^{(2)}_{j_2m_2}$. These $(2j_1+1)(2j_2+1)$ functions give a representation of the rotation group, which is the direct product $D_{j_1}\times D_{j_2}$ of the representations D_{j_1} and D_{j_2}. On decomposing it into irreducible parts, we have the possible values of the total angular momentum j of the system.

The characters of the representation $D_{j_1}\times D_{j_2}$ are equal to the products of the characters of the representations D_{j_1} and D_{j_2}. By means of formula (95.3) we find

$$\chi^{(j_1)}(\phi)\chi^{(j_2)}(\phi) = \sum_{m_1=-j_1}^{j_1} \epsilon^{m_1} \sum_{m_2=-j_2}^{j_2} \epsilon^{m_2} = \sum_{m_2} \epsilon^{m_2}\frac{\epsilon^{j_1+1}-\epsilon^{-j_1}}{\epsilon-1},$$

† The presence or absence of a centre of symmetry in the symmetry group of the external field is immaterial to this problem, since the behaviour of the wave function on inversion (the parity of the level) is unrelated to the angular momentum J.

where we have put $\epsilon = e^{i\phi}$. This expression has to be put in the form of the sum of the characters of the irreducible representations D_j, i.e. in the form

$$\sum_j \frac{\epsilon^{j+1}-\epsilon^{-j}}{\epsilon-1}.$$

Equating these two expressions, cancelling $1/(\epsilon-1)$ and effecting the multiplications, we obtain

$$\epsilon^{j_1+j_2+1}+\epsilon^{j_1+j_2}+\ldots+\epsilon^{j_1-j_2+1}-\epsilon^{-(j_1-j_2)}-\ldots-\epsilon^{-(j_1+j_2)} = \sum_j (\epsilon^{j+1}-\epsilon^{-j}).$$

On combining pairs of positive and negative terms on the left-hand side of the equation, we see that j must take the values from j_1-j_2 to j_1+j_2 once each. In other words, we must write

$$D_{j_1} \times D_{j_2} = D_{j_1+j_2}+D_{j_1+j_2-1}+\ldots+D_{j_1-j_2}. \tag{97.1}$$

This corresponds exactly to the rule which we already know for the addition of angular momenta.

The methods of group theory, however, enable us to go considerably further in investigating the problem of the addition of angular momenta. The rule which we have obtained determines only the possible values of the total angular momentum j of the system; there remains to be discussed the question of the probability that the system will have any given value of j (for given j_1, j_2 and m_1, m_2). According to the general principles of quantum mechanics, this probability is determined by the squared moduli of the coefficients in the expansion of the wave function $\psi^{(1)}_{j_1m_1}\ \psi^{(2)}_{j_2m_2}$ (which describes the state of the system for given j_1, j_2, m_1, m_2) in terms of the wave functions Ψ_{jm} of the states with given j_1, j_2, j, m. For given values m_1, m_2 of the z-components of the angular momenta of the two particles, the number m for the system is equal to the sum m_1+m_2. Hence the expansion is of the form

$$\psi^{(1)}_{j_1m_1}\ \psi^{(2)}_{j_2m_2} = \sum_j C^j_{m_1m_2}\ \Psi_{j,m_1+m_2}. \tag{97.2}$$

The squares $|C^j_{m_1m_2}|^2$ give the required probability. The quantities $C^j_{m_1m_2}$ are called the *Clebsch-Gordan coefficients*.

If the expansion (97.2) is known, we can at once write down the converse formulae which express the functions Ψ_{jm} in terms of the products $\psi^{(1)}_{j_1m_1} \times \psi^{(2)}_{j_2m_2}$. To do this, it is sufficient to notice that, since both form complete sets of normalised and orthogonal functions, the transformation of one set into the other is given by a unitary matrix (§91). Hence the transformation converse to (97.2) has the form

$$\Psi_{jm} = \sum_{m_1} C^{j*}_{m_1,m-m_1}\ \psi^{(1)}_{j_1m_1}\ \psi^{(1)}_{j_2,m-m_1}. \tag{97.3}$$

In this form, the formula determines the wave functions of the states of the system with given values of j, m in terms of the wave functions of the two particles.

The calculation of the coefficients $C^{j}_{m_1 m_2}$ requires a knowledge of the matrices of the irreducible representations of the rotation group, and not only of their characters. These matrices can be found by utilising the fact that the representation D_j can be given by the components of a symmetrical spinor of rank $2j$. Here it is evidently sufficient to consider a spinor of some particular form, which it is convenient to take as the $2j$-fold product with itself of a spinor ψ^{μ} of rank one. However, on taking the actual components of the spinor as base functions, we obtain a non-unitary representation. Hence we take, as the basis, functions $\psi(m)$ related to the components of the spinor by

$$\psi(m) = \sqrt{[(2j)!/(j+m)!\,(j-m)!]}(\psi^1)^{j+m}(\psi^2)^{j-m},$$
$$m = -j, \ldots, j \tag{97.4}$$

(see (56.2)).† These functions, regarded as the wave functions of some system for states with various values of the z-component of angular momentum, are normalised and orthogonal, so that the representation given by them is unitary.

A spatial rotation determined by the Eulerian angles ψ, θ, ϕ is equivalent to a binary transformation with parameters α, β given by (57.7). Under this transformation, the components of a spinor of rank one are transformed according to the formulae

$$\hat{G}\psi^1 = \alpha\psi^1+\beta\psi^2, \qquad \hat{G}\psi^2 = -\beta^*\psi^1+\alpha^*\psi^2,$$

where $\hat{G}$ denotes the operator of the rotation in question. The result of the action of the operator $\hat{G}$ on the function $\psi(m)$ is consequently

$$\hat{G}\psi(m) = \sqrt{[(2j)!/(j+m)!(j-m)!]}(\alpha\psi^1+\beta\psi^2)^{j+m}(-\beta^*\psi^1+\alpha^*\psi^2)^{j-m}.$$

Expanding the parentheses by the binomial theorem and expressing the products of ψ^1 and ψ^2 in terms of the functions $\psi(m)$ again, we can put the above expression in the form

$$\hat{G}\psi(m) = \sum_{m'} G^{(j)}_{m'm}\psi(m').$$

The coefficients $G^{(j)}_{m'm}$ form the required unitary matrices of the irreducible representation D_j of the rotation group. A simple calculation gives the rather complicated expression

$$G^{(j)}_{m'm} = \sum_k (-1)^k \frac{\sqrt{[(j+m)!\,(j-m)!(j+m')!\,(j-m')!]}}{(j-m-k)!\,(j+m'-k)!\,k!\,(k+m-m')!}\times$$
$$\times\alpha^{j+m'-k}\alpha^{*j-m-k}\beta^{k+m-m'}\beta^{*k}. \tag{97.5}$$

† We use the formulae of §§54–56, but write j and m in place of s and σ.

The sum is taken over all integers k, starting from zero, but it must be remembered that all terms in the sum that contain the factorial of a negative number in the denominator vanish.

Let us turn now to the problem proposed above of determining the coefficients in (97.2). The quantities $C^{j}_{m_1 m_2}$ can be regarded as the matrix elements of some unitary operator $\hat{C}$, which gives a linear transformation of the base functions of the reducible representation $D_{j_1} \times D_{j_2}$ of the rotation group. If we take as base functions the products $\psi^{(1)}_{j_1 m_1} \psi^{(2)}_{j_2 m_2}$, the elements of the matrices of this representation are equal to the products $G^{(j_1)}_{m_1' m_1} \times \times G^{(j_2)}_{m_2' m_2}$, while if the functions Ψ_{jm} are taken the elements are $G^{(j)}_{m'm}$. On the other hand, the matrices of two equivalent representations are connected by relations corresponding to the operator relation (91.7). In this case, these matrix relations take the form

$$G^{(j_1)}_{m_1' m_1} G^{(j_2)}_{m_2' m_2} = \sum_{j'} C^{j'*}_{m_1' m_2'} G^{(j')}_{m_1'+m_2', m_1+m_2} C^{j'}_{m_1 m_2}.$$

We multiply both sides of this equation by $G^{(j)*}_{m_1'+m_2', m_1+m_2}$ and integrate over the whole group. By the orthogonality relations (95.1), only the term with $j' = j$ remains in the sum over j' on the right-hand side of the equation, and we obtain

$$\int G^{(j_1)}_{m_1' m_1} G^{(j_2)}_{m_2' m_2} G^{(j)*}_{m_1'+m_2', m_1+m_2} \, d\tau_G = \frac{g}{2j+1} C^{j*}_{m_1' m_2'} C^{j}_{m_1 m_2}, \tag{97.6}$$

where $g = \int d\tau_G$.

This formula solves the problem in principle. It is found that all the $C^{j}_{m_1 m_2}$ can be taken real. It is convenient to calculate first $C^{j}_{j_1, -j_2}$, putting in (97.6) $m_1 = m_1' = j_1$, $m_2 = m_2' = -j_2$ (this coefficient is simpler in form than the rest); the remaining coefficients are then calculated by putting $m_1' = j_1$, $m_2' = -j_2$. We shall omit these calculations,† and give only the final result (E. Wigner):

$$C^{j}_{m_1 m_2} = \sqrt{\left[\frac{(j+j_1-j_2)!\,(j-j_1+j_2)!\,(j_1+j_2-j)!\,(j+m)!\,(j-m)!\,(2j+1)}{(j+j_1+j_2+1)!\,(j_1-m_1)!\,(j_1+m_1)!\,(j_2-m_2)!\,(j_2+m_2)!}\right]} \times$$
$$\times \sum_k \frac{(-1)^{k+j_2+m_2}(j+j_2+m_1-k)!(j_1-m_1+k)!}{(j-j_1+j_2-k)!\,(j+m-k)!\,k!\,(k+j_1-j_2-m)!}. \tag{97.7}$$

The summation over all integral k reduces in reality to a summation over values from the greater of 0 and $j_2 - j_1 + m$ to the smaller of $j+m$ and $j - j_1 + j_2$.

The quantities $C^{j}_{m_1 m_2}$ are quite symmetrical, though it is difficult to see this immediately from the expression (97.7), because of the impossibility of explicitly calculating the sum in (97.7). This symmetry may be put in

† A more detailed account of the calculations may be found in E. Wigner's book, *Gruppentheorie und ihre Anwendung auf die Quantenmechanik der Atomspektren*, Vieweg, Brunswick 1931, p. 198.

evidence as follows. We formally consider a third particle of angular momentum $j_3 = j$, equal to that of the system of the other two particles. For the system of three particles there is, in particular, a state in which its total angular momentum is zero. The wave function of this state is equal to the sum

$$\sum_m (-1)^{j-m}\Psi_{jm}\psi^{(3)}_{j,-m}/\sqrt{(2j+1)}, \tag{97.8}$$

where Ψ_{jm} are the wave functions of the system of particles 1 and 2, and $\psi^{(3)}_{j_3m_3}$ those of particle 3.† We introduce a new notation for the coefficients $C^{j}_{m_1m_2}$:

$$C^{j_3}_{m_1m_2} = (-1)^{-j+m_1+m_2}\sqrt{(2j+1)}S_{j_1m_1;\,j_2m_2;\,j,-m_1-m_2}, \tag{97.9}$$

which indicates by suffixes all the quantum numbers on which they depend. For greater symmetry of notation, we write j_3 instead of j, and m_3 instead of $-(m_1+m_2)$; then

$$C^{j_3}_{m_1m_2} = (-1)^{-j_3-m_3}\sqrt{(2j_3+1)}S_{j_1m_1;\,j_2m_2;\,j_3m_3}. \tag{97.10}$$

Substituting in (97.8) for Ψ_{jm} the expression (97.3) with the new notation substituted, we obtain a sum of the form

$$\sum_{m_1,m_2,m_3} S_{j_1m_1;\,j_2m_2;\,j_3m_3}\psi^{(1)}_{j_1m_1}\psi^{(2)}_{j_2m_2}\psi^{(3)}_{j_3m_3}, \tag{97.11}$$

where the summation is taken with the condition $m_1+m_2+m_3 = 0$. When the total angular momentum is zero, however, all the three particles enter the system symmetrically, and the order in which their angular momenta are added is immaterial. In other words, when the order of addition of the angular momenta is changed, the expression (97.11) must remain unchanged apart from sign. Hence it follows that, when the pairs of suffixes j_1m_1, j_2m_2, j_3m_3 are interchanged, the quantities S can only either remain unchanged or all change sign simultaneously. A more precise investigation shows that

$$\begin{aligned} S_{j_1m_1;\,j_2m_2;\,j_3m_3} &= (-1)^{j_1+j_2-j_3}S_{j_2m_2;\,j_1m_1;\,j_3m_3} \\ &= (-1)^{j_2+j_3-j_1}S_{j_1m_1;\,j_3m_3;\,j_2m_2} = (-1)^{j_1+j_2+j_3}S_{j_3m_3;\,j_2m_2;\,j_1m_1}. \end{aligned} \tag{97.12}$$

The quantities S also have the following property:

$$S_{j_1,-m_1;\,j_2,-m_2;\,j_3,-m_3} = (-1)^{j_1+j_2+j_3}S_{j_1m_1;\,j_2m_2;\,j_3m_3}. \tag{97.13}$$

This is obtained at once from (97.7) by simultaneously changing the sign of m_1 and m_2 and replacing the summation variable k by $j+j_2-j_1-k$.

† For $j = 0$, $j_1 = j_2$, $m_1 = -m_2$, formula (97.7) gives

$$C_{m_1,-m_1}{}^{0} = (-1)^{j_1-m_1}/\sqrt{(2j_1+1)}.$$

We shall rewrite formula (97.7) in the new notation:

$$S_{j_1m_1;j_2m_2;j_3m_3} = \sqrt{\left[\frac{(j_3+j_1-j_2)!\,(j_3+j_2-j_1)!\,(j_1+j_2-j_3)!\,(j_3+m_3)!\,(j_3-m_3)!}{(j_1+j_2+j_3+1)!\,(j_1-m_1)!\,(j_1+m_1)!\,(j_2-m_2)!\,(j_2+m_2)!}\right]}\times$$
$$\times\sum_k \frac{(-1)^{k+j_2+j_3-m_1}(j_2+j_3+m_1-k)!\,(j_1-m_1+k)!}{(j_3-j_1+j_2-k)!\,(j_3-m_3-k)!\,k!\,(k+j_1-j_2+m_3)!}. \quad (97.14)$$

Here it is understood that $m_1+m_2+m_3 = 0$, while j_1, j_2, j_3 have values such that each of them can be obtained by adding (vectorially) the other two (geometrically, j_1, j_2, j_3 must be the sides of a triangle); in other words, each of them lies between the difference and the sum of the other two.

A knowledge of the quantities S enables us to determine comparatively simply the dependence on the quantum number m of the matrix elements of tensor physical quantities; these dependences are analogous to the formulae (27.11), (27.13) for the matrix elements of a vector, which, of course, can equally well be found by the method given below. Let $f^{(jm)}$ be a set of $2j+1$ quantities which transform into linear combinations of themselves, under transformations of the co-ordinates, as the components of the spin wave function of a particle with spin j; the indices j, m are here entirely formal, and do not relate to any actual angular momentum. Thus, for a vector $j = 1$, for a symmetric tensor of rank two $j = 2$, and so on; it must be remembered, however, that the quantities $f^{(jm)}$ are not precisely the same as the components of the vector or tensor, but are related to them in a definite manner (see §57, including the Problem).

By the definition of the matrix elements, we can write

$$\hat{f}^{(jm)}\psi_{j_2m_2} = \sum_{j_1m_1} (f^{(jm)})_{j_2m_2}^{j_1m_1}\psi_{j_1m_1}.$$

We multiply both sides of this equation by the wave function ψ_{jm} of a particle with angular momentum j and projection thereof m, and sum over m:

$$\sum_m \psi_{jm}\hat{f}^{(jm)}\psi_{j_2m_2} = \sum_{j_1m_1,m} (f^{(jm)})_{j_2m_2}^{j_1m_1}\psi_{j_1m_1}\psi_{jm}.$$

From its transformation law, the sum $\sum_m \psi_{jm}f^{(jm)}$ is a scalar. Hence the transformation law of the expression on the left-hand side is the same as that of the functions $\psi_{j_2m_2}$. The right-hand side must therefore be transformed according to a similar law. By comparing it with equation (97.3), we can conclude that the required matrix elements must be of the form

$$(f^{(jm)})_{j_2m_2}^{j_1m_1} = (f^{(j)})_{j_2}^{j_1}(-1)^{m_2}\sqrt{(2j_2+1)}S_{j_1m_1;\,jm;\,j_2,-m_2}, \quad (97.15)$$

where the $(f^{(j)})_{j_2}^{j_1}$ are quantities independent of m_1, m_2 and m. This formula solves the problem.

Finally, by means of the formulae obtained above we can solve the problem of determining the angular dependence of the wave functions of a particle with spin s, in states with given values of the orbital angular momentum l, the total angular momentum j and its projection m. The required function is denoted by $\Psi_{sl}^{jm}(\sigma)$ ($\sigma = -s, \ -s+1, \dots, s$). The problem is solved immediately by the general formula (97.3), which we write in the form

$$\psi_{jm} = \sum_{m_s} C^j_{m_s, m-m_s} \psi^{(1)}_{sm_s} \psi^{(2)}_{l,m-m_s},$$

changing the naming of the suffixes, and taking the functions ψ_{jm} to be the required functions $\Psi_{sl}^{jm}(\sigma)$, the functions $\psi_{lm_l}{}^{(2)}$ to be the eigenfunctions of the orbital momentum (i.e. the spherical harmonics $Y_l^{m_l}(\theta,\phi)$), and the $\psi_{sm_s}{}^{(1)}$ to be the "eigenfunctions of the spin", i.e. the set of $2s+1$ components $\psi_{sm_s}{}^{(1)} = \delta_{m_s\sigma}$, of which only the component with m_s equal to the given value of σ is not zero. The sum over m_s thereby reduces to a single term, and we have

$$\begin{aligned}\Psi_{sl}^{jm}(\sigma) &= C^j_{\sigma,m-\sigma} Y_l^{m-\sigma} \\ &= (-1)^{-j+m}\sqrt{(2j+1)} S_{s\sigma; l,m-\sigma; j,-m} Y_l^{m-\sigma}. \end{aligned} \qquad (97.16)$$

This formula solves the problem.† Since the spherical harmonics are supposed normalised, the normalisation condition

$$\sum_\sigma \int |\Psi_{sl}^{jm}|^2 \, do = \sum_\sigma (C^j_{\sigma,m-\sigma})^2 = 1$$

is automatically satisfied; the coefficients C satisfy this relation automatically, since the transformation (97.3) is unitary.

Table 8 gives, for reference, the values of S for $j_2 = \frac{1}{2}, 1, \frac{3}{2}, 2$, calculated from formula (97.14). For each j_2 we give the least number of quantities S from which all the others can be obtained by means of the relations (97.12), (97.13).

TABLE 8

Formulae for the quantities $S_{j_1 m_1; j_2 m_2; j_3 m_3}$

$$S_{j,m-1;(1/2)(1/2);j-(1/2),-m+(1/2)} = (-1)^{j-m+1}\sqrt{[(j-m+1)/2j(2j+1)]}$$

$(-1)^{j-m} S_{j,m-m_2; 1m_2; j_3,-m}$

m_2 \ j_3	0	1
j	$\dfrac{m}{\sqrt{[j(j+1)(2j+1)]}}$	$-\sqrt{\left[\dfrac{(j+m)(j-m+1)}{2j(j+1)(2j+1)}\right]}$
-1	$\sqrt{\left[\dfrac{(j-m)(j+m)}{j(2j-1)(2j+1)}\right]}$	$-\sqrt{\left[\dfrac{(j-m)(j-m+1)}{2j(2j-1)(2j+1)}\right]}$

† It is easy to see that, for $s=0$, $\Psi_{0l}^{lm} = Y_l^m$, as it should.

TABLE 8—*continued*

$$(-1)^{j-m}S_{j,m-(1/2)-m_2;\ (3/2)m_2;\ j_3,-m+(1/2)}$$

j_3 \ m_2	1	$\frac{3}{2}$
$j-\frac{1}{2}$	$-(j+3m-2)\sqrt{\left[\dfrac{j-m+1}{2j(2j-1)(2j+1)(2j+2)}\right]}$	$\sqrt{\left[\dfrac{3(j-m+1)(j-m+2)(j+m-1)}{2j(2j-1)(2j+1)(2j+2)}\right]}$
$j-\frac{3}{2}$	$-\sqrt{\left[\dfrac{3(j-m)(j-m+1)(j+m-1)}{2j(2j-2)(2j-1)(2j+1)}\right]}$	$\sqrt{\left[\dfrac{(j-m+1)(j-m)(j-m+2)}{2j(2j-2)(2j-1)(2j+1)}\right]}$

$$(-1)^{j-m}S_{j,m-m_2;\,2m_2;\,j_3,-m}$$

j_3 \ m_2	0	1
j	$\dfrac{3m^2-j(j+1)}{\sqrt{[j(j+1)(2j-1)(2j+1)(2j+3)]}}$	$(1-2m)\sqrt{\left[\dfrac{3(j+m)(j-m+1)}{j(2j-1)(2j+1)(2j+2)(2j+3}\right.}$
$j-1$	$m\sqrt{\left[\dfrac{3(j-m)(j+m)}{(j-1)j(j+1)(2j-1)(2j+1)}\right]}$	$-(j+2m-1)\sqrt{\left[\dfrac{(j-m-1)(j-m)}{(j-1)j(2j-1)(2j-1)(2j+}\right.}$
$j-2$	$\sqrt{\left[\dfrac{3(j-m-1)(j-m)(j+m-1)(j+m)}{j(2j-3)(2j-2)(2j-1)(2j+1)}\right]}$	$-\sqrt{\left[\dfrac{(j-m-1)(j+m-1)(j-m)(j-m+}{(j-1)(2j-3)(2j-1)(2j+1)}\right.}$

j_3 \ m_2	2
j	$\sqrt{\left[\dfrac{3(j+m-1)(j+m)(j-m+1)(j-m+2)}{2j(j+1)(2j-1)(2j+1)(2j+3)}\right]}$
$j-1$	$\sqrt{\left[\dfrac{(j+m-1)(j-m)(j-m+1)(j-m+2)}{2(j-1)j(j+1)(2j-1)(2j+1)}\right]}$
$j-2$	$\sqrt{\left[\dfrac{(j-m-1)(j-m)(j-m+1)(j-m+2)}{2j(2j-3)(2j-2)(2j-1)(2j+1)}\right]}$

CHAPTER XIII

POLYATOMIC MOLECULES

§98. The classification of molecular vibrations

In its applications to polyatomic molecules, group theory first of all resolves at once the problem of the classification of their electron terms, i.e. of the energy levels for a given situation of the nuclei. They are classified according to the irreducible representations of the point symmetry group appropriate to the configuration of the nuclei. Here, however, we must emphasise what is really obvious, that the classification thus obtained belongs to the definite nuclear configuration considered, since the symmetry is in general destroyed when the nuclei are displaced. We usually discuss the configuration corresponding to the equilibrium position of the nuclei. In this case the classification continues to possess a certain amount of meaning even when the nuclei execute small vibrations, but of course becomes meaningless when the vibrations can no longer be regarded as small.

In the diatomic molecule this question did not arise, since its axial symmetry is of course preserved under any displacement of the nuclei. A similar situation occurs for triatomic molecules also. The three nuclei always lie in a plane, which is a plane of symmetry of the molecule. Hence the classification of the electron terms of the triatomic molecule with respect to this plane (wave functions symmetric or antisymmetric with respect to reflection in the plane) is always possible.

For the normal electron terms of polyatomic molecules there is an empirical rule according to which, in the overwhelming majority of molecules, the wave function of the normal electron state is completely symmetrical (this rule, for diatomic molecules, has already been mentioned in §75). In other words, the wave function is invariant with respect to all the elements of the symmetry group of the molecule, i.e. it belongs to the unit irreducible representation of the group.

The application of the methods of group theory is particularly significant in the investigation of molecular vibrations (E. Wigner 1930). Before beginning a quantum-mechanical investigation of this problem, a purely classical discussion of the vibrations of the molecule is necessary, in which it is regarded as a system of several interacting particles (the nuclei).

As is easily verified, a system of N particles (not lying in a straight line) has $3N-6$ vibrational degrees of freedom; of the total number of degrees of freedom $3N$, three correspond to translational and three to rotational motion of the system as a whole†. The energy of a system of particles executing

† If all the particles lie in a straight line, the number of vibrational degrees of freedom is $3N-5$; in this case, only two co-ordinates correspond to rotation, since it is meaningless to speak of the rotation of a linear molecule about its axis.

small vibrations can be written

$$E = \tfrac{1}{2}\sum_{i,k} m_{ik}\dot{u}_i\dot{u}_k + \tfrac{1}{2}\sum_{i,k} k_{ik}u_iu_k, \tag{98.1}$$

where m_{ik}, k_{ik} are constant coefficients, and the u_i are the components of the vector displacements of the particles from their equilibrium positions (the suffixes i, k denumerate both the components of the vector and the particles). By a suitable linear transformation of the quantities u_i, we can eliminate from (98.1) the co-ordinates corresponding to translational motion and rotation of the system, and take the vibrational co-ordinates in such a way that both the quadratic forms in (98.1) are transformed into sums of squares. Normalising these co-ordinates so as to make all the coefficients in the expression for the kinetic energy unity, we obtain the vibrational energy in the form

$$E = \tfrac{1}{2}\sum_{i,\alpha} \dot{Q}_{\alpha i}^2 + \tfrac{1}{2}\sum_{\alpha} \omega_\alpha^2 \sum_i Q_{\alpha i}^2. \tag{98.2}$$

The vibrational co-ordinates $Q_{\alpha i}$ are said to be *normal*; the ω_α are the frequencies of the corresponding independent vibrations. It may happen that the same frequency (which is then said to be *multiple*) corresponds to several normal co-ordinates; the suffix α to the normal co-ordinate gives the number of the frequency, and the suffix $i = 1, 2, \dots, f_\alpha$ numbers the co-ordinates belonging to a given frequency (f_α being the *multiplicity* of the frequency).

The expression (98.2) for the energy of the molecule must be invariant with respect to symmetry transformations. This means that, under any transformation belonging to the point symmetry group of the molecule, the normal co-ordinates $Q_{\alpha i}$, $i = 1, 2, \dots, f_\alpha$ (for any given α) are transformed into linear combinations of themselves, in such a way that the sum of the squares $\sum_i Q_{\alpha i}^2$ remains unchanged. In other words, the normal co-ordinates belonging to any particular eigenfrequency of the vibrations of the molecule give some irreducible representation of its symmetry group; the multiplicity of the frequency determines the dimension of the representation. The irreducibility follows from the same considerations as were given in §93 for the solutions of SCHRÖDINGER's equation. The equality of the frequencies corresponding to two different irreducible representations would be an improbable coincidence. An exception is again formed by the irreducible representations with complex conjugate systems of characters. Since the normal co-ordinates are by their physical nature real quantities, two complex conjugate representations correspond physically to one eigenfrequency of twice the multiplicity.

These considerations enable us to carry out a classification of the eigenvibrations of a molecule without solving the complex problem of actually determining its normal co-ordinates. To do so, we must first find (by the method described below) the representation given by all the vibrational co-ordinates together, which we shall call the *total* representation; this representation is reducible, and on decomposing it into irreducible parts we determine the multiplicities of the eigenfrequencies and the symmetry properties of the corresponding vibrations. Here it may happen that the same irreducible representation appears several times in the total representation; this means that there are several different frequencies of the same multiplicity and with oscillations of the same symmetry.

To find the total representation, we start from the fact that the characters of a representation are invariant with respect to a linear transformation of the base functions. Hence they can be calculated by using as base functions not the normal co-ordinates, but simply the components u_i of the vectors of the displacements of the nuclei from their equilibrium positions.

First of all, it is evident that, to calculate the character of some element G of a point group, we need consider only those nuclei which (or, more exactly, whose equilibrium positions) remain fixed under the given symmetry transformation. For if, under the rotation or reflection G in question, nucleus 1 is moved to a new position, previously occupied by a similar nucleus 2, this means that under the operation G a displacement of nucleus 1 is transformed into a displacement of nucleus 2. In other words, there will be no diagonal elements in the rows of the matrix G_{ik} which correspond to this nucleus (i.e. to its displacement u_i). The components of the displacement vector of a nucleus whose equilibrium position is not affected by the operation G, on the other hand, are evidently transformed into combinations of themselves, so that they may be considered independently of the displacement vectors of the remaining nuclei.

Let us first consider a rotation $C(\phi)$ through an angle ϕ about some symmetry axis. Let u_x, u_y, u_z be the components of the displacement vector of some nucleus, whose equilibrium position is on the axis, and hence is unaffected by the rotation. Under the rotation these components are transformed, like those of any ordinary (polar) vector, according to the formulae (the z-axis being the axis of symmetry)

$$u'_x = u_x \cos\phi + u_y \sin\phi,$$
$$u'_y = -u_x \sin\phi + u_y \cos\phi,$$
$$u'_z = u_z.$$

The character, i.e. the sum of the diagonal terms of the transformation matrix, is $1+2\cos\phi$. If altogether N_C nuclei lie on the axis in question, the total character is

$$N_C(1+2\cos\phi). \tag{98.3}$$

However, this character corresponds to the transformation of all the $3N$ displacements u_i; hence it is necessary to separate the part corresponding to the transformations of translation and (small) rotation of the molecule as a whole. The translation is determined by the displacement vector $\mathbf{U}$ of the centre of mass of the molecule; the corresponding part of the character is therefore $1+2\cos\phi$. The rotation of the molecule as a whole is determined by the vector $\delta\mathbf{\Omega}$ of the angle of rotation.† The vector $\delta\mathbf{\Omega}$ is axial, but with respect to rotations of the co-ordinate system an axial vector behaves like a polar vector. Hence a character of $1+2\cos\phi$ also corresponds to the vector $\delta\mathbf{\Omega}$. Altogether, therefore, we must subtract from (98.3) a quantity $2(1+2\cos\phi)$. Thus we finally have the character $\chi(C)$ of the rotation $C(\phi)$ in the total vibrational representation:

$$\chi(C) = (N_C-2)(1+2\cos\phi). \tag{98.4}$$

The character of the unit element is always $\chi(E) = 3N-6$ ($N_C = N, \phi = 0$).

In an exactly similar manner, we calculate the character of the rotary-reflection transformation $S(\phi)$ (a rotation through an angle ϕ about the z-axis and a reflection in the xy-plane). Here a vector is transformed according to the formulae

$$\begin{aligned} u'_x &= u_x\cos\phi+u_y\sin\phi \\ u'_y &= -u_x\sin\phi+u_y\cos\phi, \\ u'_z &= -u_z, \end{aligned}$$

to which there corresponds a character $-1+2\cos\phi$. Hence the character of the representation given by all the $3N$ displacements u_i is

$$N_S(-1+2\cos\phi), \tag{98.5}$$

where N_S is the number of nuclei left unmoved by the operation $S(\phi)$; this number is evidently either none or one. To the vector $\mathbf{U}$ of the displacement of the centre of mass there corresponds a character $-1+2\cos\phi$. The vector $\delta\mathbf{\Omega}$, being an axial vector, is unchanged by an inversion of the co-ordinate system; on the other hand, the rotary-reflection transformation $S(\phi)$ can be represented in the form

$$S(\phi) = C(\phi)\sigma_h = C(\phi)C_2I = C(\pi+\phi)I,$$

i.e. as a rotation through an angle $\pi+\phi$, followed by an inversion. Hence the character of the transformation $S(\phi)$ applied to the vector $\delta\mathbf{\Omega}$ is equal to the character of the transformation $C(\pi+\phi)$ applied to an ordinary vector, i.e. it is $1+2\cos(\pi+\phi) = 1-2\cos\phi$. The sum $(-1+2\cos\phi)+(1-2\cos\phi) = 0$, so that we reach the conclusion that the expression (98.5) is equal to the required character $\chi(S)$ of the rotary-reflection transformation $S(\phi)$ in the total representation:

$$\chi(S) = N_S(-1+2\cos\phi). \tag{98.6}$$

In particular, the character of reflection in a plane ($\phi = 0$) is $\chi(\sigma) = N_\sigma$, while that of an inversion ($\phi = \pi$) is $\chi(I) = -3N_I$.

† As is well known, the angle of a small rotation can be regarded as a vector $\delta\mathbf{\Omega}$, whose modulus is equal to the angle of rotation and which is directed along the axis of rotation in the direction determined by the corkscrew rule. The vector $\delta\mathbf{\Omega}$ so defined is clearly axial.

Having thus determined the characters χ of the total representation, we have only to decompose it into irreducible representations, which is done at once by formula (91.16) and the character tables given in §92 (see the Problems at the end of the present section).

To classify the vibrations of a linear molecule there is no need to have recourse to group theory. The total number of vibrational degrees of freedom is $3N-5$. Among the vibrations, we must distinguish those in which the atoms remain in a straight line, and those where this does not happen.† The number of degrees of freedom in the motion of N particles in a straight line is N; of these, one corresponds to the translational motion of the molecule as a whole. Hence the number of normal co-ordinates of the vibrations which leave the atoms in a straight line is $N-1$; in general, $N-1$ different eigenfrequencies correspond to them. The remaining $(3N-5)-(N-1) = 2N-4$ normal co-ordinates relate to vibrations which destroy the collinearity of the molecule; to these, there correspond $N-2$ different double frequencies (two normal co-ordinates, corresponding to the same vibrations in two mutually perpendicular planes, belong to each frequency).‡

PROBLEMS

PROBLEM 1. Classify the normal vibrations of the molecule NH_3 (an equilateral triangula pyramid, with the N atom at the vertex and the H atoms at the corners of the base; Fig. 43).

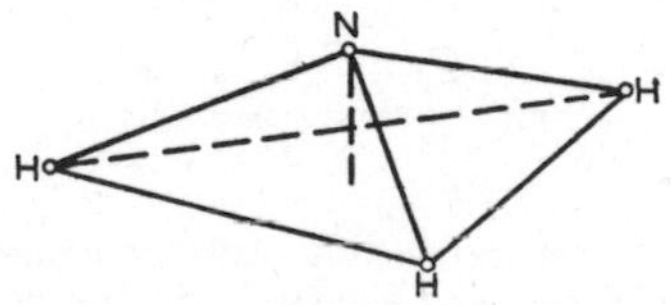

FIG. 43

SOLUTION. The point symmetry group of the molecule is C_{3v}. Rotations about an axis of the third order leave only one atom (N) fixed, while reflections in planes each leave two atoms fixed (N and one H). From formulae (98.4), (98.6) we find the characters of the total representation:

E	$2C_3$	$3\sigma_v$
6	0	2

Decomposing this representation into irreducible parts, we find that it contains the representations A_1 and E twice each. Thus there are two simple frequencies corresponding to vibrations of the type A_1, which conserve the complete symmetry of the molecule (what are called *totally symmetric* vibrations), and two double frequencies with corresponding normal co-ordinates which are transformed into combinations of each other by the representation E.

PROBLEM 2. The same as Problem 1, but for the molecule H_2O (Fig. 44).

SOLUTION. The symmetry group is C_{2v}. The transformation C_2 leaves the O atom fixed; the transformation σ_v (a reflection in the plane of the molecule) leaves all three atoms fixed;

† If the molecule is symmetrical about its centre, a further characteristic of the vibrations appears; see Problem 10 at the end of this section.

‡ Using the notation for the irreducible representations of the group $C_{\infty v}$ (see (95.4)), we can say that there are $N-1$ vibrations of the type A_1, and $N-2$ of the type E_1.

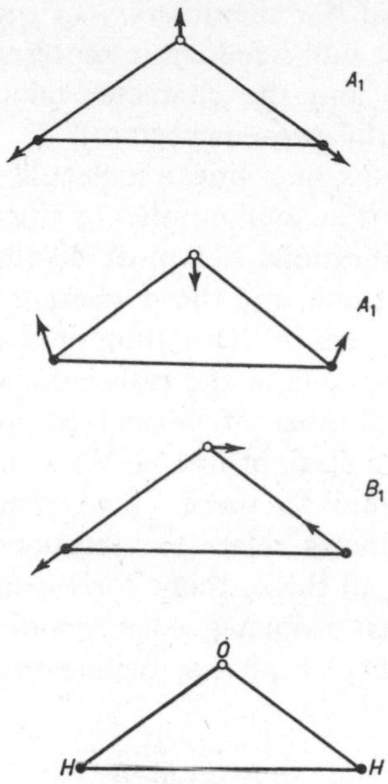

FIG. 44

the reflection σ'_v leaves only the O atom fixed. The characters of the total representation are

E	C_2	σ_v	σ'_v
3	1	3	1

This representation divides into the irreducible representations $2A_1$, $1B_1$, i.e. there are two totally symmetric vibrations and one with the symmetry given by the representation B_1; all the frequencies are simple. Fig. 44 shows the corresponding normal vibrations.

PROBLEM 3. The same as Problem 1, but for the molecule $CHCl_3$ (Fig. 45a).

SOLUTION. The symmetry group of the molecule is $\boldsymbol{C}_{3v}$. By the same method we find that there are three totally symmetric vibrations A_1 and three double vibrations of the type E.

PROBLEM 4. The same as Problem 1, but for the molecule CH_4 (the C atom is at the centre of a tetrahedron with the H atoms at the vertices; Fig. 45b).

SOLUTION. The symmetry of the molecule is $\boldsymbol{T}_d$. The vibrations are $1A_1$, $1E$, $2F_2$.

PROBLEM 5. The same as Problem 1, but for the molecule C_6H_6 (Fig. 45c).

SOLUTION. The symmetry of the molecule is $\boldsymbol{D}_{6h}$. The vibrations are $2A_{1g}$, $1A_{2g}$, $1A_{2u}$, $1B_{1g}$, $1B_{1u}$, $1B_{2g}$, $3B_{2u}$, $1E_{1g}$, $3E_{1u}$, $4E_{2g}$, $2E_{2u}$.

PROBLEM 6. The same as Problem 1, but for the molecule OsF_8 (the Os atom is at the centre of a cube with the F atoms at the vertices; Fig. 45d).

SOLUTION. The symmetry of the molecule is $\boldsymbol{O}_h$. The vibrations are $1A_{1g}$, $1A_{2u}$, $1E_g$, $1E_u$, $2F_{1u}$, $2F_{2g}$, $1F_{2u}$.

PROBLEM 7. The same as Problem 1, but for the molecule UF_6 (the U atom is at the centre of an octahedron with the F atoms at the vertices; Fig. 45e).

SOLUTION. The symmetry of the molecule is $\boldsymbol{O}_h$. The vibrations are $1A_{1g}$, $1E_g$, $2F_{1u}$, $1F_{2g}$, $1F_{2u}$.

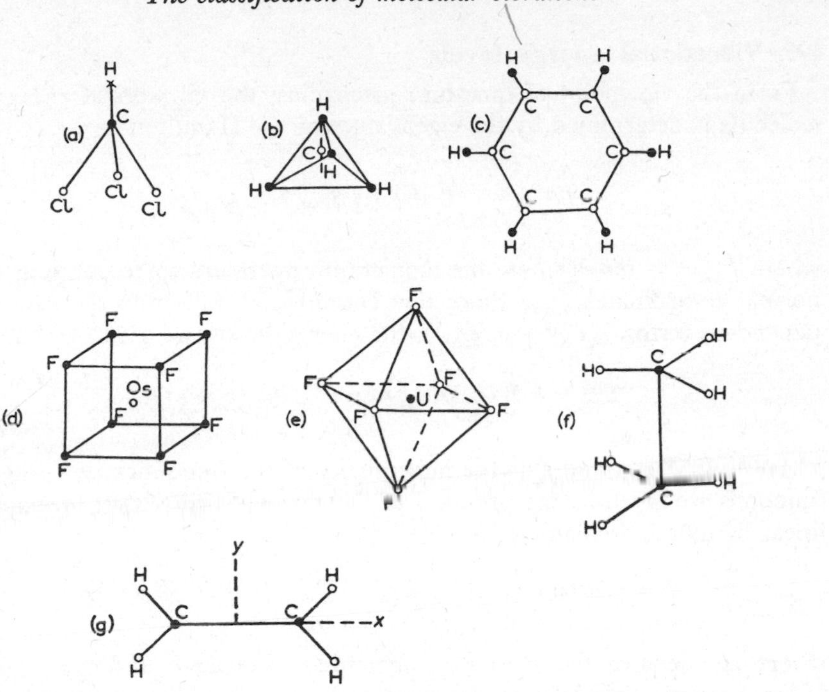

FIG. 45

PROBLEM 8. The same as Problem 1, but for the molecule C_2H_6 (Fig. 45f).

SOLUTION. The symmetry of the molecule is D_{3d}. The vibrations are $3A_{1g}$, $1A_{1u}$, $2A_{2u}$, $3E_g$, $3E_u$.

PROBLEM 9. The same as Problem 1, but for the molecule C_2H_4 (Fig. 45g; all the atoms are coplanar).

SOLUTION. The symmetry of the molecule is D_{2h}. The vibrations are $3A_{1g}$, $1A_{1u}$, $2B_{1g}$, $1B_{1u}$, $2B_{3u}$, $1B_{2g}$, $2B_{2u}$; the axes of co-ordinates are taken as shown in the figure.

PROBLEM 10. The same as Problem 1, but for a linear molecule of N atoms symmetrical about its centre.

SOLUTION. To the classification of the vibrations of a linear molecule considered in the text, we must add the classification from the behaviour with respect to inversion in the centre. There are two distinct cases, according as N is even or odd.

If N is even ($N = 2p$), there is no atom at the centre of the molecule. On giving to the p atoms in one half of the molecule independent displacements along the line, and to the remaining p atoms equal and opposite displacements, we find that p of the vibrations leaving the atoms in line are symmetrical with respect to the centre, while the remaining $(2p-1)-p = p-1$ vibrations of this type are antisymmetrical. Next, p atoms have $2p$ degrees of freedom for motions in which the atoms do not remain in line. On giving equal and opposite displacements to symmetrically placed atoms, we should obtain $2p$ symmetrical vibrations; of these, however, the two corresponding to a rotation of the molecule must be removed. Thus there are $p-1$ double frequencies of vibrations which bring the atoms out of line and are symmetrical about the centre, and the same number $[(2p-2)-(p-1) = p-1]$ which are antisymmetrical. Using the notation for the irreducible representations of the group $D_{\infty h}$ (see (95.4)), we can say that there are p vibrations of the type A_{1g} and $p-1$ of the types A_{1u}, E_{1g}, E_{1u}.

If N is odd ($N = 2p+1$), similar arguments show that there are p vibrations of each of the types A_{1g}, A_{1u}, E_{1u} and $p-1$ of the type E_{1g}.

§99. Vibrational energy levels

From the viewpoint of quantum mechanics, the vibrational energy of a molecule is determined by the eigenvalues of the Hamiltonian

$$\hat{H}^{(v)} = \tfrac{1}{2}\sum_{\alpha}\sum_{i=1}^{f_\alpha}\hat{P}_{\alpha i}^2+\tfrac{1}{2}\sum_{\alpha}\omega_\alpha^2\sum_{i=1}^{f_\alpha}Q_{\alpha i}^2, \tag{99.1}$$

where $\hat{P}_{\alpha i} = -i\hbar\partial/\partial Q_{\alpha i}$ are the momentum operators corresponding to the normal co-ordinates $Q_{\alpha i}$. Since this Hamiltonian falls into the sum of independent terms $\frac{1}{2}(\hat{P}_{\alpha i}^2+\omega_\alpha^2Q_{\alpha i}^2)$, the energy levels are given by the sums

$$E^{(v)} = \hbar\sum_{\alpha}\omega_\alpha\sum_{i}(v_{\alpha i}+\tfrac{1}{2}) = \sum_{\alpha}\hbar\omega_\alpha(v_\alpha+\tfrac{1}{2}f_\alpha), \tag{99.2}$$

where $v_\alpha = \Sigma\, v_{\alpha i}$, and f_α is the multiplicity of the frequency ω_α. The wave functions are given by the products of the corresponding wave functions for linear harmonic oscillators:

$$\psi = \text{constant}\times\exp\{-\tfrac{1}{2}\sum_{\alpha}c_\alpha^2\sum_{i}Q_{\alpha i}^2\}\prod_{\alpha}\prod_{i}H_{v_{\alpha i}}(c_\alpha Q_{\alpha i}), \tag{99.3}$$

where H_v denotes the Hermite polynomial of order v, and $c_\alpha = \sqrt{(\omega_\alpha/\hbar)}$. If there are multiple frequencies among the ω_α, the vibrational energy levels are in general degenerate. The energy (99.2) depends only on the sums $v_\alpha = \Sigma\, v_{\alpha i}$. Hence the degree of degeneracy of the level is equal to the number of ways of forming the given set of numbers v_α from the $v_{\alpha i}$. For a single number v_α it is†

$$(v_\alpha+f_\alpha-1)!/v_\alpha!(f_\alpha-1)!$$

Hence the total degree of degeneracy is

$$\prod_{\alpha}\frac{(v_\alpha+f_\alpha-1)!}{v_\alpha!(f_\alpha-1)!}. \tag{99.4}$$

For double frequencies, the factors in this product are $v_\alpha+1$, while for triple frequencies they are $\frac{1}{2}(v_\alpha+1)(v_\alpha+2)$.

It must be borne in mind that this degeneracy occurs only so long as we consider purely harmonic vibrations.

When terms of higher order in the normal co-ordinates are taken into account in the Hamiltonian (*anharmonic* vibrations), the degeneracy is in general removed, though not completely (see §102 for a further discussion of this point).

The wave functions belonging to the same degenerate vibrational term give some representation (in general reducible) of the symmetry group of the molecule. The wave functions (99.3) can be represented as the products of

† This is the number of ways in which v_α balls can be distributed among f_α urns.

functions

$$\exp\{-\tfrac{1}{2}c_\alpha^2 \, \Sigma \, Q_{\alpha i}^2\} \, \Pi \, H_{v_{\alpha i}}(c_\alpha Q_{\alpha i}), \tag{99.5}$$

belonging to the individual frequencies ω_α. The functions belonging to different frequencies are transformed independently of one another. Hence the representation given by all the functions (99.3) is the product of the representations given by the functions (99.5), so that we need consider only the latter.

The exponential factor in (99.5) is invariant with respect to all the symmetry transformations. In the Hermite polynomials, the terms of any given degree are transformed only into similar terms; a symmetry transformation evidently does not change the degree of any term. Since, on the other hand, each Hermite polynomial is completely determined by its highest term, it follows that it is sufficient to consider only the highest term, writing

$$\prod_{i=1}^{f_\alpha} H_{v_{\alpha i}}(c_\alpha Q_{\alpha i}) = \text{constant} \times Q_{\alpha 1}^{v_{\alpha 1}} Q_{\alpha 2}^{v_{\alpha 2}} \ldots Q_{\alpha f_\alpha}^{v_{\alpha f_\alpha}} + \\ + \text{terms of lower degree.}$$

The functions for which the sum $v_\alpha = \Sigma \, v_{\alpha i}$ has the same value belong to the same term. Thus we have a representation given by the products of v_α quantities $Q_{\alpha i}$; this just the symmetric product (see §91) of the irreducible representation given by the $Q_{\alpha i}$ with itself v_α times.

For one-dimensional representations, the finding of the characters of their symmetric products with themselves v times is trivial:†

$$\chi_v(G) = [\chi(G)]^v.$$

For two- and three-dimensional representations it is convenient to use the following mathematical device.‡ The sum of the squared base functions of an irreducible representation is invariant with respect to all symmetry transformations. Hence we can formally regard these functions as the components of a vector in two or three dimensions, and the symmetry transformations as some rotations (or reflections) applied to these vectors. We emphasise that there is in general no relation between these rotations and reflections and the actual symmetry transformations, the former depending (for any given element G of the group) also on the particular representation considered.

Let us consider two-dimensional representations more closely. Let $\chi(G)$ be the character of some element of the group in the two-dimensional representation concerned, with $\chi(G) \neq 0$. The sum of the diagonal elements of the transformation matrix for the components x, y of a two-dimensional

---

† We use the notation $\chi_v(G)$ in place of the cumbersome $[\chi^v](G)$.

‡ It was applied to this problem by A. S. Kompaneets (1940).

vector on rotation through an angle ϕ in a plane is $2\cos\phi$. Putting

$$2\cos\phi = \chi(G), \tag{99.6}$$

we find the angle of the rotation which formally corresponds to the element G in the irreducible representation considered. The symmetric product of the representation with itself v times is the representation whose basis is formed by the $v+1$ quantities x^v, $x^{v-1}y, \ldots, y^v$. The characters of this representation are†

$$\chi_v(G) = \sin(v+1)\phi/\sin\phi. \tag{99.7}$$

The case where $\chi(G) = 0$ requires special consideration, since a zero character corresponds both to a rotation through $\frac{1}{2}\pi$ and to a reflection. If $\chi(G^2) = -2$, we have a rotation through $\frac{1}{2}\pi$, and for $\chi_v(G)$ we obtain

$$\chi_v(G) = -\tfrac{1}{2}[1+(-1)^v]. \tag{99.8}$$

If $\chi(G^2) = 2$, on the other hand, $\chi(G)$ must be regarded as the character of a reflection (i.e. a transformation $x \to x$, $y \to -y$); then

$$\chi_v(G) = \tfrac{1}{2}[1+(-1)^v]. \tag{99.9}$$

We can similarly obtain the formulae for the symmetric products of three-dimensional representations. The finding of the rotation or reflection which formally corresponds to an element of the group in a given representation is easily accomplished with the aid of Table 6. This is the transformation which corresponds to the given $\chi(G)$ in that isomorphous group in which the co-ordinates are transformed by the representation in question. Thus, for the representation F_1 of the groups $\boldsymbol{O}$ and $\boldsymbol{T}_d$ we must take a transformation from the group $\boldsymbol{O}$, but for the representation F_2 we must take one from the group $\boldsymbol{T}_d$. We shall not pause here to derive the corresponding formulae for the characters $\chi_v(G)$.

§100. Stability of symmetrical configurations of the molecule

For a symmetrical position of the nuclei, an electron term of the molecule may be degenerate, if there are among the irreducible representations of the symmetry group one or more whose dimensions exceed unity. We may ask whether such a symmetrical configuration is a stable equilibrium configuration of the molecule. Here we shall entirely neglect the effect of spin (if any), since this effect is usually insignificant in polyatomic molecules. The degeneracy of the electron terms of which we shall speak is therefore only the "orbital" degeneracy, and is unrelated to the spin.

† For purposes of calculation it is convenient to take the base functions in the form

$$(x+iy)^v, (x+iy)^{v-1}(x-iy), \ldots, (x-iy)^v;$$

the matrix of the rotation is then diagonal, and the sum of the diagonal elements takes the form

$$e^{iv\phi} + e^{i(v-2)\phi} + \ldots + e^{-iv\phi}.$$

If the configuration in question is stable, the energy of the molecule as a function of the distances between the nuclei must be a minimum for the given position of the nuclei. This means that the change in the energy due to a small displacement of the nuclei must contain no terms linear in the displacements.

Let $\hat{H}$ be the Hamiltonian of the electron state of the molecule, the distances between the nuclei being regarded as parameters. We denote by $\hat{H}_0$ the value of this Hamiltonian for the symmetrical configuration considered. The quantities defining the small displacements of the nuclei can be taken as the normal vibrational co-ordinates $Q_{\alpha i}$. The expansion of $\hat{H}$ in powers of the $Q_{\alpha i}$ is of the form

$$\hat{H} = \hat{H}_0 + \sum_{\alpha,i} V_{\alpha i} Q_{\alpha i} + \sum_{\alpha,\beta,i,k} W_{\alpha i,\beta k} Q_{\alpha i} Q_{\beta k} + \dots . \tag{100.1}$$

The expansion coefficients V, W, ... are functions only of the co-ordinates of the electrons. Under a symmetry transformation, the quantities $Q_{\alpha i}$ are transformed into combinations of one another, and the sums in (100.1) are changed into other sums of the same form. Hence we can formally regard the symmetry transformation as a transformation of the coefficients in these sums, the $Q_{\alpha i}$ remaining unchanged. Here, in particular, the coefficients $V_{\alpha i}$ (for any given α) will be transformed by the same representation of the symmetry group as the corresponding co-ordinates $Q_{\alpha i}$. This follows at once from the fact that, by virtue of the invariance of the Hamiltonian under all symmetry transformations, the group of terms of any given order in its expansion must be invariant also, and in particular the linear terms must be invariant.†

Let us consider some electron term E_0 which is degenerate in the symmetrical configuration. A displacement of the nuclei which destroys the symmetry of the molecule generally results in a splitting of the term. The amount of the splitting is determined, as far as terms of the first order in the displacements of the nuclei, by the secular equation formed from the matrix elements of the linear term in the expansion (100.1),

$$V_{\rho\sigma} = \sum_{\alpha,i} Q_{\alpha i} \int \psi_\rho V_{\alpha i} \psi_\sigma \, dq, \tag{100.2}$$

where ψ_ρ, ψ_σ are the wave functions of electron states belonging to the degenerate term in question (and are chosen to be real). The stability of the symmetrical configuration requires that the splitting linear in Q should be zero, i.e. all the roots of the secular equation must vanish identically. This means that the matrix $V_{\rho\sigma}$ must itself be zero. Here, of course, we must consider only those normal vibrations which destroy the symmetry of the molecule, i.e. we must omit the totally symmetric vibrations (which correspond to the unit representation of the group).

† Strictly speaking, the quantities $V_{\alpha i}$ must be transformed by the representation which is the complex conjugate of that by which the $Q_{\alpha i}$ are transformed. However, as we have already pointed out, if two complex conjugate representations are not the same, they must physically be considered together as one representation of twice the dimension. The above remark is therefore unimportant.

Since the $Q_{\alpha i}$ are arbitrary, the matrix elements (100.2) vanish only if all the integrals

$$\int \psi_\rho V_{\alpha i} \psi_\sigma \, dq \tag{100.3}$$

vanish. Let D^{el} be the irreducible representation by which the electron wave functions ψ_ρ are transformed, and D_α the same for the quantities $V_{\alpha i}$; as we have already remarked, the representations D_α are those by which the corresponding normal co-ordinates $Q_{\alpha i}$ are transformed. According to the results of §94, the integrals (100.3) will be non-zero if the product $[D^{(el)2}] \times D_\alpha$ contains the unit representation or, what is the same thing, if $[D^{(el)2}]$ contains D_α. Otherwise all the integrals vanish.

Thus a symmetrical configuration is stable if the representation $[D^{(el)2}]$ does not contain any (except the unit representation) of the irreducible representations D_α which characterise the vibrations of the molecule. This condition is always satisfied for non-degenerate electron states, since the symmetric product of a one-dimensional representation with itself is the unit representation.

Let us consider, for instance, a molecule of the type CH_4, in which one atom (C) is at the centre of a tetrahedron, with four atoms (H) at the vertices. This configuration has the symmetry T_d. The degenerate electron terms correspond to the representations E, F_1, F_2 of this group. The molecule has one normal vibration A_1 (a totally symmetric vibration), one double vibration E, and two triple vibrations F_2 (see §98, Problem 4). The symmetric products of the representations E, F_1, F_2 with themselves are

$$[E^2] = A_1 + E, \qquad [F_1{}^2] = [F_2{}^2] = A_1 + E + F_2.$$

We see that each of these contains at least one of the representations E, F_2, and hence the tetrahedral configuration considered is unstable when there are degenerate electron states.

This result constitutes a general rule (H. Jahn and E. Teller 1937). A more thorough investigation than that given above, considering all possible types of symmetrical configuration of the nuclei, shows that, when there is a degenerate electron state, any symmetrical position of the nuclei (except when they are collinear) is unstable. As a result of this instability, the nuclei move in such a way that the symmetry of their configuration is destroyed, the degeneracy of the term being completely removed. In particular, we can say that the normal electron term of a symmetrical (non-linear) molecule can only be non-degenerate.

As we have just mentioned, the linear molecules alone form an exception. This is easily seen, without using group theory. A displacement of a nucleus whereby it moves off the axis of the molecule is an ordinary vector with ξ and η components (the ζ-axis being along the axis of the molecule). We have seen in §84 that such vectors have matrix elements only for transitions in which the angular momentum Λ about the axis changes by unity. On the other hand, to a degenerate term of a linear molecule there correspond states with angular momenta Λ and $-\Lambda$ about the axis ($\Lambda \geqslant 1$). A transition between them changes the angular momentum by at least 2, and therefore the matrix elements always vanish. Thus the linear position of the nuclei in the molecule may be stable, even if the electron state is degenerate.

§101. Quantisation of the rotation of a rigid body

The investigation of the rotational levels of a polyatomic molecule is often hampered by the necessity of considering the rotation simultaneously with the vibrations. As a preliminary example, let us consider the rotation of a molecule as a solid body, i.e. with the atoms "rigidly fixed".

Let ξ, η, ζ be a system of co-ordinates with axes along the three principal axes of inertia of a rigid body, and rotating with it. The corresponding Hamiltonian is obtained by replacing the components J_ξ, J_η, J_ζ of the angular momentum of the rotation, in the classical expression for the energy, by the corresponding operators:

$$\hat{H} = \tfrac{1}{2}\hbar^2\left(\frac{\hat{J}_\xi^2}{I_A}+\frac{\hat{J}_\eta^2}{I_B}+\frac{\hat{J}_\zeta^2}{I_C}\right), \tag{101.1}$$

where I_A, I_B, I_C are the principal moments of inertia of the body.

The commutation rules for the operators $\hat{J}_\xi$, $\hat{J}_\eta$, $\hat{J}_\zeta$ of the angular momentum components in a rotating system of co-ordinates are not obvious, since the usual derivation of the commutation rules relates to the components $\hat{J}_x$, $\hat{J}_y$, $\hat{J}_z$ in a fixed system of co-ordinates. They are, however, easily obtained by using the formula

$$(\hat{\mathbf{J}}\cdot\mathbf{a})(\hat{\mathbf{J}}\cdot\mathbf{b})-(\hat{\mathbf{J}}\cdot\mathbf{b})(\hat{\mathbf{J}}\cdot\mathbf{a}) = -i\hat{\mathbf{J}}\cdot\mathbf{a}\times\mathbf{b}, \tag{101.2}$$

where **a**, **b** are any two commuting vectors which characterise the body in question. This formula is easily verified by calculating the left-hand side of the equation in the fixed system of co-ordinates x, y, z, using the general rules for the commutation of angular momentum components with one another and with the components of an arbitrary vector.

Let **a** and **b** be unit vectors along the ξ and η axes. Then $\mathbf{a}\times\mathbf{b}$ is a unit vector along the ζ-axis, and (101.2) gives

$$\hat{J}_\xi\hat{J}_\eta-\hat{J}_\eta\hat{J}_\xi = -i\hat{J}_\zeta. \tag{101.3}$$

Two other relations are obtained similarly. Thus we reach the result that the commutation rules for the operators of the angular momentum components in the rotating system of co-ordinates differ from those in a fixed system only in the sign on the right-hand side of the equation. Hence it follows that all the results which we have previously obtained from the commutation rules, relating to the eigenvalues and matrix elements, hold for J_ξ, J_η, J_ζ also, with the difference that all expressions must be replaced by their complex conjugates. In particular, the eigenvalues of J_ζ (as of J_z) are the integers $k = -J, \dots, J$.

The finding of the eigenvalues of the energy of a rotating body (a *top*, as it is called) is simplest for the case where all three principal moments of inertia of the body are equal: $I_A = I_B = I_C \equiv I$ (a *spherical top*). This holds for a molecule in cases where it has the symmetry of one of the cubic point groups. The Hamiltonian (101.1) takes the form

$$\hat{H} = \hbar^2 \hat{\mathbf{J}}^2/2I,$$

and its eigenvalues are

$$E = \hbar^2 J(J+1)/2I. \tag{101.4}$$

Every energy level is degenerate, as usual, with respect to the $2J+1$ directions of the angular momentum in space, and in addition, for a spherical top, there is a $(2J+1)$-fold degeneracy with respect to the directions of the angular momentum relative to the body itself (i.e. with respect to the values of $J_\zeta = k$). The total degree of the degeneracy is therefore $(2J+1)^2$.

There is also no difficulty in calculating the energy levels in the case where only two of the moments of inertia of the body are the same: $I_A = I_B \neq I_C$ (a *symmetrical top*). This holds for molecules having one axis of symmetry of order above the second. The Hamiltonian (101.1) takes the form

$$\begin{aligned}\hat{H} &= \hbar^2(\hat{J}_\xi^2+\hat{J}_\eta^2)/2I_A+\hbar^2\hat{J}_\zeta^2/2I_C \\ &= \hbar^2\hat{\mathbf{J}}^2/2I_A+\tfrac{1}{2}\hbar^2\left(\frac{1}{I_C}-\frac{1}{I_A}\right)\hat{J}_\zeta^2.\end{aligned} \tag{101.5}$$

Hence we see that, in a state with given values of J and k, the energy is

$$E = \frac{\hbar^2}{2I_A}J(J+1)+\tfrac{1}{2}\hbar^2\left(\frac{1}{I_C}-\frac{1}{I_A}\right)k^2, \tag{101.6}$$

which determines the energy levels of a symmetrical top.

The degeneracy with respect to values of k which occurred for a spherical top is here partly removed. The values of the energy are the same only for values of k differing in sign alone, corresponding to opposite directions of the angular momentum relative to the axis of the top. Thus the total degree of degeneracy of the levels of a symmetrical top is (for $k \neq 0$) $2(2J+1)$.

For $I_A \neq I_B \neq I_C$ (an *asymmetrical top*), the calculation of the energy levels in a general form is impossible. The degeneracy with respect to the directions of the angular momentum relative to the body is here removed completely, so that $2J+1$ different levels (degenerate only with respect to the direction of the angular momentum in space) correspond to any given J. The calculation of these levels involves the solution of SCHRÖDINGER's equation in matrix form; this amounts to solving a secular equation of degree $2J+1$, formed from the matrix elements $H^{Jk}_{Jk'}$ with the given value of J (O. KLEIN 1929). The matrix elements $H^{Jk}_{Jk'}$ are defined with respect to the wave functions ψ_{Jk} of states in which the absolute value and the

ζ-component of the angular momentum have definite values (but the energy has no definite value). On the other hand, in the stationary states of an asymmetrical top the projection J_ζ of the angular momentum has, of course, no definite values, i.e. no definite values of k can be assigned to the energy levels.

The operators $\hat{J}_\xi$, $\hat{J}_\eta$ have matrix elements only for transitions in which k changes by unity, while $\hat{J}_\zeta$ has only diagonal elements (see formulae (25.13), in which we must write J, k instead of L, M). Hence the operators $\hat{J}_\xi^2$, $\hat{J}_\eta^2$, $\hat{J}_\zeta^2$, and therefore $\hat{H}$, have matrix elements only for transitions with $k \to k$ or $k \pm 2$. The absence of matrix elements for transitions between states with even and odd k has the result that the secular equation of degree $2J+1$ immediately falls into two independent equations of degrees J and $J+1$. One of these contains matrix elements for transitions between states with even k, and the other contains those for transitions between states with odd k. Each of these equations, in turn, can be reduced to two equations of lower degree. To do this, we must use the matrix elements defined, not with respect to the functions ψ_{Jk}, but with respect to the functions

$$\begin{aligned} \psi_{Jk}^+ &= (\psi_{Jk}+\psi_{J,-k})/\sqrt{2}, \\ \psi_{Jk}^- &= (\psi_{Jk}-\psi_{J,-k})/\sqrt{2} \qquad (k \neq 0); \end{aligned} \tag{101.7}$$

the function ψ_{J0} is, of course, the same as ψ_{J0}^+. Functions differing in the index + and − are of different symmetry (with respect to a reflection in a plane passing through the ζ-axis, which changes the sign of k), and hence the matrix elements for transitions between them vanish. Consequently we can form the secular equations separately for the + and − states.

The Hamiltonian (101.1), and the commutation rules (101.3), have an unusual symmetry: they are invariant with respect to a simultaneous change in sign of any two of the operators $\hat{J}_\xi$, $\hat{J}_\eta$, $\hat{J}_\zeta$. This symmetry formally corresponds to the group $\boldsymbol{D}_2$. Hence the terms of an asymmetrical top can be classified in accordance with the irreducible representations of this group. Thus there are four types of non-degenerate† term, corresponding to the representations A, B_1, B_2, B_3 (see Table 6).

In calculating the matrix elements of the various vector quantities characterising a symmetrical top (including the unit vector along its axis), it should be borne in mind that the problem of the motion of such a top is formally identical with that of the rotation of a diatomic molecule (of zero spin), the electron momentum Λ about the axis of the molecule playing the part of the angular momentum k of the rotation of the top about its axis.‡ Hence all the

---

† Here, of course, we ignore the physically unimportant $(2J+1)$-fold degeneracy with respect to the directions of the angular momentum in space.

‡ The wave functions for a symmetrical top are the same as the angular part of the wave functions of the diatomic molecule. Thus, if we describe the rotation by means of the Eulerian angles θ, ϕ, ψ (Fig. 22), the wave function of the state with the values J, M_J, k is

$$e^{iM_J\psi}e^{ik\phi}\,\Theta_{kJM_J}(\theta),$$

where Θ are the functions calculated in §79, Problem.

formulae (84.1)–(84.4) obtained in §84 can be applied directly to the symmetrical top also, replacing K, M_K, Λ respectively by the angular momentum J of the top, its projection M_J on the fixed z-axis, and its projection k on the moving ζ-axis.

The calculation of the matrix elements for the asymmetrical top is more complex. Representing the wave functions of its stationary states as linear combinations of the functions ψ_{Jk}, $\psi_{J,-k}$ (which are the wave functions of the symmetrical top), we reduce the required matrix elements to combinations of the known matrix elements for the symmetrical top.

For the asymmetrical top there are selection rules for the matrix elements of transitions between states of the types A, B_1, B_2, B_3; these rules are easily obtained from symmetry considerations in the usual way. Thus, for the components of a vector physical quantity **A** we have the selection rules

$$\begin{array}{lll} \text{for } A_\xi: & A \leftrightarrow B_3^{(\xi)}, & B_1^{(\zeta)} \leftrightarrow B_2^{(\eta)}, \\ \text{for } A_\eta: & A \leftrightarrow B_2^{(\eta)}, & B_1^{(\zeta)} \leftrightarrow B_3^{(\xi)}, \\ \text{for } A_\zeta: & A \leftrightarrow B_1^{(\zeta)}, & B_2^{(\eta)} \leftrightarrow B_3^{(\xi)}. \end{array}$$

For clarity we show, as an index to the symbol for the representation, the axis about which a rotation has the character $+1$ in the representation concerned.

PROBLEMS

PROBLEM 1. Calculate the matrix elements $H^{Jk}_{Jk'}$ for an asymmetrical top.

SOLUTION. From formula (25.13) we find

$$(J_\xi^2)^k_k = (J_\eta^2)^k_k = \tfrac{1}{2}[J(J+1)-k^2],$$

$$(J_\xi^2)^k_{k+2} = (J_\xi^2)^{k+2}_k = -(J_\eta^2)^k_{k+2} = -(J_\eta^2)^{k+2}_k$$

$$= \tfrac{1}{4}\sqrt{[(J-k)(J-k-1)(J+k+1)(J+k+2)]};$$

for brevity, we everywhere omit the diagonal suffixes J, J of the matrix elements. Hence we have for the required matrix elements of H:

$$\begin{aligned} H^k_k &= \tfrac{1}{4}\hbar^2\left(\frac{1}{I_A}+\frac{1}{I_B}\right)[J(J+1)-k^2]+\hbar^2k^2/2I_C, \\ H^k_{k+2} = H^{k+2}_k &= \tfrac{1}{8}\hbar^2\left(\frac{1}{I_A}-\frac{1}{I_B}\right)\sqrt{[(J-k)(J-k-1)(J+k+1)(J+k+2)]}. \end{aligned} \tag{1}$$

The matrix elements with respect to the functions (101.7) are expressed in terms of the elements in formulae (1) by

$$H^{k+}_{k+} = H^{k-}_{k-} = H^k_k \; (k \neq 1), \quad H^{1+}_{1+} = H^1_1 + H^1_{-1}, \quad H^{1-}_{1-} = H^1_1 - H^1_{-1},$$

$$H^{k+}_{(k+2)+} = H^{k-}_{(k+2)-} = H^k_{k+2} \; (k \neq 0), \quad H^{0+}_{2+} = \sqrt{2}H^0_2.$$

PROBLEM 2. Determine the energy levels for an asymmetrical top with $J = 1$.

SOLUTION. The secular equation, of the third degree, falls into three linear equations. One of these is $E_1 = H^{0+}_{0+}$, whence

$$E_1 = \tfrac{1}{2}\hbar^2\left(\frac{1}{I_A}+\frac{1}{I_B}\right).$$

From this we can at once write down the other two energy levels, since it is obvious that the three moments of inertia I_A, I_B, I_C enter the problem in a symmetrical manner. Hence it is sufficient simply to replace the moments of inertia I_A, I_B once by I_A, I_C and once by I_B, I_C. Thus

$$E_2 = \tfrac{1}{2}\hbar^2\left(\frac{1}{I_A}+\frac{1}{I_C}\right), \qquad E_3 = \tfrac{1}{2}\hbar^2\left(\frac{1}{I_B}+\frac{1}{I_C}\right).$$

The levels E_1, E_2, E_3 belong† to the types B_1, B_2, B_3 respectively, if I_A, I_B, I_C are the moments of inertia about the ξ, η, ζ axes.

PROBLEM 3. The same as Problem 2, but for $J = 2$.

SOLUTION. The secular equation, of the fifth degree, falls into three linear equations and one quadratic. One of the linear equations is of the form $E_1 = H^{2-}_{2-}$, whence

$$E_1 = \frac{2\hbar^2}{I_C}+\tfrac{1}{2}\hbar^2\left(\frac{1}{I_A}+\frac{1}{I_B}\right),$$

a level of the type B_1. Hence we at once conclude that there must be two other levels, of the types B_2 and B_3:

$$E_2 = \frac{2\hbar^2}{I_B}+\tfrac{1}{2}\hbar^2\left(\frac{1}{I_C}+\frac{1}{I_A}\right), \qquad E_3 = \frac{2\hbar^2}{I_A}+\tfrac{1}{2}\hbar^2\left(\frac{1}{I_B}+\frac{1}{I_C}\right).$$

The equation of the second degree is

$$\begin{vmatrix} H^{0+}_{0+}-E & H^{2+}_{0+} \\ H^{2+}_{0+} & H^{2+}_{2+}-E \end{vmatrix} = 0. \qquad (1)$$

Solving this, we obtain

$$E_{4,5} = \hbar^2\left(\frac{1}{I_A}+\frac{1}{I_B}+\frac{1}{I_C}\right)\pm\hbar^2\sqrt{\left[\left(\frac{1}{I_A}+\frac{1}{I_B}+\frac{1}{I_C}\right)^2-3\left(\frac{1}{I_AI_B}+\frac{1}{I_BI_C}+\frac{1}{I_AI_C}\right)\right]}.$$

These levels belong to the type A.

PROBLEM 4. The same as Problem 2, but for $J = 3$.

SOLUTION. The secular equation, of the seventh degree, falls into one linear equation and three quadratic. The linear equation is of the form $E_1 = H^{2-}_{2-}$, whence

$$E_1 = 2\hbar^2\left(\frac{1}{I_A}+\frac{1}{I_B}+\frac{1}{I_C}\right),$$

a level of the type A. One of the quadratic equations is equation (1) of Problem 3, with a

† This follows at once from considerations of symmetry. The energy E_1, for instance, is symmetrical with respect to the moments of inertia I_A and I_B, and this property belongs to the energy of a state whose symmetry about the ξ and η axes is the same, i.e. a state of the type B_1.

different value of J. Its roots are

$$E_{2,3} = \frac{5\hbar^2}{2}\left(\frac{1}{I_A}+\frac{1}{I_B}\right)+\frac{\hbar^2}{I_C}\pm\hbar^2\sqrt{\left[4\left(\frac{1}{I_A}-\frac{1}{I_B}\right)^2+\frac{1}{I_C^2}+\frac{1}{I_AI_B}-\frac{1}{I_AI_C}-\frac{1}{I_BI_C}\right]},$$

a level of the type B_1. The remaining levels are obtained from these by permuting I_A, I_B and I_C.

§102. The interaction between the vibrations and the rotation of the molecule

Hitherto we have regarded the rotation and the vibrations as independent motions of the molecule. In reality, however, the simultaneous presence of both motions results in a peculiar interaction between them (E. TELLER, L. TISZA and G. PLACZEK 1932–33).

Let us start by considering linear polyatomic molecules. A linear molecule can execute vibrations of two types (see the end of §98): longitudinal vibrations with simple frequencies and transverse ones with double frequencies. We shall here be interested in the latter. A molecule executing transverse vibrations has in general some angular momentum. This is evident from simple mechanical considerations†, but it can also be shown by a quantum-mechanical discussion. The latter also enables us to determine the possible values of this angular momentum in a given vibrational state.

Let us suppose that some one double frequency ω_α has been excited in the molecule. The energy level with the vibrational quantum number v_α is $(v_\alpha+1)$-fold degenerate. To this level there correspond the $v_\alpha+1$ wave functions

$$\psi_{v_{\alpha1}v_{\alpha2}} = \text{constant}\times e^{-\frac{1}{2}c_\alpha^2(Q_{\alpha1}^2+Q_{\alpha2}^2)}H_{v_{\alpha1}}(c_\alpha Q_{\alpha1})H_{v_{\alpha2}}(c_\alpha Q_{\alpha2}),$$

where $v_{\alpha1}+v_{\alpha2}=v_\alpha$, or any linearly independent combinations of them. The total degree (in $Q_{\alpha1}$ and $Q_{\alpha2}$ together) of the polynomial by which the exponential factor is multiplied is the same in all these functions, and is equal to v_α. It is evident that we can always take, as the fundamental functions, linear combinations of the functions $\psi_{v_{\alpha1}v_{\alpha2}}$ of the form

$$\psi_{v_\alpha l_\alpha} = \text{constant}\times e^{-\frac{1}{2}c_\alpha^2(Q_{\alpha1}^2+Q_{\alpha2}^2)}\left[(Q_{\alpha1}+iQ_{\alpha2})^{\frac{1}{2}(v_\alpha+l_\alpha)}(Q_{\alpha1}-iQ_{\alpha2})^{\frac{1}{2}(v_\alpha-l_\alpha)}+\ldots\right]. \tag{102.1}$$

The square brackets contain a determinate polynomial, of which we have written out only the highest term. l_α is an integer, which can take the $v_\alpha+1$ different values v_α, $v_\alpha-2$, $v_\alpha-4$, ..., $-v_\alpha$.

The normal co-ordinates $Q_{\alpha1}$, $Q_{\alpha2}$ of the transverse vibration are two mutually perpendicular displacements off the axis of the molecule. Under a

† For example, two mutually perpendicular transverse vibrations with a phase difference of $\frac{1}{2}\pi$ can be regarded as a pure rotation of a bent molecule about a longitudinal axis.

rotation through an angle ϕ about this axis, the highest term of the polynomial (and therefore the whole function $\psi_{v_\alpha l_\alpha}$) is multiplied by

$$e^{\frac{1}{2}i\phi(v_\alpha+l_\alpha)}e^{-\frac{1}{2}i\phi(v_\alpha-l_\alpha)} = e^{il_\alpha\phi}.$$

Hence we see that the function $\psi_{v_\alpha l_\alpha}$ corresponds to a state with angular momentum l_α about the axis.

Thus we reach the result that, in a state where the double frequency ω_α is excited (with quantum number v_α), the molecule has an angular momentum (about its axis) which takes the values

$$l_\alpha = v_\alpha, v_\alpha-2, v_\alpha-4, \ldots, -v_\alpha. \tag{102.2}$$

This is called the *vibrational angular momentum.* If several transverse vibrations are excited simultaneously, the total vibrational angular momentum is equal to the sum $\sum_\alpha l_\alpha$. On being added to the electron orbital angular momentum, it gives the total angular momentum l of the molecule about its axis.

The total angular momentum J of the molecule cannot be less than the angular momentum about the axis (just as in a diatomic molecule), i.e. J takes the values

$$J = |l|, \quad |l|+1, \ldots .$$

In other words, there are no states with $J = 0, 1, \ldots, |l|-1$.

For harmonic vibrations, the energy depends only on the numbers v_α, and not on l_α. The degeneracy of the vibrational levels (with respect to the values of l_α) is removed by the presence of anharmonic vibrations. The removal is not complete, however: the levels remain doubly degenerate, the same energy belonging to states differing by a simultaneous change of sign of all the l_α and of l. In the next approximation (after that of harmonic motion), a term quadratic in the angular momenta l_α, of the form $\sum_{\alpha,\beta} g_{\alpha\beta} l_\alpha l_\beta$ (the $g_{\alpha\beta}$ being constants), appears in the energy.†

When we turn to non-linear molecules, we must first of all make the following remark, which has a purely mechanical significance. For an arbitrary (non-linear) system of particles, the question arises how we can at all separate the vibrational motion from the rotation; in other words, what we are to understand by a "non-rotating system". At first sight it might be thought that the vanishing of the angular momentum,

$$\sum \mu \mathbf{r}\times\mathbf{v} = 0 \tag{102.3}$$

(the summation being over the particles in the system), could serve as a criterion of the absence of rotation. However, the expression on the left-hand side is not the complete derivative, with respect to time, of any function of the co-ordinates. Hence the above equation cannot be integrated with respect to time in such a way as to be formulated as the vanishing of some

† The remaining double degeneracy is removed by an effect similar to the Λ-doubling in diatomic molecules.

function of the co-ordinates. This, however, is necessary if a reasonable definition of the concepts of "pure vibrations" and "pure rotation" is to be possible.

As a definition of the absence of rotation, we must therefore use the condition

$$\Sigma\, \mu \mathbf{r}_0 \times \mathbf{v} = 0, \tag{102.4}$$

where $\mathbf{r}_0$ are the radius vectors of the equilibrium positions of the particles. Putting $\mathbf{r} = \mathbf{r}_0 + \mathbf{u}$, where $\mathbf{u}$ are the displacements in small vibrations, we have $\mathbf{v} = \dot{\mathbf{r}} = \dot{\mathbf{u}}$. The equation (102.4) can be integrated with respect to time, giving

$$\Sigma\, \mu \mathbf{r}_0 \times \mathbf{u} = 0. \tag{102.5}$$

The motion of the molecule can be regarded as a combination of the purely vibrational motion, in which the condition (102.5) is satisfied, and the rotation of the molecule as a whole.†

Writing the angular momentum in the form

$$\Sigma\, \mu \mathbf{r} \times \mathbf{v} = \Sigma\, \mu \mathbf{r}_0 \times \mathbf{v} + \Sigma\, \mu \mathbf{u} \times \mathbf{v},$$

we see that, in accordance with the definition (102.4) of the absence of rotation, the vibrational angular momentum must be understood as the sum $\Sigma\, \mu\, \mathbf{u} \times \mathbf{v}$. However, it must be borne in mind that this angular momentum, being only a part of the total angular momentum of the system, is not conserved. Hence only a mean value of the vibrational angular momentum can be ascribed to each vibrational state.

Molecules having no axis of symmetry of order above the second belong to the asymmetrical-top type. In a molecule of this type, all the frequencies are simple (their symmetry groups have only one-dimensional irreducible representations). Hence none of the vibrational levels is degenerate. In any non-degenerate state, however, the mean angular momentum vanishes (see §24). Thus, in a molecule of the asymmetrical-top type, the mean vibrational angular momentum vanishes in every state.

If, among the symmetry elements of the molecule, there is one axis of order higher than the second, the molecule is of the symmetrical-top type. Such a molecule has vibrations with both simple and double frequencies. The mean vibrational angular momentum of the former again vanishes. To the double frequencies, however, there corresponds a non-zero mean angular momentum about the axis of the molecule. Since the vibrational angular momentum alone is not conserved, we cannot assert that its mean value must be integral. Instead of the expression $\sum_\alpha l_\alpha$ which we had for linear molecules, we here obtain for the mean vibrational angular momentum an expression of the form

$$\sum_\alpha \zeta_\alpha l_\alpha,$$

† The translational motion is supposed removed from the start, by choosing a system of co-ordinates in which the centre of mass of the molecule is at rest.

where the numbers l_α take their previous values (102.2), and ζ_α are constants characterising the vibrations in question, and can take values in the range from -1 to $+1$.

There is no difficulty in obtaining an expression for the energies of the rotational levels of molecules (of the symmetrical-top type), taking into account the vibrational angular momentum. The Hamiltonian of a "purely rotational" motion of the molecule, instead of (101.5), now takes the form

$$\hat{H}_{\text{rot}} = \hbar^2[(\hat{J}_\xi - \hat{J}_\xi^{(v)})^2 + (\hat{J}_\eta - \hat{J}_\eta^{(v)})^2]/2I_A + \hbar^2(\hat{J}_\zeta - \hat{J}_\zeta^{(v)})^2/2I_C,$$

where $\mathbf{J}^{(v)}$ denotes the vibrational angular momentum and $\mathbf{J}$ denotes, as before, the total angular momentum of the molecule. The rotational energy is the mean value: $E_{\text{rot}} = \overline{\hat{H}_{\text{rot}}}$. In effecting the averaging, it must be borne in mind that the total angular momentum is conserved; for the vibrational angular momentum, the mean values of the transverse components $\overline{J_\xi^{(v)}}$, $\overline{J_\eta^{(v)}}$ are zero, while $\overline{J_\zeta^{(v)}} = \sum_\alpha \zeta_\alpha l_\alpha$. As a result we have

$$E_{\text{rot}} = \frac{\hbar^2}{2I_A}J(J+1) + \tfrac{1}{2}\hbar^2\left(\frac{1}{I_C} - \frac{1}{I_A}\right)k^2 - \frac{\hbar^2}{I_C}k\sum_\alpha \zeta_\alpha l_\alpha; \tag{102.6}$$

as in §101, the integer k is the projection of the total angular momentum on the axis of the molecule. The last term in (102.6) is the required effect of the interaction between the vibrations of the molecule and its rotation. It is called the *Coriolis interaction* (since it corresponds to the Coriolis forces in classical mechanics).

Finally, let us consider molecules of the spherical-top type. These include molecules whose symmetry is that of any of the cubic groups. Such molecules have simple, double and triple frequencies (there being one-, two- and three-dimensional irreducible representations of the cubic groups). The degeneracy of the vibrational levels is, as usual, partly removed by the presence of anharmonic motion; when these effects have been taken into account there remain, apart from the non-degenerate levels, only doubly and triply degenerate levels. Here we shall discuss these levels that are split by the presence of anharmonic motion.

It is easy to see that, for a molecule of the spherical-top type, the mean vibrational angular momentum vanishes not only in the non-degenerate vibrational states but also in the doubly degenerate ones. This follows at once from considerations based on group theory. From the way in which the angular momentum is formed from the co-ordinates and velocities, it is clear that its symmetry properties are determined by the antisymmetric product with itself (see §91) of the irreducible representation to which the co-ordinates of the vibration concerned (regarded in a purely classical manner) belong. But the antisymmetric product of a two-dimensional representation with itself is a one-dimensional representation. On the other hand, for the symmetry of the cubic groups the components of the angular momentum, like those of any vector, must be transformed by a three-dimensional irreducible representation of the group. Hence it follows that the angular momentum must in this case vanish identically.

To the triply degenerate vibrational levels, however, there corresponds a non-zero mean angular momentum.† It can be shown from considerations of symmetry (using group theory) that the angular momentum of a triply degenerate vibrational state must be given by an operator of the form $\zeta\hat{\mathbf{l}}$, where ζ is a constant characterising the state in question ($|\zeta| < 1$), and $\hat{\mathbf{l}}$ is the operator of an angular momentum equal to unity.

The Hamiltonian of the rotational motion of the molecule is

$$\begin{aligned}\hat{H}_{\text{rot}} &= \hbar^2(\hat{\mathbf{J}}-\zeta\hat{\mathbf{l}})^2/2I \\ &= \hbar^2\hat{\mathbf{J}}^2/2I-\hbar^2\zeta\hat{\mathbf{J}}.\hat{\mathbf{l}}/I+\hbar^2\zeta^2\hat{\mathbf{l}}^2/2I.\end{aligned}$$

On averaging to find the rotational energy, the last term gives an unimportant constant $(\hbar^2\zeta^2/2I).2$, which is independent of the rotational quantum number and can be omitted. Thus

$$E_{\text{rot}} = \hbar^2 J(J+1)/2I-\hbar^2\zeta\mathbf{l}\,.\,\mathbf{J}/I. \tag{102.7}$$

The quantity $\mathbf{l}\,.\,\mathbf{J}$ is calculated in the usual way; for a given J, it can take three different values, corresponding to the values $J+1$, J, $J-1$ of the vector $\mathbf{l}+\mathbf{J}$. As a result we obtain

$$\left.\begin{aligned}E^{(+)}_{\text{rot}} &= \hbar^2[J(J+1)+2\zeta(J+1)]/2I, \\ E^{(-)}_{\text{rot}} &= \hbar^2[J(J+1)-2\zeta J]/2I, \\ E^{(0)}_{\text{rot}} &= \hbar^2[J(J+1)+2\zeta]/2I.\end{aligned}\right\} \tag{102.8}$$

Thus the Coriolis interaction completely removes the degeneracy of a triply degenerate vibrational level.

PROBLEM

Determine the wave functions of vibrations with a double frequency which correspond to given values of the vibrational angular momentum.

SOLUTION. Let Q_1, Q_2 be the normal co-ordinates corresponding to the given frequency ω (we omit the suffix α). We introduce the radius vector $r = \sqrt{(Q_1^2+Q_2^2)}$ and the polar angle ϕ in the Q_1Q_2 plane. SCHRÖDINGER's equation takes the form

$$\frac{1}{r}\frac{\partial}{\partial r}\left(r\frac{\partial\psi}{\partial r}\right)+\frac{1}{r^2}\frac{\partial^2\psi}{\partial\phi^2}+\frac{2}{\hbar^2}[\hbar\omega(v+1)-\tfrac{1}{2}\omega^2r^2]\psi = 0,$$

where we have put $E = \hbar\omega(v+1)$ for the energy. Putting $\psi = e^{il\phi}R(r)$, we obtain for the "radial" function $R(r)$ the equation

$$\frac{1}{r}\frac{\mathrm{d}}{\mathrm{d}r}\left(r\frac{\mathrm{d}R}{\mathrm{d}r}\right)+\frac{2}{\hbar^2}[\hbar\omega(v+1)-\tfrac{1}{2}\omega^2r^2-\tfrac{1}{2}\hbar^2l^2/r^2]R = 0.$$

† The antisymmetric product of a three-dimensional representation with itself is another three-dimensional representation; by actually calculating its characters (from formula (91.20)), it is easy to see that, for all three-dimensional representations of cubic groups, this product is the representation by which the components of an axial vector are transformed.

Introducing the new variable

$$\rho = \omega r^2/\hbar,$$

we have the equation

$$R''+R'/\rho+[-\tfrac{1}{4}+\tfrac{1}{2}(v+1)/\rho-\tfrac{1}{4}l^2/\rho^2]R = 0,$$

which is analogous to (36.4). We look for R in the form

$$R = e^{-\frac{1}{2}\rho}\rho^{\frac{1}{2}|l|}w(\rho),$$

obtaining for $w(\rho)$ the equation

$$\rho w''+(|l|+1-\rho)w'+\tfrac{1}{2}(v-|l|)w = 0,$$

which is satisfied by the confluent hypergeometric function

$$w = F(-\tfrac{1}{2}v+\tfrac{1}{2}|l|,\quad |l|+1,\quad \rho).$$

$\frac{1}{2}(v-|l|)$ must be a positive integer (so that F reduces to a polynomial), and hence we again have for l the series of values (102.2). The required wave functions are thus

$$\psi_{vl} = \text{constant}\times e^{-\omega r^2/2\hbar}F(-\tfrac{1}{2}(v-|l|),\quad |l|+1,\quad \omega r^2/\hbar)r^{|l|}e^{il\phi}.$$

§103. The classification of molecular terms

The wave function of a molecule is the product of the electron wave function, the wave function of the vibrational motion of the nuclei, and the rotational wave function. We have already discussed the classification and types of symmetry of these functions separately. It now remains for us to examine the question of the classification of molecular terms as a whole, i.e. of the possible symmetry of the total wave function.

It is clear that, if the symmetry of all three factors with respect to some transformation is given, the symmetry of the product with respect to that transformation is determined. For a complete description of the symmetry of the term, we must also specify the behaviour of the total wave function when the co-ordinates of all the particles in the molecule (electrons and nuclei) are inverted simultaneously. The term is said to be *negative* or *positive*, according as the wave function does or does not change sign under this transformation.†

It must be mentioned that the characterisation of the term with respect to inversion is significant only for molecules which do not possess stereoisomers. If stereoisomerism is present, the molecule assumes on inversion a configuration which can by no rotation in space be made to coincide with the original configuration; these are the "right-hand" and "left-hand" modifications of the substance.‡ Hence, when stereoisomerism is present, the wave functions

† We use the same customary, though unfortunate, terminology as for diatomic molecules (§83).

‡ For stereoisomerism to be possible, the molecule must have no symmetry element pertaining to reflection (i.e. no centre of symmetry, plane of symmetry, or rotary-reflection axis).

obtained from each other on inversion belong essentially to different molecules, and it is meaningless to compare them.†

Let us consider a molecule whose atoms do not lie in one plane, and imagine all the atoms to be numbered. Then, on inversion, we obtain a configuration which can by no rotation of the molecule in space be made to coincide with the original one (without altering the numbering of the atoms). Forming the sum and difference of the wave functions corresponding to these two configurations, we obtain two states (one positive and one negative), corresponding to the same energy level. Thus each rotational level has an additional double degeneracy.

It must be noticed that this double degeneracy may be removed as a consequence of the following unusual effect. The two configurations obtained from each other on inversion are separated (in configuration space) by a potential barrier, which in general is very high. The passage of the nuclei "through the barrier" can effect the transition of the molecule from one configuration to the other. The existence of a non-zero probability for the transition between the two mutually degenerate states results in a splitting of the corresponding energy level (see §50, Problem 3). However, it must be borne in mind that, in the majority of molecules, the probability of the transition in question is extremely small, and so the corresponding splitting of the levels is not observable.‡

For a plane molecule, inversion gives a configuration which can always be made to coincide with the original one (even when the atoms are numbered) by a spatial rotation of the molecule as a whole. Hence the double degeneracy mentioned above, and the corresponding splitting, do not occur here. Each level is either positive or negative.

We have seen in §83 that, for diatomic molecules, the spin of the nuclei exerts an important indirect effect on the arrangement of the molecular terms by determining their degree of degeneracy, and in some cases entirely forbidding levels of a certain symmetry. The same is true for polyatomic molecules. Here, however, the investigation of the problem is considerably more complex, and requires the application of the methods of group theory to each particular case.

The idea of the method is as follows. The total wave function must contain, besides the co-ordinate part (the only part we have considered so far), a spin factor, which is a function of the projections of the spins of all the nuclei on some chosen direction in space. The projection σ of the spin of a nucleus takes $2i+1$ values (where i is the spin of the nucleus); by giving to all the $\sigma_1, \sigma_2, \dots, \sigma_N$ (where N is the number of atoms in the molecule) all possible values, we obtain altogether $(2i_1+1)(2i_2+1)\dots(2i_N+1)$ different values of the spin factor. In each symmetry transformation, certain nuclei (of the same

† Strictly speaking, quantum mechanics always gives a non-zero probability for the transition from one modification to the other. This probability, however, which relates to the passage of nuclei through a barrier (see below), is so small that the phenomenon can always be neglected.

‡ Such a splitting is in fact observed, for example in NH_3, a molecule which is an equilateral triangular pyramid with the N atom at the vertex and the H atoms at the corners of the base.

kind) change places, and if we imagine the spin values to "remain fixed", the transformation is equivalent to an interchange of spin values among the nuclei. Accordingly, the various spin factors will be transformed into one another, thus giving some representation (in general reducible) of the symmetry group of the molecule. Decomposing this into irreducible parts, we find the possible types of symmetry for the spin wave function.

A general formula can easily be written down for the characters $\chi_{sp}(G)$ of the representation given by the spin factors. To do this, it is sufficient to notice that, in a transformation, only those spin factors are unchanged in which the nuclei changing places have the same σ_a; otherwise, one spin factor changes into another and contributes nothing to the character. Bearing in mind that σ_a takes $2i_a+1$ values, we find that

$$\chi_{sp}(G) = \Pi\,(2i_a+1), \tag{103.1}$$

where the product is taken over the groups of atoms which change places under the transformation G considered (there being one factor in the product from each group).

We are, however, interested not so much in the symmetry of the spin function as in that of the co-ordinate wave function (by which we mean its symmetry with respect to interchanges of the co-ordinates of the nuclei, the co-ordinates of the electrons remaining unchanged). These two symmetries are directly related, however, since the total wave function must remain unchanged or change sign when any pair of nuclei are interchanged, according as they obey Bose statistics or Fermi statistics (in other words, it must be multiplied by $(-1)^{2i}$, where i is the spin of the nuclei that are interchanged). Introducing the appropriate factor and the characters (103.1), we obtain the system of characters $\chi(G)$ for the representation containing all the irreducible representations by which the co-ordinate wave functions are transformed:

$$\chi(G) = \Pi(2i_a+1)(-1)^{2i_a(n_a-1)}, \tag{103.2}$$

where n_a is the number of nuclei in each group which change places under the transformation in question. Decomposing this representation into irreducible parts, we at once obtain the possible types of symmetry of the co-ordinate wave functions of the molecule, together with the degrees of degeneracy of the corresponding energy levels (here and later we mean the degeneracy with respect to the different spin states of the system of nuclei).†

Each type of symmetry of the terms is related to definite values of the total spin of the nuclei in the molecule. This relation is not one-to-one; each type of symmetry can, in general, be brought about with various values of the total spin. The relation can also be established, in any particular case, by means of group theory; we shall not, however, pause to discuss this here.‡

† The degree of degeneracy of the level in this respect is often called its *statistical weight*.

‡ We shall merely remark that, to establish the relation, it is necessary to consider the representations given not only by all possible spin factors simultaneously, but also by factors belonging to every possible value of the projection of the total spin, from the greatest downwards.

As an example, let us consider a molecule of the asymmetrical-top type, the ethylene molecule $C^{12}{}_2H^1{}_4$ (Fig. 45g), with the symmetry group D_{2h}. The index to the chemical symbol indicates the isotope to which the nucleus belongs; this indication is necessary, since the nuclei of different isotopes have different spins. In this case, the spin of the H^1 nucleus is $\frac{1}{2}$, while the C^{12} nucleus has no spin. Hence we need consider only the hydrogen atoms.

We take the system of co-ordinates shown in Fig. 45g; the z-axis is perpendicular to the plane of the molecule, while the x-axis is along the axis of the molecule. A reflection in the xy-plane leaves all the atoms fixed, while other reflections and rotations interchange the hydrogen atoms in pairs. From formula (103.2) we have the following characters of the representation:

E	$\sigma(xy)$	$\sigma(xz)$	$\sigma(yz)$	I	$C_2(x)$	$C_2(y)$	$C_2(z)$
16	16	4	4	4	4	4	4

Decomposing this representation into irreducible parts, we find that it contains the following irreducible representations of the group D_{2h}: $7A_g$, $3B_{1g}$, $3B_{2u}$, $3B_{3u}$. The figures show the number of times each irreducible representation appears in the reducible one; these numbers are also the "nuclear" degrees of degeneracy (the nuclear statistical weights) of the levels with the corresponding symmetry.†

The classification of the terms of the ethylene molecule thus obtained relates to the symmetry of the total (co-ordinate) wave function, including the electron, vibrational and rotational parts. Usually, however, it is of interest to arrive at these results from a different point of view. Knowing the possible symmetries of the total wave function, we can find at once which rotational levels are possible (and with what statistical weights) for any prescribed electron and vibrational state.

Let us consider, for instance, the rotational structure of the lowest vibrational level (that for which the vibrations are not excited at all) of the normal electron term, assuming that the electron wave function of the normal state is completely symmetrical (as is the case for practically all polyatomic molecules). Then the symmetry of the total wave function with respect to rotations about the axes of symmetry is the same as the symmetry of the rotational wave function. Comparing this with the results obtained above, we therefore conclude that the rotational levels of the types A and B_1 (see §101) can only be positive, while those of the types B_2 and B_3 can only be negative.

As with diatomic molecules (see the end of §83), owing to the extreme weakness of the interaction between the nuclear spins and the electrons, transitions between states of different nuclear symmetry do not usually occur in practice. Hence molecules in states of different nuclear symmetry behave

† The total spin of the molecule $C^{12}{}_2H^1{}_4$ can take the values 2, 1, 0, and these can occur in one, three and two ways respectively. The terms of symmetry A_g correspond to the spins 2 and 0, and those of symmetry B_{1g}, B_{2u}, B_{3u} to the spin 1.

almost like different modifications of the substance. Thus ethylene $C^{12}{}_2H^1{}_4$ has four modifications, with nuclear statistical weights 7, 3, 3, 3.

Let us consider another example, the ammonia molecule $N^{14}H^1{}_3$, of the symmetrical-top type (Fig. 43), whose symmetry group is C_{3v}. The spin of the nucleus N^{14} is 1, and that of H^1 is $\frac{1}{2}$. Using formula (103.2), we find the characters of the representation of the group C_{3v} in which we are interested:

E	$2C_3$	$3\sigma_v$
24	6	-12

It contains the following irreducible representations of the group C_{3v}: $12A_2$, $6E$. Thus two types of level are possible; their nuclear statistical weights are† 12 and 6.

The rotational levels of a symmetrical top are classified (for a given J) according to the values of the quantum number k. Let us consider, as in the previous example, the rotational structure of the normal electron and vibrational state of the NH_3 molecule (i.e. we suppose the electron and vibrational wave functions to be completely symmetrical). In determining the symmetry of the rotational wave function, we must bear in mind that it is meaningful to speak of its behaviour only with respect to rotations about axes. Hence we replace the planes of symmetry by axes of symmetry of the second order perpendicular to them, a reflection in a plane being equivalent to a rotation about such an axis, followed by an inversion. In the present case, therefore, instead of the group C_{3v} we have to consider the isomorphous point group D_3.

The rotational wave functions with $k = \pm|k|$ are multiplied by $e^{\pm 2\pi i|k|/3}$ respectively under a rotation C_3 about a vertical axis of the third order, while under a rotation U_2 about a horizontal axis of the second order they change into each other, thus giving a two-dimensional representation of the group D_3. If $|k|$ is not a multiple of three, this representation is irreducible; it is E. The representation of the group C_{3v} corresponding to the total wave function is obtained by multiplying the character $\chi(U_2)$ by 1 or -1, according as the term is positive or negative. Since, however, in the representation E we have $\chi(U_2) = 0$, we obtain the same representation E in either case (but this time as a representation of the group C_{3v}, and not D_3). Bearing in mind the results obtained above, we thus conclude that, when $|k|$ is not a multiple of three, both positive and negative levels are possible, with nuclear statistical weights of 6 (the symmetry of the total co-ordinate wave function being of the type E).

When $|k|$ is a multiple of three (but not zero), the rotational functions give a representation (of the group D_3) with characters

E	$2C_3$	$3U_2$
2	2	0

† A total spin of the hydrogen nuclei of 3/2 corresponds to the terms of symmetry A_2, and one of 1/2 to those of symmetry E.

This representation is reducible, and divides into the representations A_1, A_2. In order that the total wave function should belong to the representation A_2 of the group C_{3v}, the rotational level A_1 must be negative and A_2 positive. Thus, when $|k|$ is a multiple of three and not zero, both positive and negative levels are possible, with nuclear statistical weights of 12 (levels of the type A_2).

Finally, only one rotational function corresponds to a projected angular momentum $k = 0$; it gives a representation with characters†

E	$2C_3$	$3U_2$
1	1	$(-1)^J$

If the total wave function has the symmetry A_2, its behaviour with respect to inversion must therefore be given by the factor $(-1)^{J+1}$. Thus, for $k = 0$, levels with even and odd J can only be negative and positive respectively; the statistical weight is 6 in either case (levels of the type A_2).

An example of a molecule of the spherical-top type is discussed in Problem 4.

PROBLEMS

PROBLEM 1. Determine the types of symmetry of the total (co-ordinate) wave functions, and the statistical weights of the corresponding levels, for the molecules $C^{12}{}_2H^2{}_4$, $C^{13}{}_2H^1{}_4$, $N^{14}{}_2O^{16}{}_4$ (all these molecules are of the same form; the spins are $i(H^2) = 1$, $i(C^{13}) = \frac{1}{2}$, $i(N^{14}) = 1$).

SOLUTION. By the method shown in the text for the molecule $C^{12}{}_2H^1{}_4$, we find the following terms (the axes of co-ordinates being taken the same as above):

for the molecule $C^{12}{}_2H^2{}_4$: $27A_g$, $18B_{1g}$, $18B_{2u}$, $18B_{3u}$;
for the molecule $C^{13}{}_2H^1{}_4$: $16A_g$, $12B_{1g}$, $12B_{2u}$, $24B_{3u}$;
for the molecule $N^{14}{}_2O^{16}{}_4$: $6A_g$, $3B_{3u}$.

PROBLEM 2. The same as Problem 1, but for the molecule $N^{14}H^2{}_3$.

SOLUTION. In the way shown in the text for the molecule $N^{14}H^1{}_3$, we find the terms $30A_1$, $3A_2$, $24E$.

In the normal electron and vibrational state, the following terms are possible for various values of the quantum number k (+ and − denoting positive and negative terms):

		+	−
	$\lvert k\rvert$ not a multiple of 3	$24E$	$24E$
	$\lvert k\rvert$ a multiple of 3	$30A_1$, $3A_2$	$30A_1$, $3A_2$
$k = 0$	J even	$30A_1$	$3A_2$
$k = 0$	J odd	$3A_2$	$30A_1$

PROBLEM 3. The same as Problem 1, but for the molecule $C^{12}{}_2H^1{}_6$ (see Fig. 45f; the symmetry is D_{3d}).

SOLUTION. The possible terms are of the types $7A_{1g}$, $1A_{1u}$, $3A_{2g}$, $13A_{2u}$, $9E_g$, $11E_u$.

In the normal electron and vibrational state, the following levels are obtained:

		+	−
	$\lvert k\rvert$ not a multiple of 3	$9E_g$	$11E_u$
	$\lvert k\rvert$ a multiple of 3	$7A_{1g}$, $3A_{2g}$	$1A_{1u}$, $13A_{2u}$
$k = 0$	J even	$7A_{1g}$	$1A_{1u}$
$k = 0$	J odd	$3A_{2g}$	$13A_{2u}$

† On rotation through an angle π, the eigenfunction of the angular momentum with magnitude J and projection zero is multiplied by $(-1)^J$ (see §77).

PROBLEM 4. The same as Problem 1, but for the methane molecule $C^{12}H^1_4$ (the C atom is at the centre of a tetrahedron with the H atoms at the vertices).

SOLUTION. The molecule is of the spherical-top type, and has the symmetry T_d. Following the same method, we find that the possible terms are of the types; $5A_2$, $1E$, $3F_1$ (corresponding to a total spin of the molecule of 2, 0, 1 respectively).

The rotational terms of a spherical top are classified according to the values of the total angular momentum J. The $2J+1$ rotational functions belonging to a particular value of J give a $(2J+1)$-dimensional representation of the group O, which is isomorphous with the group T_d; it is obtained from the latter by replacing all planes of symmetry by axes of the second order perpendicular to them. The characters in this representation are the same as those of the corresponding rotations in the $(2J+1)$-dimensional irreducible representation of the rotation group (formula (95.3)). Thus, for example, for $J = 3$ we obtain a representation with characters

E	$8C_3$	$6C_2$	$6C_4$	$3C_4^2$
7	1	−1	−1	−1

This contains the following irreducible representations of the group O, A_2, F_1, F_2. Again considering the rotational structure of the normal electron and vibrational term, we therefore conclude that, for $J = 3$, the levels with a symmetry A_2 of the total wave function can only be positive, while those of type F_1 can be either positive or negative. For the first few values of J we thus obtain the following levels (which we write together with their statistical weights):

	+	−
$J = 0$	—	$5A_2$
$J = 1$	$3F_1$	—
$J = 2$	$1E$	$1E$, $3F_1$
$J = 3$	$5A_2$, $3F_1$	$3F_1$
$J = 4$	$1E$, $3F_1$	$5A_2$, $1E$, $3F_1$

§104. An electron in a periodic field

In this section we shall discuss the motion of an electron in an electric field that is periodic in space (F. BLOCH 1929). Though not of direct physical interest, this is a very important auxiliary problem in the theory of the conductivity of metallic and other crystals.

The symmetry of the periodic field is that of some crystal lattice. The basis of this symmetry is a spatial periodicity, given by three fundamental periods $\mathbf{a}_1$, $\mathbf{a}_2$, $\mathbf{a}_3$. The field $U(\mathbf{r})$ is unchanged in a parallel translation over any vector of the form

$$\mathbf{a} = n_1\mathbf{a}_1 + n_2\mathbf{a}_2 + n_3\mathbf{a}_3 \tag{104.1}$$

(where n_1, n_2, n_3 are positive or negative integers):

$$U(\mathbf{r}+\mathbf{a}) = U(\mathbf{r}). \tag{104.2}$$

Hence the SCHRÖDINGER's equation which describes the motion of the electron in the periodic field is invariant under any transformation $\mathbf{r} \to \mathbf{r}+\mathbf{a}$.

From this we can draw an important conclusion. If $\psi(\mathbf{r})$ is the wave function of some stationary state, the function $\psi(\mathbf{r}+\mathbf{a})$ is also a solution of SCHRÖDINGER's equation, and describes the same state of the electron. This means that the functions $\psi(\mathbf{r})$ and $\psi(\mathbf{r}+\mathbf{a})$ must be the same apart from a constant factor: $\psi(\mathbf{r}+\mathbf{a}) = \text{constant} \times \psi(\mathbf{r})$. It is evident that the constant must be of modulus unity, since otherwise the wave function would become infinite on repeating the displacement through **a** (or **−a**) an unlimited number of times. The most general function having this property is

$$\psi_{n\mathbf{k}}(\mathbf{r}) = e^{i\mathbf{k}.\mathbf{r}}u_{n\mathbf{k}}(\mathbf{r}), \tag{104.3}$$

where **k** is an arbitrary real constant vector, and $u_{n\mathbf{k}}(\mathbf{r})$ is a periodic function:

$$u_{n\mathbf{k}}(\mathbf{r}+\mathbf{a}) = u_{n\mathbf{k}}(\mathbf{r}). \tag{104.4}$$

The suffix n is explained below.

The function (104.3) bears some similarity to the wave function of a freely moving electron $\psi = \text{constant} \times e^{(i/\hbar)\mathbf{p}.\mathbf{r}}$, the part of the conserved momentum **p** being taken by the constant vector $\hbar\mathbf{k}$. We shall see below that this vector is analogous to the momentum in a number of other respects (though there are at the same time various important differences between them). For this reason the vector $\hbar\mathbf{k}$ is called the *quasi-momentum* of the electron in the periodic field. It must be emphasised that there is no actual conserved momentum in this case, since there is no law of conservation of momentum in a field which varies in space. Nevertheless, it is noteworthy that an electron in a periodic field is still characterised by a certain constant vector.†

Thus, to each stationary state of an electron in a periodic field, there corresponds some value of the quasi-momentum **k**. This correspondence, however, is not one-to-one; for a given **k**, the energy of the electron can in general take a discrete series of values. For this reason we have introduced in the wave functions (104.3) the suffix n, which numbers the energy levels for a given **k**. The energy E of the electron can be regarded as a many-valued function of the quasi-momentum: $E = E_n(\mathbf{k})$, where the suffix n numbers the different branches of the function. Geometrically, the functional dependence of E on k_x, k_y, k_z is represented by a four-dimensional hypersurface. Different sheets of this surface correspond to different branches of the function.

Here the hypersurface $E = E(k_x, k_y, k_z)$ may intersect itself, i.e. its sheets need not be completely separate, but may intersect. Such intersections may occur both for "chance" values of the quasi-momentum and for values of the vector **k** distinguished by the symmetry of their position with respect to the reciprocal lattice of the crystal. In the first case, intersections can occur only in a manifold of one (not two) dimensions, i.e. in a line (cf. §76). In practice, the presence of such intersections could be established only by actually solving SCHRÖDINGER's equation for the given function $U(\mathbf{r})$.

On the other hand, a detailed general investigation of intersections due to

† In a stationary state with a given quasi-momentum **k**, the true momentum can have, with various probabilities, an infinite number of values of the form $\hbar(\mathbf{k}+2\pi\mathbf{b})$, where **b** is a vector of the form (104.6). This follows from the fact that the expansion of a function of the type (104.3) in plane waves is

$$e^{i\mathbf{k}.\mathbf{r}} \sum_{\mathbf{b}} a_{\mathbf{b}} e^{2\pi i \mathbf{b}.\mathbf{r}}.$$

the symmetry of the crystal can be made by using group theory. We shall not pause here to discuss this question,† but merely mention that in this case many different types of intersection are possible, not only in lines, but also in two-dimensional surfaces.

All the functions $\psi_{n\mathbf{k}}$ with different n or $\mathbf{k}$ are, of course, orthogonal. In particular, it follows from the orthogonality of $\psi_{n\mathbf{k}}$ with different n and the same $\mathbf{k}$ that

$$\int u_{m\mathbf{k}}{}^* u_{n\mathbf{k}}\,\mathrm{d}V = 0 \qquad (m \neq n). \tag{104.5}$$

Thus the functions $u_{n\mathbf{k}}$ with a given value of $\mathbf{k}$ form a system of orthogonal functions.

A very important property of the quasi-momentum, in which it differs from the true momentum, is its many-valuedness. The definition of the quasi-momentum is essentially a matter of determining the behaviour of the wave function under a parallel translation. The transformation $\mathbf{r} \rightarrow \mathbf{r}+\mathbf{a}$ multiplies the function (104.3) by $e^{i\mathbf{k}.\mathbf{a}}$. The values of $\mathbf{k}$ for which this factor is the same (for each possible $\mathbf{a}$) are physically equivalent, and correspond to the same state of the electron. For a given $\mathbf{k}$, this property is possessed by all $\mathbf{k}+2\pi\mathbf{b}$, where $\mathbf{b}$ is a vector of the form

$$\mathbf{b} = m_1\mathbf{b}_1+m_2\mathbf{b}_2+m_3\mathbf{b}_3, \tag{104.6}$$

with m_1, m_2, m_3 any integers, and the vectors $\mathbf{b}_1$, $\mathbf{b}_2$, $\mathbf{b}_3$ giving on multiplication by $\mathbf{a}_1$, $\mathbf{a}_2$, $\mathbf{a}_3$

$$\mathbf{a}_i\,.\,\mathbf{b}_k = \delta_{ik}. \tag{104.7}$$

For

$$e^{i(\mathbf{k}+2\pi\mathbf{b}).\mathbf{a}} = e^{i\mathbf{k}.\mathbf{a}}e^{2\pi i(n_1m_1+n_2m_2+n_3m_3)} = e^{i\mathbf{k}.\mathbf{a}}.$$

The vectors $\mathbf{b}_1$, $\mathbf{b}_2$, $\mathbf{b}_3$ are called in crystallography the *fundamental periods of the reciprocal lattice* corresponding to the periods $\mathbf{a}_1$, $\mathbf{a}_2$, $\mathbf{a}_3$. From the definitions (104.7) we have at once the relations

$$\mathbf{b}_1 = \mathbf{a}_2\times\mathbf{a}_3/V, \qquad \mathbf{b}_2 = \mathbf{a}_3\times\mathbf{a}_1/V, \qquad \mathbf{b}_3 = \mathbf{a}_1\times\mathbf{a}_2/V, \tag{104.8}$$

where $V = \mathbf{a}_1\,.\,\mathbf{a}_2\times\mathbf{a}_3$ is the volume of an elementary cell.

Thus the values of the quasi-momentum that differ by any period $\mathbf{b}$ (multiplied by 2π) of the reciprocal lattice are physically equivalent. We may say that the physically different values of the quasi-momentum lie in a single elementary cell of the reciprocal lattice. Hence, in particular, it follows that the energy of the electron as a function of $\mathbf{k}$ must be unaltered when $\mathbf{k}$ is replaced by $\mathbf{k}+2\pi\mathbf{b}$:

$$E_n(\mathbf{k}+2\pi\mathbf{b}) = E_n(\mathbf{k}). \tag{104.9}$$

In other words, the energy is a periodic function of the quasi-momentum, with fundamental periods $\mathbf{b}_1$, $\mathbf{b}_2$, $\mathbf{b}_3$.

† See L. P. Bouckaert, R. Smoluchowski and E. P. Wigner, *Physical Review* 50, 58, 1936; F. Hund, *Zeitschrift für Physik* 99, 119, 1936; C. Herring, *Physical Review* 52, 361, 365, 1937.

Next, let us suppose that there are two electrons in the periodic field. Considering them together as one system, and applying to its wave function $\psi(\mathbf{r}_1, \mathbf{r}_2)$ the same arguments as were used to derive (104.3), we find that, under the transformation $\mathbf{r}_1 \rightarrow \mathbf{r}_1+\mathbf{a}$, $\mathbf{r}_2 \rightarrow \mathbf{r}_2+\mathbf{a}$, it is multiplied by $e^{i\mathbf{k}.\mathbf{a}}$; the constant vector $\mathbf{k}$ may be called the quasi-momentum of the system of two electrons. On the other hand, if the electrons are sufficiently far apart for their interaction to be negligible, the wave function of the system is the product of those of the two electrons separately, and under a parallel translation it is multiplied by $e^{i\mathbf{k}_1.\mathbf{a}}\, e^{i\mathbf{k}_2.\mathbf{a}}$, where $\mathbf{k}_1$, $\mathbf{k}_2$ are the quasi-momenta of the two electrons. Since we must have $e^{i\mathbf{k}.\mathbf{a}} = e^{i(\mathbf{k}_1+\mathbf{k}_2).\mathbf{a}}$, it follows that

$$\mathbf{k} = \mathbf{k}_1+\mathbf{k}_2+2\pi\mathbf{b},$$

i.e. the quasi-momentum of the system is equal, apart from a vector of the form $2\pi\mathbf{b}$, to the sum of the quasi-momenta of the electrons separately. Hence, in particular, it follows that, if we consider the collision of two electrons moving in a periodic field, the sum of their quasi-momenta $\mathbf{k}_1$, $\mathbf{k}_2$ before the collision is equal (apart from $2\pi\mathbf{b}$) to the sum of their quasi-momenta $\mathbf{k}_1'$, $\mathbf{k}_2'$ after the collision:

$$\mathbf{k}_1+\mathbf{k}_2 = \mathbf{k}_1'+\mathbf{k}_2'+2\pi\mathbf{b}. \tag{104.10}$$

A further analogy between the quasi-momentum and the true momentum is seen when we determine the mean velocity of the electron. To calculate this, we must know the velocity operator $\hat{\mathbf{v}} = \hat{\dot{\mathbf{r}}}$ in the $\mathbf{k}$ representation. The operators in the $\mathbf{k}$ representation act on the coefficients $a_{n\mathbf{k}}$ in an expansion of an arbitrary wave function ψ in terms of the eigenfunctions $\psi_{n\mathbf{k}}$:

$$\psi = \sum_n \int a_{n\mathbf{k}}\psi_{n\mathbf{k}}\, d\tau_{\mathbf{k}}; \tag{104.11}$$

cf. the derivation of the expression for the operators of the co-ordinates in the $\mathbf{p}$ representation in §13. We have identically

$$\mathbf{r}\psi_{n\mathbf{k}} = -i\partial\psi_{n\mathbf{k}}/\partial\mathbf{k}+ie^{i\mathbf{k}.\mathbf{r}}\,\partial u_{n\mathbf{k}}/\partial\mathbf{k}.$$

Hence

$$\mathbf{r}\psi = \sum_n \int \mathbf{r}a_{n\mathbf{k}}\psi_{n\mathbf{k}}\, d\tau_{\mathbf{k}}$$

$$= -i\sum_n a_{n\mathbf{k}}\frac{\partial\psi_{n\mathbf{k}}}{\partial\mathbf{k}}\, d\tau_{\mathbf{k}}+i\sum_n \int e^{i\mathbf{k}.\mathbf{r}}a_{n\mathbf{k}}\frac{\partial u_{n\mathbf{k}}}{\partial\mathbf{k}}\, d\tau_{\mathbf{k}}.$$

In the first term we integrate by parts, while in the second term we expand the function $\partial u_{n\mathbf{k}}/\partial\mathbf{k}$ (which, like $u_{n\mathbf{k}}$ itself, is periodic) in terms of the system of mutually orthogonal functions $u_{n\mathbf{k}}$ with the same $\mathbf{k}$:

$$\partial u_{n\mathbf{k}}/\partial\mathbf{k} = \sum_m \boldsymbol{\lambda}^{(\mathbf{k})}_{mn}\, u_{m\mathbf{k}}. \tag{104.12}$$

We then have

$$\mathbf{r}\psi = i\sum_n \int \psi_{n\mathbf{k}} \frac{\partial a_{n\mathbf{k}}}{\partial \mathbf{k}} d\tau_{\mathbf{k}} + i\sum_{n,m} \int a_{n\mathbf{k}} \boldsymbol{\lambda}^{(\mathbf{k})}_{mn} \psi_{m\mathbf{k}} d\tau_{\mathbf{k}}$$

$$= \sum_n \int \left\{ i\frac{\partial a_{n\mathbf{k}}}{\partial \mathbf{k}} + i\sum_m a_{m\mathbf{k}} \boldsymbol{\lambda}^{(\mathbf{k})}_{nm} \right\} \psi_{n\mathbf{k}}\, d\tau_{\mathbf{k}}.$$

On the other hand, from the definition of an operator in the **k** representation we must have

$$\hat{\mathbf{r}}\psi = \sum_n \int \mathbf{b}_{n\mathbf{k}}\psi_{n\mathbf{k}}\, d\tau_{\mathbf{k}},$$

where $\mathbf{b}_{n\mathbf{k}} = \hat{\mathbf{r}}a_{n\mathbf{k}}$. Comparing this with the expression obtained above, we find that the operator $\hat{\mathbf{r}}$ has the form

$$\hat{\mathbf{r}} = i\partial/\partial\mathbf{k} + \hat{\boldsymbol{\Omega}}, \tag{104.13}$$

where the operator $\hat{\boldsymbol{\Omega}}$ is defined by

$$\hat{\boldsymbol{\Omega}} a_{n\mathbf{k}} = \sum_m \boldsymbol{\lambda}^{(\mathbf{k})}_{nm} a_{m\mathbf{k}}. \tag{104.14}$$

It is important to notice that $\boldsymbol{\Omega}$ has non-zero matrix elements only for transitions between states with the same **k**: $\boldsymbol{\Omega}^{m\mathbf{k}}_{n\mathbf{k}} = i\boldsymbol{\lambda}^{(\mathbf{k})}_{nm}$ (including the diagonal elements $\boldsymbol{\Omega}^{n\mathbf{k}}_{n\mathbf{k}}$).

The velocity operator is obtained, according to the general rule, by commuting the operator $\hat{\mathbf{r}}$ with the Hamiltonian. In the **k** representation, the Hamiltonian is just the energy $E(\mathbf{k})$ expressed as a function of **k**. Hence the operator $\hat{\mathbf{v}}$ in the **k** representation is

$$\hat{\mathbf{v}} = (i/\hbar)(E\hat{\mathbf{r}} - \hat{\mathbf{r}}E) = -\frac{1}{\hbar}\left(E\frac{\partial}{\partial\mathbf{k}} - \frac{\partial}{\partial\mathbf{k}}E\right) + \frac{i}{\hbar}(E\hat{\boldsymbol{\Omega}} - \hat{\boldsymbol{\Omega}}E),$$

or

$$\hat{\mathbf{v}} = (1/\hbar)\partial E(\mathbf{k})/\partial\mathbf{k} + \hat{\dot{\boldsymbol{\Omega}}}. \tag{104.15}$$

The matrix elements of $\dot{\boldsymbol{\Omega}}$ are related to those of $\boldsymbol{\Omega}$ by

$$\dot{\boldsymbol{\Omega}}^{n\mathbf{k}}_{m\mathbf{k}} = (1/\hbar)[E_n(\mathbf{k}) - E_m(\mathbf{k})]\boldsymbol{\Omega}^{n\mathbf{k}}_{m\mathbf{k}}.$$

We see from this that $\dot{\boldsymbol{\Omega}}^{n\mathbf{k}}_{n\mathbf{k}} = 0$, i.e. $\dot{\boldsymbol{\Omega}}$ has no diagonal matrix elements.

The mean value of the velocity is equal to the diagonal matrix element of the operator (104.15). Using the above result we have

$$\bar{\mathbf{v}} = \partial E(\mathbf{k})/\hbar\partial\mathbf{k}. \tag{104.16}$$

Thus the mean velocity is found by differentiating the energy with respect to the quasi-momentum, in complete analogy to the classical relation between energy, momentum and velocity.

Finally, let us suppose that a homogeneous electric field, in which a force **F** acts on the electron, is superposed on the periodic field considered above.

Then the quasi-momentum of the electron will not be conserved. Let us determine its derivative with respect to time. The homogeneous field adds to the Hamiltonian a term $-\mathbf{F.r}$. The quasi-momentum operator in the $\mathbf{k}$ representation is simply $\mathbf{k}$ itself. Hence

$$\hat{\dot{\mathbf{k}}} = -(i/\hbar)\mathbf{F}(\hat{\mathbf{r}}.\mathbf{k}-\mathbf{k}.\hat{\mathbf{r}})$$

$$= \frac{\mathbf{F}}{\hbar}\left(\frac{\partial}{\partial \mathbf{k}}.\mathbf{k}-\mathbf{k}.\frac{\partial}{\partial \mathbf{k}}\right)-\frac{i}{\hbar}\mathbf{F}(\hat{\boldsymbol{\Omega}}.\mathbf{k}-\mathbf{k}.\hat{\boldsymbol{\Omega}})$$

$$= (1/\hbar)\mathbf{F}-(i/\hbar)\mathbf{F}(\hat{\boldsymbol{\Omega}}.\mathbf{k}-\mathbf{k}.\hat{\boldsymbol{\Omega}}).$$

It is easy to see that the operator $\hat{\boldsymbol{\Omega}}.\mathbf{k}-\mathbf{k}.\hat{\boldsymbol{\Omega}}$ is identically zero. For the matrix of $\mathbf{k}$ is diagonal in the $\mathbf{k}$ representation, its diagonal elements being simply the values of $\mathbf{k}$. The matrix of $\boldsymbol{\Omega}$, on the other hand, has elements only for transitions without change of $\mathbf{k}$. Hence all the matrix elements of $\boldsymbol{\Omega}.\mathbf{k}-\mathbf{k}.\boldsymbol{\Omega}$ vanish. Thus we have

$$\hbar\hat{\dot{\mathbf{k}}} = \mathbf{F}. \tag{104.17}$$

We see that the operator of the derivative of the quasi-momentum with respect to time is equal to the force acting on the electron due to the homogeneous field, just as would be true for the derivative of the true momentum in the absence of the periodic field.

PROBLEM

Determine the energy as a function of the quasi-momentum of the electron in the periodic field shown in Fig. 46.

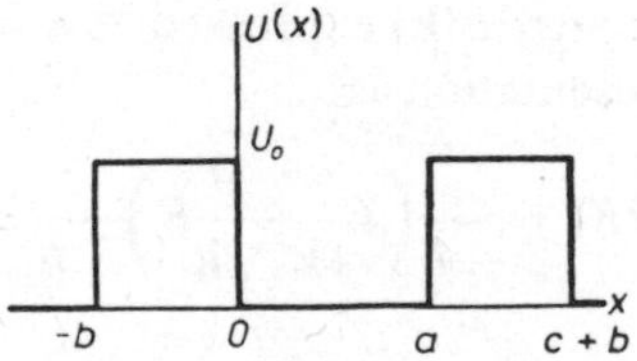

Fig. 46

SOLUTION. The wave function in the region of the well $0 < x < a$ is of the form

$$\psi = c_1 e^{i\kappa_1 x}+c_2 e^{-i\kappa_1 x}, \quad \kappa_1 = \sqrt{(2\mu E)}/\hbar, \tag{1}$$

and in the barrier region $(-b < x < 0)$ it is

$$\psi = c_3 e^{i\kappa_2 x}+c_4 e^{-i\kappa_2 x}, \quad \kappa_2 = \sqrt{[2\mu(E-U_0)]}/\hbar; \tag{2}$$

κ_2 is purely imaginary for $E < U_0$. In the region of the next barrier $(a < x < a+b)$, ψ must differ from (2) only by the factor $e^{ik(a+b)}$ ($a+b$ being the period of the field), i.e. it has the form

$$\psi = c_3 e^{ik(a+b)}e^{i\kappa_2(x-a-b)}+c_4 e^{ik(a+b)}e^{-i\kappa_2(x-a-b)}. \tag{3}$$

The continuity conditions on ψ and $d\psi/dx$ at the points $x = 0$ and $x = a$ give four equations for c_1, c_2, c_3, c_4; the condition for the compatibility of these equations leads to the equation

$$\cos k(a+b) = \cos \kappa_1 a . \cos \kappa_2 b - \tfrac{1}{2}\left(\frac{\kappa_1}{\kappa_2}+\frac{\kappa_2}{\kappa_1}\right)\sin \kappa_1 a . \sin \kappa_2 b,$$

which implicitly determines the required function.

CHAPTER XIV

THE THEORY OF ELASTIC COLLISIONS

§105. The general theory of scattering

In classical mechanics, collisions of two particles are entirely determined by their velocities and impact parameter (i.e. the distance at which they would pass if they did not interact). In quantum mechanics the very wording of the problem must be changed, since in motion with definite velocities the concept of the path is meaningless, and therefore so is the impact parameter. The purpose of the theory is here only to calculate the probability that, as a result of the collision, the particles will deviate (or, as we say, be *scattered*) through any given angle. We are speaking here of what are called *elastic collisions*, in which the internal state of the colliding particles (if these are complex) is left unchanged.

The problem of an elastic collision, like any problem of two bodies, amounts to a problem of the scattering of a single particle, with the reduced mass, in the field $U(r)$ of a fixed centre of force. This simplification is effected by passing to a system of co-ordinates in which the centre of mass of the two particles is at rest. The scattering angle in this system we denote by θ. It is simply related to the angles ϑ_1 and ϑ_2 giving the deviations of the two particles in a system of co-ordinates in which the second particle (say) was at rest before the collision. In the centre-of-mass system, the momenta of the two particles are the same in magnitude and opposite in direction. After the collision, the momenta in this system are simply interchanged, remaining opposite and equal in magnitude, the latter result following from the conservation of energy. The formulae (105.1) are obtained by returning to the original system of co-ordinates.

$$\tan\vartheta_1 = \mu_2\sin\theta/(\mu_1+\mu_2\cos\theta), \qquad \vartheta_2 = \tfrac{1}{2}(\pi-\theta), \tag{105.1}$$

where μ_1, μ_2 are the masses of the particles. In particular, if the masses of the two particles are the same ($\mu_1 = \mu_2$), we have simply

$$\vartheta_1 = \tfrac{1}{2}\theta, \qquad \vartheta_2 = \tfrac{1}{2}(\pi-\theta); \tag{105.2}$$

the sum $\vartheta_1+\vartheta_2 = \frac{1}{2}\pi$, i.e. the particles diverge at right angles.

In what follows, we shall always use (unless the contrary is specifically stated) a system of co-ordinates in which the centre of mass is at rest.

A free particle moving in the positive direction of the z-axis is described by a plane wave, constant$\times e^{ikz}$ (where $k = \mu v/\hbar$). We take the constant to be unity; the function $\psi = e^{ikz}$ corresponds to a probability current density v. The scattered particles must be described, at a great distance from the scattering centre, by an outgoing spherical wave of the form $f(\theta)e^{ikr}/r$, where

$f(\theta)$ is some function of the scattering angle θ (the angle between the z-axis and the direction of the scattered particle). Thus the exact wave function, which is a solution of SCHRÖDINGER's equation with potential energy $U(r)$, must have at large distances the asymptotic form

$$\psi \approx e^{ikz}+f(\theta)e^{ikr}/r. \tag{105.3}$$

The probability per unit time that the scattered particle will pass through a surface element $\mathrm{d}S = r^2\mathrm{d}o$ (where $\mathrm{d}o$ is an element of solid angle) is $(v/r^2)\,|f(\theta)|^2\,\mathrm{d}S = v|f(\theta)|^2\,\mathrm{d}o$.† Its ratio to the probability density in the incident wave is

$$\mathrm{d}\sigma = |f(\theta)|^2\,\mathrm{d}o. \tag{105.4}$$

This quantity has the dimensions of area, and is called the *effective cross-section* for scattering into the solid angle $\mathrm{d}o$. If we put $\mathrm{d}o = 2\pi\sin\theta\,\mathrm{d}\theta$, we obtain for the effective cross-section

$$\mathrm{d}\sigma = 2\pi\sin\theta\,|f(\theta)|^2\,\mathrm{d}\theta \tag{105.5}$$

for scattering through angles in the range from θ to $\theta+\mathrm{d}\theta$.

The determination of the function $f(\theta)$ (the *scattering amplitude*) requires, in general, the solution of the exact SCHRÖDINGER's equation, with the conditions of finiteness in all space and assumption of the asymptotic form (105.3) as $r \to \infty$.

Every solution of SCHRÖDINGER's equation in a centrally symmetric field can be written as a sum of products of spherical harmonics with radial functions $R_l(r)$ that satisfy the equations

$$\frac{1}{r^2}\frac{\mathrm{d}}{\mathrm{d}r}\left(r^2\frac{\mathrm{d}R_l}{\mathrm{d}r}\right)+\left[k^2-\frac{l(l+1)}{r^2}-\frac{2\mu}{\hbar^2}U(r)\right]R_l = 0. \tag{105.6}$$

The asymptotic form of the functions R_l is (see (33.16))

$$R \approx \frac{a_l\sin(kr-\frac{1}{2}l\pi+\delta_l)}{r}. \tag{105.7}$$

We shall show how the scattering amplitude $f(\theta)$ can be expressed in terms of the phases. The general axially symmetric (about the z-axis) solution of SCHRÖDINGER's equation is a sum of products $R_l(r)P_l(\cos\theta)$, and the solution describing the scattering must therefore be of this form. Accordingly, the general asymptotic form of the solution is

$$\psi \approx \sum_l A_lP_l(\cos\theta)\frac{\sin(kr-\frac{1}{2}l\pi+\delta_l)}{kr}. \tag{105.8}$$

---

† It is supposed that the incident beam of particles is defined by a wide (to avoid diffraction effects) but finite diaphragm, as happens in actual experiments on scattering. There is therefore no interference between the two terms of the expression (105.3); the squared modulus $|\psi|^2$ is taken at poinıs where there is no incident wave.

We have to choose the constants A_l such that this function has the form (105.3). To do this, we use the expansion of a plane wave in terms of spherical waves, obtained in §34. The asymptotic form of this expansion is (34.1a):

$$e^{ikz} \approx \sum_l i^l(2l+1)P_l(\cos\theta)\frac{\sin(kr-\frac{1}{2}l\pi)}{kr}.$$

Subtracting e^{ikz} from (105.8), we have

$$\psi - e^{ikz} \approx \sum_l \frac{1}{kr}P_l(\cos\theta)\{A_l\sin(kr-\tfrac{1}{2}l\pi+\delta_l)-i^l(2l+1)\sin(kr-\tfrac{1}{2}l\pi)\}.$$

This difference must represent an outgoing wave. For this to be so, the term in e^{-ikr} must vanish for each pair of terms in the braces, which can be written

$$\frac{1}{2i}e^{i(kr-\frac{1}{2}l\pi)}[A_le^{i\delta_l}-i^l(2l+1)]-\frac{1}{2i}e^{-i(kr-\frac{1}{2}l\pi)}[A_le^{-i\delta_l}-i^l(2l+1)].$$

Hence we find for the required coefficients A_l

$$A_l = i^l(2l+1)e^{i\delta_l}. \tag{105.9}$$

For the coefficients of e^{ikr}/r in the difference $\psi - e^{ikz}$ we obtain

$$f(\theta) = \frac{1}{2ik}\sum_{l=0}^{\infty}(2l+1)[e^{2i\delta_l}-1]P_l(\cos\theta). \tag{105.10}$$

This formula solves the problem of expressing the scattering amplitude, and therefore the effective cross-section, in terms of the phases δ_l (FAXÉN and HOLTSMARK 1927).

If we integrate $d\sigma$ over all angles θ, we obtain the total effective scattering cross-section σ, which is the ratio of the total probability (per unit time) that the particle will be scattered to the probability current density in the incident wave. Substituting (105.10) in the integral

$$\sigma = 2\pi\int_0^{\pi}|f(\theta)|^2\sin\theta\,d\theta,$$

and recalling that the Legendre polynomials with different l are orthogonal, while

$$\int_0^{\pi} P_l^2(\cos\theta)\sin\theta\,d\theta = 2/(2l+1),$$

we have for the total effective cross-section

$$\sigma = \frac{4\pi}{k^2} \sum_{l=0}^{\infty} (2l+1) \sin^2 \delta_l. \tag{105.11}$$

Taking the value of $f(\theta)$ for $\theta = 0$ (with $P_l(1) = 1$) and comparing with (105.11), we easily see that the relation

$$\operatorname{Im} f(0) = k\sigma/4\pi \tag{105.12}$$

holds. We shall see below (§117) that this relation between the total effective cross-section and the scattering amplitude in the forward direction is actually more general, and is not for elastic scattering only.

The problem of whether the scattering potential $U(r)$ can in principle be expressed in terms of the phases δ_l, supposed known, is of considerable interest.† If there are no discrete levels in the field $U(r)$, it is found that, to do so, it is sufficient to know the phase $\delta_0(k)$ as a function of the wave number from $k = 0$ to $k = \infty$. If there are discrete (negative) energy levels E_n, however, these levels also must be known, together with the coefficients a_n in the asymptotic (for $r \to \infty$) expressions

$$R_{n0} \approx \frac{a_n}{r} e^{-\kappa_n r}, \qquad \kappa_n = \sqrt{(2\mu|E_n|)}/\hbar, \tag{105.13}$$

for the radial wave functions of the corresponding states (normalised by the condition $\int\limits_0^\infty R_{n0}\, r^2 \,\mathrm{d}r = 1$). The problem of expressing the potential energy $U(r)$ in terms of these quantities amounts to solving the following equations.‡ We form the function

$$F(r) = \sum_n a_n^2 e^{-\kappa_n r} - \frac{1}{2\pi} \int_{-\infty}^{\infty} [e^{2i\delta_0(k)} - 1] e^{ikr} \,\mathrm{d}k, \tag{105.14}$$

and from it the linear integral equation

$$F(x+y) + A(x,y) + \int_x^\infty A(x,t) F(y+t) \,\mathrm{d}t = 0, \tag{105.15}$$

in which the unknown function is $A(x, y)$, containing two variables. If this

† It is assumed, of course, that these phases are finite; for this to be so, $U(r)$ must diminish more rapidly than $1/r$ as $r \to \infty$ (see §106).

‡ These results are due to I. M. Gel'fand, B. M. Levitan and V. A. Marchenko. The derivation of equations (105.14)–(105.16) is given by V. A. Marchenko, *Doklady Akademii Nauk SSSR* **104**, 695, 1955.

equation is solved, the required function $U(r)$ can be found from the formula

$$U(r) = -\frac{\hbar^2}{\mu}\frac{d}{dr}A(r,r). \tag{105.16}$$

§106. An investigation of the general formula

The formulae which we have obtained are in principle applicable to scattering in any field $U(r)$ which vanishes at infinity. The question remains, however, of the convergence of the series which represent the effective cross-sections.

To estimate the order of magnitude of the phases δ_l for large values of l, we use the fact that the motion is quasi-classical for large l (see §49). Hence the phase of the wave function is determined by the integral

$$\int_{r_0}^{r}\sqrt{\left[k^2-\frac{(l+\frac{1}{2})^2}{r^2}-\frac{2\mu U(r)}{\hbar^2}\right]}\,dr+\tfrac{1}{4}\pi,$$

where r_0 is a zero of the expression under the radical ($r > r_0$ being the classically accessible region of motion). Subtracting from this the phase

$$\int_{r_0}^{r}\sqrt{\left[k^2-\frac{(l+\frac{1}{2})^2}{r^2}\right]}\,dr+\tfrac{1}{4}\pi$$

of the wave function of free motion, and letting $r \to \infty$, we obtain, by definition, the quantity δ_l. For large values of l, the value of r_0 also becomes large; $U(r)$ is therefore small throughout the range of integration, and we have approximately

$$\delta_l = -\int_{r_0}^{\infty}\mu U(r)\,dr\Big/\hbar^2\sqrt{\left[k^2-\frac{(l+\frac{1}{2})^2}{r^2}\right]}. \tag{106.1}$$

In order of magnitude this integral (if convergent) is

$$\delta_l \sim \mu U(r_0)r_0/k\hbar^2. \tag{106.2}$$

The order of magnitude of r_0 is $r_0 \sim l/k$.

If $U(r)$ vanishes at infinity as $1/r^n$ with $n > 1$, the integral (106.1) converges, and the phases δ_l are finite. On the other hand, for $n \leqslant 1$ the integral diverges, so that the phases δ_l are infinite. This holds for any l, since the convergence or divergence of the integral (106.1) depends on the behaviour of $U(r)$ for large r, while at large distances (where the field $U(r)$ is weak) the radial motion is quasi-classical for all l. We shall show below how the formulae (105.10), (105.11) are to be interpreted when δ_l is infinite.

Let us first consider the convergence of the series (105.11) which gives the total effective cross-section. For large l, the phases $\delta_l \ll 1$, as is seen from (106.2) if we take into account the fact that $U(r)$ decreases more rapidly than $1/r$. Hence we can put $\sin^2\delta_l \cong \delta_l^2$, and so the sum of the high terms in the series (105.11) will be of the order of $\sum_{l\gg 1} l\delta_l^2$. From the well-known integral test for the convergence of series, we conclude that the series in question converges if the integral $\int^{\infty} l\delta_l^2 dl$ does so. Substituting here (106.2) and replacing l by kr_0, we obtain the integral

$$\int^{\infty} U^2(r_0)r_0^3\, dr_0.$$

If $U(r)$ decreases at infinity as $1/r^n$ with $n > 2$, this integral converges, and the total effective cross-section is finite. If, on the other hand, the field $U(r)$ decreases not more rapidly than $1/r^2$, the total effective cross-section appears to be infinite. The physical reason for this is that, when the field falls off only slowly with distance, the probability of scattering through small angles becomes extremely large. In this connection we may recall that, in classical mechanics, in any field which vanishes only as $r \to \infty$, a particle passing at any finite impact parameter, however large, always undergoes a deviation through some angle which, though small, is not zero; hence the total effective scattering cross-section is infinite for any law of decrease of $U(r)$. In quantum mechanics, this argument is invalid, since we can speak of scattering through a certain angle only if this angle is large compared with the indeterminacy in the direction of motion of the particle. If the impact parameter is known to within $\Delta\rho$, an indeterminacy $\hbar/\Delta\rho$ is caused in the transverse component of momentum, i.e. an indeterminacy $\sim \hbar/\mu v\Delta\rho$ in the angle.

In view of the important part played by small-angle scattering when $U(r)$ decreases only slowly, the question naturally arises whether the scattering amplitude $f(\theta)$ diverges for $\theta = 0$, even when $U(r)$ decreases more rapidly than $1/r^2$. Putting $\theta = 0$ in (105.10), we obtain for the high terms in the sum an expression proportional to $\sum_{l\gg 1} l\delta_l$. Arguing as in the previous case, our search for the criterion of the convergence of the sum leads us to the integral

$$\int^{\infty} U(r_0)r_0^2\, dr_0,$$

which diverges for $U(r) \sim 1/r^n$ with $n \leqslant 3$. Thus the differential effective scattering cross-section becomes infinite at $\theta = 0$ for fields which decrease not more rapidly than $1/r^3$.

Finally, let us consider the case where the phase δ_l itself is infinite, as happens when $U(r) \sim 1/r^n$ with $n \leqslant 1$. It is evident from the results obtained above that, when the field decreases so slowly, both the total effective cross-section and the scattering amplitude for $\theta = 0$ will be infinite. There remains, however, the problem of calculating $f(\theta)$ for $\theta \neq 0$. First of all, we notice that the formula†

$$\sum_{l=0}^{\infty} (2l+1)P_l(\cos\theta) = 2\delta(1-\cos\theta) \tag{106.3}$$

holds. In other words, the sum vanishes for all $\theta \neq 0$. Hence, in the expression (105.10) for the scattering amplitude, we can omit unity in the square brackets in each term of the sum when $\theta \neq 0$, leaving

$$f(\theta) = \frac{1}{2ik}\sum_{l=0}^{\infty} (2l+1)P_l(\cos\theta)e^{2i\delta_l}. \tag{106.4}$$

If we multiply the right-hand side of the equation by the constant factor $e^{-2i\delta_0}$, the effective cross-section will be unchanged, since it is determined by the squared modulus $|f(\theta)|^2$, while the phase of the complex function $f(\theta)$ is changed only by an unimportant constant. On the other hand, the divergent integral of $U(r)$ cancels in the difference $\delta_l - \delta_0$ of expressions such as (106.1), and a finite quantity remains. Thus, to calculate the scattering amplitude in the case considered, we can use the formula

$$f(\theta) = \frac{1}{2ik}\sum_{l=0}^{\infty} (2l+1)P_l(\cos\theta)e^{2i(\delta_l-\delta_0)}. \tag{106.5}$$

§107. The relation between the scattering law and the discrete energy levels

From the theory of analytic functions we can establish a certain relation which exists between the scattering law for particles (of positive energy) in a given field and the discrete spectrum of negative energy levels in that field.

To simplify the discussion, let us consider motion with angular momentum $l = 0$ (though the results obtained are valid for any l). Let $U(r)$ be a field negative in all space and vanishing at infinity more rapidly than $1/r$. The asymptotic form of the wave function for a particle with positive energy is

$$\psi = \{a(k)e^{ikr}+b(k)e^{-ikr}\}/r, \tag{107.1}$$

where $k = \sqrt{(2\mu E)}/\hbar$ is the wave number of the particle, and $a(k)$ and $b(k)$ are constants depending on k. The wave function is supposed normalised by some definite condition, say $\psi(0) = 1$. The functions $a(k)$ and $b(k)$ are not

† This formula is the expansion of the delta function in Legendre polynomials, and can be immediately verified by multiplying both sides by $\sin\theta\ P_l(\cos\theta)$ and integrating over θ.

independent, but are simply related. One relation between them follows immediately from the fact that ψ must be real:

$$b(k) = a^*(k). \tag{107.2}$$

We shall formally regard k as a complex variable. Then $a(k)$ and $b(k)$ will be functions of a complex variable, related as before by the equation (107.2) (the symbol $a^*(k)$ now signifying that we take the complex conjugate function to $a(k)$, leaving k unchanged), and also by the equation

$$a(-k) = b(k), \tag{107.3}$$

which follows from the definition of a and b in formula (107.1). The function with complex k, being the analytical continuation of the solution of SCHRÖDINGER's equation with real k, is still a solution of SCHRÖDINGER's equation and satisfies the same condition at the origin. However, this function does not in general satisfy the condition of finiteness in all space; as $r \to \infty$, the first or second term (depending on the sign of im k) becomes infinite.

In particular, when k is purely imaginary, (107.1) determines the asymptotic form of the solution of SCHRÖDINGER's equation with negative energy. However, if this solution corresponds to a stationary state of the discrete spectrum, ψ must satisfy the condition of finiteness at infinity. To each negative energy value, there corresponds a pair of purely imaginary values of k, differing in sign. It follows from what was said above that negative eigenvalues of the energy must correspond to zeros of the function $b(k)$ on the upper half of the imaginary axis (in the complex plane of k), so that the second term in the expression (107.1) is absent, and to zeros of the function $a(k)$ on the lower half of the imaginary axis.†

On the other hand, comparing (107.1) with the asymptotic expression for the wave function of a particle with positive energy, written in the form (105.7):

$$\psi \approx a_0[e^{i(kr+\delta_0)} - e^{-i(kr+\delta_0)}]/2ir, \tag{107.4}$$

we see that the ratio $a(k)/b(k)$ is related to the phase δ_0 by

$$e^{2i\delta_0(k)} = -a(k)/b(k). \tag{107.5}$$

Hence we can say that poles of the function $e^{2i\delta_0(k)}$ in the upper half-plane of the complex variable k correspond to the discrete energy levels.

In an entirely similar manner, the corresponding result can be obtained for levels with non-zero angular momentum l. For these, the function $e^{2i\delta_l(k)}$ has singularities in the upper half-plane.

The quantities $e^{2i\delta_l}$ are, however, just those which appear in the general formula (105.10) for the scattering amplitude. We see that the scattering amplitude, formally regarded as a function of the complex variable k, has

† There are no zeros of the functions $a(k)$ and $b(k)$ in the lower and upper half-planes respectively, except for those lying on the imaginary axis. This follows at once from the fact that SCHRÖDINGER's equation has only real eigenvalues.

singular points for values of k which lie in the upper half-plane and correspond to the discrete energy levels.

It must be emphasised that the converse does not hold: the function $e^{2i\delta_0} = -a/b$ (and similarly for $l \neq 0$) can become infinite in the upper half-plane not only at the zeros of the function $b(k)$, but also at poles of the function $a(k)$, the existence of which is entirely possible, and to which negative energy levels of the discrete spectrum do not correspond. Thus there is no one-to-one correspondence between the poles of the scattering amplitude and the energy levels of the discrete spectrum (D. TER HAAR and S. MA 1946).

§108. The scattering of slow particles

The effective scattering cross-section is a function of the velocity of the scattered particles, and we can propose the question of the limit to which it tends for small velocities (i.e. small k). The solution of this problem requires an elucidation of the dependence of the phases δ_l on k when the latter is small.

Let r_0 be some value of r, so large that $U(r_0)$ may be considered small, but yet small in comparison with $1/k$. For $r \ll r_0$ we can neglect the term in k^2 in the exact SCHRÖDINGER's equation (105.6):

$$R_l''+2R_l'/r-l(l+1)R_l/r^2 = 2\mu U(r)R_l/\hbar^2. \tag{108.1}$$

In the range $r_0 \ll r \ll 1/k$, on the other hand, we can also omit the term in $U(r)$, leaving

$$R_l''+2R_l'/r-l(l+1)R_l/r^2 = 0. \tag{108.2}$$

The general solution of this equation is of the form

$$R_l = c_1 r^l + c_2/r^{l+1}. \tag{108.3}$$

The values of the constants c_1 and c_2 can in principle be determined only by solving equation (108.1) for a particular function $U(r)$; they are, of course, different for different l. At still greater distances, $r \sim 1/k$, the term in $U(r)$ can be omitted from SCHRÖDINGER's equation, but the term in k^2 cannot be neglected, so that we have

$$R_l''+\frac{2}{r}R_l'+\left[k^2-\frac{l(l+1)}{r^2}\right]R_l = 0. \tag{108.4}$$

The solution of this equation is† (see §33)

$$R_l = c_1(-1)^l\frac{(2l+1)!!}{k^{2l+1}}r^l\left(\frac{\mathrm{d}}{r\,\mathrm{d}r}\right)^l\frac{\sin kr}{r}+ +c_2(-1)^l\frac{r^l}{(2l-1)!!}\left(\frac{\mathrm{d}}{r\,\mathrm{d}r}\right)^l\frac{\cos kr}{r}. \tag{108.5}$$

† The symbol !! denotes the product of all integers of the same parity up to and including the number in question.

The constant coefficients have been chosen so that, for $kr \ll 1$, this solution becomes (108.3); this ensures the "joining" of the solution (108.3) in the region $r \ll 1/k$ to the solution (108.5) in the region $r \sim 1/k$.

Finally, for $kr \gg 1$ the solution (108.5) takes the asymptotic form (§33)

$$R_l \approx c_1(2l+1)!!\frac{\sin(kr-\frac{1}{2}l\pi)}{rk^{l+1}}+\frac{c_2k^l}{(2l-1)!!\,r}\cos(kr-\tfrac{1}{2}l\pi).$$

This expression can be put in the form

$$R_l \approx \text{constant}\times\frac{\sin(kr-\frac{1}{2}l\pi+\delta_l)}{r}, \tag{108.6}$$

where the phase δ_l is given by the equation

$$\tan\delta_l = c_2k^{2l+1}/c_1(2l-1)!!\,(2l+1)!! \tag{108.7}$$

In particular

$$\tan\delta_0 = \beta k, \qquad \beta = c_2/c_1. \tag{108.8}$$

Since $k \ll 1$, $\tan\delta_l \cong \delta_l$, and we reach the result that, in the limiting case of small velocities, the phase δ_l is proportional to k^{2l+1}:

$$\delta_l \sim k^{2l+1}. \tag{108.9}$$

Thus all the phases δ_l with $l \neq 0$ are small in comparison with δ_0. We accordingly neglect all terms except the first in formulae (105.10) and (105.11), obtaining for the scattering amplitude

$$f(\theta) \cong (e^{2i\delta_0}-1)/2ik \cong \delta_0/k = \beta,$$

so that

$$d\sigma = \beta^2 do, \tag{108.10}$$

and the total effective cross-section is

$$\sigma = 4\pi\beta^2. \tag{108.11}$$

We consequently arrive at the important result that, for small velocities, the scattering is isotropic, and the effective cross-section is independent of the velocity.†

Formulae (108.10) and (108.11) are applicable for velocities at which $1/k$ (i.e. the de Broglie wavelength of the particle) is large compared with the distance r_0 at which the field $U(r)$ becomes small. This we have in essence assumed from the start by considering SCHRÖDINGER's equation in the range $r_0 \ll r \ll 1/k$. To estimate the distance r_0 in practice, we can take the value for which $U(r)$ is comparable with the total energy of the scattered particle.

† If the colliding particles possess spin, the total angular momentum of the system is (for $l = 0$) the same as the total spin S. The scattering amplitude is in general different for different S.

We have not concerned ourselves hitherto with the conditions which must be satisfied by the field $U(r)$ in order that the calculations we have performed should be valid. Let us estimate the error involved in neglecting $U(r)$ in equation (108.1). To do this, we solve this equation by successive approximations. Putting $R_l = R_l^{(0)}+R_l^{(1)}$, where $R_l^{(0)}$ is the solution of equation (108.1) with the right-hand side omitted, and $R_l^{(1)}$ is a small correction, we have

$$R_l^{(1)\prime\prime}+2R_l^{(1)\prime}/r-l(l+1)R_l^{(1)}/r^2 = 2\mu U(r)R_l^{(0)}/\hbar^2. \tag{108.12}$$

In $R_l^{(0)}$ we omit the term in $r^{-(l+1)}$, which is small for large r. Let $U(r)$ decrease at large distances as $1/r^n$ (an exponential decrease corresponding to $n \to \infty$). Then the right-hand side of the equation is proportional to r^{l-n}, and so $R_l^{(1)}$ is proportional to r^{2+l-n}. If the above calculations are justifiable, $R_l^{(1)}$ must be small compared with the two terms in (108.3) at large distances. This requires that $2+l-n < -(l+1)$, or

$$n > 2l+3.$$

Thus the law (108.9) for the dependence of δ_l on k holds only when $n > 2l+3$. In particular, δ_0 is proportional to k when $n > 3$. This is also the condition for the results obtained above to be applicable: as $k \to 0$, the effective cross-section tends to a constant limit only in a field $U(r)$ which decreases at large distances more rapidly than $1/r^3$.

We shall obtain the dependence on k of the phases δ_l for $l > \frac{1}{2}(n-3)$ by means of the following qualitative method. For small δ_l, the asymptotic expression (108.6) for the wave function can be written in the form

$$R_l = \text{constant} \times \left\{\frac{\sin(kr-\frac{1}{2}l\pi)}{r}+\delta_l\frac{\cos(kr-\frac{1}{2}l\pi)}{r}\right\}.$$

From this we see that, in order of magnitude, the phase δ_l is equal to the relative value of the correction to the wave function for free motion (the first term in the braces) when $kr \sim 1$. From this, for example, we could obtain the law (108.9) without deriving the quantitative formula (108.7); we should merely take the ratio of the second term in (108.3) to the first for $r \sim 1/k$.

For $2l > n-3$, we must take as the correction to the wave function of free motion not c_2/r^{l+1}, as in (108.3), but the solution $R_l^{(1)}$ of equation (108.12). Since $R_l^{(1)} \sim r^{2+l-n}$, we take its ratio to $c_1 r^l$ for $r \sim 1/k$, finding that δ_l is proportional to k^{n-2} for $r \sim 1/k$.

Thus, instead of (108.9), it is more correct to write

$$\delta_l \sim k^{2l+1} \quad (\text{for } 2l < n-3), \qquad \delta_l \sim k^{n-2} \quad (\text{for } 2l > n-3). \tag{108.13}$$

All the δ_l with $l \neq 0$, of course, are small compared with δ_0 (for $n > 3$), as before.

PROBLEMS

PROBLEM 1. Determine the effective scattering cross-section for a spherical potential well of depth U_0 and radius a:

$$U(r) = -U_0 \text{ for } r < a, \; U(r) = 0 \text{ for } r > a.$$

The radius is supposed small in comparison with the de Broglie wavelength of the particle ($ka \ll 1$).

SOLUTION. We are interested only in the phase δ_0. Hence we put $l = 0$ in equation (108.1), and obtain for the function $\chi(r) = rR_0(r)$, for $r < a$, the equation

$$\chi'' + \kappa^2\chi = 0, \quad \kappa = \sqrt{(2\mu U_0)}/\hbar.$$

The solution which vanishes at $r = 0$ (χ/r must be finite at $r = 0$) is

$$\chi = A \sin \kappa r \qquad (r < a). \tag{1}$$

For $r > a$, the function χ satisfies the equation $\chi'' + k^2\chi = 0$ (i.e. equation (108.4) with $l = 0$), whence

$$\chi = B \sin(kr + \delta_0) \qquad (r > a). \tag{2}$$

Equating the logarithmic derivatives of (1) and (2) at $r = a$, we obtain the equation

$$\kappa \cot \kappa a = k \cot(ka + \delta_0) \cong k/(ka + \delta_0),$$

from which we determine δ_0. As a result, we have for the effective cross-section†

$$\sigma = 4\pi\left(\frac{\tan \kappa a - \kappa a}{\kappa}\right)^2.$$

If we change the sign of U_0 (which means replacing κ by $i\kappa$), we obtain for the effective scattering cross-section for a "potential hump" ($U(r) = U_0$ for $r < a$, $U(r) = 0$ for $r > a$) the formula

$$\sigma = 4\pi\left(\frac{\tanh \kappa a - \kappa a}{\kappa}\right)^2.$$

For $U_0 \to \infty$ we have

$$\sigma = 4\pi a^2.$$

This corresponds to scattering from an impenetrable sphere of radius a; we note that classical mechanics would give a result four times smaller ($\sigma = \pi a^2$).

PROBLEM 2. Determine the effective scattering cross-section for particles of low energy in a field $U = \alpha/r^4$, $\alpha > 0$.‡

SOLUTION. Equation (108.1) with $l = 0$ is

$$\chi'' - 2\mu\alpha\chi/\hbar^2 r^4 = 0.$$

By the substitutions

$$\chi = \phi\sqrt{r}, \qquad r = (i/\hbar)\sqrt{(2\mu\alpha)}/x$$

† This formula becomes inapplicable if the width and depth of the well are such that κa is close to an odd multiple of $\frac{1}{2}\pi$. For such values of κa the discrete spectrum of negative energy levels includes one which is close to zero (see §33, Problem), and the scattering is described by formulae which we shall derive in the next section.

‡ The same method can be used to solve the problem for the general case $U = \alpha/r^n$.

it can be brought to the form

$$\frac{d^2\phi}{dx^2}+\frac{1}{x}\frac{d\phi}{dx}+\left(1-\frac{1}{4x^2}\right)\phi = 0,$$

i.e. Bessel's equation of order $\frac{1}{2}$. The solution which vanishes at $r = 0$ (i.e. $x = \infty$) is, apart from a constant factor,

$$\chi = \sqrt{r}H_{1/2}^{(1)}(i\sqrt{(2\mu\alpha)}/\hbar r), \tag{1}$$

where $H_{1/2}^{(1)}$ is the Hankel function of the first kind, of order $\frac{1}{2}$. Using the well-known formulae

$$H_p^{(1)}(z) = i[e^{-ip\pi}J_p(z)-J_{-p}(z)]/\sin p\pi,$$

$$J_p(z) \cong z^p/2^p\Gamma(p+1) \qquad (z \ll 1),$$

we obtain for the function χ at large distances ($\sqrt{(2\mu\alpha)} \ll r \ll 1/k$) the expression

$$\chi = \text{constant}\times[r(\hbar^2/2\mu\alpha)^{1/4}-(2\mu\alpha/\hbar^2)^{1/4}].$$

This formula corresponds to (108.3), so that the ratio of the coefficients in it determines δ_0 immediately:

$$\delta_0 = -\sqrt{(2\mu\alpha)}k/\hbar,$$

and the effective cross-section is

$$\sigma = 8\pi\mu\alpha/\hbar^2.$$

The condition for the applicability of this formula is $k \ll \hbar/\sqrt{(\mu\alpha)}$, i.e. the argument of the Hankel function in (1) must be small for $r \sim 1/k$.

§109. Resonance scattering

Special consideration must be given to the scattering of slow particles in an attractive field, in the case where there is, among the discrete spectrum of negative energy levels, one which is close to zero (and has angular momentum $l = 0$); we shall denote this level by $-\epsilon$ ($\epsilon > 0$). The energy E of the scattered particle, being a small positive quantity, is close to the level $-\epsilon$, i.e. it is, as we say, almost in resonance with it. This, as we shall see, leads to a marked increase in the effective scattering cross-section.

The presence of a shallow level can be taken into account in the theory of scattering by means of a convenient formal method, based on the following considerations. SCHRÖDINGER's equation determining the stationary state with energy $-\epsilon$ is of the form

$$\chi''-2\mu[\epsilon+U(r)]\chi/\hbar^2 = 0 \tag{109.1}$$

($\chi = rR_0$). In the region of small r, where $|U(r)|$ is large compared with ϵ, we can write

$$\chi''-2\mu\chi U(r)/\hbar^2 = 0. \tag{109.2}$$

Solving this equation with the boundary condition $\chi(0) = 0$, we obtain a function determinate apart from an unimportant constant factor (the logarithmic derivative χ'/χ does not contain this constant). In the region of large r, on the other hand, we can neglect $U(r)$ compared with ϵ, so that we have

$$\chi'' - 2\mu\epsilon\chi/\hbar^2 = 0.$$

The solution of this equation which does not diverge as $r \to \infty$ is

$$\chi = \text{constant} \times e^{-\sqrt{(2\mu\epsilon)}r/\hbar}. \tag{109.3}$$

This has to be "joined" to the solution of equation (109.2) by the condition that χ'/χ is continuous at $r = r_0$, where r_0 gives the dimensions of the region where the field $U(r)$ is noticeably different from zero. Thus we have

$$[\chi'/\chi]_{r=r_0} = -\sqrt{(2\mu\epsilon)}/\hbar. \tag{109.4}$$

We see that the magnitude ϵ of the level is determined by the value at $r = r_0$ of the logarithmic derivative of the solution of equation (109.2).

In solving the problem of scattering, we can neglect altogether the region of small r in which the field $U(r)$ acts, and formally take into account the level $-\epsilon$ (supposing ϵ known) by imposing on the wave function of the scattered particle the condition

$$[\chi'/\chi]_{r\to 0} = -\sqrt{(2\mu\epsilon)}/\hbar. \tag{109.5}$$

We have seen in the previous section that, outside the range of action of the field, the scattered particle is described by the wave function

$$\chi = rR_0 = c_1 r + c_2;$$

cf. formula (108.3), with $l = 0$. Substituting in (109.5), we find

$$c_1/c_2 = -\sqrt{(2\mu\epsilon)}/\hbar.$$

Consequently, from (108.8), we have for the phase δ_0

$$\tan\delta_0 = -\hbar k/\sqrt{(2\mu\epsilon)} = -\sqrt{(E/\epsilon)}. \tag{109.6}$$

Since ϵ is small, the phase δ_0 may be large in this case.

The phases δ_l with $l \neq 0$ remain small, as before. Hence we can again neglect all terms with $l \neq 0$ in the scattering amplitude, so that the scattering remains isotropic. For the total effective cross-section, however, we now have

$$\sigma = (4\pi/k^2)\sin^2\delta_0 = 4\pi/k^2(1+\cot^2\delta_0),$$

or, substituting (109.6),

$$\sigma = 2\pi\hbar^2/\mu(E+\epsilon). \tag{109.7}$$

Thus the effective cross-section for resonance elastic scattering depends on the energy of the scattered particle, and is large compared with the cross-section in the absence of a resonance.†

† Formula (109.7) was obtained by Wigner (1933). The derivation used here is due to Bethe and Peierls (1935).

The function $\sigma(E)$ determined by formula (109.7) has a singular point at $E = -\epsilon$, in complete accordance with the general statements made in §107.

The formula we have obtained is rather more general in character than was supposed in deriving it. If we change the function $U(r)$ slightly, the logarithmic derivative $(\chi'/\chi)_{r=r_0}$ will change, since it is calculated from the solution of equation (109.2). By a suitable change of $U(r)$, this derivative may be made to vanish and then become small and positive. Formally defining the quantity ϵ by equation (109.4) with a change of sign,

$$[\chi'/\chi]_{r=r_0} = \sqrt{(2\mu\epsilon)}/\hbar,$$

we obtain the same formula (109.7) for the scattering. The quantity ϵ is a constant characterising the field $U(r)$, but is not now an energy level in this field. In such cases we say that there is a *virtual level* in the field, bearing in mind that, though in reality there is no level close to zero, nevertheless a small change in the field would be sufficient for such a level to appear.

§110. Born's formula

The effective scattering cross-section can be calculated in a general form in a very important case, namely that where the scattering field may be regarded as a perturbation. It has been shown in §45 that this is possible when either of the two conditions

$$|U(r)| \ll \hbar^2/\mu r^2 \tag{110.1}$$

or

$$|U(r)| \ll \hbar v/r \tag{110.2}$$

holds. In particular, we see from the second condition that the approximation in question is always applicable for sufficiently fast particles. When the first condition is satisfied, however, the approximation is valid for all velocities.

In accordance with §45, we seek the wave function in the form $\psi = \psi^{(0)}+\psi^{(1)}$, where $\psi^{(0)} = e^{i\mathbf{p}.\mathbf{r}/\hbar}$ corresponds to an incident particle having momentum $\mathbf{p}$. From formula (45.3) we then have

$$\psi^{(1)}(x,y,z) = -\frac{\mu}{2\pi\hbar^2}\int U(x',y',z')e^{i(\mathbf{p}.\mathbf{r}'+pR)/\hbar}\frac{\mathrm{d}V'}{R}. \tag{110.3}$$

Taking the origin at the scattering centre, we introduce the radius vector $\mathbf{R}_0$ from the origin to the point where the value of $\psi^{(1)}$ is required, and denote by $\mathbf{n}$ a unit vector along $\mathbf{R}_0$. Let the radius vector of a volume element $\mathrm{d}V'$ be $\mathbf{r}'$; clearly $\mathbf{R} = \mathbf{R}_0-\mathbf{r}'$. At large distances from the centre, $R_0 \gg r'$, so that

$$R = |\mathbf{R}_0-\mathbf{r}'| \cong R_0-\mathbf{r}'.\mathbf{n}.$$

Substituting this in (110.3) and renaming the variable of integration, we have the following asymptotic expression for $\psi^{(1)}$:

$$\psi^{(1)} \approx -\frac{\mu}{2\pi\hbar^2}\frac{e^{ipR_0/\hbar}}{R_0}\int U(\mathbf{r}')e^{i(\mathbf{p}-\mathbf{p}').\mathbf{r}'/\hbar}\,\mathrm{d}V'$$

(where $\mathbf{p}' = p\mathbf{n}$ is the momentum of the particle after scattering). Comparing this with the scattering amplitude given by formula (105.3), we find for the latter the expression

$$f = -\frac{\mu}{2\pi\hbar^2}\int Ue^{i\mathbf{q}.\mathbf{r}}\,\mathrm{d}V, \tag{110.4}$$

where we have renamed the variable of integration and introduced the vector

$$\mathbf{q} = (\mathbf{p}-\mathbf{p}')/\hbar,$$

whose absolute magnitude is

$$q = (2p/\hbar)\sin\tfrac{1}{2}\theta,$$

θ being the angle between $\mathbf{p}$ and $\mathbf{p}'$, i.e. the scattering angle.

Finally, squaring the modulus of the scattering amplitude, we have the following expression† for the effective cross-section for scattering into the solid angle element $\mathrm{d}o$:

$$\mathrm{d}\sigma = \frac{\mu^2}{4\pi^2\hbar^4}\left|\int Ue^{i\mathbf{q}.\mathbf{r}}\,\mathrm{d}V\right|^2\mathrm{d}o. \tag{110.5}$$

We see that the scattering with a momentum change $\hbar\mathbf{q}$ is determined by the squared modulus of the corresponding Fourier component of the field U.

Formula (110.5) can also be obtained by another method (which, however, does not determine the phase of the scattering amplitude). We can start from the general formula (43.1), according to which the transition probability between states of the continuous spectrum is given by the expression

$$\mathrm{d}w_{\nu_0\nu} = (2\pi/\hbar)|U_{\nu\nu_0}|^2\,\delta(E_\nu - E_{\nu_0})\mathrm{d}\nu.$$

In the case under consideration, we have to apply this formula to a transition from the state of the incident particle with a given initial momentum $\mathbf{p}$ to the state of the particle, with momentum $\mathbf{p}'$, scattered into the element of solid angle $\mathrm{d}o'$. As the "interval" of states $\mathrm{d}\nu$ we can take the volume element $\mathrm{d}p'_x\,\mathrm{d}p'_y\,\mathrm{d}p'_z$ in momentum space. Substituting for $E_\nu - E_{\nu_0}$ the difference $(p'^2-p^2)/2\mu$ of the energies of the free particles with momenta $\mathbf{p}'$ and $\mathbf{p}$, we obtain

$$\mathrm{d}w_{\mathbf{pp}'} = (4\pi\mu/\hbar)|U_{\mathbf{pp}'}|^2\delta(p'^2-p^2)\,\mathrm{d}p'_x\,\mathrm{d}p'_y\,\mathrm{d}p'_z. \tag{110.6}$$

The wave functions of the incident and scattered particles are the functions

† This formula was first obtained by M. Born (1926). In the theory of collisions, the approximation considered here is often called the *Born approximation*.

for free motion, i.e. plane waves:

$$\psi_{\mathbf{p}} = \text{constant} \times e^{i\mathbf{p}.\mathbf{r}/\hbar}, \quad \psi_{\mathbf{p}'} = \text{constant} \times e^{i\mathbf{p}'.\mathbf{r}/\hbar}.$$

Since we have taken as the "interval" $d\nu'$ an element of momentum space, the wave function $\psi_{\mathbf{p}'}$ must be normalised by the delta function in momentum space:

$$\psi_{\mathbf{p}'} = e^{(i/\hbar)\mathbf{p}'.\mathbf{r}}/(2\pi\hbar)^{3/2} \tag{110.7}$$

(see (13.8)). We normalise the function $\psi_{\mathbf{p}}$ to unit current density:

$$\psi_{\mathbf{p}} = \sqrt{(\mu/p)}e^{(i/\hbar)\mathbf{p}.\mathbf{r}}. \tag{110.8}$$

Then the probability (110.6) will have the dimensions of area, and is the differential effective scattering cross-section.

The presence of the delta function in formula (110.6) means that $p' = p$, i.e. the absolute magnitude of the momentum is unchanged, as it should be in elastic scattering. We can remove the delta function by changing to "spherical co-ordinates" in momentum space (i.e. by replacing $dp'_x\, dp'_y\, dp'_z$ by $p'^2 dp'\, do' = \frac{1}{2}p' d(p'^2) do'$) and integrating over p'^2. The integration amounts to replacing p' by p in the integrand, and we obtain

$$d\sigma = (2\pi\mu p/\hbar) \Big| \int \psi_{\mathbf{p}'}{}^* U \psi_{\mathbf{p}} dV \Big|^2 do'.$$

Substituting the functions (110.7), (110.8), we reach once more the final expression (110.5).

In the form shown above, this formula is applicable to scattering in a field $U(x, y, z)$ which is any function of the co-ordinates, and not only a function of r. In the case $U = U(r)$, however, this formula can be further transformed. In the integral

$$\int U(r) e^{i\mathbf{q}.\mathbf{r}}\, dV$$

we use spherical space co-ordinates r, ϑ, ϕ, with the polar axis in the direction of the vector $\mathbf{q}$, denoting the polar angle by ϑ to distinguish it from the scattering angle θ. The integration over ϑ and ϕ can be effected, and we obtain

$$\int_0^\infty \int_0^{2\pi} \int_0^\pi U(r) e^{iqr\cos\vartheta} r^2 \sin\vartheta\, d\vartheta\, d\phi\, dr = 4\pi \int_0^\infty U(r) \frac{\sin qr}{q} r\, dr.$$

Substituting this expression in (110.5), we obtain the following formula for the effective scattering cross-section in a centrally symmetric field:

$$d\sigma = do \frac{4\mu^2}{\hbar^4} \left| \int_0^\infty U(r) \frac{\sin qr}{q} r\, dr \right|^2. \tag{110.9}$$

For $\theta = 0$ (i.e. $q = 0$), the integral diverges when $U(r)$ decreases at infinity not more rapidly than $1/r^3$ (in accordance with the general results of §106).

We may call attention to the following interesting fact. The momentum p of the particle and the scattering angle θ enter (110.9) only through q. Thus, in the Born approximation, the effective-section depends on p and θ only in the combination $p \sin \frac{1}{2}\theta$.

In the limiting case of small velocities, we can put $e^{i\mathbf{q}.\mathbf{r}} \cong 1$ in (110.5), so that

$$d\sigma = \frac{\mu^2}{4\pi^2\hbar^4}\left|\int U\,dV\right|^2 do, \tag{110.10}$$

while if $U = U(r)$,

$$d\sigma = \frac{4\mu^2}{\hbar^4}\left|\int_0^\infty U(r)r^2\,dr\right|^2 do. \tag{110.11}$$

Here the scattering is isotropic and independent of the velocity, in accordance with the general results of §108.

In the opposite limiting case of large q (which presupposes large velocities and not too small scattering angles), the factor $e^{i\mathbf{q}.\mathbf{r}}$ is a rapidly oscillating function, and the integral of its product with the slowly varying function U is nearly zero. Thus, as the velocity increases, the effective cross-section (for not too small θ) tends to zero, as we should expect.

It is easy to see that, for large velocities, the total effective cross-section is (if the integral $\int d\sigma$ converges) inversely proportional to the square of the velocity, i.e. to the energy. For, at large velocities, the scattering is mainly through small angles. Hence we can put $\sin \frac{1}{2}\theta \approx \frac{1}{2}\theta$, so that the differential effective cross-section is of the form $d\sigma = f(v\theta)\,do$. The integral over θ converges so rapidly for large θ that the integration can be extended to infinity without any great error:

$$\sigma = 2\pi \int_0^\infty f(v\theta)\theta\,d\theta.$$

Taking $v\theta$ as the new variable of integration, we have the result stated.

In some physical applications† of collision theory, the integral

$$\int (1-\cos\theta)\,d\sigma$$

appears as a quantity characterising the scattering. By arguments exactly similar to those just given, it can be shown that at large velocities this quantity is inversely proportional to the square of the energy.

† For example, in considering diffusion.

Born's formula can also be obtained, of course, from the general theory of scattering developed in §105. The Born approximation corresponds to the case where all the phases δ_l are small; in addition, it is necessary that these phases should be calculable from SCHRÖDINGER's equation, with the potential energy in the latter regarded as a perturbation.

PROBLEMS

PROBLEM 1. Determine, in the Born approximation, the effective scattering cross-section in a field $U = U_0 e^{-\alpha r^2}$.

SOLUTION. Taking the x-axis in the direction of the vector $\mathbf{q}$, we have from (110.6)

$$d\sigma = \frac{\mu^2 U_0^2}{4\pi^2\hbar^4}\left|\int\limits_{-\infty}^{\infty}\int\limits_{-\infty}^{\infty}\int\limits_{-\infty}^{\infty} e^{-\alpha(x^2+y^2+z^2)+iqx}\,dx dy dz\right|^2 do.$$

Effecting the integration, we find

$$d\sigma = \frac{\pi\mu^2 U_0^2}{4\alpha^3\hbar^4} e^{-(2p^2/\hbar^2\alpha)\sin^2\frac{1}{2}\theta}\, do.$$

The total effective cross-section is of the form

$$\sigma = \frac{\pi^2 U_0^2}{2\alpha^2\hbar^2 v^2}(1-e^{-2\mu^2v^2/\hbar^2\alpha}).$$

These formulae hold for all velocities if $U_0 \ll \hbar^2\alpha^2/\mu$ (the condition (110.1) with $r \sim 1/\alpha$).

PROBLEM 2. Find the effective scattering cross-section in a field $U = \alpha/r^3$ ($\alpha > 0$). It is assumed that the particle moves so slowly that its wave number $k \ll \hbar^2/\mu\alpha$.

SOLUTION. Let r_0 be some value of r, such that $1/k \gg r_0 \gg \mu\alpha/\hbar^2$. We shall regard the scattering as being due to the superposition of two fields, of which one is zero for $r < r_0$, while the other is zero for $r > r_0$. For $r > r_0$, the condition (110.1) is satisfied, and so the Born approximation is applicable in this field. For the corresponding part of the scattering amplitude we have, by (110.9),

$$\frac{2\mu}{\hbar^2}\int\limits_{r_0}^{\infty}\frac{\alpha}{r^3}\frac{\sin qr}{q} r\, dr = \frac{2\mu\alpha}{\hbar^2 q}\int\limits_{r_0}^{\infty}\frac{\sin qr}{r^2}\, dr = \frac{2\mu\alpha}{\hbar^2}\int\limits_{qr_0}^{\infty}\frac{\sin\xi}{\xi^2}\, d\xi.$$

The most important range in the integral is that of small ξ, where the integral diverges logarithmically. Hence, for $qr_0 \ll 1$ (which follows from $kr_0 \ll 1$), this integral is equal to an expression of the form $\log(c/qr_0)$, where c is some number, so that the scattering amplitude is

$$(2\mu\alpha/\hbar^2)\log(c/qr_0). \tag{1}$$

For the scattering in the field which is cut off at $r = r_0$, we can use the results of §108, according to which the scattering amplitude for slow particles (in a field which decreases sufficiently rapidly with distance) is a constant. By adding this to the amplitude (1), we merely change the constant c. Squaring the total amplitude, we finally have the effective cross-section in the form

$$d\sigma = (4\mu^2\alpha^2/\hbar^4)\ \mathrm{og}^2(\mathrm{constant}/q)\, do,$$

where the constant is of the order of $\hbar^2/\mu\alpha$.

§111. The quasi-classical case

It is of interest to investigate the manner in which the passage occurs from the quantum-mechanical theory of scattering to the limit of the classical theory.

It is evident that the field $U(r)$ and the energy E of the scattered particle must be such that the conditions for quasi-classical motion are satisfied. However, it is found that this is not sufficient to ensure quasi-classical scattering.

Omitting from consideration a scattering angle θ of zero, we can write the scattering amplitude given by the exact quantum-mechanical theory in the form (106.4):

$$f(\theta) = (1/2ik)\sum_{l=0}^{\infty}(2l+1)P_l(\cos\theta)e^{2i\delta_l}. \tag{111.1}$$

We know that the quasi-classical wave functions are characterised by having large phases. It is therefore natural to suppose that large phases δ_l correspond to the passage to the limit of the classical theory of scattering. The value of the sum (111.1) is mainly determined by the terms with large l. Hence we can replace P_l (cos θ) by the asymptotic expression (49.6a), which we write in the form

$$P_l(\cos\theta) \approx -\frac{i}{\sqrt{(2\pi l\sin\theta)}}[e^{i(l+\frac{1}{2})\theta+\frac{1}{4}i\pi}-e^{-i(l+\frac{1}{2})\theta-\frac{1}{4}i\pi}].$$

Substituting this expression in (111.1), we obtain

$$f(\theta) = \frac{1}{k}\sum_{l}\sqrt{\frac{l}{2\pi\sin\theta}}\{e^{i[2\delta_l-(l+\frac{1}{2})\theta-\frac{1}{4}\pi]}-e^{i[2\delta_l+(l+\frac{1}{2})\theta+\frac{1}{4}\pi]}\}. \tag{111.2}$$

The exponential factors, regarded as functions of l, are rapidly oscillating functions, since their phases are large. The majority of the terms in the sum in (111.2) therefore cancel. The sum is mainly determined by the range of values of l near that for which one of the exponents has an extremum, i.e. near the root of the equation

$$2\,\mathrm{d}\delta_l/\mathrm{d}l \pm \theta = 0. \tag{111.3}$$

In this region there are a large number of terms in the series for which the exponential factors have almost the same value (since the exponents vary slowly near the extremum), and which therefore will not cancel.

The phases δ_l in the quasi-classical case can be written (see §106) as the limit to which the difference between the phase

$$\tfrac{1}{4}\pi+\frac{1}{\hbar}\int_{r_0}^{r}\sqrt{\{2\mu[E-U(r)]-\hbar^2(l+\tfrac{1}{2})^2/r^2\}}\,\mathrm{d}r$$

of the quasi-classical wave function in the field $U(r)$ and the phase

$$kr - \tfrac{1}{2}l\pi$$

(see §33) of the wave function of free motion tends as $r \to \infty$. Thus

$$\delta_l = \int_{r_0}^{\infty} \left\{\frac{1}{\hbar}\sqrt{[2\mu(E-U) - \hbar^2(l+\tfrac{1}{2})^2/r^2]} - k\right\} \mathrm{d}r + \tfrac{1}{2}\pi(l+\tfrac{1}{2}) - kr_0. \qquad (111.4)$$

This expression is to be substituted in equation (111.3). In finding the derivative of the integral, it must be remembered that the limit of integration r_0 also depends on l; the term $k\,\mathrm{d}r_0/\mathrm{d}l$ arising from this, however, cancels with the derivative of the term $-kr_0$ in δ_l.

$\hbar(l+\frac{1}{2})$ is the angular momentum of the particle. In classical mechanics, it can be written in the form $\mu\rho v$, where ρ is the impact parameter, and v is the velocity of the particle at infinity. We make this substitution; equation (111.3) then takes the final form

$$\int_{r_0}^{\infty} \frac{\mu v \rho \,\mathrm{d}r}{r^2\sqrt{[2\mu(E-U) - (\mu v\rho/r)^2]}} = \tfrac{1}{2}(\pi \mp \theta). \qquad (111.5)$$

In a repulsive field this equation has a root (for ρ) only for a minus sign in front of θ on the right-hand side, and in an attractive field only for a plus sign.

Equation (111.5) is exactly the same as the classical equation which determines the scattering angle from the impact parameter.† It is easy to see that the classical expression for the effective cross-section is in fact obtained.‡

The derivation given above shows that the conditions for classical scattering through a given angle θ are that the value of l for which (111.3) holds should be large, and that δ_l should also be large for this value of l. This latter condition has a simple physical interpretation. If we can speak of classical scattering through an angle θ when the particle is incident at an impact parameter ρ, it is necessary that the quantum-mechanical indeterminacies of these two quantities should be relatively small: $\Delta\rho \ll \rho$, $\Delta\theta \ll \theta$. The indeterminacy in the scattering angle is of the order of magnitude $\Delta\theta \sim \Delta p/p$, where p is the momentum of the particle and Δp is the indeterminacy in its transverse component. Since $\Delta p \sim \hbar/\Delta\rho \gg \hbar/\rho$, we have $\Delta\theta \gg \hbar/p\rho$, and thus

$$\theta \gg \hbar/\rho\mu v. \qquad (111.6)$$

Replacing the angular momentum $\mu\rho v$ by $\hbar l$, we obtain $\theta l \gg 1$, which is the same as $\delta_l \gg 1$ (since $\delta_l \sim l\theta$, as we see from (111.3)).

† See, for instance, *Mechanics*, §21, Moscow 1940.

‡ The calculation is effected by replacing the summation over l in (111.2) by an integration over a region round the extremum point of the exponent.

The classical angle of deviation of the particle is (if small) equal in order of magnitude to the force $U'(\rho)$ acting on the particle at the distance ρ, multiplied by the "collision time" ρ/v and divided by the momentum μv:

$$\theta \sim |U'(\rho)|\rho/\mu v^2.$$

Hence we can rewrite the condition (111.6), for scattering through small angles, as

$$|U'(\rho)|\rho^2 \gg \hbar v. \tag{111.7}$$

From this we can draw the following conclusions. If the field $U(r)$ decreases more rapidly than $1/r$, the condition (111.7) always ceases to be satisfied for sufficiently large ρ. Small θ, however, correspond to large ρ; thus scattering through sufficiently small angles is never classical. If, on the other hand, the field decreases less rapidly than $1/r$, the scattering through small angles is classical; whether the scattering through large angles is classical in this case depends on the behaviour of the field at small distances.

For a Coulomb field, $U = \alpha/r$, the condition (111.7) is satisfied if $\alpha \gg \hbar v$. This is the opposite condition to that for which the Coulomb field can be regarded as a perturbation. We shall see, however, that the quantum theory of scattering in a Coulomb field leads to a result which, as it happens, is always in agreement with the classical result.

PROBLEM

Find the total effective cross-section for quasi-classical scattering in a field which has the form $U = \alpha/r^s$ $(s > 2)$ at sufficiently large distances.

SOLUTION. Bearing in mind that the phases δ_l with large l are the most important, we calculate them from (106.1):

$$\delta_l = -\frac{\mu\alpha}{\hbar^2}\int\limits_{l/k}^{\infty}\frac{dr}{r^s\sqrt{(k^2-l^2/r^2)}}. \tag{1}$$

Making the substitution $l^2/k^2r^2 = \xi$, we reduce the integral to EULER's well-known form, obtaining

$$\delta_l = -\frac{\mu\alpha k^{s-2}}{2\hbar^2 l^{s-1}}\frac{\Gamma(\frac{1}{2})\Gamma(\frac{1}{2}s-\frac{1}{2})}{\Gamma(\frac{1}{2}s)}. \tag{2}$$

Replacing the summation in (105.11) by an integration, we write

$$\sigma = \frac{4\pi}{k^2}\int\limits_0^{\infty} 2l\sin^2\delta_l\,dl.$$

To integrate, we substitute $\delta_l = u$ and integrate once by parts with respect to u, reducing the integral to a gamma function. The result is

$$\sigma = 2\pi^{s/(s-1)}\sin\left[\tfrac{1}{2}\pi.\frac{s-3}{s-1}\right]\Gamma\left(\frac{s-3}{s-1}\right)\left[\frac{\Gamma(\frac{1}{2}s-\frac{1}{2})}{\Gamma(\frac{1}{2}s)}\right]^{2/(s-1)}\left(\frac{\alpha}{\hbar v}\right)^{2/(s-1)}$$

The chief condition for the applicability of this formula is that $l \gg 1$ for $\delta_l \sim 1$; this gives the inequality

$$\mu \alpha k^{s-2}/\hbar^2 \gg 1.$$

The field $U(r)$ must have the form in question from distances

$$r \sim l/k \sim (\mu\alpha/\hbar^2 k)^{1/(s-1)}$$

outwards (l being obtained from $\delta_l \sim 1$), these distances playing the principal part in the integral (1).

§112. Rutherford's formula

Scattering in a Coulomb field is of particular interest from the point of view of physical applications. It is also of interest in that, for this case, the quantum-mechanical collision problem can be solved exactly.

When there is a direction (in this case, the direction of incidence of the particle) which can be distinguished from the remainder, SCHRÖDINGER's equation in the Coulomb field is conveniently solved in parabolic co-ordinates ξ, η, ϕ (§37). The problem of the scattering of a particle in a central field is axially symmetric. Hence the wave function ψ is independent of the angle ϕ. We write the particular solution of SCHRÖDINGER's equation (37.6) in the form

$$\psi = f_1(\xi) f_2(\eta); \tag{112.1}$$

this is (37.7) with $m = 0$. Accordingly, after separating the variables, we obtain† equations (37.8) with $m = 0$:

$$\begin{aligned} &\frac{\mathrm{d}}{\mathrm{d}\xi}\left(\xi \frac{\mathrm{d}f_1}{\mathrm{d}\xi}\right) + (\tfrac{1}{4}k^2\xi - \beta_1) f_1 = 0, \\ &\frac{\mathrm{d}}{\mathrm{d}\eta}\left(\eta \frac{\mathrm{d}f_2}{\mathrm{d}\eta}\right) + (\tfrac{1}{4}k^2\eta - \beta_2) f_2 = 0, \quad \beta_1 + \beta_2 = 1. \end{aligned} \tag{112.2}$$

The energy of the scattered particle is, of course, positive; we have put $E = \frac{1}{2}k^2$. The signs in equations (112.2) are for the case of a repulsive field; exactly the same final result is obtained for the scattering cross-section in an attractive field.

We have to find that solution of SCHRÖDINGER's equation which, for negative z and large r, has the form of a plane wave:

$$\psi \sim e^{ikz} \quad \text{for } -\infty < z < 0, \quad r \to \infty,$$

corresponding to a particle incident in the positive direction of the z-axis. We shall see from what follows that the condition imposed can be satisfied by a single particular integral (112.1); a sum of integrals with various values of β_1, β_2 is not needed.

† We are here using Coulomb units.

In parabolic co-ordinates, this condition takes the form

$$\psi \sim e^{\frac{1}{2}ik(\xi-\eta)} \quad \text{for } \eta \to \infty \text{ and all } \xi.$$

This can be satisfied only if

$$f_1(\xi) = e^{\frac{1}{2}ik\xi} \tag{112.3}$$

and $f_2(\eta)$ is subject to the condition

$$f_2(\eta) \sim e^{-\frac{1}{2}ik\eta} \quad \text{for } \eta \to \infty. \tag{112.4}$$

Substituting (112.3) in the first of equations (112.2), we see that this function does in fact satisfy the equation, provided that the constant $\beta_1 = \frac{1}{2}ik$. The second equation (112.2), with $\beta_2 = 1-\beta_1$, then takes the form

$$\frac{d}{d\eta}\left(\eta\frac{df_2}{d\eta}\right)+(\tfrac{1}{4}k^2\eta-1+\tfrac{1}{2}ik)f_2 = 0.$$

Let us seek its solution in the form

$$f_2(\eta) = e^{-\frac{1}{2}ik\eta}w(\eta), \tag{112.5}$$

where the function $w(\eta)$ tends to a constant as $\eta \to \infty$. For $w(\eta)$ we have the equation

$$\eta w''+(1-ik\eta)w'-w = 0, \tag{112.6}$$

which, by introducing the new variable $\eta_1 = ik\eta$, can be reduced to the equation for a confluent hypergeometric function with parameters $\alpha = -i/k$, $\gamma = 1$. We have to choose that solution of equation (112.6) which, on being multiplied by $f_1(\xi)$, contains only an outgoing (i.e. scattered) and not an ingoing spherical wave. This solution is the function (see below)

$$w = \text{constant} \times F(-i/k, 1, ik\eta).$$

Thus, on assembling the expressions obtained, we find the following exact solution of SCHRÖDINGER's equation, describing the scattering:

$$\psi = e^{-\pi/2k}\Gamma(1+i/k)e^{\frac{1}{2}ik(\xi-\eta)}F(-i/k, 1, ik\eta). \tag{112.7}$$

We have chosen the normalising constant in ψ such that the incident plane wave has unit amplitude (see below).

In order to separate the incident and scattered waves in this function, we must consider its form at large distances from the scattering centre. Using the first two terms of the asymptotic expansion (formula (d.14) in the Mathematical Appendices) for the confluent hypergeometric function, we have for large η

$$F(-i/k, 1, ik\eta) \approx \frac{(-ik\eta)^{i/k}}{\Gamma(1+i/k)}\left(1+\frac{1}{ik^3\eta}\right)+\frac{(ik\eta)^{-i/k}}{\Gamma(-i/k)}\frac{e^{ik\eta}}{ik\eta}$$

$$= \frac{e^{\pi/2k}}{\Gamma(1+i/k)}\left(1+\frac{1}{ik^3\eta}\right)e^{(i/k)\log(k\eta)}-\frac{(i/k)e^{\pi/2k}}{\Gamma(1-i/k)}\frac{e^{ik\eta}}{ik\eta}e^{-(i/k)\log(k\eta)}.$$

Substituting this in (112.7) and changing to spherical co-ordinates ($\xi-\eta = 2z$, $\eta = r-z = r(1-\cos\theta)$), we have the following final asymptotic expression for the wave function:

$$\psi = \left[1+\frac{1}{ik^3r(1-\cos\theta)}\right]e^{ikz+(i/k)\log(kr-kr\cos\theta)}+\frac{f(\theta)}{r}e^{ikr-(i/k)\log(2kr)}, \quad (112.8)$$

where†

$$f(\theta) = -\frac{1}{2k^2\sin^2\frac{1}{2}\theta}e^{-(2i/k)\log\sin\frac{1}{2}\theta}\frac{\Gamma(1+i/k)}{\Gamma(1-i/k)}. \quad (112.9)$$

The first term in (112.8) represents the incident wave. We see that, in consequence of the slow decrease of the Coulomb field, the plane wave is distorted even at large distances from the centre, as is shown by the presence of the logarithmic term in the phase and of the $1/r$ term in the amplitude. The distorting logarithmic term in the phase is found also in the scattered spherical wave given by the second term in (112.8). These differences from the usual asymptotic form of the wave function (105.3) are unimportant, however, since they give a correction to the current density which tends to zero as $r \to \infty$.

Thus we obtain for the effective scattering cross-section $d\sigma = |f(\theta)|^2 do$ the formula

$$d\sigma = do/4k^4\sin^4\tfrac{1}{2}\theta,$$

or, in ordinary units,

$$d\sigma = (\alpha/2\mu v^2)^2\, do/\sin^4\tfrac{1}{2}\theta, \quad (112.10)$$

where we have introduced the velocity $v = k\hbar/\mu$ of the particle. This is the familiar *Rutherford's formula* given by classical mechanics. Thus, for scattering in a Coulomb field, quantum and classical mechanics give the same result (N. Mott, and W. Gordon, 1928). Born's formula (110.9) naturally leads to the same expression (112.10) also.

Finally, we shall give for reference the expression for the scattering amplitude (112.9), written as a sum of spherical harmonics. This is obtained by substituting in (106.5) the phases δ_l from (36.28), i.e.‡

$$e^{2i\delta_l} = \Gamma(l+1+i/k)/\Gamma(l+1-i/k). \quad (112.11)$$

Thus we find

$$f(\theta) = \frac{1}{2ik}\sum_l (2l+1)\frac{\Gamma(l+1+i/k)}{\Gamma(l+1-i/k)}P_l(\cos\theta). \quad (112.12)$$

† The signs in the scattering amplitude (112.9) correspond to a repulsive field. In an attractive Coulomb field, formula (112.9) is replaced by the complex conjugate expression. We may point out that $f(\theta)$ then becomes infinite at the poles of the function $\Gamma(1-i/k)$, i.e. at points where the argument of the gamma function is a negative integer or zero (when $\mathrm{Im}\, k > 0$ and the function ψ decreases at infinity). The corresponding energy values are $\frac{1}{2}k^2 = -1/2n^2$ ($n = 1, 2, 3, \ldots$), and coincide with those of the discrete spectrum in the Coulomb field (cf. §107).

‡ The value of δ_l in this formula differs from the true (divergent) Coulomb phase by a quantity which is the same for all l.

§113. The system of wave functions of the continuous spectrum

The formulae obtained in the last section for the wave functions describing scattering are of interest from another point of view also. We have seen in §105 that functions of the form

$$\psi = c_k \sum_{l=0}^{\infty} i^l(2l+1)e^{i\delta_l}P_l(\cos\theta)R_{kl}(r), \tag{113.1}$$

where c_k is a constant, describe a stationary state of a particle in a centrally symmetric field, there being at infinity a plane wave propagated in the positive direction of the z-axis and an outgoing spherical wave. In this formula, θ is the angle between the radius vector $\mathbf{r}$ and the z-axis, which coincides with the direction of the wave vector of the incident wave. If we substitute $\cos\theta = \mathbf{k}\cdot\mathbf{r}/kr$, the expression (113.1) will not involve any particular choice of the axes of co-ordinates. By giving the vector $\mathbf{k}$ all possible values, we obtain, as we shall now show, a complete set of orthogonal wave functions of the continuous spectrum. We shall denote these functions by $\psi^+_{\mathbf{k}}$:

$$\psi^+_{\mathbf{k}} = \frac{1}{4\pi k}\sum_{l=0}^{\infty} i^l(2l+1)e^{i\delta_l}R_{kl}(r)P_l(\mathbf{k}\cdot\mathbf{r}/kr). \tag{113.2}$$

We have chosen the constant c_k in (113.1) such that the functions are normalised in the usual manner for the continuous spectrum, i.e. by the delta function in $\mathbf{k}$-space:†

$$\int \psi^+_{\mathbf{k}'}\psi^+_{\mathbf{k}}\,dV = \delta(\mathbf{k}'-\mathbf{k}); \tag{113.3}$$

this will be confirmed by the subsequent calculation. Thus, together with the usual system of wave functions $\psi = R_{kl}(r)Y_{lm}(\theta,\phi)$ (corresponding to a stationary state with definite values of the energy $\hbar^2k^2/2\mu$, angular momentum l and projection thereof m), we have for the continuous spectrum another system of functions which describe states with a definite energy (but not a definite angular momentum or projection thereof). In these states there is at infinity, besides the outgoing wave, a plane wave incident in a definite direction $\mathbf{k}$. This system of functions is very useful in solving a number of problems relating to collisions.

We now go on to prove (113.3), and denote by θ and θ' the angles between the radius vector and $\mathbf{k}$, $\mathbf{k}'$ respectively; the angle between $\mathbf{k}$ and $\mathbf{k}'$ is denoted by α. The product $\psi^+_{\mathbf{k}'}{}^*\psi^+_{\mathbf{k}}$ is expressed as a double sum (over l and l') of terms containing the products $P_{l'}(\cos\theta')P_l(\cos\theta)$. Noticing that

$$\cos\theta' = \cos\theta\cos\alpha+\sin\theta\sin\alpha\cos\phi,$$

† For this normalisation, the incident plane wave has, at infinity, the form

$$(2\pi,^{-3/2}e^{i\mathbf{k}\cdot\mathbf{r}}.$$

where ϕ is the angle between the planes $(\mathbf{r}, \mathbf{k})$ and $(\mathbf{k}, \mathbf{k}')$, and using the addition theorem for spherical harmonics (formula (c.8) in the Mathematical Appendices), we obtain

$$P_{l'}(\cos\theta')P_l(\cos\theta) = P_l(\cos\theta)P_{l'}(\cos\theta)P_{l'}(\cos\alpha)+$$

$$+2P_l(\cos\theta)\sum_{m'=1}^{\infty}\frac{(l'-m')!}{(l'+m')!}P_{l'}^{m'}(\cos\theta)P_{l'}^{m'}(\cos\alpha)\cos m'\phi. \tag{113.4}$$

We first multiply $\psi^+_{\mathbf{k}'}{}^*\psi^+_{\mathbf{k}}$ by $\mathrm{d}o = \sin\theta\,\mathrm{d}\theta\,\mathrm{d}\phi$ and integrate over all angles. The integration over ϕ reduces to zero all the terms in (113.4) except the first. The latter gives zero on integration over θ if $l \neq l'$ (by the orthogonality of the Legendre polynomials), while for $l = l'$

$$\int_0^{\pi} P_l^2(\cos\theta)\sin\theta\,\mathrm{d}\theta = 2/(2l+1).$$

Thus we obtain

$$\int \psi^+_{\mathbf{k}'}{}^*\psi^+_{\mathbf{k}}\,\mathrm{d}V = \frac{1}{4\pi kk'}\sum_{l=0}^{\infty}(2l+1)e^{i[\delta_l(k)-\delta_l(k')]}P_l(\cos\alpha)\int_0^{\infty}R_{k'l}(r)R_{kl}(r)r^2\,\mathrm{d}r.$$

The radial functions R_{kl} are orthogonal, however, and are normalised by

$$\int_0^{\infty} R_{k'l}R_{kl}r^2\,\mathrm{d}r = \delta(k'-k).$$

Hence we can put $k = k'$ in the coefficients in front of the integrals; using also the relation (106.3), we have

$$\int \psi^+_{\mathbf{k}'}{}^*\psi^+_{\mathbf{k}}\,\mathrm{d}V = \frac{1}{4\pi k^2}\delta(k'-k)\sum_{l=0}^{\infty}(2l+1)P_l(\cos\alpha)$$

$$= \frac{1}{2\pi k^2}\delta(k'-k)\delta(1-\cos\alpha).$$

The expression on the right, on being multiplied by $2\pi k^2 \sin\alpha\,\mathrm{d}k\,\mathrm{d}\alpha$ and integrated over all **k**-space, gives 1; in other words, it is the delta function in **k**-space, which proves formula (113.3).

Together with the system of functions $\psi^+_{\mathbf{k}}$, we can also introduce a system corresponding to states in which there are at infinity a plane wave and an ingoing spherical wave. These functions, which we denote by $\psi^-_{\mathbf{k}}$, are obtained directly from the $\psi^+_{\mathbf{k}}$. We first take the complex conjugate, obtaining from the outgoing wave an ingoing one ($\sim e^{-ikr}/r$), while the plane wave takes the form: $\sim e^{-i\mathbf{k}.\mathbf{r}}$. In order to keep the previous definition of $\mathbf{k}$ (with the plane wave $\sim e^{i\mathbf{k}.\mathbf{r}}$), we must then reverse the direction of $\mathbf{k}$, i.e. replace it by $-\mathbf{k}$. Noticing that $P_l(-\cos\theta) = (-1)^l P_l(\cos\theta)$, we obtain from (113.2)

$$\psi^-_{\mathbf{k}} = \frac{1}{4\pi k}\sum_{l=0}^{\infty} i^l(2l+1)e^{-i\delta_l}R_{kl}(r)P_l(\mathbf{k}\cdot\mathbf{r}/kr); \tag{113.5}$$

the functions R_{kl} are supposed real.

The case of a Coulomb field is of great importance. Here the functions $\psi^+_{\mathbf{k}}$ (and $\psi^-_{\mathbf{k}}$) can be written in a closed form, which is obtained directly from formula (112.7) (the latter must be multiplied by $(2\pi)^{-3/2}$; see the first footnote to the present section). We express the parabolic co-ordinates by

$$\tfrac{1}{2}k(\xi-\eta) = kz = \mathbf{k}\cdot\mathbf{r}, \qquad k\eta = k(r-z) = kr-\mathbf{k}\cdot\mathbf{r}.$$

Thus we obtain for a repulsive Coulomb field†

$$\psi^+_{\mathbf{k}} = \frac{1}{(2\pi)^{3/2}}e^{-\pi/2k}\Gamma(1+i/k)e^{i\mathbf{k}\cdot\mathbf{r}}F(-i/k, 1, ikr-i\mathbf{k}\cdot\mathbf{r}), \tag{113.6}$$

$$\psi^-_{\mathbf{k}} = \frac{1}{(2\pi)^{3/2}}e^{-\pi/2k}\Gamma(1-i/k)e^{i\mathbf{k}\cdot\mathbf{r}}F(i/k, 1, -ikr-i\mathbf{k}\cdot\mathbf{r}). \tag{113.7}$$

The wave functions for an attractive Coulomb field are found by simultaneously changing the signs of k and r:

$$\psi^+_{\mathbf{k}} = \frac{1}{(2\pi)^{3/2}}e^{\pi/2k}\Gamma(1-i/k)e^{i\mathbf{k}\cdot\mathbf{r}}F(i/k, 1, ikr-i\mathbf{k}\cdot\mathbf{r}), \tag{113.8}$$

$$\psi^-_{\mathbf{k}} = \frac{1}{(2\pi)^{3/2}}e^{\pi/2k}\Gamma(1+i/k)e^{i\mathbf{k}\cdot\mathbf{r}}F(-i/k, 1, -ikr-i\mathbf{k}\cdot\mathbf{r}). \tag{113.9}$$

The action of the Coulomb field on the motion of the particle near the origin may be characterised by the ratio of the squared modulus of $\psi^+_{\mathbf{k}}$ or $\psi^-_{\mathbf{k}}$ at the point $r = 0$ to the squared modulus of the wave function $\psi_{\mathbf{k}} = (2\pi)^{-3/2}e^{i\mathbf{k}\cdot\mathbf{r}}$ for free motion; this ratio is important in certain problems (see, for instance, §118). A simple calculation gives, for a repulsive field,

$$\frac{|\psi^+_{\mathbf{k}}(0)|^2}{|\psi_{\mathbf{k}}|^2} = \frac{|\psi^-_{\mathbf{k}}(0)|^2}{|\psi_{\mathbf{k}}|^2} = \frac{2\pi}{k(e^{2\pi/k}-1)}, \tag{113.10}$$

and for an attractive field,

$$\frac{|\psi^+_{\mathbf{k}}(0)|^2}{|\psi_{\mathbf{k}}|^2} = \frac{|\psi^-_{\mathbf{k}}(0)|^2}{|\psi_{\mathbf{k}}|^2} = \frac{2\pi}{k(1-e^{-2\pi/k})}. \tag{113.11}$$

† In Coulomb units.

The functions $\psi^{-}_{\mathbf{k}}$ play an important part in a number of problems relating to the application of perturbation theory in the continuous spectrum. Let us suppose that, as a result of some perturbation, the particle enters a state of the continuous spectrum (the initial state may belong to either the discrete or the continuous spectrum).† The problem then arises of calculating the probability that the freely moving particle resulting from this transition will have a definite direction in space. It can be shown that, for this to be so, we must take the function $\psi^{-}_{\mathbf{k}}$ as the wave function of the final state of the particle, **k** being the wave vector of the particle at infinity.

For let us consider the function

$$\psi^{-}_{\mathbf{k}_0}+\frac{\sqrt{(2\mu^3)}}{\hbar^3}\iint\frac{V_{\mathbf{k}\mathbf{k}_0}}{E_0-E}\psi^{-}_{\mathbf{k}}\sqrt{E}\,\mathrm{d}E\,\mathrm{d}o.$$

This is the function (43.3), in which the functions $\psi_\nu^{(0)}$ have been taken to be $\psi^{-}_{\mathbf{k}}$, and instead of $\mathrm{d}\nu$ we have written $k^2\,\mathrm{d}k\,\mathrm{d}o = [\sqrt{(2\mu^3)}/\hbar^3]\sqrt{E}\,\mathrm{d}E\,\mathrm{d}o$. It describes the state of the particle occurring as a result of a constant perturbation, the unperturbed wave functions being $\psi^{-}_{\mathbf{k}}$. The integration over E is taken along a path which passes round the point $E = E_0$ (in the plane of the complex variable E) below. Let us consider large values of r; we shall show that the terms in $\psi^{-}_{\mathbf{k}}$ which contain the ingoing wave vanish on integration over E. To show this, it is sufficient to displace the contour of integration slightly into the lower half-plane. Then we have $\mathrm{im}\, E < 0$ on the contour, and so $\mathrm{im}\, k < 0$ (the root $k = \sqrt{(2\mu E)}/\hbar$ is defined so that it is positive on the positive real E-axis). The ingoing wave contains the factor e^{-ikr}; for $\mathrm{im}\, k < 0$ and large r it can be made arbitrarily small, and this proves the above statement. Thus, as a result of the integration over E, only the plane wave remains (at infinity) from the function $\psi^{-}_{\mathbf{k}}$, and this corresponds to a particle moving in a definite direction.

§114. Collisions of like particles

The case where two identical particles collide requires special consideration. The identity of the particles leads in quantum mechanics, as we know, to the appearance of a peculiar exchange interaction between them. This has an important effect on scattering also (N. F. Mott 1930).

The orbital wave function of a system of two particles must be symmetric or antisymmetric with respect to the particles, according as their total spin is even or odd (see §60). The wave function which describes the scattering, and which is obtained by solving the usual Schrödinger's equation, must therefore be symmetrised or antisymmetrised with respect to the particles. An interchange of the particles is equivalent to reversing the direction of the

† For example, an electron colliding with an atom and emitting an X-ray quantum, thereby changing its energy and its direction of motion.

radius vector joining them. In the co-ordinate system in which the centre of mass is at rest, this means that r remains unchanged, while the angle θ is replaced by $\pi-\theta$ (and so $z = r\cos\theta$ becomes $-z$). Hence, instead of the asymptotic expression (105.3) for the wave function, we must write

$$\psi = e^{ikz} \pm e^{-ikz} + e^{ikr}[f(\theta) \pm f(\pi-\theta)]/r. \tag{114.1}$$

By virtue of the identity of the particles it is, of course, impossible to say which of them scatters and which is scattered. In the co-ordinate system in which the centre of mass is at rest, we have two equal incident plane waves, propagated in opposite directions (e^{ikz} and e^{-ikz} in (114.1)). The outgoing spherical wave in (114.1) takes into account the scattering of both particles, and the probability current calculated from it gives the probability that either of the particles will be scattered into the element do of solid angle considered. The effective cross-section is the ratio of this current to the current density in either of the incident plane waves, i.e. it is given, as before, by the squared modulus of the coefficient of e^{ikr}/r in the wave function (114.1).

Thus, if the total spin of the colliding particles is even, the effective scattering cross-section is of the form

$$d\sigma_s = |f(\theta)+f(\pi-\theta)|^2 \, do, \tag{114.2}$$

while if the total spin is odd, it is

$$d\sigma_a = |f(\theta)-f(\pi-\theta)|^2 \, do. \tag{114.3}$$

The appearance of the "interference" term $f(\theta)f^*(\pi-\theta)+f^*(\theta)f(\pi-\theta)$ characterises the exchange interaction. If the particles were different, as they are in classical mechanics, the probability that either of them would be scattered into a given element of solid angle do would simply be equal to the sum of the probabilities that one particle is deviated through an angle θ and the other through $\pi-\theta$; in other words, the effective cross-section would be

$$\{|f(\theta)|^2+|f(\pi-\theta)|^2\} \, do.$$

In formulae (114.2), (114.3) it is supposed that the total spin of the colliding particles has a definite value. Usually, however, we have to deal with the collision of particles which are not in definite spin states. To determine the effective cross-section in this case, it is necessary to average over all possible spin states, assuming them to be all equally probable. We have shown in §60 that, of the total number of $(2s+1)^2$ different spin states of a system of two particles with spin s, $s(2s+1)$ states correspond to an even total spin and $(s+1)(2s+1)$ to an odd total spin (if s is half-integral), or *vice versa* if s is integral. Let us first suppose that the spin s of the particles is half-integral. Then the probability that the system of two colliding particles will have even S is $s(2s+1)/(2s+1)^2 = s/(2s+1)$, while the probability of odd S is $(s+1)/(2s+1)$. Hence the effective cross-section is

$$d\sigma = \frac{s}{2s+1}\, d\sigma_s + \frac{s+1}{2s+1}\, d\sigma_a.$$

Substituting here (114.2), (114.3), we obtain

$$d\sigma = \{|f(\theta)|^2 + |f(\pi-\theta)|^2 - \frac{1}{2s+1}[f(\theta)f^*(\pi-\theta) + f^*(\theta)\, f(\pi-\theta)]\}\, do. \tag{114.4}$$

Similarly, we find for integral s

$$d\sigma = \{|f(\theta)|^2 + |f(\pi-\theta)|^2 + \frac{1}{2s+1}[f(\theta)f^*(\pi-\theta) + f^*(\theta)f(\pi-\theta)]\}\, do. \tag{114.5}$$

As an example, we shall write out the formulae for the collision of two electrons interacting by Coulomb's law ($U = e^2/r$). Substitution of the expression (112.9) in the formula (114.4) with $s = \frac{1}{2}$ gives (in ordinary units), after a simple calculation,

$$d\sigma = \left(\frac{e^2}{\mu_0 v^2}\right)^2 \left[\frac{1}{\sin^4 \frac{1}{2}\theta} + \frac{1}{\cos^4 \frac{1}{2}\theta} - \frac{1}{\sin^2 \frac{1}{2}\theta \cos^2 \frac{1}{2}\theta} \cos\left(\frac{e^2}{\hbar v} \log \tan^2 \tfrac{1}{2}\theta\right)\right] do, \tag{114.6}$$

where we have introduced the mass μ_0 of the particles in place of the reduced mass $\mu = \frac{1}{2}\mu_0$. This formula is considerably simplified if the velocity is so large that $e^2 \ll v\hbar$; we notice that this is just the condition for perturbation theory to be applicable to a Coulomb field. Then the cosine in the third term can be replaced by unity, and we have

$$d\sigma = \left(\frac{2e^2}{\mu_0 v^2}\right)^2 \frac{4 - 3\sin^2\theta}{\sin^4\theta}\, do. \tag{114.7}$$

The opposite limiting case, $e^2 \gg v\hbar$, corresponds to the passage to the limit of classical mechanics (see the end of §111). In formula (114.6) this transition occurs in a very curious way. For $e^2 \gg v\hbar$, the cosine in the third term in the square brackets is a rapidly oscillating function. For any given θ, formula (114.6) gives for the effective cross-section a value which in general differs considerably from the Rutherford value.† However, on averaging over even a small range of values of θ, the oscillating term in (114.6) vanishes, and we obtain the classical formula.

All the formulae (114.2)–(114.6) for the effective cross-section refer to

† See, for instance, *Mechanics*, §22, Moscow 1940.

a system of co-ordinates in which the centre of mass is at rest. The transition to a system in which one of the particles is at rest before the collision is effected (according to (105.2)) simply by replacing θ by 2ϑ. Thus, for a collision of electrons we have from (114.6)

$$d\sigma = \left(\frac{2e^2}{\mu_0 v^2}\right)^2 \left[\frac{1}{\sin^4\vartheta} + \frac{1}{\cos^4\vartheta} - \frac{1}{\sin^2\vartheta\cos^2\vartheta}\cos\left(\frac{e^2}{\hbar v}\log\tan^2\vartheta\right)\right]\cos\vartheta\, do, \tag{114.8}$$

where do is the element of solid angle in the new system of co-ordinates.†

PROBLEM

Determine the effective scattering cross-section for two identical particles of spin $\frac{1}{2}$, with definite values $\sigma = +\frac{1}{2}$ of the projection of the spin on axes at an angle α with each other.

SOLUTION. Let the spinors χ^μ and ξ^μ be the spin wave functions of the particles. The wave function of the system of the two colliding particles is the product $\chi^\mu\xi^\nu$. We write it in the form

$$\chi^\mu\xi^\nu = \tfrac{1}{2}(\chi^\mu\xi^\nu + \chi^\nu\xi^\mu) + \tfrac{1}{2}(\chi^\mu\xi^\nu - \chi^\nu\xi^\mu).$$

The first term is a symmetrical spinor of rank two, and corresponds to a state of the system with total spin $S = 1$; the second is an antisymmetrical spinor, which reduces to a scalar and corresponds to a state with $S = 0$. Hence the probabilities for the system to have spin 1 and 0 are respectively

$$\begin{aligned} w_1 &= \tfrac{1}{4}[\chi^\mu\xi^\nu + \chi^\nu\xi^\mu]^2 = \tfrac{1}{2}(1 + |\chi^{\nu *}\xi^\nu|^2), \\ w_0 &= \tfrac{1}{4}[\chi^\mu\xi^\nu - \chi^\nu\xi^\mu]^2 = \tfrac{1}{2}(1 - |\chi^{\nu *}\xi^\nu|^2); \end{aligned} \tag{1}$$

summation over repeated spinor indices is understood, and it must be recalled that $|\chi^\mu|^2 = |\xi^\mu|^2 = 1$. The required effective cross-section is

$$d\sigma = w_0\, d\sigma_s + w_1\, d\sigma_a. \tag{2}$$

We take a system of co-ordinates with the z-axis that along which the projected spin of the first particle has a definite value ($\sigma = +\frac{1}{2}$); then $\chi^1 = 1$, $\chi^2 = 0$. The components of the spinor ξ are $\xi^1 = \cos\frac{1}{2}\alpha$, $\xi^2 = i\sin\frac{1}{2}\alpha$ (see the transformation formulae (57.7); in the system of co-ordinates along whose z-axis the projected spin of the second particle has a definite value, we should have $\xi^1 = 1$, $\xi^2 = 0$). Substituting these values in (1), we find the effective cross-section (2) in the form

$$d\sigma = \tfrac{1}{4}(1 - \cos\alpha)\, d\sigma_s + \tfrac{1}{4}(3 + \cos\alpha)\, d\sigma_a. \tag{3}$$

§115. Elastic collisions between fast electrons and atoms

Born's formula (110.5) can be applied not only to collisions of two elementary particles, but also to an elastic collision between, say, an electron and an atom, if the potential energy $U(r)$ is suitably defined. The condition for the Born approximation to be applicable to such a collision requires that the

† In replacing θ by 2ϑ, the element of solid angle do must be replaced by $4\cos\vartheta\, do$, since $\sin\theta\, d\theta d\phi = 4\cos\vartheta\sin\vartheta\, d\vartheta d\phi$.

velocity of the incident electron should be large in comparison with those of the atomic electrons.

In deriving formula (110.5), we have calculated the matrix element $U_{\mathbf{p}'\mathbf{p}}$ of the interaction energy with respect to the wave functions of a free particle before and after the collision.† In a collision with an atom, however, it is clearly necessary to take into account also the wave functions describing the internal state of the atom. In an elastic collision, the state of the atom is left unchanged. Hence $U_{\mathbf{p}'\mathbf{p}}$ must be determined as the matrix element with respect to the wave functions $\psi_{\mathbf{p}}$ and $\psi_{\mathbf{p}'}$ of the electron; it is diagonal with respect to the wave function of the atom. In other words, $U(r)$ in formula (110.5) must be taken to be the potential energy of the interaction of the electron with the atom, averaged with respect to the wave function of the latter. It is $e\phi(r)$, where $\phi(r)$ is the potential of the field at the point r due to the mean distribution of charges in the atom.

Denoting the density of the charge distribution in the atom by $\rho(r)$, we have, for the potential ϕ, Poisson's equation:

$$\Delta\phi = -4\pi\rho(r).$$

The required matrix element $U_{\mathbf{p}'\mathbf{p}}$ is essentially the Fourier component of U (i.e. of ϕ) corresponding to the wave vector $\mathbf{q}$. Applying Poisson's equation to each Fourier component separately, we have

$$\Delta\phi_{\mathbf{q}}e^{-i\mathbf{q}.\mathbf{r}} = -q^2\phi_{\mathbf{q}}e^{-i\mathbf{q}.\mathbf{r}} = -4\pi\rho_{\mathbf{q}}e^{-i\mathbf{q}.\mathbf{r}},$$

so that

$$\phi_{\mathbf{q}} = 4\pi\rho_{\mathbf{q}}/q^2,$$

i.e.

$$\int \phi e^{i\mathbf{q}.\mathbf{r}}\,dV = (4\pi/q^2)\int \rho e^{i\mathbf{q}.\mathbf{r}}\,dV.$$

The charge density $\rho(\mathbf{r})$ consists of the electron charges and the charge on the nucleus:

$$\rho = -en(r)+Ze\delta(\mathbf{r}),$$

where $en(r)$ is the electron charge density in the atom. Multiplying by $e^{i\mathbf{q}.\mathbf{r}}$ and integrating, we have

$$\int \rho e^{i\mathbf{q}.\mathbf{r}}\,dV = -e\int ne^{i\mathbf{q}.\mathbf{r}}\,dV+Ze.$$

† In view of the great difference in mass between the electron and the atom, the latter may be regarded as immovable in the collision, and the system of co-ordinates in which the centre of mass is at rest is the same as that in which the atom is fixed. p and p' then denote the momentum of the electron before and after the collision, μ its mass, and the angle θ is the same as the angle of deviation ϑ of the electron.

Thus we obtain for the integral in question the expression

$$\int Ue^{i\mathbf{q}\cdot\mathbf{r}}\,\mathrm{d}V = \frac{4\pi e^2}{q^2}[Z-F(q)], \tag{115.1}$$

where $F(q)$ is defined by the formula

$$F(q) = \int ne^{i\mathbf{q}\cdot\mathbf{r}}\,\mathrm{d}V \tag{115.2}$$

and is called the *atomic form factor*. It is a function of the scattering angle and of the velocity of the incident electron.

Finally, substituting (115.1) in (110.5), we obtain the following expression for the effective cross-section for the elastic scattering of fast electrons by an atom:

$$\begin{aligned}\mathrm{d}\sigma &= \frac{4\mu^2 e^4}{\hbar^4 q^4}[Z-F(q)]^2\,\mathrm{do} \\ &= \left(\frac{e^2}{2\mu v^2}\right)^2\left[Z-F\left(\frac{2\mu v}{\hbar}\sin\tfrac{1}{2}\vartheta\right)\right]^2\frac{\mathrm{do}}{\sin^4\frac{1}{2}\vartheta}.\end{aligned} \tag{115.3}$$

Let us consider the limiting case of small q; we have in mind values of q which are small compared with the "reciprocal atomic radius", i.e. with $1/a_0$, where a_0 is of the order of magnitude of the dimensions of the atom ($qa_0 \ll 1$). Small scattering angles correspond to small q; $\vartheta \ll v_0/v$, where $v_0 \sim \hbar/\mu a_0$ is of the order of magnitude of the velocities of the atomic electrons.

Let us expand $F(q)$ as a series of powers of q. The zero-order term is $\int n\mathrm{d}V$, which is the total number Z of electrons in the atom. The first-order term is proportional to $\int \mathbf{r}n(r)\,\mathrm{d}V$, i.e. to the mean value of the dipole moment of the atom; this vanishes identically (see §72).

We must therefore continue the expansion up to the second-order term, obtaining

$$Z-F(q) = \frac{1}{6}q^2\int nr^2\,\mathrm{d}V;$$

substituting in (115.3), we obtain

$$\mathrm{d}\sigma = \left|\frac{\mu e^2}{3\hbar^2}\int nr^2\,\mathrm{d}V\right|^2\mathrm{do}. \tag{115.4}$$

Thus, in the range of small angles, the effective cross-section is independent of the scattering angle, and is given by the mean square distance of the atomic electrons from the nucleus.

In the opposite limiting case of large q ($qa_0 \gg 1$, i.e. $\vartheta \gg v_0/v$), the factor $e^{i\mathbf{q}\cdot\mathbf{r}}$ in the integrand in (115.2) is a rapidly oscillating function, and therefore the whole integral is nearly zero. Consequently, we can neglect $F(q)$

in comparison with Z, so that

$$d\sigma = \left(\frac{Ze^2}{2\mu v^2}\right)^2 \frac{do}{\sin^4 \frac{1}{2}\vartheta}. \tag{115.5}$$

In other words, we have Rutherford scattering at the nucleus of the atom.

In applications, the value of the integral

$$\int (1-\cos\vartheta)\,d\sigma$$

is often of interest. In the range of angles $\vartheta \ll v_0/v$ we have, according to (115.4), $d\sigma = \text{constant} \times \sin\vartheta\, d\vartheta = \text{constant} \times \vartheta\, d\vartheta$, where the constant is independent of ϑ. Hence, in this region, the integrand in the above integral is proportional to ϑ^3, so that the integral converges rapidly at the lower limit. In the region $1 \gg \vartheta \gg v_0/v$ we have $d\sigma \cong \text{constant} \times d\vartheta/\vartheta^3$; the integrand is proportional to $1/\vartheta$, and the integral diverges logarithmically. Hence we see that this range of angles plays the chief part in the integral, and we need integrate only over this range. The lower limit of integration can be taken as of the order of v_0/v; we shall write it in the form $e^2/\gamma\hbar v$, where γ is a dimensionless constant. It is important that the value of the integral depends only slightly on the choice of this constant, since it enters only in a logarithm, and divided by the large quantity $e^2/\hbar v$. As a result we have the formula

$$\int (1-\cos\vartheta)\,d\sigma = 4\pi(Ze^2/\mu v^2)^2 \log(\gamma\hbar v/e^2). \tag{115.6}$$

An exact calculation of the constant γ requires a consideration of scattering through angles $\vartheta > v_0/v$, and cannot be carried out in a general form.

For a numerical calculation of the atomic form factor for heavy atoms, we can use the Thomas-Fermi distribution of the density $n(r)$. We have seen that, in the Thomas-Fermi model, $n(r)$ has the form (69.9):

$$n(r) = Z^2 f(rZ^{1/3}/b);$$

all quantities in this and the following formulae are measured in atomic units. It is easy to see that the integral (115.2), when calculated with such a function $n(r)$, will contain q only in the combination $qZ^{-1/3}$:

$$F(q) = Z\phi(bqZ^{-1/3}) \tag{115.7}$$

or, in ordinary units,

$$F(q) = Z\phi(0{\cdot}885\hbar^2 qZ^{-1/3}/\mu e^2).$$

Table 9 gives, for reference, the values of the function $\phi(x)$, which holds for all atoms.†

† It must be borne in mind that this formula is not applicable for small q, since the integral of nr^2 cannot in practice be calculated by the Thomas-Fermi method (see the fifth note to §126).

TABLE 9

The atomic form factor on the Thomas-Fermi model

x	$\phi(x)$	x	$\phi(x)$	x	$\phi(x)$
0	1·000	1·08	0·422	2·17	0·224
0·15	0·922	1·24	0·378	2·32	0·205
0·31	0·796	1·39	0·342	2·48	0·189
0·46	0·684	1·55	0·309	2·64	0·175
0·62	0·589	1·70	0·284	2·79	0·167
0·77	0·522	1·86	0·264	2·94	0·156
0·93	0·469	2·02	0·240		

With the atomic form factor (115.7), the effective cross-section (115.3) will have the form

$$d\sigma = (4Z^2/q^4)[1-\phi(bqZ^{-1/3})]^2 = Z^{2/3}\Phi(Z^{-1/3}v\sin\tfrac{1}{2}\vartheta), \qquad (115.8)$$

where $\Phi(x)$ is a new function holding for all atoms. The total effective cross-section may be obtained by integration. The chief part in the integral is played by the range of small ϑ. Hence we can write

$$d\sigma \cong Z^{2/3}\Phi(Z^{-1/3}v\vartheta/2)2\pi\vartheta\, d\vartheta,$$

and extend the integration over ϑ to infinity:

$$\sigma = 2\pi Z^{2/3}\int_0^\infty \Phi(Z^{-1/3}v\vartheta/2)\vartheta\, d\vartheta = (8\pi/v^2)Z^{4/3}\int_0^\infty \Phi(x)\, dx.$$

Thus σ is of the form

$$\sigma = \text{constant}\times Z^{4/3}/v^2. \qquad (115.9)$$

Similarly, it is easy to see that the constant γ in formula (115.6) will be proportional to $Z^{-1/3}$.

PROBLEM

Calculate the effective cross-section for the elastic scattering of fast electrons by a hydrogen atom in the ground state.

SOLUTION. The wave function of the normal state of the hydrogen atom is $\psi = \pi^{-1/2}e^{-r}$, so that $n = e^{-2r}/\pi$ (we are using atomic units). The integration over angles in (115.2) is effected as in the derivation of formula (110.9); we have

$$F = \frac{4\pi}{q}\int\limits_0^\infty n(r)\sin qr \,.\, r\,\mathrm{d}r = \frac{1}{(1+\frac{1}{4}q^2)^2}.$$

Substituting in (115.3), we obtain

$$\mathrm{d}\sigma = \frac{4(8+q^2)^2}{(4+q^2)^4}\,\mathrm{d}o,$$

where $q = 2v\sin\frac{1}{2}\vartheta$. The total effective cross-section is conveniently calculated by putting $\mathrm{d}o = 2\pi\sin\vartheta\,\mathrm{d}\vartheta = (2\pi/v^2)q\,\mathrm{d}q$ and integrating over q; here, of course, only the term of the highest degree in v need be retained. The result is

$$\sigma = 7\pi/3v^2.$$

CHAPTER XV

THE THEORY OF INELASTIC COLLISIONS

§116. The principle of detailed balancing

COLLISIONS are said to be *inelastic* when they are accompanied by a change in the internal state of the colliding particles. Here we understand "a change in the internal state" in the widest sense; in particular, the very nature of the particles may be altered, as in fact usually happens in nuclear reactions.

Starting from the symmetry with respect to a change in the sign of the time, we can obtain a very general relation between the effective cross-section for some inelastic collision and that for the converse process.

To derive this, we shall suppose, in a purely formal manner, that the motion of the colliding particles takes place in a large but finite volume V, our object being to pass subsequently to the limit $V \to \infty$. At the boundaries of this volume we must formally impose such boundary conditions as would permit the description of the particles at large distances by plane waves. Then the energy spectrum of the relative motion of the particles is no longer continuous, but discrete (the intervals between the levels being very small, and tending to zero as $V \to \infty$).

Let w_{12} be the probability for the transition of the system of the two colliding particles from some state 1 to state 2. Each of these states is characterised by definite internal states of the particles, and by velocities of the particles which are definite in both magnitude and direction. If we change the sign of the time, the velocities and the projected angular momenta of the particles change sign. The states differing from 1 and 2 by a reversal of the directions of the velocities and angular momenta are denoted by 1* and 2*. Furthermore, the initial state becomes the final state, and *vice versa*. It follows from the symmetry with respect to a change in the sign of the time that the transition probabilities $1 \to 2$ and $2^* \to 1^*$ must be the same:

$$w_{12} = w_{2^*1^*}. \tag{116.1}$$

Although the above statement is evident from the simple considerations given, it is also useful to show how it can be verified in terms of the general mathematical formalism of quantum mechanics.

Let Ψ and Ψ' be the wave functions of the system at times t and t' ($t' > t$). The relation between them can be written

$$\Psi' = \hat{S}\Psi, \tag{116.2}$$

where $\hat{S}$ is some linear integral operator (whose form can be found by solving the corresponding SCHRÖDINGER's equation). The normalisation of the wave function must be unchanged with time, i.e. we must have

$$\int \Psi^*\Psi \, dq = \int \Psi'^*\Psi' \, dq = \int \hat{S}^*\Psi^*\hat{S}\Psi \, dq = \int \Psi^*\tilde{\hat{S}}^*\hat{S}\Psi \, dq.$$

It follows from this that

$$\tilde{\hat{S}}^*\hat{S} = 1, \tag{116.3}$$

i.e. the operator $\hat{S}$ is unitary.

When the sign of the time is changed, the parts played by the instants t and t' are interchanged, the initial instant being now t'. The wave functions Ψ and Ψ' are replaced by Ψ'^* and Ψ^*. The symmetry with respect to this operation means that, besides (116.2), we must have also

$$\Psi^* = \hat{S}\Psi'^*,$$

with the same operator $\hat{S}$. Substituting here from (116.2) $\Psi'^* = \hat{S}^*\Psi^*$, we have $\hat{S}\hat{S}^* = 1$, and by comparison with $\tilde{\hat{S}}\hat{S}^* = 1$ (116.3) we see that

$$\hat{S} = \tilde{\hat{S}}, \tag{116.4}$$

i.e. the operator $\hat{S}$ is the same as its transpose.

Now let Ψ_1 and Ψ_2 be the wave functions of two states of a system of colliding particles. The probability amplitude for the transition from the state Ψ_1 to the state Ψ_2 is proportional, by the general rules of quantum mechanics, to the integral $\int \Psi_2^*\hat{S}\Psi_1 \, dq$. Using (116.4), we have

$$\int \Psi_2^*\hat{S}\Psi_1 \, dq = \int \Psi_1\tilde{\hat{S}}\Psi_2^* \, dq = \int \Psi_1\hat{S}\Psi_2^* \, dq.$$

The integral on the right gives the probability amplitude for the transition from the state Ψ_2^* to the state Ψ_1^*, and, taking the squared moduli of the amplitudes, we have equation (116.1).

Let us change from probabilities to effective cross-sections. Let $d\sigma_{12}$ be the effective cross-section for a collision with a given change in the internal states of the particles and with a deviation of the velocity of their relative motion into the element of solid angle do_2 (in a system of co-ordinates in which the centre of mass of the particles is at rest). The total energy of the two particles is, of course, unaltered in the collision ($E_1 = E_2$). We introduce, however, an effective cross-section which formally relates to the interval dE_2 of energies in the final state. This cross-section may be written in the form

$$d\sigma_{12} \, . \, \delta(E_2 - E_1) \, dE_2. \tag{116.5}$$

The delta function ensures that the law of conservation of energy is obeyed. From the definition of the concept of effective cross-section, the latter is obtained by dividing the probability of the process concerned by the incident current density. This density is the product of the absolute magnitude of the relative velocity v_1 of the particles before the collision and the probability density $1/V$ (one particle in the volume V). Furthermore, it must be borne in mind that the effective cross-section (116.5) is referred to the whole range of scattering angles and energies, but the probability w_{12} refers to a strictly defined change in the magnitude and direction of the velocity. Hence, to obtain the effective cross-section from w_{12}, it must be multiplied by the number of quantum states belonging to the range of velocity directions and magnitudes concerned. Since the motion of the particle in a large part of space can be regarded as free, and therefore as quasi-classical, we can use the concept of "cells" in the phase space. Then the number of quantum states belonging to the volume $V . p_2^2 \, dp_2 \, do_2$ in phase space is

$$V . p_2^2 \, dp_2 \, do_2/(2\pi\hbar)^3.$$

Summarising the above arguments, we can write down the following relation between the effective cross-section and the probability:

$$d\sigma_{12}\delta(E_2-E_1)\,dE_2 = \frac{w_{12}}{v_1/V}\frac{V . p_2^2 \, dp_2 \, do_2}{(2\pi\hbar)^3}.$$

Hence

$$w_{12} = \frac{(2\pi\hbar)^3}{V^2}\frac{v_1 \, d\sigma_{12}\delta(E_2-E_1)\,dE_2}{p_2^2 \, dp_2 \, do_2}.$$

Writing $w_{2^*1^*}$ in the same form and equating it to w_{12}, we obtain

$$\frac{(2\pi\hbar)^3}{V^2}\frac{v_1 \, d\sigma_{12}\delta(E_2-E_1)\,dE_2}{p^2 \, dp_2 \, do_2} = \frac{(2\pi\hbar)^3}{V^2}\frac{v_2 \, d\sigma_{2^*1^*}\delta(E_1-E_2)\,dE_1}{p_1^2 \, dp_1 \, do_1}.$$

Taking into account that $dE_1/dp_1 = v_1$, $dE_2/dp_2 = v_2$, and cancelling the common factors, we finally have

$$d\sigma_{12}/p_2^2 \, do_2 = d\sigma_{2^*1^*}/p_1^2 \, do_1. \qquad (116.6)$$

The volume V does not appear in this relation, which therefore preserves the same form when we pass to the limit $V \to \infty$.

The relation (116.6) is the content of what is called the *principle of detailed balancing*. It relates the effective cross-sections for the two processes $1 \to 2$, $2^* \to 1^*$, which, although they are not direct and converse in the literal sense ($1 \to 2$, $2 \to 1$), are very close to being so in their physical significance.

From (116.6) we can obtain an analogous relation for the integrated effective cross-section. The cross-section integrated over all directions of the velocity after the collision, and also summed over all directions of the spins of the particles after the collision and averaged over the directions of the velocities and spins of the particles in their initial states, is what is usually of physical interest. We denote this cross-section by $\bar{\sigma}_{12}$:

$$\bar{\sigma}_{12} = \frac{1}{4\pi(2J_1^{(1)}+1)(2J_1^{(2)}+1)} \sum_{M_2^{(1)},M_2^{(2)}} \sum_{M_1^{(1)},M_1^{(2)}} \iint d\sigma_{12} do_1, \qquad (116.7)$$

where $J_1^{(1)}$, $J_1^{(2)}$ are the spins of the particles before the collision, and $M_1^{(1)}$, $M_1^{(2)}$, $M_2^{(1)}$, $M_2^{(2)}$ are the projections of their spins before and after the collision. Writing (116.6) in the form

$$p_1^2 \, d\sigma_{12} \, do_1 = p_2^2 \, d\sigma_{2^*1^*} \, do_2$$

and effecting the integration and summation, we obtain the relation

$$(2J_1^{(1)}+1)(2J_1^{(2)}+1)p_1^2\bar{\sigma}_{12} = (2J_2^{(1)}+1)(2J_2^{(2)}+1)p_2^2\bar{\sigma}_{2^*1^*}. \qquad (116.8)$$

When applied to an elastic collision of two particles, the relation (116.6) reduces to an identity (the effective cross-section depends only on the scattering angle). For elastic scattering in a field $U(x, y, z)$ which is not centrally symmetric, however, the relation

$$d\sigma_{12}/do_2 = d\sigma_{2^*1^*}/do_1 \qquad (116.9)$$

($p_1 = p_2$) gives some properties of the dependence of the effective cross-section on direction.

We may notice that, in the Born approximation, the relation (116.9) holds not only for the transitions $1 \to 2$, $2^* \to 1^*$, but also for direct and converse transitions in the literal sense ($1 \to 2$, $2 \to 1$):

$$d\sigma_{12}/do_2 = d\sigma_{21}/do_1. \qquad (116.10)$$

This follows at once from formula (110.9). It does not hold, however, in even the next approximation of perturbation theory.†

§117. The general theory of inelastic scattering

In the general case of inelastic scattering, the asymptotic form of the wave function of the system of the two colliding particles is a sum, in which there is a term corresponding to every possible result of the collision (taking into account the nature, internal state, and kinetic energy of the resulting particles); in addition there is, of course, a term describing the particles before the collision. Each of these terms is the product of the wave functions of the internal states of the particles, and of a function describing the free relative motion of the particles (in a system of co-ordinates in which the centre of mass is at rest). Among these terms there is, in particular, a term corresponding to elastic scattering. We shall consider this term, combining it with the

† At first sight, formula (43.5) for the second approximation of perturbation theory is also symmetrical with respect to an interchange of the initial and final states. In reality, this symmetry is lost, because the contour of integration is changed (as regards the direction in which it passes round the singular point) when we take the complex conjugate formula.

term which describes the incident particles. Separating the wave functions of the unchanged internal state of the particles, we obtain the wave function of the relative motion, which depends only on the distance between the particles and on the scattering angle. We denote this function by ψ, and seek its asymptotic form.

The calculations are effected in a manner exactly similar to those in §105. The only difference is that the asymptotic expression for the radial functions $R_l(r)$ cannot be taken in the form of a stationary wave (105.7). The stationary wave is the sum of ingoing and outgoing waves with the same amplitudes. In elastic scattering, this accords with the physical significance of the problem, but in inelastic scattering the amplitude of the outgoing wave must be less than that of the ingoing wave. Hence, instead of (105.7), we have

$$R_l(r) \approx a_l \frac{\alpha_l e^{i(kr-\frac{1}{2}l\pi)} - e^{-i(kr-\frac{1}{2}l\pi)}}{2ikr}, \tag{117.1}$$

where α_l is some (generally complex) quantity whose modulus is less than unity. For the asymptotic expression of the wave function ψ, we obtain the expression

$$\psi = \sum_l i^l(2l+1)\frac{\alpha_l e^{i(kr-\frac{1}{2}l\pi)} - e^{-i(kr-\frac{1}{2}l\pi)}}{2ikr}P_l(\cos\theta). \tag{117.2}$$

The coefficients are chosen so that, when the incident plane wave e^{ikz} is subtracted, only an outgoing wave remains. For the coefficient of e^{ikr}/r in this difference, we obtain the expression

$$f(\theta) = \frac{1}{2ik}\sum_{l=0}^{\infty}(2l+1)(\alpha_l-1)P_l(\cos\theta), \tag{117.3}$$

replacing formula (105.10). The square $|f(\theta)|^2$ determines the differential cross-section for the scattering of the particle in an unchanged state, i.e. the effective cross-section for elastic scattering. For the total elastic scattering cross-section, we have instead of (105.11) the formula

$$\sigma_{el} = \frac{\pi}{k^2}\sum_{l=0}^{\infty}(2l+1)|1-\alpha_l|^2. \tag{117.4}$$

The total inelastic scattering cross-section (for all possible final states of the particles) can also be expressed in terms of the quantities α_l. To do this, it is sufficient to notice that, for each value of l, the intensity of the outgoing wave is reduced in the ratio $|\alpha_l|^2$ in comparison with that of the ingoing wave. This reduction must be entirely due to inelastic scattering.

Hence it is clear that

$$\sigma_{\text{in}} = \frac{\pi}{k^2}\sum_{l=0}^{\infty}(2l+1)(1-|\alpha_l|^2), \tag{117.5}$$

and the total effective cross-section

$$\sigma = \sigma_{\text{el}}+\sigma_{\text{in}} = \frac{\pi}{k^2}\sum_{l}(2l+1)(2-\alpha_l-\alpha_l^*). \tag{117.6}$$

Taking the value of $f(\theta)$ for $\theta = 0$ and comparing with the expression (117.6), we have the relation

$$\text{Im}\, f(0) = k\sigma/4\pi, \tag{117.7}$$

which is a generalisation of the formula (105.12) obtained previously. Here $f(0)$ is, as before, the elastic scattering amplitude in the forward direction, but the total cross-section σ now includes the inelastic part also.

Each of the terms in the sums (117.4), (117.5) can be regarded as the effective cross-section for the scattering of a particle incident with a definite angular momentum l:

$$\sigma_{l,\text{el}} = (\pi/k^2)(2l+1)|1-\alpha_l|^2, \quad \sigma_{l,\text{in}} = (\pi/k^2)(2l+1)(1-|\alpha_l|^2). \tag{117.8}$$

If $|\alpha_l| = 1$, there is no inelastic scattering, and the elastic scattering cross-section must lie between the limits

$$0 \leqslant \sigma_{l,\text{el}} \leqslant 4\pi(2l+1)/k^2.$$

The lower limit is reached for $\alpha_l = 1$; both inelastic and elastic scattering are then absent. It is of interest that the presence of inelastic scattering necessarily results in the simultaneous presence of elastic scattering.

We may also notice the case $\alpha_l = 0$. Here

$$\sigma_{l,\text{in}} = \sigma_{l,\text{el}} = \pi(2l+1)/k^2,$$

i.e. the effective cross-sections for elastic and inelastic scattering are the same.

PROBLEM

Neutrons are scattered by a heavy nucleus whose "radius" a is large compared with the de Broglie wavelength of the neutrons (so that a quasi-classical discussion is possible). All neutrons incident with orbital angular momentum $l < l_0 \equiv ka$ (i.e. with impact parameter $\rho = \hbar l/\mu v = l/k < a$) undergo inelastic scattering, while those with $l > l_0$ do not interact with the nucleus at all. Determine the effective cross-section for elastic scattering through small angles.

SOLUTION. According to the conditions of the problem, we have $\alpha = 0$ for $l < l_0$ and $\alpha_l = 1$ for $l > l_0$. The elastic scattering amplitude is therefore

$$f(\theta) = -\frac{1}{2ik}\sum_{l=0}^{l_0}(2l+1)P_l(\cos\theta).$$

The chief part in the sum is played by the terms with large l (we recall that l_0 is large). We therefore write $2l$ in place of $2l+1$, use the approximate expression (49.6) for $P_l(\cos\theta)$ with θ small, and change from summation to integration:

$$f(\theta) = \frac{i}{k}\int_0^{l_0} lJ_0(l\theta)\,\mathrm{d}l = \frac{i}{k\theta}l_0J_1(l_0\theta) = \frac{ia}{\theta}J_1(ka\theta).$$

The effective cross-section is

$$\mathrm{d}\sigma_{\mathrm{el}} = \pi a^2\frac{J_1^2(ka\theta)}{\pi\theta^2}\,\mathrm{do}.$$

We note that this formula is formally identical with the expression† for the intensity of light undergoing Fraunhofer diffraction from a black sphere of radius a.

§118. Inelastic scattering of slow particles

The derivation of the limiting law of inelastic scattering at small velocities is carried out by a method exactly similar to that used in §108 for elastic scattering.

The scattering with $l = 0$ is the most important at small velocities (small k). The radial wave function with $l = 0$ (in the region $r_0 \ll r \ll 1/k$) is of the form

$$R_0 = c_1+c_2/r; \tag{118.1}$$

see (108.3). In elastic scattering, the constants c_1, c_2 can always be determined as real quantities, since both SCHRÖDINGER's equation and its boundary condition (the asymptotic form of the stationary wave) are real. In inelastic scattering, the condition at infinity (the asymptotic form (117.1)) is complex; hence the constants c_1, c_2 are in general complex also.

In the region $r \gtrsim 1/k$, the wave function (with $l = 0$) is of the form

$$R_0 = c_1[(ik\beta-1)e^{-ikr}+(ik\beta+1)e^{ikr}]/2ikr, \tag{118.2}$$

where $\beta = c_2/c_1$. The coefficients of the ingoing and outgoing waves are chosen so that for $rk \ll 1$ the function (118.2) becomes (118.1).

Comparing (118.2) with the general asymptotic expression (117.1), we find that

$$\alpha_0 = (1+ik\beta)/(1-ik\beta) \cong 1+2ik\beta.$$

Substituting this expression in the formulae

$$\sigma_{\mathrm{el}} \cong \sigma_{0,\mathrm{el}} = (\pi/k^2)|1-\alpha_0|^2, \qquad \sigma_{\mathrm{in}} \cong \sigma_{0,\mathrm{in}} = (\pi/k^2)(1-|\alpha_0|^2),$$

† See, for instance, *The Classical Theory of Fields*, §7–9, Problem 3, Addison-Wesley Press, Cambridge (Mass.) 1951; the problem of diffraction from a black sphere is equivalent to that of diffraction from a circular aperture cut in an opaque screen.

we have for the effective cross-sections the final expressions

$$\sigma_{el} = 4\pi\beta\beta^*, \tag{118.3}$$

$$\sigma_{in} = 2\pi i(\beta^*-\beta)/k. \tag{118.4}$$

Thus, for elastic scattering, we obtain our previous result: the effective cross-section is independent of the velocity. The effective cross-section for inelastic scattering, on the other hand, is inversely proportional to the velocity (BETHE 1935). Consequently, as the velocity diminishes, inelastic scattering becomes more and more important in comparison with elastic scattering.

In an entirely similar manner, we could investigate the velocity dependence of the effective cross-sections $\sigma_{l,in}$ with $l \neq 0$. We shall, however, merely give the result:

$$\sigma_{l,in} \sim k^{2l-1}. \tag{118.5}$$

The elastic cross-sections $\sigma_{l,el}$ are, as before, proportional to k^{4l}, i.e. they decrease with the velocity more rapidly than $\sigma_{l,in}$ with the same l.

The $1/v$ law for the effective inelastic scattering cross-section can easily be obtained by another method, which is more comprehensible, though less rigorous. To do this, we suppose that the inelastic scattering is proportional to the squared modulus, at the point $r = 0$, of the wave function of the incident particle when not perturbed by the scattering field. Physically, this supposition represents the fact that, for example, a slow neutron colliding with a nucleus can cause a reaction only by "penetrating" into the nucleus. Dividing $|\psi(0)|^2$ by the current density, we obtain (apart from a constant) the effective cross-section. Taking ψ in the form of a plane wave normalised to unit current density, we have $|\psi|^2 = 1/v$, which is the desired result.

The method just described makes it easy to deduce the limits of applicability of the $1/v$ law. It is evident that the scattering field must be such that the square $|\psi(0)|^2$ in that field is of the same order of magnitude as the squared modulus of the wave function for free motion. For this to be so, the field must fall off with distance more rapidly than $1/r^2$.

The important case of a Coulomb interaction between the colliding particles therefore requires special consideration. Near the origin, the Coulomb field noticeably affects the plane wave incident from infinity. The effective cross-section is obtained by multiplying $1/v$ by the ratio of the squared moduli of the Coulomb and free wave functions (at the origin); this ratio is given by formulae (113.10), (113.11). Thus we find (in Coulomb units)

$$\sigma_{in} \sim \pm 1/vk(e^{\pm 2\pi/k}-1);$$

the upper signs hold for a repulsive field, and the lower for an attractive field. For velocities which are small even in comparison with the Coulomb unit, we have in a repulsive field (in ordinary units)†

$$\sigma_{\text{in}} \sim e^{-2\pi Z_1 Z_2 e^2/\hbar v}/v^2, \tag{118.6}$$

where Z_1e, Z_2e are the charges on the colliding particles. In an attractive field,

$$\sigma_{\text{in}} \sim 1/v^2. \tag{118.7}$$

Finally, we may consider the case of inelastic scattering in which the relative velocity of the colliding particles before the collision is not small, but its value v' after the collision is small (for example, a nuclear reaction with the emission of a slow neutron).

This process is, in a sense, the converse of the inelastic scattering of a slow particle. The dependence of the cross-section on the velocity of the resulting particle is obtained immediately from the $1/v$ law, using the principle of detailed balancing. We conclude at once from (116.8) that, for the process in question,

$$\sigma_{\text{in}} \sim v', \tag{118.8}$$

i.e. the effective cross-section is proportional to the velocity of the resulting slow particle.

§119. Breit and Wigner's formula

A system which can disintegrate does not, strictly speaking, have a discrete energy spectrum. The particle (or particles) leaving it when it disintegrates recedes to infinity; in this sense, the motion of the system is infinite, and hence the energy spectrum is continuous.

It may happen, however, that the disintegration probability of the system is very small. The simplest example of this kind is given by a particle surrounded by a fairly high and wide potential barrier. Another example is a neutron in a heavy nucleus. Although the total energy of the particles in the nucleus is large, during the greater part of the time it is distributed more or less uniformly among the particles, so that each of them has an energy which is insufficient to overcome the attraction of the remaining particles and so allow the particle considered to leave the nucleus. Only comparatively rarely is enough energy for this purpose concentrated on one particle.

For such systems with a small disintegration probability, we can introduce the concept of *quasi-stationary* states, in which the particles move "inside the system" for a considerable period of time, leaving it only when a fairly long time interval τ has elapsed; τ may be called the *lifetime* of the almost stationary state concerned ($\tau \sim 1/w$, where w is the disintegration probability per unit time). The energy spectrum of these states will be *quasi-discrete*; it consists of a series of broadened levels, whose "width" is related

† The exponential factor is the probability of passing through the Coulomb potential barrier (see §50, Problem 2).

to the lifetime by $\Gamma \sim \hbar/\tau$ (see (44.7)). The widths of the quasi-discrete levels are small compared with the distances between them.

In discussing the quasi-stationary states, we can use the following somewhat unusual method. Until now we have always considered solutions of SCHRÖDINGER's equation with a boundary condition requiring the finiteness of the wave function at infinity. Instead of this, we shall now look for solutions which represent an outgoing spherical wave at infinity; this corresponds to the particle finally leaving the system when it disintegrates. Since such a boundary condition is complex, we cannot assert that the eigenvalues of the energy must be real. On the contrary, by solving SCHRÖDINGER's equation, we obtain a set of complex values, which we write in the form

$$E = E_0 - i\Gamma, \tag{119.1}$$

where E_0 and Γ are two constants, which are positive (see below).

It is easy to see the physical significance of the complex energy values. The time factor in the wave function of a quasi-stationary state is of the form

$$e^{-(i/\hbar)Et} = e^{-(i/\hbar)E_0 t} e^{-(\Gamma/\hbar)t}.$$

Hence all the probabilities given by the squared modulus of the wave function decrease† with time as $e^{-(2\Gamma/\hbar)t}$. In particular, the probability of finding the particle "inside the system" decreases according to this law. Thus Γ determines the lifetime of the state; the disintegration probability per unit time is

$$w = 2\Gamma/\hbar. \tag{119.2}$$

The quantity Γ is‡ the *width* of the level of energy E_0.

At first sight there seems to be a contradiction between the diminution of the square $|\psi|^2$ with time and the fact that the normalisation integral $\int |\psi|^2 \, dV$ must be a constant, as follows immediately from the wave equation. In fact, however, there is no contradiction, since the normalising integral for the wave functions in question diverges. This is seen from the fact that, at large distances, the wave function (an outgoing wave) contains the factor e^{ikr} (where $k = \sqrt{[2\mu(E_0 - i\Gamma)]}/\hbar$, im $k < 0$), which increases exponentially as $r \to \infty$.

We shall normalise the wave function by the condition that the integral $\int |\psi|^2 \, dV$, taken over the volume "inside the system", is unity. For an arbitrary energy E, the asymptotic form of the radial part of the wave function (for a given angular momentum l of the particle about the origin) is a combination of ingoing and outgoing waves:

$$R_l \approx [\alpha_l(E) e^{-ikr} + \alpha_l^*(E) e^{ikr}]/r, \tag{119.3}$$

where the coefficient $\alpha_l(E)$ may be regarded as a function of the complex

† We see from this the physical necessity for Γ to be positive. It is, in fact, automatically positive (as may be shown from the wave equation) if the given condition is imposed at infinity.

‡ Often, however, a quantity twice this is called the width of the level and denoted by Γ.

variable E. The coefficients of the ingoing and outgoing waves are written so that R_l is real for real E (as it should be for the wave functions of the true stationary states).

For E equal to any of the complex eigenvalues $E_0 - i\Gamma$ (for given l), only the outgoing wave must remain in the asymptotic expression for the wave function. In other words, the eigenvalues of the energy are zeros of the function $\alpha_l(E)$. Thus

$$\alpha_l(E_0 - i\Gamma) = 0. \tag{119.4}$$

For values of the energy which lie close to an eigenvalue, we can expand $\alpha_l(E)$ as a series of powers of the difference $E-(E_0-i\Gamma)$. The zero-order term of the expansion vanishes by (119.4); taking only the first-order term, we have

$$\alpha_l(E) = a_l.(E-E_0+i\Gamma), \tag{119.5}$$

where a_l is a constant. Substituting this expression in (119.3), we obtain the following formula for the wave function of a state close to a quasi-stationary one:

$$R_l = [a_l(E-E_0+i\Gamma)e^{-ikr} + a_l^*(E-E_0-i\Gamma)e^{ikr}]/r. \tag{119.6}$$

The modulus of the constant a_l is easily determined by noticing that, in the quasi-stationary state with the normalisation we have adopted (one particle inside the system), the total probability current in the outgoing wave must be equal to the decay probability per unit time. For $E = E_0 - i\Gamma$, the function (119.6) reduces to

$$R_l = -2i\Gamma a_l^* e^{ikr}/r.$$

The corresponding total probability current is $v|2i\Gamma a_l^*|^2$, where the velocity $v = \sqrt{(2E_0/\mu)}$ (we suppose that $\Gamma \gg E_0$). Equating this current to the probability (119.2), we find

$$|a_l|^2 = 1/2\hbar v\Gamma. \tag{119.7}$$

The asymptotic form of the ordinary wave function of the continuous spectrum with the real energy E (a stationary spherical wave), normalised by the delta function of energy, is

$$\begin{aligned} R_l &\approx \sqrt{\frac{2}{\pi\hbar v}}\frac{1}{r}\sin(kr - \tfrac{1}{2}l\pi + \delta_l) \\ &= \frac{i}{\sqrt{(2\pi\hbar v)}}\frac{1}{r}[e^{-i(kr-\frac{1}{2}l\pi+\delta_l)} - e^{i(kr-\frac{1}{2}l\pi+\delta_l)}]. \end{aligned} \tag{119.8}$$

The ratio of the squared modulus of the normalisation coefficient in this formula to that of the corresponding coefficient in the function (119.6), with a_l given by (119.7), is

$$\Gamma/\pi[(E-E_0)^2+\Gamma^2]. \tag{119.9}$$

Since the function (119.6) is so normalised that the integral of its squared modulus over the region "inside the system" is unity, it is clear that the expression (119.9) gives the value of this integral for the state described by the wave function (119.8). We may point out that "far from the resonance" ($|E-E_0| \gg \Gamma$) this quantity is proportional to the width Γ of the level, while "close to the resonance" ($|E-E_0| \ll \Gamma$) it is inversely proportional to Γ.

Comparing (119.6) and (119.8), we see that the phase δ_l of the function (119.6) is determined by the relation

$$e^{2i\delta_l} = e^{2i\delta_l^{(0)}}\frac{E-E_0-i\Gamma}{E-E_0+i\Gamma} = e^{2i\delta_l^{(0)}} - e^{2i\delta_l^{(0)}}\frac{2i\Gamma}{E-E_0+i\Gamma}, \qquad (119.10)$$

where

$$e^{2i\delta_l^{(0)}} = -e^{i\pi l}a^*/a. \qquad (119.11)$$

For $|E-E_0| \gg \Gamma$, the phase δ_l is equal to $\delta_l^{(0)}$; in other words, $\delta_l^{(0)}$ is the value of the phase "far from the resonance".

It is seen from formula (119.10) that, in the region of the resonance, δ_l varies considerably with energy. If we rewrite this formula as

$$\delta_l = \delta_l^{(0)} + \tan^{-1}[\Gamma/(E_0-E)],$$

we see at once that, in passing through the entire region of the resonance (from $E \ll E_0$ to $E \gg E_0$), the phase changes by π.

The results obtained above enable us to discuss the problem of the elastic scattering of a particle whose energy E is close to some quasi-discrete level E_0 of the *compound system* formed by the scattering system together with the scattered particle (in the case of scattering by a nucleus, we speak of a *compound nucleus*). In the general formula (105.10) for the scattering amplitude, we have to substitute the expression (119.10) in the term for the angular momentum value l to which the level E_0 corresponds. We then obtain

$$f(\theta) = f^{(0)}(\theta) - \frac{2l+1}{k}\frac{\Gamma}{E-E_0+i\Gamma}e^{2i\delta_l^{(0)}}P_l(\cos\theta), \qquad (119.12)$$

where $f^{(0)}(\theta)$ is the scattering amplitude far from the resonance (given by formula (105.10) with $\delta_l = \delta_l^{(0)}$ in all the terms of the sum).

The formula which we have obtained gives the elastic scattering in a resonance region. Its range of applicability is restricted only by the requirement that the difference $|E-E_0|$ is small compared with the distance D between neighbouring quasi-discrete levels of the compound system:

$$|E-E_0| \ll D. \qquad (119.13)$$

The amplitude $f^{(0)}(\theta)$ is often called the *potential scattering amplitude*, and the other term in formula (119.12) the *resonance scattering amplitude*.

If we are dealing with the scattering of a charged particle (for instance, a proton) by a nucleus, we must use the expression (112.11) for $e^{2i\delta_l^{(0)}}$. In ordinary units this has the form

$$e^{2i\delta_l^{(0)}} = \Gamma(l+1+iZze^2\mu/\hbar^2k)/\Gamma(l+1-iZze^2\mu/\hbar^2k). \tag{119.14}$$

Here Ze is the charge on the nucleus, ze that on the scattered particle, μ the reduced mass of particle and nucleus, and $\Gamma(x)$ the gamma function.

The scattering of neutral particles (scattering of neutrons by nuclei) is of particular interest. The forces of interaction between a neutron and a nucleus fall off rapidly with distance, and if the neutrons are sufficiently slow we can apply the results of §108 (the neutron velocity must be such that $\hbar/p$ is large compared with the "radius" of the nucleus). In the scattering of slow particles, only the scattering with $l = 0$ is important; we shall suppose that the level E_0 belongs, in fact, to the motion with angular momentum $l = 0$. The potential scattering amplitude $f^{(0)}(\theta)$ is now simply some real constant β (see §108). In the second term, we put $l = 0$ and replace $e^{2i\delta_l^{(0)}}$ by unity (since $\delta_l^{(0)} \ll 1$). Thus we obtain the following formula for the elastic scattering amplitude when slow neutrons are scattered by nuclei:

$$f(\theta) = \beta - \Gamma/k(E-E_0+i\Gamma). \tag{119.15}$$

In all the preceding derivations (from formula (119.5) onwards) it has been tacitly supposed that the energy E_0 of the level itself is not too small. The case where E_0 is small in comparison with the distance between the levels requires special investigation. We shall here consider collisions between slow neutrons and nuclei, when only the scattering with $l = 0$ is important.

The coefficient $\alpha(E)$ in the wave function (119.3) now has to be expanded in powers of the energy E; we omit, for brevity, the suffix $l = 0$ in α_l. In order to determine the nature of the first few terms in the expansion, we note that the expression (119.3), regarded as a function of the complex variable E, must be a one-valued function (by the uniqueness of the solution of SCHRÖDINGER's equation for any given E). If, starting from some positive real value of E, we go completely round the origin in the complex plane, returning to the initial value, the square root $\sqrt{E}$ changes sign, and therefore so does $k = \sqrt{(2\mu E)}/\hbar$. The function (119.3), on the other hand, must remain unchanged. In other words, when $\sqrt{E}$ is replaced by $-\sqrt{E}$, the function $\alpha(E)$ must become $\alpha^*(E)$. It follows from these considerations that the first terms in the expansion of $\alpha(E)$ are of the form

$$\alpha(E) = a.(E-\epsilon_0+i\gamma\sqrt{E}), \tag{119.16}$$

where ϵ_0 and γ are real constants.† This expression replaces the formula (119.5) in this case; the remaining formulae must be changed correspondingly (replacing everywhere E_0 by ϵ_0 and Γ by $\gamma\sqrt{E}$). Thus the elastic scattering

† The relation between the constants ϵ_0 and γ, the energy E_0 of the level, and its width Γ, is given by the equation $\alpha_l(E_0-i\Gamma) = 0$, i.e. $E_0-i\Gamma-\epsilon_0+i\gamma\sqrt{E} = 0$. If, in particular $\epsilon_0 \gg \gamma^2$, we have $E_0 = \epsilon_0$, $\Gamma = \gamma\sqrt{E_0}$.

amplitude for slow neutrons now has the form

$$f(\theta) = \beta - \hbar\gamma/\sqrt{(2\mu)}(E-\epsilon_0+i\gamma\sqrt{E}); \tag{119.17}$$

we have substituted $k = \sqrt{(2\mu E)}/\hbar$, where μ is the reduced mass of the neutron and nucleus. As $E \to 0$, the scattering amplitude tends to a constant, as the general theory requires (the passage to the limit $E \to 0$, of course, cannot be made in formula (119.15)). We may note that this result could also be used to prove the necessity of replacing Γ by $\gamma\sqrt{E}$ for small E.

Formula (119.17) is applicable not only to scattering in the presence of a quasi-discrete level close to zero, but also to the case where there is an actual discrete level of the compound system close to zero; we denote this by $-\epsilon$. The relation between ϵ and the constants ϵ_0 and γ can be determined from the condition that the scattering amplitude becomes infinite for $E = -\epsilon$ (§107). The value of the square root $\sqrt{-\epsilon}$ must here be taken as $+i\sqrt{\epsilon}$, as shown in §107. Thus we have the condition

$$\epsilon+\gamma\sqrt{\epsilon}+\epsilon_0 = 0. \tag{119.18}$$

For $\epsilon_0 < 0$, this equation gives a real value for ϵ, in accordance with the existence of a true discrete level, whose width is zero. For negative ϵ_0 not too close to zero, we have from (119.18) simply $\epsilon = -\epsilon_0$.

We shall show how the formula (119.17) is related to WIGNER's formula (109.7). Suppose $|\epsilon_0| \ll \gamma^2$. For energies $E \ll \gamma^2$ we can neglect the first term E in the denominator of the resonance scattering amplitude (119.17). Next, in view of the smallness of this denominator, we can neglect the potential scattering amplitude β altogether. We then have for the effective cross-section the expression

$$4\pi|f|^2 = 2\pi\hbar^2/\mu(E+\epsilon_0^2/\gamma^2),$$

which is the same as WIGNER's formula, the energy of the level being $\epsilon = \epsilon_0^2/\gamma^2$; this value is also obtained from equation (119.18) when $\epsilon_0 \ll \gamma^2$. This level is real or virtual (see the end of §109), according as the constant ϵ_0 is negative or positive; for positive ϵ_0, equation (119.18) has no solution (we recall that $\sqrt{\epsilon}$ must be positive).

The whole of the above discussion presupposes that the scattering is entirely elastic. If inelastic scattering is possible as well as elastic (as usually happens in nuclear processes), the investigation given above requires modification. Following the general theory explained in §117, we must write the asymptotic expression for the wave function describing the incident and elastically scattered particles. This expression has the form of a sum of ingoing and outgoing waves, but the amplitudes of these waves need not be the same in absolute magnitude, as they are in (119.3). Expanding each in a series, we obtain an expression analogous to (119.6):

$$rR_l(r) = a_l(E-E_0+i\Gamma)e^{-ikr}+a_l'(E-E_0+b_l+ic_l)e^{ikr},$$

where the a_l, a_l' are complex constants, and the b_l, c_l are real constants;

the coefficient of the ingoing wave must vanish, as before, for $E = E_0 - i\Gamma$. Comparing this expression with formula (117.1), we can determine the quantity α_l in the latter, and then the effective cross-sections for elastic and inelastic scattering, using the general formulae of §117. We may note that the constants a_l, a_l', b_l, c_l must satisfy certain inequalities derived from the condition $|\alpha_l|^2 < 1$.

The formulae thus obtained are rather cumbersome and are of little interest. They are simpler in the case most important in nuclear physics, where the inelastic scattering occurs only via an intermediate stage, the formation of a compound nucleus. Because of the very rapid fall-off of the specifically nuclear forces of interaction, inelastic scattering which is accompanied by a reconstruction of the nucleus usually occurs in such a way that the incident particle is first absorbed by the nucleus. The compound nucleus so formed then decays in some manner, passing into a stable state.

Since the inelastic scattering is of this nature, we can say that it has no effect on the potential elastic scattering (which does not depend on the nearness of E to the level E_0), and merely alters the magnitude of the resonance scattering. In order to take account of this in mathematical terms, we rewrite the expression (119.6) for the wave function in the absence of inelastic scattering in the form

$$rR_l = (E - E_0 + i\Gamma)(a_l e^{-ikr} + a_l^* e^{ikr}) - 2i\Gamma a_l^* e^{ikr}.$$

Here the first term clearly corresponds to the potential elastic scattering; the phase of the scattered wave in this term is $\delta_l^{(0)}$, by (119.11). The second term, consequently, corresponds to the resonance scattering. Taking $2\Gamma/\hbar$ to be the total probability of any decay (elastic or inelastic) of the compound nucleus, we now have to replace Γ in the resonance term by some other quantity $\Gamma_e < \Gamma$, where $2\Gamma_e/\hbar$ denotes the probability of elastic decay. We then obtain

$$R_l = \frac{E - E_0 + i\Gamma}{r}\left\{ a_l e^{-ikr} + a_l^* \left(1 - \frac{2i\Gamma_e}{E - E_0 + i\Gamma}\right) e^{ikr} \right\}.$$

A comparison with the general expression (117.1) shows that the quantity α_l in the latter is, in this case,

$$\alpha_l = e^{2i\delta_l^{(0)}}\left[1 - \frac{2i\Gamma_e}{E - E_0 + i\Gamma}\right]. \tag{119.19}$$

Having found α_l, we can immediately determine all the effective cross-sections. Substituting in (117.3) the expression (119.19) for one of the α_l (with the l which corresponds to the level E_0), and $\alpha_l = e^{2i\delta_l^{(0)}}$ for the remainder, we find the elastic scattering amplitude in the form

$$f(\theta) = f^{(0)}(\theta) - \frac{2l+1}{k}\frac{\Gamma_e}{E - E_0 + i\Gamma} e^{2i\delta_l^{(0)}} P_l(\cos\theta), \tag{119.20}$$

which differs from (119.12) in that Γ in the numerator of the resonance scattering amplitude is replaced by Γ_e.

The effective inelastic scattering cross-section is obtained by substituting the same values for the α_l in the general formula (117.5). Only one term remains out of the sum over l in (117.5); this is quite natural, in view of the purely resonance character of the inelastic scattering. After an elementary transformation, we obtain

$$\sigma_{\text{in}} = (2l+1)\frac{4\pi}{k^2}\frac{\Gamma_e\Gamma_u}{(E-E_0)^2+\Gamma^2}, \tag{119.21}$$

where $\Gamma_u = \Gamma - \Gamma_e$. Evidently $2\Gamma_u/\hbar$ is the probability for an inelastic decay of the compound nucleus. The quantities Γ_e and Γ_u are often called the *elastic* and *inelastic widths* of the level.†

It is of interest to find the value of the effective inelastic scattering cross-section integrated over the range of energies near the resonance value $E = E_0$. Since σ_{in} falls off rapidly as $|E-E_0|$ increases, the integration over E can be extended from $-\infty$ to $+\infty$, and we obtain

$$\int \sigma_{\text{in}}\, dE = (2l+1)\frac{4\pi^2}{k^2}\frac{\Gamma_e\Gamma_u}{\Gamma}. \tag{119.22}$$

When slow neutrons are scattered by nuclei, the elastic scattering amplitude is of the form

$$f(\theta) = \beta - \Gamma_e/k(E-E_0+i\Gamma),$$

instead of (119.15). The total effective elastic scattering cross-section $\sigma_{\text{el}} = 4\pi|f|^2$ is

$$\sigma_{\text{el}} = 4\pi\beta^2 + \frac{4\pi}{k^2}\frac{\Gamma_e^2 - 2\beta k\Gamma_e(E-E_0)}{(E-E_0)^2+\Gamma^2}. \tag{119.23}$$

The term $\sigma_0 = 4\pi\beta^2$ may be called the *effective potential scattering cross-section*; we see, however, that in the resonance region there is interference between the potential scattering and the resonance scattering.

In the immediate neighbourhood of the level, the potential scattering may be neglected,‡ and the formula for the effective elastic scattering cross-section for slow neutrons becomes

$$\sigma_{\text{el}} = \frac{4\pi}{k^2}\frac{\Gamma_e^2}{(E-E_0)^2+\Gamma^2}. \tag{119.24}$$

† If, in a given collision, several different types of inelastic scattering are possible, σ_{in} is the total effective cross-section for all these types together. For each type separately a similar formula is obtained, Γ_u being replaced by the part of the level width that relates to the process in question.

‡ We recall that the product βk, which is equal to the phase $\delta_0^{(0)}$, is supposed small.

The total effective cross-section for both elastic and inelastic scattering is

$$\sigma = \sigma_{el}+\sigma_{in} = \frac{4\pi}{k^2}\frac{\Gamma_e\Gamma}{(E-E_0)^2+\Gamma^2}, \tag{119.25}$$

where σ_{in} is got from (119.21) with $l = 0$.†

If the energy of the level is small ($E_0 \ll D$), then, as we have already remarked, the formulae in which the width of the level is regarded as constant are invalid. For the same reasons as above, we must replace E_0 in formulae (119.19)–(119.25) by some constant ϵ_0 related to it, and Γ_e by $\gamma_e\sqrt{E}$. The inelastic width Γ_u must be regarded as constant, as before. This is seen from the fact that only with this condition will σ_{in} (119.21) increase as $1/\sqrt{E}$ for $E \to 0$, as is required by the general theory of inelastic scattering (see §118).‡

Finally, it remains for us to examine the effect of the spins of the colliding particles on the scattering, an effect which we have entirely neglected so far. In the general case, taking the spin into account leads to very cumbersome formulae, and we shall restrict ourselves to the simplest, though important, case, that of the scattering of slow neutrons. Let i be the spin of the nucleus, and $s = \frac{1}{2}$ that of the neutron; we suppose that $i \neq 0$, since otherwise there is no change in the formulae. Since the scattering occurs with orbital angular momentum $l = 0$, the angular momentum of the compound nucleus is obtained by adding $\mathbf{i}$ and $\mathbf{s}$, i.e. it can take the values $j = i\pm\frac{1}{2}$. Each quasi-discrete level of the compound nucleus belongs, in general, to one definite value of j. Hence the effective cross-section for inelastic scattering is obtained by multiplying the expression (119.21) (with $l = 0$) by the probability that the system nucleus + neutron will have the necessary value of j.

We shall suppose that either the incident current of neutrons is "unpolarised" (i.e. the spins of the neutrons in it are oriented entirely at random), or the nuclear spins in the irradiated substance are "unpolarised", or both. Altogether there are $(2i+1)(2s+1)$ possible orientations of the pair of spins $\mathbf{i}$, $\mathbf{s}$. Of these, $2j+1$ orientations correspond to a given value j of the total angular momentum. Assuming that all orientations are equally probable, we find that the probability of the given value of j is

$$(2j+1)/(2s+1)(2i+1) = (2j+1)/2(2i+1).$$

Hence the effective inelastic scattering cross-section is

$$\sigma_{in} = \frac{2j+1}{2i+1}\frac{2\pi}{k^2}\frac{\Gamma_e\Gamma_u}{(E-E_0)^2+\Gamma^2}. \tag{119.26}$$

In elastic scattering we have to take into account, firstly, that resonance

† The formulae (119.24), (119.25) were obtained by G. Breit and E. Wigner (1936).
‡ The necessity of this treatment of the widths Γ_e and Γ_u at low energies was pointed out by Bethe and Placzek (1937).

scattering occurs only for a definite value of j and, secondly, that the potential scattering amplitude β also depends on j. The total effective elastic scattering cross-section is

$$\sigma_{\text{el}} = \sum \frac{2j+1}{(2s+1)(2i+1)} \sigma_{\text{el}}^{(j)}, \tag{119.27}$$

where $\sigma_{\text{el}}^{(j)}$ is the effective scattering cross-section with a given value of j. In a term of the sum for which j corresponds to a resonance level, we must substitute the expression (119.23), while for other j the scattering is purely potential scattering, i.e. $\sigma_{\text{el}}^{(j)} = \sigma_0^{(j)} = 4\pi\beta_j^2$. Thus we find

$$\sigma_{\text{el}} = \sigma_0 + \frac{2j+1}{2i+1}\frac{2\pi}{k^2}\frac{\Gamma_e^2 - k\sqrt{(\sigma_0^{(j)}/\pi)}\Gamma_e(E-E_0)}{(E-E_0)^2+\Gamma^2}, \tag{119.28}$$

where

$$\sigma_0 = \sum_j \frac{2j+1}{(2s+1)(2i+1)}\sigma_0^{(j)} = \frac{i+1}{2i+1}\sigma_0^{(i+\frac{1}{2})} + \frac{i}{2i+1}\sigma_0^{(i-\frac{1}{2})} \tag{119.29}$$

is the total potential scattering cross-section.

§120. **Inelastic collisions between fast electrons and atoms**

A method similar to that used for elastic scattering can be applied to calculate the effective cross-section for inelastic collisions of fast electrons with atoms. The condition for the Born approximation to be applicable to inelastic collisions is, as before, that the velocity of the incident electron should be large compared with those of the atomic electrons.†

An inelastic collision is accompanied by a change in the internal state of the atom. The atom may go from the normal state into an excited state of the discrete or continuous spectrum; the latter case signifies an ionisation of the atom. In deriving the general formulae, we can consider these two cases together.

We start (as in §110) from the general formula for the transition probability between states of the continuous spectrum, and apply it to the system consisting of the incident electron and the atom. Let **p**, **p**′ be the momenta of the incident electron before and after the collision, and E_0, E_n the corresponding energies of the atom. For the transition probability, we have instead of (110.6) the expression

$$dw_n = \frac{2\pi}{\hbar}\left|U_{E_n\mathbf{p}'}^{E_0\mathbf{p}}\right|^2 \delta\left(\frac{p'^2-p^2}{2\mu}+E_n-E_0\right) dp'_x\,dp'_y\,dp'_z, \tag{120.1}$$

† The energy loss in the collision may have any value. If the electron loses a considerable part of its energy in the collision, the atom is ionised, the energy being transferred to one of its electrons. However, we shall always regard as the scattered electron that which has the greater velocity after the collision; thus, if the velocity of the incident electron is large, that of the scattered electron is large also.

where $U_{En\mathbf{p}'}^{E_0\mathbf{p}}$ is the matrix element of the energy of interaction between the incident electron and the atom,

$$U = Ze^2/r - \sum_{a=1}^{Z} e^2/|\mathbf{r}-\mathbf{r}_a|;$$

here $\mathbf{r}$ is the radius vector of the incident electron, $\mathbf{r}_a$ those of the atomic electrons; the origin is at the nucleus of the atom, and μ is the mass of the electron.

The wave functions $\psi_{\mathbf{p}}$, $\psi_{\mathbf{p}'}$ of the electron are determined by the previous formulae (110.7), (110.8); then dw is the effective cross-section dσ for the collision. The wave functions of the atom in the initial and final states we denote by ψ_0, ψ_n. If the final state of the atom belongs to the discrete spectrum, then, ψ_n (like ψ_0) is normalised to unity in the usual manner. If, on the other hand, the atom enters a state of the continuous spectrum, the wave function is normalised by the delta function of the parameters ν which determine these states (these parameters may be, for instance, the energy of the atom, and the momentum components of the electron which leaves the atom in the ionisation). The effective cross-sections thus obtained give the probability of a collision in which the atom enters states of the continuous spectrum lying in the range of parameters between ν and $\nu+\mathrm{d}\nu$.

Integration of (120.1) over the absolute magnitude p' gives

$$\mathrm{d}\sigma_n = \frac{2\pi\mu p'}{\hbar}|U_{n\mathbf{p}'}^{0\mathbf{p}}|^2 \mathrm{d}o',$$

where p' is determined from the law of conservation of energy:

$$(p^2-p'^2)/2\mu = E_n - E_0. \tag{120.2}$$

Substituting in the matrix element $U_{n\mathbf{p}'}^{0\mathbf{p}}$ the wave functions of the electron from (110.7), (110.8), we obtain

$$\mathrm{d}\sigma_n = \frac{\mu^2}{4\pi^2\hbar^4}\frac{p'}{p}\left|\int\int Ue^{i\mathbf{q}\cdot\mathbf{r}}\psi_n^*\psi_0\,\mathrm{d}\tau\mathrm{d}V\right|^2 \mathrm{d}o, \tag{120.3}$$

where $\mathrm{d}\tau = \mathrm{d}V_1\,\mathrm{d}V_2 \ldots \mathrm{d}V_Z$ is the element of configuration space of the Z electrons in the atom, and we omit the prime to do. In this form, this is a general formula of perturbation theory, applicable not only to collisions of electrons with an atom, but also to any inelastic collisions of two particles, and gives the effective scattering cross-section in a system of co-ordinates in which the centre of mass of the particles is at rest; μ is then the reduced mass of the two particles. For $n = 0$ and $p = p'$, (120.3) becomes the formula for the effective elastic scattering cross-section.

In collisions of an atom with electrons, the system of co-ordinates in which the centre of mass is at rest can, as we have already remarked, be identified with a system in which the atom is at rest; we shall, in fact, use this latter system below.

Since the functions ψ_n and ψ_0 are orthogonal, the term in U which contains the interaction Ze^2/r with the nucleus vanishes on integration over τ, and so we have for inelastic collisions

$$d\sigma_n = \frac{\mu^2}{4\pi^2\hbar^4}\frac{p'}{p}\left|\sum_a \iint \frac{e^2}{|\mathbf{r}-\mathbf{r}_a|} e^{i\mathbf{q}\cdot\mathbf{r}}\psi_n^*\psi_0 \, d\tau dV\right|^2 do. \qquad (120.3a)$$

The integration over V can be effected as in §115. The integral

$$\phi_{\mathbf{q}}(\mathbf{r}_a) = \int e^{i\mathbf{q}\cdot\mathbf{r}} \, dV/|\mathbf{r}-\mathbf{r}_a|$$

is formally the same as the potential at a point $\mathbf{r}_a$ due to charges distributed in space with density $\rho_{\mathbf{q}}(\mathbf{r}) = e^{i\mathbf{q}\cdot\mathbf{r}}$. Hence it satisfies Poisson's equation

$$\Delta\phi_{\mathbf{q}}(\mathbf{r}) = -4\pi e^{i\mathbf{q}\cdot\mathbf{r}},$$

whence we conclude at once that

$$\phi_{\mathbf{q}}(\mathbf{r}_a) \equiv \int e^{i\mathbf{q}\cdot\mathbf{r}} \, dV/|\mathbf{r}-\mathbf{r}_a| = 4\pi e^{i\mathbf{q}\cdot\mathbf{r}_a}/q^2. \qquad (120.4)$$

Substituting this expression in (120.3a), we finally obtain the following general expression for the effective inelastic scattering cross-section†:

$$d\sigma_n = \left(\frac{e^2\mu}{\hbar^2}\right)^2 \frac{4k'}{kq^4}\left|\int \sum_a e^{i\mathbf{q}\cdot\mathbf{r}_a}\psi_n^*\psi_0 \, d\tau\right|^2 do; \qquad (120.5)$$

here we have introduced, in place of the momenta $\mathbf{p}'$, $\mathbf{p}$, the wave vectors $\mathbf{k}' = \mathbf{p}'/\hbar$, $\mathbf{k} = \mathbf{p}/\hbar$, which are more convenient in subsequent calculations. This formula gives the probability of a collision in which the electron is scattered into an element of solid angle do and the atom enters the nth excited state. The vector $\hbar\mathbf{q}$ is the momentum given to the atom by the electron in the collision.

In effecting the calculations, it is more convenient to refer the effective cross-section, not to the element of solid angle, but to the element dq of the absolute magnitudes of the vector $\mathbf{q}$. The vector $\mathbf{q}$ is defined by $\mathbf{q} = \mathbf{k}-\mathbf{k}'$; for its absolute magnitude we have

$$q^2 = k^2+k'^2-2kk' \cos\vartheta. \qquad (120.6)$$

Hence, for given k, k', i.e. for a given loss of energy by the electron,

$$q dq = kk' \sin\vartheta \, d\vartheta = (kk'/2\pi) \, do. \qquad (120.7)$$

Substituting in formula (120.5) $do = 2\pi(q \, dq/kk')$, we have

$$d\sigma_n = 8\pi\left(\frac{e^2}{\hbar v}\right)^2 \frac{dq}{q^3}\left|\int \sum_a e^{i\mathbf{q}\cdot\mathbf{r}_a}\psi_n^*\psi_0 \, d\tau\right|^2. \qquad (120.8)$$

† This, like most of the subsequent formulae in §§120–122, was obtained by Bethe (1930).

The vector $\mathbf{q}$ plays an important part in all the following calculations. Let us examine more closely its relation to the scattering angle ϑ and to the energy $E_n - E_0$ transferred in the collision. We shall see below that the most important collisions are those which cause scattering through small angles ($\vartheta \ll 1$), with a transfer of energy which is small in comparison with the energy $E = \frac{1}{2}\mu v^2$ of the incident electron: $E_n - E_0 \ll E$. The difference $k - k'$ in the absolute magnitudes of the wave vectors of the incident and scattered electrons is in this case also small ($k - k' \ll k$), and, writing

$$E_n - E_0 = \hbar^2(k^2 - k'^2)/2\mu \cong \hbar^2 k(k-k')/\mu,$$

we find that

$$k - k' \cong \mu(E_n - E_0)/\hbar^2 k = (E_n - E_0)/\hbar v.$$

Since ϑ is small, we have from (120.6)

$$q^2 \cong (k-k')^2 + kk'\vartheta^2,$$

and finally

$$q = \sqrt{[\{(E_n - E_0)/\hbar v\}^2 + (k\vartheta)^2]}. \tag{120.9}$$

Let us apply the general formula (120.8) to the case of small q ($qa_0 \ll 1$). This condition means, as we see from (120.9), that the angle of deviation is small:

$$\vartheta \ll v_0/v,$$

and that the excitation energies of the atom are not too large.† (In these inequalities, a_0 and v_0 are of the order of magnitude of the dimensions of the atom and the velocity of the atomic electrons respectively.) In this case we can expand the exponential factors $e^{i\mathbf{q}\cdot\mathbf{r}_a}$ as series of powers of $\mathbf{q}$:

$$e^{i\mathbf{q}\cdot\mathbf{r}_a} \cong 1 + i\mathbf{q}\cdot\mathbf{r}_a = 1 + iqx_a;$$

we choose a co-ordinate system with the x-axis along the vector $\mathbf{q}$. On substituting this expansion in (120.8), the terms containing 1 give zero, by the orthogonality of the wave functions ψ_0 and ψ_n, and we obtain

$$d\sigma_n = 8\pi\left(\frac{e}{\hbar v}\right)^2 \frac{dq}{q}|(d_x)_{0n}|^2 = \left(\frac{2e}{\hbar v}\right)^2 |(d_x)_{0n}| \frac{do}{\vartheta^2}, \tag{120.10}$$

where $d_x = e\sum_a x_a$ is the x-component of the dipole moment of the atom. We see that the effective cross-section (for small q) is given by the squared modulus of the matrix element of the dipole moment for the transition which corresponds to the change in state of the atom.‡

† We must have, in fact, $E_n - E_0 \ll \mu v v_0$.

‡ The effective cross-section $d\sigma_n$, summed over all directions of the angular momentum of the atom in the final state and averaged over the directions of the angular momentum in the initial state, is what is of physical interest. After this summation and averaging, the square $|(d_x)_{0n}|^2$ is independent of the direction of the x-axis.

It may happen, however, that the matrix element of the dipole moment vanishes identically for the transition considered, on account of the selection rules (a *forbidden transition*). Then the expansion $e^{i\mathbf{q}.\mathbf{r}_a}$ must be continued to the next term,† and we obtain

$$d\sigma_n = 2\pi\left(\frac{e^2}{\hbar v}\right)^2 |(\sum_a x_a{}^2)_{0n}|^2 q\, dq. \tag{120.11}$$

Let us now consider the opposite limiting case of large q ($qa_0 \gg 1$). If q is large, this means that the atom receives a momentum which is large compared with the original intrinsic momentum of the atomic electrons. It is evident from physical considerations that, in this case, we can regard the atomic electrons as free, and the collision with the atom as an elastic collision between the incident electron and the atomic electrons, the latter being originally at rest. This can also be seen from the general formula (120.8). For large q, the integrand contains a rapidly oscillating factor $e^{i\mathbf{q}.\mathbf{r}_a}$, and the integral is almost zero if ψ_n does not contain a similar factor. Such a function ψ_n corresponds to an ionised atom, with the electron emitted from it with momentum $\hbar\mathbf{q} = \mathbf{p}-\mathbf{p}'$, i.e. with the momentum given by the law of conservation of momentum, as it should be in a collision of two free electrons.

In a collision with a large transfer of momentum, the incident electron and the atomic electron may have final velocities that are comparable in magnitude. The exchange effect arising from the identity of the colliding particles therefore becomes important, although it was not taken into account in the general formula (120.8). The effective scattering cross-section for fast electrons when exchange is allowed for is given by formula (114.8) (the cosine in the last term being put equal to unity); this formula relates to a co-ordinate system in which one of the electrons is at rest before the collision.

Multiplying by the number of electrons in the atom, Z, we obtain the effective cross-section for the collision of an electron with an atom, in the form

$$d\sigma = 4Z\left(\frac{e^2}{\mu v^2}\right)^2\left[\frac{1}{\sin^4\vartheta}+\frac{1}{\cos^4\vartheta}-\frac{1}{\sin^2\vartheta\cos^2\vartheta}\right]\cos\vartheta\, do. \tag{120.12}$$

In this formula it is convenient to express the scattering angle in terms of the energy which the electrons have after the collision. As is well known, when a particle of energy $E = \frac{1}{2}\mu v^2$ collides with one of the same mass at rest, the energy of the particles after the collision is

$$\epsilon = E\sin^2\vartheta, \qquad E-\epsilon = E\cos^2\vartheta.$$

In order to find the effective cross-section referred to the interval $d\epsilon$, we

† Or, in general, to the next non-vanishing term.

express do in terms of $d\epsilon$ by the relation $\cos\vartheta\, do = 2\pi \sin\vartheta \cos\vartheta\, d\vartheta = (\pi/E)\, d\epsilon$. Substituting in (120.12), we obtain the final formula

$$d\sigma_\epsilon = \pi Z e^4 \left[\frac{1}{\epsilon^2} + \frac{1}{(E-\epsilon)^2} - \frac{1}{\epsilon(E-\epsilon)}\right]\frac{d\epsilon}{E}. \tag{120.13}$$

If one of the energies ϵ and $E-\epsilon$ is small compared with the other, only one of the three terms in this formula (the first or the second) is important. This is as it should be, since, for a great difference between the energies of the two electrons, the exchange effect becomes insignificant, and we then return to the familiar Rutherford's formula.†

The integration of the differential effective cross-section over all angles (or, what is the same thing, over q) gives the total effective cross-section σ_n for a collision in which the atom is excited to the state in question. The dependence of σ_n on the velocity of the incident electron is closely related to the existence or otherwise of the matrix element, for the corresponding transition, of the dipole moment of the atom. Let us first suppose that this matrix element is not zero. Then, for small q, $d\sigma_n$ is given by formula (120.10), and we see that, as q diminishes, the integral over q diverges logarithmically. In the region of large q, on the other hand, the effective cross-section (for a given energy transfer $E_n - E_0$) decreases exponentially as q increases, because of the presence (already pointed out) of a rapidly oscillating factor in the integrand of (120.8). Thus the region of small q plays the principal part in the integral over q, and we can restrict ourselves to an integration from the minimum value

$$q_{\min} = (E_n - E_0)/\hbar v$$

(formula (120.9) with $\vartheta = 0$) to some value of the order of $1/a_0$.

As a result we obtain

$$\sigma_n = 8\pi(e/\hbar v)^2 |(d_x)_{0n}|^2 \log(\beta_n v\hbar/e^2), \tag{120.14}$$

where β_n is a dimensionless constant, which cannot be calculated in a general form.‡

If, on the other hand, the matrix element of the dipole moment vanishes for the transition in question, the integral over q converges rapidly both for small q (as we see from (120.11)) and for large q. The most important range in the integral is in this case $q \sim 1/a_0$. No general quantitative formula

† For a collision of a positron with an atom there is no exchange effect, and Rutherford's formula

$$d\sigma_\epsilon = (\pi Z e^4/E)\, d\epsilon/\epsilon^2$$

holds for all $q \gg 1/a_0$.

‡ We suppose that $E_n - E_0$ is of the order of the energy ϵ_0 of the atomic electrons. For larger energy transfers ($E_n - E_0 \sim E \gg \epsilon_0$), the formulae (120.10), (120.14) are both inapplicable, since the matrix element of the dipole moment becomes very small, and it is not possible to take only the first term of the expansion in powers of q.

such as (120.14) can be obtained, and we can deduce only that σ_n is inversely proportional to the square of the velocity:

$$\sigma_n = \text{constant}/v^2. \tag{120.15}$$

This follows at once from the general formula (120.8), according to which $d\sigma_n$ is proportional to $1/k^2$ for $q \sim 1/a_0$.

Let us determine the effective cross-section $d\sigma_{\text{in}}$ for inelastic scattering into a given element of solid angle regardless of the state entered by the atom. To do this, we have to sum the expression (120.8) for all $n \neq 0$, i.e. over all the states of the atom (of both the discrete and the continuous spectrum) except the normal state. We omit from consideration the ranges of large and small angles, and suppose that $1 \gg \vartheta \gg (v_0/v)^2$. Then, by (120.9), we have $q \cong \mu v\vartheta/\hbar$ ($\gg v_0/a_0 v$), i.e. q is independent of the amount of energy transferred.†

The latter circumstance makes it easy to calculate the sum

$$d\sigma_{\text{in}} = \sum_{n\neq 0} d\sigma_n = 8\pi\left(\frac{e^2}{\hbar v}\right)^2 \sum_{n\neq 0} |(\sum_a e^{i\mathbf{q}\cdot\mathbf{r}_a})_{0n}|^2 \frac{dq}{q^3}$$

$$= \left(\frac{2e^2}{\mu v^2}\right)^2 \sum_{n\neq 0} |(\sum_a e^{i\mathbf{q}\cdot\mathbf{r}_a})_{0n}|^2 \frac{do}{\vartheta^4}. \tag{120.16}$$

To do so, we note that, for any quantity f, we have by the multiplication rule for matrices

$$\sum_n |f_{0n}|^2 = \sum_n f_{0n} f^*_{0n} = \sum_n f_{0n}(f^+)_{n0} = (ff^+)_{00}.$$

The summation here is over all n, including $n = 0$. Hence

$$\sum_{n\neq 0} |f_{0n}|^2 = \sum_n |f_{0n}|^2 - |f_{00}|^2 = (ff^+)_{00} - |f_{00}|^2. \tag{120.17}$$

Applying this relation for $f = \sum e^{i\mathbf{q}\cdot\mathbf{r}_a}$, we have

$$d\sigma_{\text{in}} = \left(\frac{2e^2}{\mu v^2}\right)^2 \left\{\overline{|\sum_a e^{i\mathbf{q}\cdot\mathbf{r}_a}|^2} - \left|\overline{\sum_a e^{i\mathbf{q}\cdot\mathbf{r}_a}}\right|^2\right\}\frac{do}{\vartheta^4}, \tag{120.18}$$

where the bar denotes averaging with respect to the normal state of the atom (i.e. taking the diagonal matrix element 00). The mean value $\overline{\sum e^{i\mathbf{q}\cdot\mathbf{r}_a}}$ is, by definition, the atomic form factor $F(q)$ for the atom in the normal state. In the first term in the braces we can write

$$\left|\sum_{a=1}^{Z} e^{i\mathbf{q}\cdot\mathbf{r}_a}\right|^2 = Z + \sum_{a\neq b} e^{i\mathbf{q}\cdot(\mathbf{r}_a-\mathbf{r}_b)}.$$

† Here it is assumed that $E_n - E_0 \sim \epsilon_0$, so that the first term under the radical in (120.9) can be neglected in comparison with the second. In practice, the summation in (120.16) is taken over states with $E_n - E_0 \gg \epsilon_0$ also. However, the effective cross-section for transitions with a large energy transfer is small, and these terms in the sum are unimportant. The condition $\vartheta \ll 1$ is imposed so that the exchange effects need not be taken into account.

Thus we find the general formula

$$d\sigma_{\text{in}} = \left(\frac{2e^2}{\mu v^2}\right)^2 \{Z - F^2(q) + \overline{\sum_{a\neq b} e^{i\mathbf{q}\cdot(\mathbf{r}_a-\mathbf{r}_b)}\}} \frac{do}{\vartheta^4}. \tag{120.19}$$

This formula is much simplified for small q, when we can expand in powers of q ($v_0/a_0 v \ll q \ll 1/a_0$, corresponding to angles $(v_0/v)^2 \ll \vartheta \ll v_0/v$). Instead of effecting the expansion from formula (120.19), it is more convenient to sum again over n, using for $d\sigma_n$ the expression (120.10). Summing with the aid of the relation (120.17) with $f = d_x$, and recalling that $\bar{d}_x = 0$, we have

$$d\sigma_{\text{in}} = (2e/\hbar v)^2 \overline{d_x^2}\, do/\vartheta^2. \tag{120.20}$$

It is of interest to compare this expression with the effective cross-section (115.4) for elastic scattering through small angles; whereas the latter is independent of ϑ, the effective cross-section for inelastic scattering into the solid angle element do increases as $1/\vartheta^2$ when ϑ decreases.

For angles ϑ such that $1 \gg \vartheta \gg v_0/v$ (so that $qa_0 \gg 1$), the second and third terms in the braces in (120.19) are small, and we have simply

$$d\sigma_{\text{in}} = Z(2e^2/\mu v^2)^2\, do/\vartheta^4. \tag{120.21}$$

As we should expect, we have obtained Rutherford scattering from the Z atomic electrons (without allowance for exchange). We recall that, for elastic scattering, we had the result (115.5), which differs only in that the differential cross-section is proportional to Z^2 and not to Z.

Finally, integrating over angles, we have the total effective cross-section σ_{in} for inelastic scattering at all angles and with any excitation of the atom. In an exactly similar manner to the calculation of σ_n (120.14), we obtain

$$\sigma_{\text{in}} = 8\pi(e/\hbar v)^2 \overline{d_x^2} \log(\beta v\hbar/e^2). \tag{120.22}$$

As well as the case of fast electrons considered in this section, the opposite limiting case, that of collisions between atoms and electrons of small energy, only a little above the ionisation threshold of the atom, is also of interest. In these conditions the collision process may be regarded as quasi-classical. WANNIER† has given a general solution of this difficult problem. The probability of a single ionisation of a neutral atom is found to be proportional to

$$(E-I)^\alpha, \qquad \alpha = \frac{1}{4}\left(\sqrt{\frac{91}{3}} - 1\right),$$

where $E-I$ is the amount by which the energy of the electron exceeds the ionisation threshold.

PROBLEMS

PROBLEM 1. Determine the angular distribution from the inelastic scattering of fast electrons by a hydrogen atom (in the normal state).

† G. H. WANNIER, *Physical Review* **90**, 817, 1953.

Solution. For the hydrogen atom, the third term in the braces in (120.19) vanishes, while the atomic form factor $F(q)$ has been calculated in §115, Problem. Substituting, we find†

$$d\sigma_{in} = \frac{4}{v^4\vartheta^4}\frac{(1+v^2\vartheta^2/4)^4-1}{(1+v^2\vartheta^2/4)^4}do.$$

Problem 2. Determine the differential effective cross-section for collisions of electrons with a hydrogen atom in the normal state, the latter being excited to the nth level of the discrete spectrum (where n is the principal quantum number).

Solution. The matrix elements are conveniently calculated in parabolic co-ordinates. We take the z-axis in the direction of the vector $\mathbf{q}$; then

$$e^{i\mathbf{q}\cdot\mathbf{r}} = e^{iqz} = e^{\frac{1}{2}iq(\xi-\eta)}.$$

The wave function of the normal state is

$$\psi_{000} = \pi^{-\frac{1}{2}}e^{-\frac{1}{2}(\xi+\eta)}.$$

The matrix elements are non-zero only for transitions to states with $m = 0$. The wave functions of these states are the functions

$$\psi_{n_1n_20} = (1/\sqrt{\pi n^2})e^{-\frac{1}{2}(\xi+\eta)/n}F(-n_1, 1, \xi/n)F(-n_2, 1, \eta/n)$$

($n = n_1+n_2+1$). The required matrix elements are the integrals

$$(e^{i\mathbf{q}\cdot\mathbf{r}})^{000}_{n_1n_20} = \int_0^\infty\int_0^\infty e^{\frac{1}{2}iq(\xi-\eta)}\psi_{000}\psi_{n_1n_20}\frac{\xi+\eta}{4}2\pi\, d\xi d\eta.$$

The integration is effected immediately by means of the formulae of § f in the Mathematical Appendices. The result is

$$|(e^{i\mathbf{q}\cdot\mathbf{r}})^{000}_{n_1n_20}|^2 = 2^8n^6q^2\frac{[(n-1)^2+(qn)^2]^{n-3}}{[(n+1)^2+(qn)^2]^{n+3}}[(n_1-n_2)^2+(qn)^2].$$

All states with the same $n_1+n_2 = n-1$ have the same energy. Summing over all possible values of n_1-n_2 for the given n, and substituting the result in (120.8), we obtain the required cross-section:

$$d\sigma_n = 2^{11}\pi\frac{1}{v^2}n^7[\tfrac{1}{3}(n^2-1)+(qn)^2]\frac{[(n-1)^2+(qn)^2]^{n-3}}{[(n+1)^2+(qn)^2]^{n+3}}\frac{dq}{q}.$$

Problem 3. Determine the total effective cross-section for the excitation of the first excited state of the hydrogen atom.‡

---

† We use atomic units in all the Problems.

‡ It can also be calculated for arbitrary n. By numerical calculation, we can obtain also the total effective cross-section for inelastic scattering by a hydrogen atom:

$$\sigma_{in} = 4\pi \log(v^2/0{\cdot}160).$$

This includes the following contributions from collisions in which states of the discrete spectrum are excited, and from those in which the atom is ionised:

$$\sigma_{ex} = 4\pi\times0{\cdot}715 \log(v^2/0{\cdot}45),$$

$$\sigma_{io} = 4\pi\times0{\cdot}285 \log(v^2/0{\cdot}012).$$

SOLUTION. We have to integrate

$$d\sigma_2 = 2^8\pi\frac{1}{v^2}\frac{dq}{q(q^2+9/4)^5}$$

over all q from $q_{\min} = (E_2-E_1)/v = 3/8v$ to $q_{\max} = 2v$, only the terms of the highest degree in v being retained. The integration is elementary, and the result is

$$\sigma_2 = \frac{2^{18}\pi}{3^{10}v^2}\left[\log(4v)-\frac{25}{24}\right].$$

PROBLEM 4. Determine the effective cross-section for the ionisation of a hydrogen atom (in the normal state), with the emission of a secondary electron in a given direction; the energy of the secondary electron is small in comparison with that of the primary, and so exchange effects are unimportant (MASSEY and MOHR 1933).

SOLUTION. The wave function of the atom in the initial state is $\psi_0 = e^{-r}/\sqrt{\pi}$. In the final state, the atom is ionised, and the secondary electron emitted from it has a wave vector which we denote by $\varkappa$ (and energy $\epsilon = \frac{1}{2}\varkappa^2$). This state is described by a function ψ^-_κ (113.9), in which the outgoing part consists (at infinity) only of a plane wave propagated in the direction of $\varkappa$. The function ψ^-_κ is normalised by the delta function in $\varkappa$-space; hence the effective cross-section calculated from it will relate to $d\kappa_x\, d\kappa_y\, d\kappa_z$, or to $\kappa^2\, d\kappa\, do_\kappa$, where do_κ is an element of solid angle about the direction of the secondary electron. Thus

$$d\sigma = \frac{4k'\kappa^2}{kq^4}|(e^{i\mathbf{q}.\mathbf{r}})_{0\kappa}|^2\, do\, do_\kappa d\kappa,$$

where do is an element of solid angle about the direction of the scattered electron, and

$$(e^{i\mathbf{q}.\mathbf{r}})_{0\kappa} = \int \psi^-_\kappa{}^* e^{i\mathbf{q}.\mathbf{r}}\psi_0\, dV = \frac{e^{\pi/2\kappa}(1+i/\kappa)}{2^{3/2}\pi^2}I,$$

$$I = \left[-\frac{\partial}{\partial\lambda}\int e^{i\mathbf{q}.\mathbf{r}-i\boldsymbol{\varkappa}.\mathbf{r}-\lambda r}F(-i/\kappa, 1, -i(\kappa r+\boldsymbol{\varkappa}.\mathbf{r}))\frac{dV}{r}\right]_{\lambda=1}.$$

We effect the integration in parabolic co-ordinates, with the z-axis in the direction of $\varkappa$ and the angle ϕ measured from the $(\mathbf{q}, \varkappa)$ plane:

$$I = \left[-\tfrac{1}{2}\frac{\partial}{\partial\lambda}\int_0^\infty\int_0^\infty\int_0^{2\pi} \exp\{\tfrac{1}{2}iq(\xi-\eta)\cos\gamma+iq\sqrt{(\xi\eta)}\sin\gamma\cos\phi-\tfrac{1}{2}\lambda(\xi+\eta)-\tfrac{1}{2}i\kappa(\xi-\eta)\}\times\right.$$

$$\left.\times F(-i/\kappa, 1, -i\kappa\xi)\, d\phi\, d\xi\, d\eta\right]_{\lambda=1},$$

where γ is the angle between $\varkappa$ and $\mathbf{q}$. The integration over ϕ and η is easily performed by substituting $\sqrt{\eta}\cos\phi = u$, $\sqrt{\eta}\sin\phi = v$, which gives

$$\frac{I}{2\pi} = \left[\frac{\partial}{\partial\lambda}\int_0^\infty \exp\left\{\frac{-q^2\sin^2\gamma+\lambda^2+(\kappa-q\cos\gamma)^2}{2[i(\kappa-q\cos\gamma)-\lambda]}\xi\right\}\times\frac{F(-i/\kappa, 1, -i\kappa\xi)\, d\xi}{i(\kappa-q\cos\gamma)-\lambda}\right]_{\lambda=1}.$$

The integral here is found from the formula

$$\int_0^\infty e^{-\lambda t}F(\alpha, 1, kt)\, dt = \lambda^{\alpha-1}(\lambda-k)^{-\alpha};$$

see §f of the Mathematical Appendices. The subsequent calculations, though lengthy, are elementary, and give as a result the following expression for the effective cross-section:

$$d\sigma = \frac{2^8 k'\kappa[q^2-2q\kappa\cos\gamma+(\kappa^2+1)\cos^2\gamma]}{\pi k q^2[q^2-2q\kappa\cos\gamma+1+\kappa^2]^4[(q+\kappa)^2+1][(q-\kappa)^2+1](1-e^{-2\pi/\kappa})}\times$$

$$\times e^{-(2/\kappa)\tan^{-1}[2\kappa/(q^2-\kappa^2+1)]}\, do\, do_\kappa\, d\kappa.$$

The integration over all angles of emission of the secondary electron is elementary, and gives the distribution of scattering over directions, for a given energy $\frac{1}{2}\kappa^2$ of the emitted electron:

$$d\sigma = \frac{2^{10}k'\kappa}{kq^2}\frac{[q^2+\frac{1}{3}(1+\kappa^2)]e^{-(2/\kappa)\tan^{-1}[2\kappa/(q^2-\kappa^2+1)]}}{[(q+\kappa)^2+1]^3[(q-\kappa)^2+1]^3(1-e^{-2\pi/\kappa})}\, do\, d\kappa.$$

For $q \gg 1$, this expression has a sharp maximum at $\kappa \cong q$; near the maximum,

$$d\sigma = \frac{2^5}{3\pi\kappa^4}\frac{d\kappa\, do}{[1+(q-\kappa)^2]^3}.$$

Integrating over o, with $do = 2\pi q\, dq/k^2 \cong (2\pi\kappa/k^2)d(q-\kappa)$, we obtain the expression $8\pi\, d\kappa/k^2\kappa^3$; this is the same as the first term in formula (120.13), as it should be.

§121. The effective retardation

In applications of collision theory, the calculation of the mean energy lost by a colliding particle is of great importance. This energy loss is conveniently characterised by the quantity

$$d\kappa = \sum_n (E_n - E_0)\, d\sigma_n, \tag{121.1}$$

which we shall call the (differential) *effective retardation*; the summation is taken, of course, over states of both the discrete and the continuous spectrum. $d\kappa$ relates to scattering into a given element of solid angle.†

The general formula for the effective retardation of fast electrons is

$$d\kappa = 8\pi\left(\frac{e^2}{\hbar v}\right)^2 \sum_n (E_n - E_0)|(\sum_a e^{i\mathbf{q}\cdot\mathbf{r}_a})_{0n}|^2 \frac{dq}{q^3}, \tag{121.2}$$

where $d\sigma_n$ has been taken from (120.8). As in the derivation of (120.19), we exclude from consideration the region of very small angles, and suppose that $1 \gg \vartheta \gg (v_0/v)^2$. Then $q \cong \mu v\vartheta/\hbar$ is independent of the amount of energy transferred, and the sum over n can therefore be calculated in a general form.

This is done by means of a summation theorem derived as follows. The matrix elements of some quantity f, a function of the co-ordinates, and of

† If an electron is passing through a gas, the scattering at various atoms is independent, and $N d\kappa$ (where N is the number of gas atoms per unit volume) is the energy lost by the electron in unit path by collisions in which it deviates into the given element of solid angle.

its derivative $\dot{f}$ with respect to time are related by

$$(\dot{f})_{0n} = -(i/\hbar)(E_n - E_0)f_{0n}.$$

Hence, using (11.9), we have

$$\sum_n (E_n - E_0)|f_{0n}|^2 = \sum_n (E_n - E_0)f_{0n}f_{0n}^*$$

$$= \sum_n (E_n - E_0)f_{0n}(f^+)_{n0} = i\hbar \sum_n (\dot{f})_{0n}(f^+)_{n0} = i\hbar(\dot{f}f^+)_{00}.$$

The wave functions of the stationary states of the atom can be taken real. Then $(f_{0n})^* = (f^+)_{0n}$, and we can also write the sum in question as

$$\sum_n (E_n - E_0)|f_{0n}|^2 = \sum_n (E_n - E_0)f_{0n}^*(f^+)_{n0}^*$$

$$= \sum_n (E_n - E_0)(f^+)_{0n}f_{n0} = -i\hbar \sum_n (f^+)_{0n}(\dot{f})_{n0} = -i\hbar(f^+\dot{f})_{00}.$$

Taking half the sum of these two equations, we have the required theorem:

$$\sum_n (E_n - E_0)|f_{0n}|^2 = \tfrac{1}{2}i\hbar(\dot{f}f^+ - f^+\dot{f})_{00}. \tag{121.3}$$

We apply it to the quantity

$$f = \sum_a e^{i\mathbf{q}\cdot\mathbf{r}_a}.$$

According to (17.2), its derivative with respect to time is represented by the operator

$$\hat{\dot{f}} = (\hbar/2\mu) \sum_a (e^{i\mathbf{q}\cdot\mathbf{r}_a}(\mathbf{q}\cdot\nabla_a) + (\mathbf{q}\cdot\nabla_a)e^{i\mathbf{q}\cdot\mathbf{r}_a}].$$

The result of commuting $\hat{\dot{f}}$ and f^+ is easily calculated directly:

$$\hat{\dot{f}}f^+ - f^+\hat{\dot{f}} = -(i\hbar/\mu)q^2 Z.$$

Substituting in (121.3), we obtain the formula

$$\sum_n \frac{2\mu}{\hbar^2 q^2}(E_n - E_0)|(\sum_a e^{i\mathbf{q}\cdot\mathbf{r}_a})_{0n}|^2 = Z, \tag{121.4}$$

which effects the summation required.†

Thus we find for the differential effective retardation the formula

$$\mathrm{d}\kappa = 4\pi\frac{Ze^4}{\mu v^2}\frac{\mathrm{d}q}{q} = \frac{2Ze^4}{\mu v^2}\frac{\mathrm{do}}{\vartheta^2}. \tag{121.5}$$

† In deriving this relation we have nowhere used the fact that the state denoted by the suffix 0 is the normal state of the atom. The relation therefore holds for any initial state.

The range of applicability of this formula is given by the inequality

$$(v_0/v)^2 \ll \vartheta \ll 1, \text{ i.e. } v_0/v \ll a_0 q \ll v/v_0.$$

Next, let us determine the total effective retardation $\kappa(q_1)$ for all collisions in which the transfer of momentum does not exceed some value q_1 such that $v_0/v \ll a_0 q_1 \ll v/v_0$:

$$\kappa(q_1) = \sum_n \int_{q_{\min}}^{q_1} (E_n - E_0)\, d\sigma_n; \tag{121.6}$$

$q_{\min} = (E_n - E_0)/\hbar v$ is the smallest possible value of q for the given $E_n - E_0$. The integration and summation signs cannot be transposed, since $q_{\min}$ depends on n.

We divide the range of integration into two parts, from $q_{\min}$ to q_0 and from q_0 to q_1, where q_0 is some value of q such that $v_0/v \ll q_0 a_0 \ll 1$. Then, over the whole range of integration from $q_{\min}$ to q_0, we can use for $d\sigma_n$ the expression (120.10):

$$\kappa(q_0) = 8\pi\left(\frac{e}{\hbar v}\right)^2 \sum_n |(d_x)_{0n}|^2 (E_n - E_0) \int_{q_{\min}}^{q_0} \frac{dq}{q},$$

whence

$$\kappa(q_0) = 8\pi\left(\frac{e}{\hbar v}\right)^2 \sum_n |(d_x)_{0n}|^2 (E_n - E_0) \log\frac{q_0 \hbar v}{E_n - E_0}. \tag{121.7}$$

In the range from q_0 to q_1, on the other hand, we can first sum over n, which gives the expression (121.5) for $d\kappa$, and then on integrating over q we have

$$\kappa(q_1) - \kappa(q_0) = 4\pi(Ze^4/\mu v^2)\log(q_1/q_0). \tag{121.8}$$

To transform the above expressions, we use the summation theorem obtained from formula (121.3) by putting there

$$f = d_x/e = \sum_a x_a, \qquad \dot{f} = (1/\mu)\sum_a p_{xa}.$$

Commuting $\dot{f}^+$ and f gives (in the present case, f^+ is the same as f)

$$\dot{f}f^+ - f^+\dot{f} = -i\hbar Z/\mu,$$

so that†

$$\sum_n N_{0n} = \sum_n (2\mu/e^2\hbar^2)(E_n - E_0)|(d_x)_{0n}|^2 = Z. \tag{121.9}$$

We have introduced the special notation N_{0n} for the summand, since it is

† The remark made concerning (121.4) applies to this relation also.

frequently needed. The quantities N_{0n} are called the *oscillator strengths* for the corresponding transitions.

We introduce some mean energy I of the atom, defined by the formula

$$\log I = \sum_n N_{0n} \log(E_n - E_0) / \sum_n N_{0n}$$
$$= (1/Z) \sum_n N_{0n} \log(E_n - E_0). \quad (121.10)$$

Then, using the summation theorem (121.9). we can rewrite formula (121.7) in the form

$$\kappa(q_0) = (4\pi Ze^4/\mu v^2)\log(q_0 \hbar v/I).$$

Adding this to (121.8), we have finally

$$\kappa(q_1) = (4\pi Ze^4/\mu v^2) \log(q_1 \hbar v/I). \quad (121.11)$$

Only one constant characterising the atom concerned appears in this formula.†

Expressing q_1 in terms of the scattering angle ϑ_1 by means of $q_1 = \mu v \vartheta_1/\hbar$, we obtain the effective retardation in scattering through all angles $\vartheta \leqslant \vartheta_1$:

$$\kappa(\vartheta_1) = (4\pi Ze^4/\mu v^2) \log(\mu v^2 \vartheta_1/I). \quad (121.12)$$

If $q_1 a_0 \gg 1$ (i.e. $\vartheta_1 \gg v_0/v$), we can express κ as a function of the greatest amount of energy that can be transferred from the incident electron to the atom. We have shown in the previous section that, for $qa_0 \gg 1$, the atom is ionised, almost all the momentum $\hbar\mathbf{q}$ and energy being given to one atomic electron. Hence $\hbar\mathbf{q}$ and ϵ are related by being the momentum and energy of an electron, i.e. by $\epsilon = \hbar^2 q^2/2\mu$. Substituting in (121.11) $q_1^2 = 2\mu\epsilon_1/\hbar^2$, we obtain the effective retardation in collisions where the energy transfer is $\epsilon \leqslant \epsilon_1$:

$$\kappa(\epsilon_1) = (2\pi Ze^4/\mu v^2) \log(2\mu\epsilon_1 v^2/I^2). \quad (121.13)$$

For heavy atoms we should expect to get good accuracy on calculating the constant I by the Thomas-Fermi method. This calculation has not yet been carried out. However, it is easy to establish from general considerations how the values of I thus calculated will depend on Z. In the quasi-classical Thomas-Fermi model, the eigenfrequencies of the system of charges correspond to the differences of the energy levels. The mean eigenfrequency of the atom is of the order of v_0/a_0; hence we can deduce that $I \sim \hbar v_0/a_0$. The velocities of the atomic electrons in the Thomas-Fermi model depend on Z as $Z^{2/3}$, while the dimensions of the atom vary as $Z^{-1/3}$. Thus we find that I should be proportional‡ to Z:

$$I = \text{constant} \times Z.$$

† For hydrogen, $I = 0{\cdot}55\mu e^4/\hbar^2 = 14{\cdot}9$ eV (Bethe).

‡ From experimental results it can be found that the constant is of the order of magnitude of 10 eV.

In conclusion, we may make the following remark. The energy levels of the discrete spectrum of an atom mainly involve excitations of a single (outer) electron; the excitation of even two electrons usually requires an energy sufficient to ionise the atom. Hence, in the sum of oscillator strengths, the transitions to states of the discrete spectrum form only a part, of the order of unity, while those which involve ionisation form a part of the order of Z. Hence it follows that the main part in retardation (by heavy atoms) is played by those collisions which are accompanied by ionisation.

PROBLEM

Determine the total effective retardation of an electron by a hydrogen atom ($I = 0{\cdot}55$ atomic units); for large energy transfers, the faster of the two colliding electrons is taken to be the primary.

SOLUTION. When the primary and secondary electrons have comparable energies after the collision, the exchange effect must be taken into account. Hence, for retardation with an energy transfer between some value ϵ_1 $(1 \ll \epsilon_1 \ll v^2)$ and the maximum value $\epsilon_{max} = \frac{1}{2}E = \frac{1}{4}v^2$ (by our definition of the primary electron), we must use the effective cross-section (120.13):

$$\kappa(\epsilon_{max}) - \kappa(\epsilon_1) = \frac{2\pi}{v^2}\int\limits_{\epsilon_1}^{\frac{1}{2}E} \epsilon\left[\frac{1}{\epsilon^2}+\frac{1}{(E-\epsilon)^2}-\frac{1}{\epsilon(E-\epsilon)}\right] d\epsilon$$

$$= \frac{2\pi}{v^2}[\log(E/8\epsilon_1)+1].$$

Adding this to (121.13), we obtain†

$$\kappa = \frac{4\pi}{v^2}\log\left[\frac{v^2}{2I}\sqrt{(\tfrac{1}{2}e)}\right] = \frac{4\pi}{v^2}\log\frac{v^2}{1{\cdot}3}.$$

§122. Inelastic collisions between heavy particles and atoms

The condition for the Born approximation to be applicable to collisions between heavy particles and atoms, expressed in terms of the velocity of a particle, remains the same as for electrons:

$$v \gg v_0.$$

This follows immediately from the general condition (110.2) for perturbation theory to be applicable ($Ua_0/\hbar v \ll 1$), if we notice that the mass of the particle does not appear there, while $Ua_0/\hbar$ is of the order of magnitude of the velocity of the atomic electrons.

In a system of co-ordinates in which the centre of mass of the atom and the

† For collisions between a positron and a hydrogen atom there is no exchange effect, and the total retardation is obtained by simply substituting $\epsilon_{max} = E = \frac{1}{2}v^2$ in place of ϵ_1 in (121.13):

$$\kappa = (4\pi/v^2)\log(v^2/0{\cdot}55).$$

particle is at rest, the effective cross-section is given by the general formula (120.3), in which μ is the reduced mass of the particle and the atom. It is more convenient, however, to consider the collision in a system of co-ordinates in which the scattering atom is at rest before the collision. To do this, we start from formula (120.1); in a system of co-ordinates in which the atom is at rest before the collision, the argument of the delta function which expresses the law of conservation of energy is of the form

$$\tfrac{1}{2}p'^2/M-\tfrac{1}{2}p^2/M+\tfrac{1}{2}(\mathbf{p}'-\mathbf{p})^2/M_a+E_n-E_0, \qquad (122.1)$$

where M is the mass of the incident particle and M_a that of the atom. The third term is the kinetic "recoil" energy of the atom (and could be entirely neglected when considering a collision between an atom and an electron).

For a collision of a fast heavy particle with an atom, the change in the momentum of the particle is almost always small in comparison with its original momentum. If this condition holds, we can neglect the recoil energy of the atom in the argument of the delta function, and we then arrive at exactly the same formula (120.1), except that μ in the latter must be replaced by the mass M of the incident particle (and not by the reduced mass of the particle and the atom). Thus we have again the formula (120.3) (with μ replaced by M) for the effective cross-section in a system of co-ordinates in which the atom is at rest before the collision; bearing in mind that the transfer of momentum is supposed small in comparison with the original momentum, we put $p \cong p'$:

$$\mathrm{d}\sigma_n = (M^2/4\pi^2\hbar^4)\left|\iint Ue^{i\mathbf{q}\cdot\mathbf{r}}\psi_n{}^*\psi_0\,\mathrm{d}\tau\mathrm{d}V\right|^2 \mathrm{d}o. \qquad (122.2)$$

Taking into account the fact that the charge on the particle may differ from that on the electron, we write ze^2 in place of e^2, where ze is the charge on the incident particle. The general formula for inelastic scattering, written in the form (120.8):

$$\mathrm{d}\sigma_n = 8\pi\left(\frac{ze^2}{\hbar v}\right)^2\left|\left(\sum_a e^{i\mathbf{q}\cdot\mathbf{r}_a}\right)_{0n}\right|^2\frac{\mathrm{d}q}{q^3}, \qquad (122.3)$$

does not contain the mass of the particle. Hence it follows that all the formulae derived from it remain applicable at once to collisions with heavy particles, provided that these formulae are expressed in terms of v and q.

It is easy to see how the formulae must be modified when they are expressed in terms of the scattering angle ϑ (the angle of deviation of the heavy particle on colliding with the atom). To see this, we notice first of all that the angle ϑ is always small in an inelastic collision with a heavy particle. For, when the momentum transfer is large (compared with the momenta of the atomic electrons), we can regard the inelastic collision with the atom as an elastic collision with free electrons; when a heavy particle collides with a light one (the electron), however, the heavy particle hardly deviates at all. In other words, the transfer of momentum from the heavy particle to the atom is small in comparison with the original momentum of the particle; an exception is formed by elastic scattering through large angles, but this is extremely improbable.

Thus, over the whole range of angles, we can put

$$q = \sqrt{\{[(E_n - E_0)/v]^2 + (Mv\vartheta)^2\}}/\hbar, \tag{122.4}$$

which in practice reduces to

$$qh \cong Mv\vartheta \tag{122.5}$$

everywhere except for very small angles. On the other hand, when considering the collisions of electrons with an atom, we had (for small angles)

$$q = \sqrt{\{[(E_n - E_0)/v]^2 + (\mu v\vartheta)^2\}}/\hbar.$$

Hence we can deduce that the formulae which we obtained for collisions between electrons and atoms, if expressed in terms of the velocity and the angle of deviation, become formulae for the collision of heavy particles if we everywhere make the substitution

$$v \to v, \qquad \vartheta \to M\vartheta/\mu \tag{122.6}$$

(including the element of solid angle $do = 2\pi \sin\vartheta\, d\vartheta \cong 2\pi\vartheta\, d\vartheta$). Qualitatively, this means that the whole picture of small-angle scattering is (for a given velocity) compressed in the ratio μ/M.

The rules obtained above relate also to elastic scattering through small angles. Making the transformation (122.6) in formula (115.3) with $\vartheta \ll 1$, we have the effective cross-section

$$d\sigma_{el} = 8\pi(ze^2/Mv^2)^2[Z - F(Mv\vartheta/\hbar)]^2\, d\vartheta/\vartheta^3. \tag{122.7}$$

The elastic scattering of heavy particles through angles $\vartheta \sim 1$ reduces to Rutherford scattering at the nucleus of the atom.

Inelastic scattering in which the atom is ionised with a large transfer of momentum requires special consideration. Unlike the situation for ionisation by an electron, there are of course no exchange effects. For heavy particles it is characteristic that a large momentum transfer ($qa_0 \gg 1$) does not mean a deviation through a large angle; ϑ always remains small. The effective cross-section for ionisation with the emission of an electron of energy between ϵ and $\epsilon + d\epsilon$ is found immediately from formula (120.21), which we write in the form

$$d\sigma_{in} = 8\pi(ze^2/\hbar v)^2 Z\, dq/q^3,$$

putting $\hbar^2 q^2/2\mu = \epsilon$ (the whole of the momentum $\hbar q$ is given to a single atomic electron). This gives

$$d\sigma_\epsilon = (2\pi Z z^2 e^4/\mu v^2)\, d\epsilon/\epsilon^2. \tag{122.8}$$

In collisions of heavy particles with atoms, the total effective cross-section and retardation are of particular interest. The total inelastic scattering cross-section is given by the previous formula (120.22). The total effective retardation is obtained by substituting the maximum possible momentum q_{max} in place of q_1 in (121.11). q_{max} is easily expressed in terms of the velocity of the particle as follows. Since even $\hbar q_{max}$ is small compared with the original momentum Mv of the particle, the change in its energy is related to the change in momentum by $\Delta E = \mathbf{v} \cdot \hbar\mathbf{q}$. On the other hand, for a large momentum transfer nearly all this energy is given to one atomic electron, so that we can write

$$\epsilon = \hbar^2 q^2/2\mu = \hbar\mathbf{v} \cdot \mathbf{q} \leqslant \hbar v q.$$

Hence we have $\hbar q \leqslant 2\mu v$, i.e.

$$\hbar q_{max} = 2\mu v, \qquad \epsilon_{max} = 2\mu v^2. \tag{122.9}$$

We may notice that the maximum angle of deviation of the particle in an inelastic collision is

$$\vartheta_{max} = \hbar q_{max}/Mv = 2\mu/M.$$

Substituting (122.9) in (121.11), we obtain the total effective retardation of a heavy particle:

$$\kappa = (4\pi Z z^2 e^4/\mu v^2) \log(2\mu v^2/I). \tag{122.10}$$

§123. Collisions with molecules

The problem of scattering by molecules can in some cases be reduced to problems of scattering by the individual atoms forming the molecule. One such case is formed by collisions of fast charged particles (electrons, protons, etc.) with molecules composed of heavy atoms (see below).

The general theory of the scattering of fast particles by molecules is given by essentially the same formulae as for scattering by atoms. We shall here consider in more detail collisions accompanied by the excitation of rotational and vibrational levels, the electron state of the molecule remaining unchanged. In view of the small excitation energy of these levels we can suppose that the momentum is unchanged in absolute value.

Let U be the energy of the interaction between the incident particle and the molecule, averaged with respect to the electron wave function of the molecule; U is a function of the co-ordinates of the incident particle and those of the nuclei in the molecule. Next, let ψ_0 and ψ_n be the initial and final wave functions of the nuclear (vibrational and rotational) motion. Then, analogously to formula (120.3), we have

$$d\sigma_n = (M^2/4\pi^2\hbar^4)\left| \iint U e^{i\mathbf{q}\cdot\mathbf{r}} \psi_n^* \psi_0 \, d\tau dV \right|^2 do. \tag{123.1}$$

Here $d\tau$ is an element of the configuration space of the nuclei, M the mass of the incident particle; we use a system of co-ordinates in which the molecule is at rest before the collision. This formula relates to both inelastic and ($n = 0$) elastic scattering.

If all the atoms in the molecule are fairly heavy, the majority of the scattering electrons belong to the inner shells of the atoms. On the other hand, the motion of the inner electrons is not greatly affected when the atoms form a molecule (this, of course, does not in general hold good for the outer electrons). Hence the "scattering field" U can be written with sufficient accuracy in the form $U = \Sigma\, U_a$, where U_a is the energy of the interaction between the incident particle and the ath atom (averaged with respect to its electron state); U_a is a function of the co-ordinates of the particle relative to the ath nucleus. Substituting in (123.1)

$$U = \sum_a U_a = \sum_a U_a e^{-i\mathbf{q}.\mathbf{R}_a} e^{i\mathbf{q}.\mathbf{R}_a},$$

where $\mathbf{R}_a$ is the radius vector of the ath nucleus, we can represent the effective cross-section in the form

$$\mathrm{d}\sigma_n = |\sum_a A_a(\mathbf{q})(e^{i\mathbf{q}.\mathbf{R}_a})_{0n}|^2\, \mathrm{d}o, \tag{123.2}$$

where the matrix element of the expression in parentheses is taken with respect to the nuclear wave functions ψ_0, ψ_n, and the quantities $A_a(\mathbf{q})$ are defined by the formula

$$A_a(\mathbf{q}) = (M/2\pi\hbar^2) \int U_a e^{i\mathbf{q}.(\mathbf{r}-\mathbf{R}_a)}\, \mathrm{d}V. \tag{123.3}$$

These have a simple physical significance. They are the scattering amplitudes for the individual atoms:

$$\mathrm{d}\sigma_{a,\mathrm{el}} = |A_a(\mathbf{q})|^2\, \mathrm{d}o \tag{123.4}$$

is the effective elastic scattering cross-section for an individual (free) atom in a co-ordinate system in which the atom was at rest before the collision. The formula which we have obtained solves the above problem in principle.

Next, let us consider a collision between a neutron and a molecule (not having a magnetic moment†). The electrons hardly scatter neutrons at all, so that practically all the scattering takes place at the nuclei. We shall suppose that the scattering is weak, in the sense that the amplitude of a wave scattered by one of the nuclei in the molecule becomes small even at the positions of the other nuclei; this condition essentially amounts to requiring that the effective cross-sections for scattering by individual atoms are small in comparison with the squares of the distances between the atoms. When this condition holds, the scattering amplitude for the molecule is given by the sum of those for the separate atoms.

† Otherwise there is a further special scattering effect due to the interaction between the magnetic moment of the neutron and that of the molecule.

However, perturbation theory cannot be applied directly to such a collision. The forces of interaction between a nucleus and a neutron, though they have a small range of action, are very large within this range, and this means that perturbation theory is inapplicable. Hence the scattering amplitudes for the separate atoms are in general functions of the two momenta **p** and **p**′ before and after the collision, and not only of their difference **q**, the result given by perturbation theory.

There is, however, a case where the scattering of neutrons is described by formulae which would also be obtained by formally applying perturbation theory (E. FERMI 1936). This is the case of slow neutrons, where the scattering amplitude (and therefore the effective cross-section) for an individual atom is independent of the velocity.

Let A_a be the (constant) scattering amplitude for neutrons at an individual atom, so that

$$\sigma_{a,\mathrm{el}} = 4\pi A_a^2 \tag{123.5}$$

is the effective elastic scattering cross-section (in a system of co-ordinates in which the centre of mass of the neutron and the atom is at rest).

The expression (123.5) can be formally obtained from perturbation theory (Born's formula), if we formally describe the interaction between the neutron and the nucleus by a potential energy

$$U_a(\mathbf{r}) = \frac{M_a+M}{M_aM}2\pi\hbar^2 A_a\delta(\mathbf{r}-\mathbf{R}_a),$$

where M_a is the mass of the atom and M that of the neutron. Accordingly, we describe the interaction between the neutron and the molecule by a potential energy

$$U(\mathbf{r}) = \frac{2\pi\hbar^2}{M}\sum_a \frac{M_a+M}{M_a}A_a\delta(\mathbf{r}-\mathbf{R}_a). \tag{123.6}$$

Substituting this expression in (120.3), we find the following formula for the effective cross-section for the scattering of neutrons by a molecule, in a co-ordinate system in which the centre of mass of the neutron and the molecule is at rest:

$$d\sigma_n = \left(\frac{M_m}{M+M_m}\right)^2 \frac{p'}{p}\left|\sum_a \frac{M_a+M}{M_a}A_a(e^{i\mathbf{q}\cdot\mathbf{R}_a})_{0n}\right|^2 do, \tag{123.7}$$

where $M_m = \Sigma M_a$ is the mass of the molecule. This formula gives the relation between the scattering of slow neutrons by a molecule and that by the separate atoms.

In the preceding formulae we have not taken into account the existence of the spin of the neutrons and nuclei. In reality, the scattering amplitude A_a depends on the total angular momentum j_a of the system nucleus + neutron;

we suppose that the spin of the nucleus is not zero, since otherwise the preceding formulae are unchanged.

Since the scattering of slow neutrons takes place with orbital angular momentum $l = 0$, j is obtained by adding the spin of the neutron ($s = \frac{1}{2}$) to the spin i_a of the nucleus, i.e. it can take the two values $j = i_a + \frac{1}{2}$ and $j = i_a - \frac{1}{2}$. We denote by A_a^+ and A_a^- the scattering amplitudes for these two values of j_a. If, as usually happens, there are in the incident beam neutrons whose spins are in different directions (or if the nuclei in the irradiated substance have spins in different directions), the effective scattering cross-section must be averaged accordingly.

This averaging is conveniently effected by means of the following formal device. We form an expression depending on j, equal to A^+ and A^- for $j = i \pm \frac{1}{2}$ respectively. It is easily verified that this is

$$A = a + b\mathbf{i} \cdot \mathbf{s}, \tag{123.8}$$

where

$$a = \{(i+1)A^+ + iA^-\}/(2i+1),$$
$$b = 2\{A^+ - A^-\}/(2i+1), \tag{123.9}$$

and $\mathbf{i} \cdot \mathbf{s}$ denotes the eigenvalue of the operator $\hat{\mathbf{i}} \cdot \hat{\mathbf{s}}$, which for any given j is

$$\mathbf{i} \cdot \mathbf{s} = \tfrac{1}{2}[j(j+1) - i(i+1) - \tfrac{3}{4}].$$

We shall suppose that the directions of the spins of the neutrons and nuclei are distributed entirely at random, i.e. all possible directions are equally probable. In averaging the square

$$\left| \sum_a \frac{M_a + M}{M_a} (a_a + b_a \mathbf{s} \cdot \mathbf{i}_a)(e^{i\mathbf{q} \cdot \mathbf{R}_a})_{0n} \right|^2$$

it must be borne in mind that the averagings with respect to the directions of the spins of the neutrons and of the nuclei are independent, and each gives zero on averaging. Hence the mean values of the products $\mathbf{s} \cdot \mathbf{i}_a$ are zero. Since the direct interaction of the nuclear spins with one another is wholly negligible, the directions of the spins of the different nuclei in the molecule are also independent, provided that the molecule does not contain similar atoms; if it does, the independence is destroyed by the necessity of a definite symmetry of the wave function of the molecule (the exchange interaction). Considering only molecules in which all the atoms are different, we therefore find that the products of the form $(\mathbf{s} \cdot \mathbf{i}_1)(\mathbf{s} \cdot \mathbf{i}_2)$ also vanish on averaging. Thus there remains

$$\left| \sum_a \frac{M_a + M}{M_a} a_a (e^{i\mathbf{q} \cdot \mathbf{R}_a})_{0n} \right|^2 + \sum_a \left| \frac{M_a + M}{M_a} b_a (e^{i\mathbf{q} \cdot \mathbf{R}_a})_{0n} \right|^2 \overline{(\mathbf{s} \cdot \mathbf{i}_a)^2}.$$

The mean values of expressions of the form $\mathbf{s} \cdot \mathbf{i}_a$ which occur here are very easily calculated:

$$\overline{(\mathbf{s}\cdot\mathbf{i})^2} = \tfrac{1}{3}\mathbf{s}^2\mathbf{i}^2 = \tfrac{1}{3}s(s+1)i(i+1) = \tfrac{1}{4}i(i+1).$$

As a result, we have the following expression for the effective cross-section:

$$\mathrm{d}\sigma_n = \left(\frac{M_m}{M+M_m}\right)^2 \frac{p'}{p}\left\{\left|\sum_a \frac{M_a+M}{M_a} a_a (e^{i\mathbf{q}\cdot\mathbf{R}_a})_{0n}\right|^2 + \right.$$

$$\left. +\tfrac{1}{4}\sum_a \left(\frac{M_a+M}{M_a}\right)^2 i_a(i_a+1) b_a{}^2 |(e^{i\mathbf{q}\cdot\mathbf{R}})_{0n}|^2\right\} \mathrm{d}o. \qquad (123.10)$$

We shall not pause here to consider the case of molecules containing similar atoms.

CHAPTER XVI

MOTION IN A MAGNETIC FIELD

§124. Schrödinger's equation in a magnetic field

In non-relativistic theory, a magnetic field can be regarded only as an external field. The magnetic interactions between particles are a relativistic effect, and a consistently relativistic theory is needed if they are to be taken into account.

The Hamiltonian of a system of particles in a magnetic field can be obtained from the classical expression for the corresponding Hamilton's function. As is known from electrodynamics, this function is of the form

$$H = \sum_a \frac{(\mathbf{p}_a - e_a \mathbf{A}_a/c)^2}{2\mu_a} + U(x, y, z),$$

where $\mathbf{p}_a$ is the generalised momentum of the ath particle, $\mathbf{A}_a$ the vector potential of the magnetic field at the point occupied by this particle, and $U(x, y, z)$ the potential energy of the interaction of the particles (or their energy in the external electric field).† For brevity, we shall write the formulae below for a single particle:

$$H = \frac{(\mathbf{p} - e\mathbf{A}/c)^2}{2\mu} + U(x, y, z).$$

If the particle has no spin, the transition to quantum mechanics can be made in the usual manner; the momentum $\mathbf{p}$ must be replaced by the operator $\hat{\mathbf{p}} = -i\hbar\nabla$, and we obtain the Hamiltonian

$$\hat{H} = \frac{(\hat{\mathbf{p}} - e\mathbf{A}/c)^2}{2\mu} + U(x, y, z). \qquad (124.1)$$

If, on the other hand, the particle has a spin, this procedure does not suffice. This is because the spin interacts directly with the magnetic field. In the classical Hamilton's function this interaction does not appear, since the spin, which is a purely quantum effect, vanishes when we pass to the limit of classical mechanics. To a particle with a spin we must also ascribe an intrinsic magnetic moment; from considerations of symmetry it is evident that this moment is parallel or antiparallel to the spin. Hence its operator is of the form $\beta\hat{\mathbf{s}}$, where $\hat{\mathbf{s}}$ is the spin operator and β is a constant characterising the particle. The correct expression for the Hamiltonian is obtained by

† See, for instance, *The Classical Theory of Fields*, §3-1, Addison-Wesley Press, Cambridge (Mass.) 1951. We here denote the generalised momentum by $\mathbf{p}$ and not by $\mathbf{P}$.

adding to (124.1) an additional term $-\beta\hat{\mathbf{s}}\,.\,\mathscr{H}$, which corresponds to the energy of the magnetic moment $\beta\mathbf{s}$ in the field $\mathscr{H}$. Thus the Hamiltonian of a particle having a spin and in a magnetic field is

$$\hat{H} = (\hat{\mathbf{p}}-e\mathbf{A}/c)^2/2\mu-\beta\hat{\mathbf{s}}\,.\,\mathscr{H}+U(x,y,z). \qquad (124.2)$$

In expanding the square $(\hat{\mathbf{p}}-e\mathbf{A}/c)^2$, we must bear in mind that $\hat{\mathbf{p}}$ does not in general commute with the vector $\mathbf{A}(x, y, z)$, which is a function of the co-ordinates. Hence we must write

$$\hat{H} = \hat{\mathbf{p}}^2/2\mu-(e/2\mu c)(\mathbf{A}\,.\,\hat{\mathbf{p}}+\hat{\mathbf{p}}\,.\,\mathbf{A})+e^2\mathbf{A}^2/2\mu c^2-\beta\hat{\mathbf{s}}\,.\,\mathscr{H}+U. \qquad (124.3)$$

According to the general rule (14.4) for the commutation of the momentum operator with any function of the co-ordinates, we have

$$\hat{\mathbf{p}}\,.\,\mathbf{A}-\mathbf{A}\,.\,\hat{\mathbf{p}} = -i\hbar\,\mathrm{div}\,\mathbf{A}. \qquad (124.4)$$

Thus $\hat{\mathbf{p}}$ and $\mathbf{A}$ commute if $\mathrm{div}\,\mathbf{A} \equiv 0$. This holds, in particular, for a homogeneous field, if its vector potential is expressed in the form

$$\mathbf{A} = \tfrac{1}{2}\mathscr{H}\times\mathbf{r}. \qquad (124.5)$$

The equation $\hat{H}\psi = E\psi$ for the eigenvalues of the operator (124.2) is a generalisation of SCHRÖDINGER's equation to the case where a magnetic field is present. The properties of the operator $\hat{\mathbf{s}}$ have been considered in detail in Chapter VIII. The wave functions on which the operator (124.2) acts are symmetrical spinors of rank $2s$.

The wave functions of the stationary states of a particle in a magnetic field are not uniquely defined, because the choice of the vector potential is not unique. If we make the substitution

$$\mathbf{A} \rightarrow \mathbf{A}+\nabla f(x,y,z), \qquad (124.6)$$

where f is any function of the co-ordinates,† the magnetic field $\mathscr{H}$ is unaffected; in other words, the vector potential is determined only to within the gradient of an arbitrary function. It is therefore clear that the transformation (124.6) cannot essentially change the eigenfunctions of the operator (124.2); in particular, the squared modulus $|\psi|^2$ must remain unchanged. In fact, it is easy to see that, on making together with (124.6) the substitution

$$\psi \rightarrow \psi\exp[-i(e/\hbar c)f(x,y,z)], \qquad (124.7)$$

we return to the original equation. Thus the phases of the wave functions

† The arbitrary function f in the transformation (124.6) may be a function of the time also. In that case, in reducing SCHRÖDINGER's equation to its original form, together with the transformation (124.6), (124.7), we must also replace the potential energy U by $U-(e/c)\partial f/\partial t$.

We may mention also that, if we are concerned with a system of several particles, the transformation of the wave function is (instead of (124.7))

$$\psi \rightarrow \psi\exp\{-(i/\hbar c)\,\Sigma\, e_a f(x_a, y_a, z_a)\},$$

the summation in the exponent being over the particles forming the system.

of the stationary states are determined only to within an arbitrary function of the co-ordinates. This non-uniqueness, however, does not affect any quantity having a physical significance; the vector potential does not appear explicitly in the definition of such a quantity.

In classical mechanics, the generalised momentum of a particle is related to its velocity by

$$\mu \mathbf{v} = \mathbf{p} - e\mathbf{A}/c.$$

In order to find the operator $\hat{\mathbf{v}}$ in quantum mechanics, we have to commute the vector $\mathbf{r}$ with the Hamiltonian. A simple calculation gives the result

$$\mu \hat{\mathbf{v}} = \hat{\mathbf{p}} - e\mathbf{A}/c, \tag{124.8}$$

which is exactly analogous to the classical expression. For the operators of the velocity components we have the commutation rules

$$\left.\begin{aligned} \{\hat{v}_x, \hat{v}_y\} &= i(e\hbar/\mu^2 c)\mathscr{H}_z, \\ \{\hat{v}_y, \hat{v}_z\} &= i(e\hbar/\mu^2 c)\mathscr{H}_x, \\ \{\hat{v}_z, \hat{v}_x\} &= i(e\hbar/\mu^2 c)\mathscr{H}_y, \end{aligned}\right\} \tag{124.9}$$

which are easily verified directly. We see that, in a magnetic field, the operators of the three velocity components of a (charged) particle do not commute. This means that the particle cannot simultaneously have definite values of the velocity components in all three directions.

The constant $\beta/\hbar$ gives the ratio of the intrinsic magnetic moment of the particle to its spin angular momentum $\hbar\mathbf{s}$. As is well known,† for the ordinary (orbital) angular momentum this ratio is $e/2\mu c$. The coefficient of proportionality between the intrinsic magnetic moment and the spin of the particle is not the same. For an electron it is

$$\beta/\hbar = -|e|/\mu c, \tag{124.10}$$

i.e. twice the usual value.‡ The intrinsic magnetic moment of the electron (spin $\frac{1}{2}$) is consequently

$$|e|\hbar/2\mu c = 0{\cdot}927 \times 10^{-20} \text{ erg/gauss}.$$

This quantity is called the *Bohr magneton.* The magnetic moment of heavy particles, on the other hand, is customarily measured in *nuclear magnetons,* defined as $e\hbar/2\mu c$ with μ the mass of the proton. The intrinsic magnetic moment of the proton is found by experiment to be 2.68 nuclear magnetons, the moment being parallel to the spin. The magnetic moment of the neutron is opposite to the spin, and is 1.91 nuclear magnetons.

---

† See, for instance, *The Classical Theory of Fields,* §5–9, Addison-Wesley Press, Cambridge (Mass.) 1951.

‡ This value of β can be obtained theoretically from DIRAC's relativistic wave equation.

§125. **Motion in a homogeneous magnetic field**

Let us apply the Hamiltonian (124.2) to determine the energy levels of a particle in a constant homogeneous magnetic field (L. LANDAU 1930). The vector potential of the homogeneous magnetic field is conveniently taken here not in the form (124.5), but as

$$A_x = -\mathscr{H}y, \qquad A_y = A_z = 0 \tag{125.1}$$

(the z-axis being taken in the direction of the field).

The Hamiltonian (124.2) becomes

$$\hat{H} = \frac{1}{2\mu}(\hat{p}_x + e\mathscr{H}y/c)^2 + \frac{\hat{p}_y^2}{2\mu} + \frac{\hat{p}_z^2}{2\mu} - \beta\hat{s}_z\mathscr{H}. \tag{125.2}$$

First of all, we notice that the operator $\hat{s}_z$ commutes with $\hat{H}$, and the coefficient of $\hat{s}_z$ in (125.2) is a constant, independent of the co-ordinates. From the first of these facts it follows that s_z is conserved; from the second, that the spin and co-ordinate variables in SCHRÖDINGER's equation are separable. In other words, the eigenfunctions can be represented as products of co-ordinate functions with spin functions which correspond to definite values σ of the z-component of the spin ($\sigma = -s, \dots, s$). For the co-ordinate function ψ we have the equation

$$\left[\frac{1}{2\mu}(\hat{p}_x + e\mathscr{H}y/c)^2 + \frac{\hat{p}_y^2}{2\mu} + \frac{\hat{p}_z^2}{2\mu} - \beta\sigma\mathscr{H}\right]\psi = E\psi. \tag{125.3}$$

The operator (125.2) does not contain the co-ordinates x and z explicitly. The operators $\hat{p}_x$ and $\hat{p}_z$ therefore commute with $\hat{H}$, i.e. the x and z components of the generalised momentum are conserved. We accordingly seek ψ in the form

$$\psi = e^{(i/\hbar)(p_x x + p_z z)}\chi(y). \tag{125.4}$$

The eigenvalues p_x and p_z take all values from $-\infty$ to $+\infty$. The momentum p_z is related to the velocity by $p_z = \mu v_z$ (see (124.8)). Thus the velocity of the particle in the direction of the field can take any value; we can say that the motion along the z-axis is "not quantised". The physical significance of p_x will be explained below.

Substituting (125.4) in (125.3), we obtain the following equation for the function $\chi(y)$:

$$\chi'' + \frac{2\mu}{\hbar^2}\left\{E + \beta\sigma\mathscr{H} - \frac{p_z^2}{2\mu} - \tfrac{1}{2}\mu\left(\frac{e\mathscr{H}}{\mu c}\right)^2(y-y_0)^2\right\}\chi = 0,$$

where we have introduced the notation

$$y_0 = -cp_x/e\mathscr{H}.$$

This equation is formally identical with SCHRÖDINGER's equation (21.6) for a linear oscillator, oscillating with frequency $\omega = |e|\mathscr{H}/\mu c$ about the point

$y = y_0$. Hence we conclude immediately that the constant $E + \beta\sigma\mathscr{H} - \frac{1}{2}p_z^2/\mu$, which takes the part of the oscillator energy, can have the values $(n+\frac{1}{2})\hbar\omega$, where n is any integer.

Thus we obtain the following expression for the energy levels of a particle in a homogeneous magnetic field:

$$E = (n+\tfrac{1}{2})|e|\hbar\mathscr{H}/\mu c + p_z^2/2\mu - \beta\sigma\mathscr{H}. \tag{125.5}$$

The corresponding wave functions are (apart from a normalising constant)

$$\psi = e^{(i/\hbar)(p_x x + p_z z)} e^{-|e|\mathscr{H}(y-y_0)^2/2c\hbar} H_n[\sqrt{(|e|\mathscr{H}/c\hbar)}(y-y_0)], \tag{125.6}$$

where the H_n are Hermite polynomials.

The energy given by the first term in (125.5) corresponds to the motion in the xy-plane. In classical mechanics this is a motion in a circle about a fixed centre. The quantity y_0, which is conserved, corresponds to the classical y co-ordinate of the centre of the circle. The quantity $x_0 = cp_y/e\mathscr{H} + x$ is also conserved; it is easy to see that the operator $x + c\hat{p}_y/e\mathscr{H}$ commutes with the Hamiltonian (125.2). This quantity x_0 corresponds to the classical x co-ordinate of the centre of the circle.† The operators $\hat{x}_0$ and $\hat{y}_0$, however, do not commute. In other words, the co-ordinates x_0 and y_0 cannot take definite values simultaneously.

Since (125.5) does not contain the quantity p_x, which assumes a continuous sequence of values, the energy levels are continuously degenerate. However the degree of degeneracy becomes finite if the motion on the x, y plane is restricted to a large, but finite, area $S = L_x L_y$. The number of (now discrete) possible values of p_x in an interval Δp_x is $(L_x/2\pi\hbar)\Delta p_x$. All values of p_x are admissible for which the orbit centre is inside S (we neglect the radius of the circle as compared to the large L_y). From the condition $0 < y_0 < L_y$ we have $\Delta p_x = eHL_y/c$. Hence the number of energy levels (for given u, p_z) is

$$eHS/2\pi\hbar c.$$

If the region of motion is bounded along the z axis too (dimensions L_z), the number of possible values of p_z in an interval Δp_z is $(L_z/2\pi\hbar)\Delta p_z$ and the number of energy levels in this interval is

$$\frac{eHS}{2\pi\hbar c}\frac{L_z}{2\pi\hbar}\Delta p_z = \frac{eHV}{y\pi^2\hbar^2 c}\Delta p_z.$$

† For, in classical motion in a circle of radius $c\mu v_t/e\mathscr{H}$ (where v_t is the projection of the velocity on the xy-plane; see *The Classical Theory of Fields*, §3-7), we have

$$y_0 = -cp_x/e\mathscr{H} = -c\mu v_x/e\mathscr{H} + y.$$

It is evident from this that y_0 is the y co-ordinate of the centre of the circle. The other co-ordinate is

$$x_0 = c\mu v_y/e\mathscr{H} + x = cp_y/e\mathscr{H} + x.$$

For an electron there is an additional degeneracy: putting in (125.5) $\beta = -|e|\hbar/\mu c$, we obtain

$$E = (n+\tfrac{1}{2}+\sigma)\,|e|\hbar\mathscr{H}/\mu c + p_z^2/2\mu, \tag{125.7}$$

where $\sigma = \pm\frac{1}{2}$; it is evident that the levels with n, $\sigma = \frac{1}{2}$ and $n+1$, $\sigma = -\frac{1}{2}$ are the same.

§126. The Zeeman effect

Let us consider an atom in a homogeneous magnetic field. Its Hamiltonian is of the form

$$\hat{H} = \frac{1}{2\mu}\sum_a (\hat{\mathbf{p}}_a + e\mathbf{A}_a/c)^2 + U(x,y,z) + \frac{e\hbar}{\mu c}\mathscr{H}\cdot\sum_a \hat{\mathbf{s}}_a,$$

where the summations are taken over all the electrons; $U(x, y, z)$ is the energy of interaction of the electrons with the nucleus and with one another.† The sum $\Sigma\,\hat{\mathbf{s}}_a$ is the operator $\hat{\mathbf{S}}$ of the total spin of the atom. Denoting by $\hat{H}_0$ the Hamiltonian of the atom in the absence of the field:

$$\hat{H}_0 = (1/2\mu)\sum_a \hat{\mathbf{p}}_a^2 + U(x,y,z),$$

we can rewrite $\hat{H}$ in the form

$$\hat{H} = \hat{H}_0 + \frac{e}{\mu c}\sum_a \mathbf{A}_a\cdot\hat{\mathbf{p}}_a + \frac{e^2}{2\mu c^2}\sum_a \mathbf{A}_a^2 + \frac{e\hbar}{\mu c}\mathscr{H}\cdot\hat{\mathbf{S}}; \tag{126.1}$$

we recall that $\hat{\mathbf{p}}_a$ and $\mathbf{A}_a$ commute in a homogeneous field with the vector potential (124.5).

Substituting $\mathbf{A} = \frac{1}{2}\mathscr{H}\times\mathbf{r}$ in (126.1) and using the identity $\mathscr{H}\times\mathbf{r}\cdot\mathbf{p} = \mathscr{H}\cdot\mathbf{r}\times\mathbf{p}$, we obtain

$$\hat{H} = \hat{H}_0 + \frac{e}{2\mu c}\mathscr{H}\cdot\sum_a \mathbf{r}_a\times\hat{\mathbf{p}}_a + \frac{e^2}{8\mu c^2}\sum_a (\mathscr{H}\times\mathbf{r}_a)^2 + \frac{e\hbar}{\mu c}\mathscr{H}\cdot\hat{\mathbf{S}}.$$

The vector $\mathbf{r}_a\times\hat{\mathbf{p}}_a$, however, is simply the operator of the orbital angular momentum of the electron, and the summation over all the electrons gives the operator $\hbar\hat{\mathbf{L}}$ of the total orbital angular momentum of the atom. Thus

$$\hat{H} = \hat{H}_0 + \beta_0(\hat{\mathbf{L}}+2\hat{\mathbf{S}})\cdot\mathscr{H} + (e^2/8\mu c^2)\sum_a (\mathscr{H}\times\mathbf{r}_a)^2, \tag{126.2}$$

where we have put $\beta_0 = e\hbar/2\mu c$ for the Bohr magneton.

Let us suppose that the magnetic field is so weak that $\beta_0\mathscr{H}$ is small compared with the distances between the energy levels of the atom, including the

† In this section we shall denote the charge on the electron by $-e$.

fine-structure intervals. Then the second and third terms in (126.2) can be regarded as a perturbation, the unperturbed levels being the separate components of the multiplets. In the first approximation we can neglect the third term, which is quadratic with respect to the field, in comparison with the second term, which is linear.

The magnetic field, by distinguishing a certain direction in space, removes the degeneracy of the levels with respect to the directions of the total angular momentum **J** of the atom. By virtue of the axial symmetry of the field, the projection of the total angular momentum on the direction of the field is conserved, and the different components of the split term are characterised by the values M_J of this projection. The energy ΔE of the splitting is determined by the mean values of the perturbation in states with the given quantum numbers† J, L, S and different values of M_J:

$$\Delta E = \beta_0\overline{(\mathbf{L}+2\mathbf{S})}\cdot\mathscr{H} = \beta_0\,\overline{(\mathbf{J}+\mathbf{S})}\cdot\mathscr{H}.$$

If we take the direction of the magnetic field to be along the z-axis, we have

$$\Delta E = \beta_0\mathscr{H}(\bar{J}_z+\bar{S}_z). \tag{126.3}$$

The operator $\beta_0(\hat{\mathbf{L}}+2\hat{\mathbf{S}})$ may be regarded as the operator of the "intrinsic" magnetic moment of the atom, which it possesses in the absence of the field.

For the vector **J**, which is conserved (in the unperturbed state), we have simply $J_z = M$. The mean value of S_z could be found immediately from the general formulae of §31 for the matrix elements of added angular momenta. Here, however, we shall give another derivation, whose significance is more easily seen. It is evident from considerations of symmetry that the mean value $\bar{\mathbf{S}}$ is a vector directed parallel to the vector **J**, the latter being the only one which is conserved. Hence we can write $\bar{\mathbf{S}} =$ constant $\times\mathbf{J}$. Multiplying both sides of this equation by **J**, we have $\overline{\mathbf{J}\cdot\mathbf{S}} = \mathbf{J}\cdot\bar{\mathbf{S}} =$ constant $\times\mathbf{J}^2$, from which the constant is determined. Thus

$$\bar{\mathbf{S}} = \mathbf{J}(\mathbf{J}\cdot\mathbf{S})/\mathbf{J}^2,$$

or

$$\bar{S}_z = M_J(\mathbf{J}\cdot\mathbf{S})/\mathbf{J}^2; \tag{126.4}$$

we have omitted the bar over $\mathbf{J}\cdot\mathbf{S}$, since this product has a definite value in the Russell-Saunders approximation. Here $\mathbf{J}^2$ is equal to its eigenvalue $J(J+1)$, while the eigenvalue of $\mathbf{J}\cdot\mathbf{S}$ is (see (30.3))

$$\mathbf{J}\cdot\mathbf{S} = \tfrac{1}{2}\{J(J+1)-L(L+1)+S(S+1)\}.$$

Collecting the above expressions and substituting in (126.3), we find the

† We assume that the case of Russell-Saunders coupling holds for the atomic terms.

following final expression for the energy of the splitting:

$$\Delta E = \beta_0 g M_J \mathscr{H}, \qquad M_J = -J, -J+1, \dots, J, \tag{126.5}$$

where

$$g = 1+[J(J+1)-L(L+1)+S(S+1)]/2J(J+1) \tag{126.6}$$

is what is called thc *Landé factor*. The splitting of the levels in a magnetic field is called the *Zeeman effect*. We see that the magnetic field completely removes the degeneracy (if $g \neq 0$), and the magnitude of the splitting is proportional to the field.

The Landé factor for the various components of the multiplet takes values lying between those corresponding to $J = L \pm S$ (if $L \geqslant S$):

$$(L+2S)/(L+S) \geqslant g \geqslant (L-2S+1)/(L-S+1),$$

or between those corresponding to $J = S \pm L$ (if $S \geqslant L$):

$$(L+2S)/(L+S) \geqslant g \geqslant (2S+2-L)/(S-L+1).$$

If there is no spin ($S = 0$, $J = L$), g is simply unity†; if $L = 0$, $g = 2$. For $J = 0$ (which can occur only for $S = L$), the expression (126.6) becomes indeterminate; the effect, however, is of course absent, since $M_J = 0$ if $J = 0$. The splitting linear with respect to the field vanishes for some terms with $J \neq 0$ also, namely for $L = 2S-1$, $J = S-1$.

The derivative $-\partial \Delta E/\partial \mathscr{H}$ is the mean value of the magnetic moment of the atom.‡ We see that an atom in a state with a definite value M_J of the component in some direction of the total angular momentum has a mean magnetic moment $-\beta_0 g M_J$ in that direction.||

If the atom has neither spin nor orbital angular momentum ($S = L = 0$), and second term in (126.2) gives no displacement of the level, either in the first approximation or in any higher one (since the matrix elements of **L** and **S** vanish). Hence, in this case, the whole effect arises from the third term in (126.2), and in the first approximation of perturbation theory the displacement of the level is equal to the mean value

$$\Delta E = \frac{e^2}{8\mu c^2} \sum_a \overline{(\mathscr{H} \times \mathbf{r}_a)^2}. \tag{126.7}$$

Putting $(\mathscr{H} \times \mathbf{r}_a)^2 = \mathscr{H}^2 r_a{}^2 \sin^2\theta$, where θ is the angle between $\mathbf{r}_a$ and $\mathscr{H}$, and averaging with respect to the directions of $\mathbf{r}_a$, we have $\overline{\sin^2\theta} = 1 - \overline{\cos^2\theta} = 2/3$ (bearing in mind that the wave function of a state with $L = S = 0$ is

† The splitting described by the general formulae (126.5), (126.6) is often called the *anomalous Zeeman effect.* This unfortunate name arose because, before the spin of the electron was discovered, the effect described by formula (126.5) with $g = 1$ was regarded as normal.

‡ See the derivation given at the end of §72 (formula (72.2)).

|| It is easy to see that the mean values of all 2^n-pole atomic magnetic moments (n even) vanish.

spherically symmetrical). Thus

$$\Delta E = \frac{e^2}{12\mu c^2}\mathscr{H}^2 \sum_a \overline{r_a{}^2}\,. \tag{126.8}$$

The derivative $-\partial\Delta E/\partial\mathscr{H}$ is the magnetic moment acquired by the atom in the magnetic field. Writing it in the form $\chi\mathscr{H}$, we can regard

$$\chi = -\frac{e^2}{6\mu c^2}\sum_a \overline{r_a{}^2} \tag{126.9}$$

as the magnetic susceptibility of the atom. It is negative, i.e. an atom with $L = S = 0$ is diamagnetic.†

If $J = 0$, but $S = L \neq 0$, the displacement linear with respect to the field again vanishes, but the quadratic effect from the perturbation $\beta_0\mathscr{H}\times(\hat{L}_z+2\hat{S}_z)$ in the second approximation exceeds the effect (126.7).‡ This is because, according to the general formula (38.9), the correction to the eigenvalue of the energy in the second approximation is given by a sum of expressions whose denominators contain the differences between the unperturbed energy levels, in this case the fine-structure intervals of the level, which are small quantities. We have remarked in §38 that the correction to the normal level in the second approximation is always negative. Hence the magnetic moment in the normal state is positive, i.e. an atom in the normal state with $J = 0$, $L = S \neq 0$ is paramagnetic.

In strong magnetic fields, where $\beta_0\mathscr{H}$ is comparable with or greater than the intervals in the fine structure, the splitting of the levels differs from that predicted by formulae (126.5), (126.6); this phenomenon is called the *Paschen-Back effect*.

The calculation of the energy of the splitting is very simple in the case where the Zeeman splitting is large in comparison with the intervals in the fine structure but still, of course, small compared with the distances between the different multiplets (when it may be shown that we can, as before, neglect the third term of the Hamiltonian (126.2) in comparison with the second).‖ In other words, the energy in the magnetic field considerably exceeds the spin-orbit interaction. Hence we can neglect this interaction in the first approximation. The projections M_L and M_S of the orbital angular momentum and spin on the z-axis are then conserved, as well as the projection of the total angular momentum. The perturbation operator $\beta_0\mathscr{H}(\hat{L}_z+2\hat{S}_z)$ can

† We may mention that the Thomas-Fermi model cannot be used to calculate the mean square distance of the electrons from the nuclei. Though the integral $\int nr^2dr$ with the Thomas-Fermi density $n(r)$ converges, it does so too slowly, and the values obtained are very different from the experimental ones.

‡ For $S = L \neq 0$, the non-diagonal matrix elements of L_z, S_z for the transitions $S, L, J \rightarrow S, L, J\pm 1$ are not in general zero.

‖ For intermediate cases, where the effect of the magnetic field is comparable with the spin-orbit interaction, the splitting cannot be calculated in a general form; the calculation for $S = \frac{1}{2}$ is given in Problem 1.

be reduced to diagonal form simultaneously with $\hat{L}_z$ and $\hat{S}_z$, so that the splitting is given by the formula

$$\Delta E = \beta_0 \mathscr{H}(M_L+2M_S). \tag{126.10}$$

The multiplet splitting is superposed on the splitting in the magnetic field. It is determined by the mean value of the operator $A\hat{\mathbf{L}}\cdot\hat{\mathbf{S}}$ (67.2) with respect to the state with the given M_L, M_S (we are considering the multiplet splitting due to the spin-orbit interaction). For a given value of one of the angular momentum components, the mean values of the other two are zero. Hence $\overline{\mathbf{L}\cdot\mathbf{S}} = M_L M_S$, so that the energy of the levels is given in the next approximation by the formula

$$\Delta E = \beta_0 \mathscr{H}(M_L+2M_S)+AM_LM_S. \tag{126.11}$$

The calculation of the Zeeman effect in the general case of any type of coupling (not Russell-Saunders) is not possible. We can say only that the splitting (in a weak field) is linear with respect to the field and proportional to the projection M_J of the total angular momentum, i.e. it has the form

$$\Delta E = \beta_0 g_{nJ} \mathscr{H} M_J, \tag{126.12}$$

where the g_{nJ} are some coefficients characterising the term in question; n denotes the assembly of all the quantum numbers, except J, which characterise the term. Though these coefficients cannot be calculated separately, it is possible to obtain a formula, useful in applications, which gives the sum $\sum_n g_{nJ}$ taken over all possible states of the atom with the given electron configuration and total angular momentum.

The quantities $g_{nJ}M_J$ are the diagonal matrix elements of the operator $\hat{L}_z+2\hat{S}_z$, calculated with respect to the wave functions ψ_{nJM_J}. The quantities $g_{SLJ}M_J$, on the other hand (where g_{SLJ} is the Russell-Saunders Landé factor), are the diagonal matrix elements of the same operator with respect to the functions ψ_{SLJM_J}. The functions ψ_{nJM_J} with given J, M_J can be represented as mutually orthogonal linear combinations of the functions ψ_{SLJM_J} with the same J, M_J. The linear transformation of one orthogonal set of functions into another is unitary (see §91). A unitary transformation of the base functions, however, leaves unchanged the sum of the diagonal elements of the matrix.† Hence we conclude that

$$\sum_n g_{nJ}M_J = \sum_{S,L} g_{SLJ}M_J,$$

or, cancelling M_J (since g_{nJ} and g_{SLJ} do not depend on M_J),

$$\sum_n g_{nJ} = \sum_{S,L} g_{SLJ}. \tag{126.13}$$

† The proof was given in §91 in connection with the characters of matrices of group representations.

The summation is taken over all states with the given value of J which are possible for the given electron configuration. This is the required relation.

PROBLEMS

PROBLEM 1. Determine the splitting of a term with $S = \frac{1}{2}$ by the Paschen-Back effect.

SOLUTION. The magnetic field and the spin-orbit interaction have to be taken into account simultaneously by perturbation theory, i.e. the perturbation operator is†

$$\hat{V} = A\,\hat{\mathbf{L}}.\hat{\mathbf{S}} + \beta_0(\hat{L}_z + 2\hat{S}_z)\mathscr{H}.$$

As the initial wave functions for the zero approximation, we take functions corresponding to states with definite values of L, $S = \frac{1}{2}$, M_L, M_S (L given; $M_L = -L, \ldots, L$; $M_S = \pm\frac{1}{2}$). In the perturbed states, only the sum $M_J = M_L + M_S$ is conserved ($\hat{V}$ commutes with $\hat{J}_z$), so that we can ascribe definite values of M_J to the components of the split term.

The values $M_J = L+\frac{1}{2}$ and $M_J = -(L+\frac{1}{2})$ can occur in only one way each: with $M_L = L$, $M_S = \frac{1}{2}$ and $M_L = -L$, $M_S = -\frac{1}{2}$ respectively. Hence the corrections to the energy of the states with these M_J are simply equal to the diagonal matrix elements $V_{M_L M_S}^{M_L M_S}$ with the indicated values of M_L and M_S. The remaining values of M_J can occur in two ways each: with $M_L = M_J - \frac{1}{2}$, $M_S = \frac{1}{2}$ and with $M_L = M_J + \frac{1}{2}$, $M_S = -\frac{1}{2}$. Here two different values of the energy correspond to each M_J; they are determined from the secular equation formed from the matrix elements for transitions between these two states. The matrix elements of $\mathbf{L}\,.\,\mathbf{S}$ are calculated by directly multiplying the matrices $\mathbf{L}_{M'_L}^{M_L}$ and $\mathbf{S}_{M'_S}^{M_S}$, and are

$$(\mathbf{L}\,.\,\mathbf{S})_{M_L M_S}^{M_L M_S} = M_L M_S,$$

$$(\mathbf{L}\,.\,\mathbf{S})_{M_J-\frac{1}{2},\frac{1}{2}}^{M_J+\frac{1}{2},-\frac{1}{2}} = (\mathbf{L}\,.\,\mathbf{S})_{M_J+\frac{1}{2},-\frac{1}{2}}^{M_J-\frac{1}{2},\frac{1}{2}} = \tfrac{1}{2}\sqrt{[(L+M_J+\tfrac{1}{2})(L-M_J+\tfrac{1}{2})]}.$$

In the absence of a magnetic field, the term is a doublet, the distance between the components being $\epsilon = A(L+\frac{1}{2})$; see (67.4). We take the lower of these levels as the origin of energy. Then the final formulae for the levels E_{M_J} in the magnetic field are

$$E_{L+\frac{1}{2}} = \epsilon + \beta_0\mathscr{H}(L+1),$$

$$E_{-(L+\frac{1}{2})} = \epsilon - \beta_0\mathscr{H}(L+1),$$

$$E_{M_J}{}^{\pm} = \tfrac{1}{2}\epsilon + \beta_0\mathscr{H}M_J \pm \sqrt{[\tfrac{1}{4}(\epsilon^2+\beta_0{}^2\mathscr{H}^2) + \beta_0\mathscr{H}M_J\epsilon/(2L+1)]},$$

$$M_J = L-\tfrac{1}{2}, \ldots, -L+\tfrac{1}{2}.$$

For small $\beta_0\mathscr{H}/\epsilon$ we have

$$E_{M_J}{}^{+} = \epsilon + \beta_0\mathscr{H}M_J\,.\,2(L+1)/(2L+1),\quad E_{M_J}{}^{-} = \beta_0\mathscr{H}M_J\,.\,2L/(2L+1),$$

in accordance with formulae (126.5), (126.6) (in which we must put $S = \frac{1}{2}$, $J = L\pm\frac{1}{2}$). For large $\beta_0\mathscr{H}/\epsilon$ we have

$$E_{M_J}{}^{\pm} = \beta_0\mathscr{H}(M_J \pm \tfrac{1}{2}),$$

in accordance with (126.10).

† We do not include in $\hat{V}$ the term proportional to $(\hat{\mathbf{L}}\,.\,\hat{\mathbf{S}})^2$ (the spin-spin interaction). It must be borne in mind, however, that, for a spin $S = \frac{1}{2}$, the expression $(\hat{\mathbf{L}}\,.\,\hat{\mathbf{S}})^2$ reduces by virtue of the properties of the Pauli matrices (as may easily be seen from (54.4)) to $\hat{\mathbf{L}}\,.\,\hat{\mathbf{S}}$, and is therefore included in the formula for $\hat{V}$ as written here.

PROBLEM 2. Determine the Zeeman splitting for the terms of a diatomic molecule in case *a*.

SOLUTION. The magnetic moment arising from the motion of the nuclei is very small in comparison with the magnetic moment of the electrons. Hence the perturbation due to the magnetic field can be written for the molecule as for a system of electrons, i.e. in the form used previously: $\hat{V} = \beta_0 \mathscr{H} \cdot (\hat{\mathbf{L}} + 2\hat{\mathbf{S}})$, where **L**, **S** are the electron orbital and spin angular momenta.

Averaging the perturbation with respect to the electron state, we have in case *a*

$$\beta_0 \mathscr{H} n_z(\Lambda + 2\Sigma) = \beta_0 \mathscr{H} n_z(2\Omega - \Lambda).$$

The mean value of n_z with respect to the rotation of the molecule is the diagonal matrix element $(n_z)_{JM_J}^{JM_J}$, which is equal to $M_J n_J^J$, n_J^J being given by formulae (84.1) (with J and Ω in place of K and Λ). Thus the required splitting is

$$\Delta E = \beta_0 \frac{\Omega(2\Omega - \Lambda)}{J(J+1)} M_J \mathscr{H}.$$

PROBLEM 3. The same as Problem 2, but for case *b*.

SOLUTION. The diagonal matrix elements $V_{\Lambda KJ}^{\Lambda KJ}$ which determine the required splitting could be calculated from the general rules given in §84. However, it is simpler and more comprehensible to perform the calculation as follows. Averaging the perturbation operator with respect to the orbital and electron states, we obtain

$$\beta_0 \mathscr{H}(\Lambda n_z + 2\hat{S}_z)$$

(the spin operator is unaffected by this averaging). Next, we average with respect to rotation of the molecule; the mean value of n_z is given by formula (84.1), and so we have

$$\beta_0 \mathscr{H}[\{\Lambda^2/K(K+1)\}\hat{K}_z + 2\hat{S}_z].$$

Lastly, we average with respect to the spin wave function; after the whole averaging, the mean values of the vectors must be directed parallel to the total angular momentum **J**, which is the only conserved vector. Hence we have (cf. (126.4))

$$\frac{\beta_0 \mathscr{H}}{J(J+1)} \left[\frac{\Lambda^2}{K(K+1)} \mathbf{K} \cdot \mathbf{J} + 2\mathbf{S} \cdot \mathbf{J}\right] M_J,$$

or finally

$$\Delta E = \frac{\beta_0}{J(J+1)} \left\{\frac{\Lambda^2}{2K(K+1)}[J(J+1) + K(K+1) - S(S+1)] + \right.$$
$$\left. + [J(J+1) - K(K+1) + S(S+1)]\right\} \mathscr{H} M_J.$$

PROBLEM 4. Determine the Zeeman splitting of the components of the hyperfine structure of an atomic term.

SOLUTION. In view of the smallness of the magnetic moment of the nucleus in comparison with the electron magnetic moment, we can neglect the former in the expression for the perturbation energy, so that we can begin from the previous formula (126.3); we suppose the field so weak that the splitting caused by it is small compared with the intervals in the hyperfine structure. However, the averaging must be performed not only with respect to the electron state, but also with respect to the directions of the nuclear spin. As a result of the former averaging we obtain $\Delta E = \beta_0 g J_z \mathscr{H}$, with the same g as before (126.6). A second averaging gives, similarly to (126.4),

$$\bar{J}_z = (\mathbf{J}\cdot\mathbf{F})M_F/F^2,$$

where $\mathbf{F} = \mathbf{J}+\mathbf{i}$ is the total conserved angular momentum of the atom. Thus we have finally

$$\Delta E = \beta_0 g \frac{F(F+1)+J(J+1)-i(i+1)}{2F(F+1)} \mathscr{H} M_F.$$

§127. A neutral particle in a magnetic field

Let us consider an electrically neutral particle having a magnetic moment, and situated in a magnetic field which is homogeneous but varies with time. We may have in mind either an elementary particle (a neutron) or a complex one (an atom). The magnetic field is supposed so weak that the magnetic energy of the particle in the field is small compared with the intervals between its energy levels. Then we can consider the motion of the particle as a whole, its internal state being given.

Let $\hat{\mathbf{s}}$ be the operator of the "intrinsic" angular momentum of the particle—the spin of an elementary particle, or the total angular momentum **J** for an atom. The magnetic moment operator can be represented in the form $\beta\hat{\mathbf{s}}$. The Hamiltonian for the motion of a neutral particle as a whole can evidently be written†

$$\hat{H} = -\beta\hat{\mathbf{s}}\cdot\mathscr{H}. \tag{127.1}$$

In a homogeneous field,‡ this operator does not contain the co-ordinates explicitly. Hence the wave function of the particle falls into a product of a co-ordinate and a spin function. Of these, the former is simply the wave function of free motion; in what follows, we shall be interested only in the spin part. We shall show that the problem of a particle with any angular momentum s can be reduced to the simpler problem of the motion of a particle of spin $\frac{1}{2}$ (MAJORANA). To do this, it is sufficient to use the method which we have already employed in §56. That is, instead of one particle of spin s, we can formally introduce a system of $2s$ "particles" of spin $\frac{1}{2}$. The operator $\hat{\mathbf{s}}$ is then represented as a sum $\Sigma\,\hat{\mathbf{s}}_a$ of the spin operators of these "particles", and the wave function as a product of $2s$ spinors of rank one. The Hamiltonian (127.1) then falls into the sum of $2s$ independent Hamiltonians:

$$\hat{H} = \sum_a \hat{H}_a, \qquad \hat{H}_a = -\beta\mathscr{H}\cdot\hat{\mathbf{s}}_a, \tag{127.2}$$

so that the motion of each of the $2s$ "particles" is determined independently of

† We write out only that part of the Hamiltonian which depends on the spin.

‡ These arguments can also be applied to the case where any particle (charged or not) moves in a homogeneous magnetic field, if its motion can be regarded as quasi-classical. The magnetic field, which varies as the particle moves along its path, can then be regarded simply as a function of time, and we can apply the same equations to the variation of the spin wave function.

the others. When this has been done, we need only reintroduce the components of an arbitrary symmetrical spinor of rank $2s$ in place of the products of components of $2s$ spinors of rank one.

PROBLEMS

PROBLEM 1. Determine the spin wave function for a neutral particle of spin $\frac{1}{2}$, in a homogeneous magnetic field which is constant in direction but varies in absolute magnitude according to an arbitrary law $\mathscr{H} = \mathscr{H}(t)$.

SOLUTION. The wave function is a spinor ψ^ν satisfying the wave equation

$$i\hbar\, \partial\psi^\nu/\partial t = -\beta\mathscr{H}\hat{s}_z\psi^\nu$$

(the direction of the field being taken as the z-axis), or, in spinor components (by (54.3)),

$$i\hbar\, \partial\psi^1/\partial t = -\tfrac{1}{2}\beta\mathscr{H}\psi^1, \qquad i\hbar\, \partial\psi^2/\partial t = \tfrac{1}{2}\beta\mathscr{H}\psi^2.$$

Hence

$$\psi^1 = c_1 e^{(i\beta/2\hbar)\int\mathscr{H}\,dt}, \quad \psi^2 = c_2 e^{-(i\beta/2\hbar)\int\mathscr{H}\,dt}.$$

The constants c_1, c_2 must be determined from the initial conditions and from the normalisation condition $|c_1|^2+|c_2|^2 = 1$.

PROBLEM 2. The same as Problem 1, but for a magnetic field constant in absolute magnitude, whose direction rotates uniformly in a plane, with angular velocity ω.

SOLUTION. We take the xy-plane as the plane of rotation of the field; then $\mathscr{H}_x = \mathscr{H}\cos\omega t$, $\mathscr{H}_y = \mathscr{H}\sin\omega t$, $\mathscr{H}_z = 0$. The wave equation is

$$i\hbar\, \partial\psi^\nu/\partial t = -\beta\mathscr{H}(\cos\omega t.\, \hat{s}_x+\sin\omega t\,.\,\hat{s}_y)\psi^\nu,$$

or, by (54.3),

$$i\hbar\, \partial\psi^1/\partial t+\tfrac{1}{2}\beta\mathscr{H}e^{-i\omega t}\psi^2 = 0, \quad i\hbar\, \partial\psi^2/\partial t+\tfrac{1}{2}\beta\mathscr{H}e^{i\omega t}\psi^1 = 0.$$

Making the substitution

$$\psi^1 e^{\frac{1}{2}i\omega t} = \phi^1, \qquad \psi^2 e^{-\frac{1}{2}i\omega t} = \phi^2,$$

we obtain a system of linear equations with constant coefficients:

$$i\hbar\, \partial\phi^1/\partial t+\tfrac{1}{2}\omega\hbar\phi^1+\tfrac{1}{2}\beta\mathscr{H}\phi^2 = 0,$$
$$i\hbar\, \partial\phi^2/\partial t-\tfrac{1}{2}\omega\hbar\phi^2+\tfrac{1}{2}\beta\mathscr{H}\phi^1 = 0.$$

Solving these, we have

$$\psi^1 = e^{-\frac{1}{2}i\omega t}(ae^{\frac{1}{2}it\Omega}+be^{-\frac{1}{2}it\Omega}),$$

$$\psi^2 = \frac{\beta\mathscr{H}}{\hbar}e^{\frac{1}{2}i\omega t}\left(\frac{a}{\omega+\Omega}e^{\frac{1}{2}it\Omega}+\frac{b}{\omega-\Omega}e^{-\frac{1}{2}it\Omega}\right), \quad \hbar\Omega = \sqrt{(\beta^2\mathscr{H}^2+\omega^2)}.$$

The constants a and b are related by

$$\frac{|a|^2}{\Omega+\omega}+\frac{|b|^2}{\Omega-\omega} = \frac{1}{2\Omega},$$

which follows from the normalisation condition $|\psi^1|^2+|\psi^2|^2 = 1$.

§128. The current density in a magnetic field

We shall now derive the quantum-mechanical expression for the current density when charged particles move in a magnetic field.

We start from the well-known formula of classical electrodynamics

$$\delta H = -(1/c)\int \mathbf{j}\,.\,\delta\mathbf{A}\,\mathrm{d}V, \tag{128.1}$$

where **j** is the current density; this determines the change in the Hamilton's function of charges distributed in space when the vector potential is varied.† In quantum mechanics this formula must be applied to the mean value of the Hamiltonian of the charged particle:

$$\bar{H} = \int \Psi^*[(\hat{\mathbf{p}}-e\mathbf{A}/c)^2/2\mu - \beta\mathcal{H}\,.\,\hat{\mathbf{s}}]\Psi\,\mathrm{d}V. \tag{128.2}$$

Effecting the variation and bearing in mind that $\delta\mathcal{H} = \mathbf{curl}\,\delta\mathbf{A}$, we find

$$\bar{H} = \int \Psi^*\left[-\frac{e}{2\mu c}(\hat{\mathbf{p}}\,.\,\delta\mathbf{A}+\delta\mathbf{A}\,.\,\hat{\mathbf{p}})+\frac{e^2}{\mu c^2}\mathbf{A}\,.\,\delta\mathbf{A}\right]\Psi\,\mathrm{d}V - \beta\int \mathbf{curl}\,\delta\mathbf{A}\,.\,\Psi^*\hat{\mathbf{s}}\Psi\,\mathrm{d}V. \tag{128.3}$$

The term in $\hat{\mathbf{p}}\,.\,\delta\mathbf{A}$ is transformed by integration by parts:

$$\int \Psi^*\hat{\mathbf{p}}\,.\,\delta\mathbf{A}\,\Psi\,\mathrm{d}V = -i\hbar\int \Psi^*\nabla(\delta\mathbf{A}\,.\,\Psi)\,\mathrm{d}V$$
$$= i\hbar\int \delta\mathbf{A}\,.\,\Psi\nabla\Psi^*\,\mathrm{d}V$$

(the integral over an infinitely distant surface vanishing in the usual way). The integration by parts is also used in the last term in (128.3), together with the well-known formula of vector analysis

$$\mathbf{a}\,.\,\mathbf{curl}\,\mathbf{b} = -\mathrm{div}(\mathbf{a}\times\mathbf{b})+\mathbf{b}\,.\,\mathbf{curl}\,\mathbf{a}.$$

The integral of the div term vanishes, so that we have

$$\int \Psi^*\hat{\mathbf{s}}\Psi\,.\,\mathbf{curl}\,\delta\mathbf{A}\,\mathrm{d}V = \int \delta\mathbf{A}\,.\,\mathbf{curl}(\Psi^*\hat{\mathbf{s}}\Psi)\,\mathrm{d}V.$$

---

† Lagrange's function for a charge in a magnetic field contains a term $e\mathbf{v}\,.\,\mathbf{A}/c$, or, if the charge is distributed in space, $(1/c)\int \mathbf{j}\,.\,\mathbf{A}\,\mathrm{d}V$ (see *The Classical Theory of Fields*, §3–1, Addison-Wesley Press, Cambridge (Mass.) 1951.

The change in the Lagrange's function when **A** is varied is therefore

$$\delta L = (1/c)\int \mathbf{j}\,.\,\delta\mathbf{A}\,\mathrm{d}V.$$

An infinitely small change in Hamilton's function is, however, equal to the change in Lagrange's function, taken with the opposite sign (see *The Classical Theory of Fields*)

The final result is

$$\delta \bar{H} = -\frac{ie\hbar}{2\mu c}\int \delta\mathbf{A}\,.(\Psi\nabla\Psi^* - \Psi^*\nabla\Psi)\,dV + \frac{e^2}{\mu c}\int \mathbf{A}\,.\delta\mathbf{A}\Psi\Psi^*\,dV -$$

$$-\beta\int \delta\mathbf{A}\,.\,\mathbf{curl}(\Psi^*\hat{\mathbf{s}}\Psi)\,dV.$$

Comparing this expression with (128.1), we find the following expression for the current density:

$$\mathbf{j} = \frac{ie\hbar}{2\mu}(\Psi\nabla\Psi^* - \Psi^*\nabla\Psi) - \frac{e^2}{\mu c}\mathbf{A}\Psi\Psi^* + \beta c\,\mathbf{curl}(\Psi^*\hat{\mathbf{s}}\Psi). \tag{128.4}$$

We emphasise that, though this expression contains the vector potential explicitly, it is nevertheless one-valued, as it should be. This is easily seen by direct calculation, recalling that the transformation (124.6) of the vector potential must be accompanied by the transformation (124.7) of the wave function.

The expression (128.4) is the mean value of the current. It may be regarded as a diagonal matrix element of the current density operator. The non-diagonal matrix elements of this operator can then be determined also. We shall not pause to write out here the explicit expression for the operator itself, which is rarely needed; we give only the matrix elements, which are evidently

$$\mathbf{j}_{nm} = \frac{ie\hbar}{2\mu}(\Psi_m\nabla\Psi_n^* - \Psi_n^*\nabla\Psi_m) - \frac{e^2}{\mu c}\mathbf{A}\Psi_m\Psi_n^* +$$

$$+\beta c\,\mathbf{curl}(\Psi_n^*\hat{\mathbf{s}}\Psi_m). \tag{128.5}$$

PROBLEM

Determine the energy of the hyperfine structure of a level for an atom containing, outside the closed shells, only one electron, which is in the *s* state. This electron is described by the wave function $\psi(r)$ of its motion in the self-consistent field of the other electrons and the nucleus (E. Fermi 1930).

Solution. The direct calculation of the energy of the splitting as the mean value of the dipole interaction between the magnetic moments of the electron and the nucleus leads to a sum of integrals, each of which diverges; hence this method is not suitable for the calculation. Instead, we calculate the energy of the splitting as the energy $E = -\beta\,\overline{\mathbf{i}.\mathscr{H}}$ of the magnetic moment $\beta\hat{\mathbf{i}}$ of the nucleus ($\mathbf{i}$ being the spin of the nucleus) in the magnetic field (at the origin) due to the electron. According to a well-known formula of classical electrodynamics, we have

$$\bar{\mathscr{H}} = \frac{1}{c}\int \nabla\left(\frac{1}{r}\right)\times\mathbf{j}\,dV, \tag{1}$$

where $\mathbf{j} = 2\beta_0 c\,\mathbf{curl}(|\psi|^2\bar{\mathbf{s}})$ is the current density due to the electron angular momentum (spin). We remove from the region of integration in (1) a small sphere of radius r_0 about the origin, and integrate over the space between this sphere and an infinitely remote surface.

On integrating by parts, the integral over the infinitely remote surface vanishes. Using well-known formulae of vector analysis, we obtain (temporarily using the notation $\mathbf{F} = 2\beta_0 c|\psi|^2\bar{\mathbf{s}}$)

$$\int \nabla\left(\frac{1}{r}\right) \times \mathbf{curl}\,\mathbf{F}\,dV = -\int (\mathbf{F}\cdot\nabla)\nabla\left(\frac{1}{r}\right) dV - \\ -\int \nabla\left(\frac{1}{r}\right) \times (\mathbf{n}\times\mathbf{F})\,df, \qquad (2)$$

where the second integral on the right is taken over the surface of the small sphere ($\mathbf{n}$ being a unit vector along the radius). Since the wave function of the s state is centrally symmetric, the vector $\mathbf{F}$ is constant in direction. Expanding the expression $(\mathbf{F}.\nabla)\nabla(1/r)$ and integrating over angles in the first integral on the right-hand side of (2), we easily see that this term vanishes identically. In the surface integral we write $df = r_0^2\,do$ and pass to the limit $r_0 \to 0$. The result of integrating over angles is $\bar{\mathcal{H}} = (8\pi/3c)\mathbf{F}(0)$ or

$$\hat{\mathcal{H}} = (16\pi\beta_0/3)|\psi(0)|^2\hat{\mathbf{s}}.$$

Hence we have at once the energy

$$E = \frac{16\pi\beta_0|\beta|}{3}|\psi(0)|^2\mathbf{s}\cdot\mathbf{i} = \frac{8\pi\beta_0|\beta|}{3}[F(F+1)-i(i+1)-\tfrac{3}{4}]|\psi(0)|^2.$$

The distance ΔE between the two levels of the doublet in the hyperfine structure ($F = i\pm\frac{1}{2}$) is

$$\Delta E = \frac{8\pi\beta_0|\beta|}{3}(2i+1)|\psi(0)|^2.$$

MATHEMATICAL APPENDICES

§a. Hermite polynomials

The equation

$$y''-2xy'+2ny = 0 \tag{a.1}$$

belongs to a class which can be solved by what is called *Laplace's method.*†

This method is applicable to any linear equation of the form

$$\sum_{m=0}^{n} (a_m+b_m x) \frac{d^m y}{dx^m} = 0,$$

whose coefficients are of degree in x not higher than the first, and consists in the following procedure. We form the polynomials

$$P(t) = \sum_{m=0}^{n} a_m t^m, \qquad Q(t) = \sum_{m=0}^{n} b_m t^m,$$

and from them the function

$$Z(t) = (1/Q)e^{\int (P/Q)\,dt},$$

which is determined to within a constant factor. Then the solution of the equation under consideration can be expressed as a complex integral:

$$y = \int_C Z(t)e^{xt}\,dt,$$

where the path of integration C is taken so that the integral is finite and non-zero, and the function

$$V = e^{xt}QZ$$

returns to its original value when t describes the contour C (which may be either closed or open).

In the case of equation (a.1) we have

$$P = t^2+2n, \qquad Q = -2t, \qquad Z = t^{-(n+1)}e^{-\frac{1}{4}t^2},$$

so that its solution is

$$y = \int e^{xt-\frac{1}{4}t^2}\,dt/t^{n+1}. \tag{a.2}$$

† See, for instance, Goursat, *Cours d'Analyse Mathématique*, Vol. II; V. I. Smirnov, *Course of Higher Mathematics*, Vol. III.

For physical applications we need only consider values $n > -\frac{1}{2}$. For these values the contour of integration can be taken as C_1 or C_2 (Fig. 47); these satisfy the required conditions†, since the function $V = \text{constant} \times \times t^{-n} e^{xt-\frac{1}{4}t^2}$ vanishes at their ends ($t = +\infty$ or $t = -\infty$).

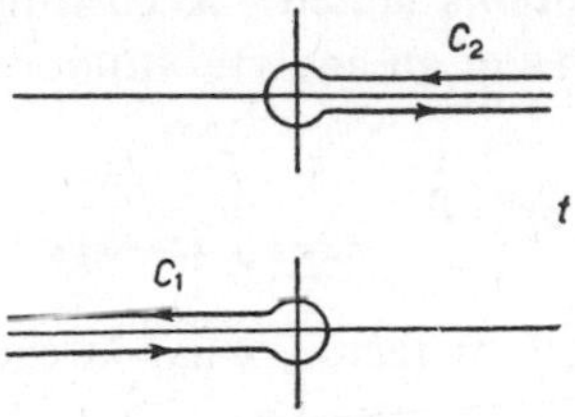

Fig. 47

Let us find the values of the parameter n for which equation (a.1) has solutions finite for all finite x, which tend to infinity, as $x \to \pm\infty$, not more rapidly than every finite power of x. First, we consider non-integral values of n. The integrals (a.2) along C_1 and C_2 then give two independent solutions of equation (a.1). We transform the integral along C_1 by introducing the variable u such that $t = 2(x-u)$. Omitting a constant factor, we find

$$y = e^{x^2} \int_{C_1'} e^{-u^2} du/(u-x)^{n+1}, \qquad \text{(a.3)}$$

where the integration is taken over the contour C_1' in the complex plane of u, as shown in Fig. 48.

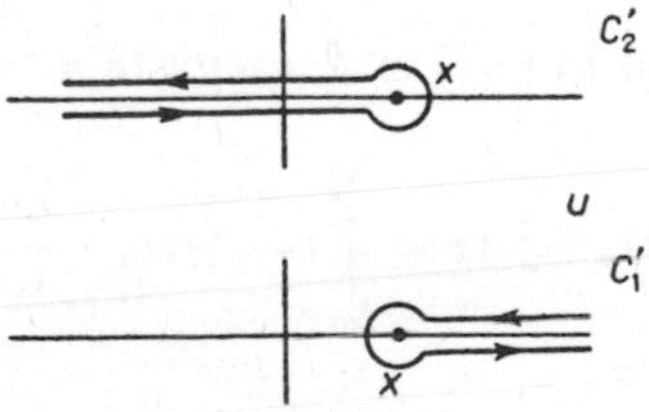

Fig. 48

As $x \to +\infty$, the whole path of integration C_1' moves to infinity, and the integral in (a.3) tends to zero as e^{-x^2}. As $x \to -\infty$, however, the path of integration extends along the whole of the real axis, and the integral in (a.3) does not tend exponentially to zero, so that the function $y(x)$ becomes infinite essentially as e^{x^2}. Similarly, it is easy to see that the integral (a.2) along the contour C_2' diverges exponentially as $x \to +\infty$.

For positive integral n (including zero), on the other hand, the integrals along the straight parts of the path of integration cancel, and the two integrals (a.3), along C_1' and C_2', reduce to an integral along a closed path round the

† These paths will not serve for negative integral n, since the integral (a.2) along them then vanishes identically.

point $u = x$. Thus we have the solution

$$y(x) = e^{x^2} \oint e^{-u^2}\, du/(u-x)^{n+1},$$

which satisfies the conditions stated. According to CAUCHY's well-known formula for the derivatives of an analytic function,

$$f^{(n)}(x) = \frac{n!}{2\pi i} \oint \frac{f(t)}{(t-x)^{n+1}}\, dt.$$

$y(x)$ is, apart from a constant factor, what is called an *Hermite polynomial*:

$$H_n(x) = (-1)^n e^{x^2} \frac{d^n}{dx^n} e^{-x^2}. \tag{a.4}$$

The polynomial H_n, expanded in decreasing powers of x, has the open form

$$H_n(x) = (2x)^n - \frac{n(n-1)}{1}(2x)^{n-2} + \frac{n(n-1)(n-2)(n-3)}{1.2}(2x)^{n-4} - \dots. \tag{a.5}$$

It contains only powers of x which are of the same parity as n. We may write out here the first few Hermite polynomials:

$$H_0 = 1, \quad H_1 = 2x, \quad H_2 = 4x^2-2, \quad H_3 = 8x^3-12x, \quad H_4 = 16x^4-48x^2+12. \tag{a.6}$$

To calculate the normalisation integral $\int_{-\infty}^{\infty} e^{-x^2} H_n^2(x)\, dx$, we replace $e^{-x^2} H_n$ by its expression in (a.4) and integrate n times by parts:

$$\int_{-\infty}^{\infty} e^{-x^2} H_n^2(x)\, dx = \int_{-\infty}^{\infty} (-1)^n H_n(x) \frac{d^n}{dx^n} e^{-x^2}\, dx$$

$$= \int_{-\infty}^{\infty} e^{-x^2} \frac{d^n}{dx^n} H_n\, dx.$$

But $d^n H_n/dx^n$ is a constant, $2^n n!$. Thus

$$\int_{-\infty}^{\infty} e^{-x^2} H_n^2(x)\, dx = 2^n n! \int_{-\infty}^{\infty} e^{-x^2}\, dx$$

or

$$\int_{-\infty}^{\infty} e^{-x^2} H_n^2(x)\, dx = 2^n n! \sqrt{\pi}. \tag{a.7}$$

§b. The Airy function

The equation

$$y''-xy = 0 \tag{b.1}$$

is of Laplace's type (see §a). Following the general method, we form the functions

$$P = t^2, \qquad Q = -1, \qquad Z = -e^{-\frac{1}{3}t^3},$$

so that the solution can be represented in the form

$$y(x) = \text{constant} \times \int_C e^{xt-\frac{1}{3}t^3}\,dt. \tag{b.2}$$

The path of integration C must be chosen so that the function $V = e^{xt-\frac{1}{3}t^3}$ vanishes at both ends of it. These ends must therefore go to infinity in the regions of the complex plane of t in which re $t^3 > 0$ (the shaded regions in Fig. 49).

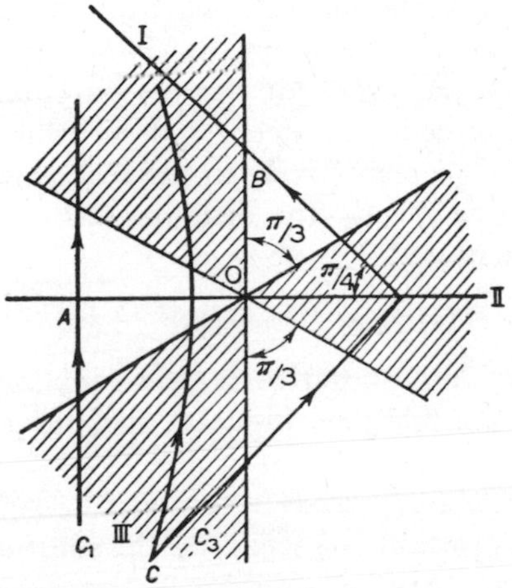

FIG. 49

A solution finite for all x is obtained by taking the path C as shown in the figure. It can be displaced in any manner provided that the ends of it go to infinity in the same two shaded sectors (I and III in Fig. 49). We notice that, by taking a path which lay in sectors III and II (say), we should obtain a solution which becomes infinite as $x \to \infty$.

Deforming the path C so that it goes along the imaginary axis, we obtain the function (b.2) in the form (substituting $t = iu$)

$$\Phi(x) = \frac{1}{\sqrt{\pi}} \int_0^\infty \cos(ux+\tfrac{1}{3}u^3)\,du. \tag{b.3}$$

The constant in (b.2) has been put equal to $-i/2\sqrt{\pi}$, and we have denoted the function thus obtained by $\Phi(x)$; it is called the *Airy function.*†

The asymptotic expression for $\Phi(x)$ for large values of x is conveniently obtained by calculating the integral (b.2) by the *saddle-point method.* For $x > 0$, the exponent in the integrand has an extremum for $t = \pm\sqrt{x}$, and the "direction of steepest descent" of the integrand is parallel to the imaginary axis. Accordingly, to obtain the asymptotic expression for large positive x, we expand the exponent in powers of $t+\sqrt{x}$ and integrate along the line C_1 (Fig. 49), which is parallel to the imaginary axis; the distance $OA = \sqrt{x}$. Making the substitution $t = -\sqrt{x}+iu$, we have

$$\Phi(x) \approx -\frac{i}{2\sqrt{\pi}}\int\limits_{-\infty}^{\infty} e^{-\frac{2}{3}x^{3/2}-u^2\sqrt{x}}\,\mathrm{d}u,$$

whence

$$\Phi(x) \approx \tfrac{1}{2}x^{-\frac{1}{4}}e^{-\frac{2}{3}x^{3/2}}. \tag{b.4}$$

Thus, for large positive x, the function $\Phi(x)$ diminishes exponentially.

To obtain the asymptotic expression for large negative values of x, we notice that, for $x < 0$, the exponent has an extremum for $t = i\sqrt{|x|}$ and $t = -i\sqrt{|x|}$, and the direction of steepest descent at these points is along lines at angles $-\frac{1}{4}\pi$ and $\frac{1}{4}\pi$ respectively to the real axis. Taking as the path of integration the broken line C_3 (the distance $OB = \sqrt{|x|}$), we have, after some simple transformations,

$$\Phi(x) = |x|^{-1/4}\sin(\tfrac{2}{3}|x|^{3/2}+\tfrac{1}{4}\pi). \tag{b.5}$$

Thus, in the region of large negative x, the function $\Phi(x)$ is oscillatory. We may mention that the first (and highest) maximum of the function $\Phi(x)$ is $\Phi(-1{\cdot}02) = 0{\cdot}95$.

The Airy function can be expressed in terms of Bessel functions of order $\frac{1}{3}$. The equation (b.1), as can easily be seen, has the solution

$$\sqrt{x}\,Z_{1/3}(\tfrac{2}{3}x^{3/2}),$$

where $Z_{1/3}(x)$ is any solution of Bessel's equation of order $\frac{1}{3}$. The solution which is the same as (b.3) is

$$\begin{aligned} \Phi(x) &= \tfrac{1}{3}\sqrt{(\pi x)}\{I_{-1/3}(\tfrac{2}{3}x^{3/2})-I_{1/3}(\tfrac{2}{3}x^{3/2})\} \text{ for } x > 0,\\ \Phi(x) &= \tfrac{1}{3}\sqrt{(\pi|x|)}\{J_{-1/3}(\tfrac{2}{3}|x|^{3/2})+J_{1/3}(\tfrac{2}{3}|x|^{3/2})\} \text{ for } x < 0, \end{aligned} \tag{b.6}$$

where $I_n(x) = i^{-n}J_n(ix)$. The coefficient here is most simply obtained by comparing the asymptotic expression (b.5) with the well-known asymptotic expression for the Bessel functions,

$$J_n(x) \approx \sqrt{(2/\pi x)}\sin(x-\tfrac{1}{2}n\pi+\tfrac{1}{4}\pi).$$

† We follow the definition proposed by V. A. Fok.

§c. Legendre polynomials

The *Legendre polynomials* $P_n(\cos\theta)$ are defined by the formula

$$P_n(\cos\theta) = \frac{1}{2^n n!}\frac{d^n}{(d\cos\theta)^n}(\cos^2\theta-1)^n, \tag{c.1}$$

or, in open form,

$$P_n(\cos\theta) = \frac{(2n)!}{2^n(n!)^2}\left[\cos^n\theta-\frac{n(n-1)}{2(2n-1)}\cos^{n-2}\theta+\frac{n(n-1)(n-2)(n-3)}{2.4.(2n-1)(2n-3)}\cos^{n-4}\theta-\ldots\right]. \tag{c.2}$$

They satisfy the differential equation

$$\frac{1}{\sin\theta}\frac{\partial}{\partial\theta}\left(\sin\theta\frac{\partial P_n}{\partial\theta}\right)+n(n+1)P_n = 0. \tag{c.3}$$

The *associated Legendre polynomials* are defined by

$$\begin{aligned}P_n^m(\cos\theta) &= \sin^m\theta\,\frac{d^m P_n(\cos\theta)}{(d\cos\theta)^m}\\ &= \frac{1}{2^n n!}\sin^m\theta\,\frac{d^{m+n}}{(d\cos\theta)^{m+n}}(\cos^2\theta-1)^n,\end{aligned} \tag{c.4}$$

with $m = 0, 1, \ldots, n$. An equivalent definition is

$$P_n^m(\cos\theta) = (-1)^m\frac{(n+m)!}{(n-m)!\,2^n n!}\sin^{-m}\theta\,\frac{d^{n-m}}{(d\cos\theta)^{n-m}}(\cos^2\theta-1)^n, \tag{c.5}$$

or, in open form,

$$\begin{aligned}P_n^m(\cos\theta) = {}&\frac{(2n)!}{2^n n!\,(n-m)!}\sin^m\theta\left\{\cos^{n-m}\theta-\frac{(n-m)(n-m-1)}{2(2n-1)}\cos^{n-m-2}\theta+\right.\\ &\left.+\frac{(n-m)(n-m-1)(n-m-2)(n-m-3)}{2.4.(2n-1)(2n-3)}\cos^{n-m-4}\theta-\ldots\right\}.\end{aligned} \tag{c.6}$$

The associated Legendre polynomials satisfy the equation

$$\frac{1}{\sin\theta}\frac{\partial}{\partial\theta}\left(\sin\theta\frac{\partial P_n^m}{\partial\theta}\right)+\left[n(n+1)-\frac{m^2}{\sin^2\theta}\right]P_n^m = 0. \tag{c.7}$$

The following "addition theorem" holds for Legendre polynomials.† Let

† There are in the mathematical literature many good accounts of the theory of spherical harmonics. Here we shall give, for reference, only a few basic relations, and make no attempt at a systematic discussion of the theory of these functions.

γ be the angle between two directions defined by the spherical angles θ, ϕ and θ', ϕ':

$$\cos\gamma = \cos\theta\cos\theta' + \sin\theta\sin\theta'\cos(\phi - \phi').$$

Then

$$P_n(\cos\gamma) = P_n(\cos\theta)P_n(\cos\theta') +$$

$$+\sum_{m=1}^{n} 2\frac{(n-m)!}{(n+m)!}P_n{}^m(\cos\theta)P_n{}^m(\cos\theta')\cos m(\phi-\phi'). \qquad \text{(c.8)}$$

We shall show how the normalisation integral for Legendre polynomials

$$\int_0^\pi [P_n(\cos\theta)]^2 \sin\theta \, d\theta = \int_{-1}^1 [P_n(\mu)]^2 \, d\mu$$

($\mu = \cos\theta$) may be calculated. Substituting for $P_n(\mu)$ the expression (c.1) and integrating n times by parts, we have

$$\int_{-1}^1 [P_n(\mu)]^2 \, d\mu = \frac{1}{2^{2n}(n!)^2}\int_{-1}^1 \frac{d^n}{d\mu^n}(\mu^2-1)^n \frac{d^n}{d\mu^n}(\mu^2-1)^n \, d\mu$$

$$= \frac{(-1)^n}{2^{2n}(n!)^2}\int_{-1}^1 (\mu^2-1)^n \frac{d^{2n}}{d\mu^{2n}}(\mu^2-1)^n \, d\mu$$

$$= \frac{(2n)!}{2^{2n}(n!)^2}\int_{-1}^1 (1-\mu^2)^n \, d\mu$$

$$= 2\frac{(2n)!}{(n!)^2}\int_0^1 u^n(1-u)^n \, du$$

($u = \frac{1}{2}(1-\mu)$), whence

$$\int_{-1}^1 [P_n(\mu)]^2 \, d\mu = 2/(2n+1). \qquad \text{(c.9)}$$

Similarly, it is easy to see that the functions $P_n(\mu)$ with different n are orthogonal:

$$\int_{-1}^{1} P_n(\mu)P_m(\mu)\,d\mu = 0 \qquad (n \neq m). \tag{c.10}$$

The calculation of the normalisation integral for the associated Legendre polynomials is easily effected by a similar method. We write $[P_n^m(\mu)]^2$ as a product of the expressions (c.4) and (c.5), and integrate $n-m$ times by parts:

$$\int_{-1}^{1} [P_n^m(\mu)]^2\,d\mu$$

$$= (-1)^m \frac{(n+m)!}{2^{2n}(n!)^2(n-m)!} \int_{-1}^{1} \frac{d^{n+m}}{d\mu^{n+m}}(\mu^2-1)^n \frac{d^{n-m}}{d\mu^{n-m}}(\mu^2-1)^n\,d\mu$$

$$= \frac{(n+m)!\,(2n)!}{2^{2n}(n!)^2(n-m)!} \int_{-1}^{1} (1-\mu^2)^n\,d\mu,$$

or

$$\int_{-1}^{1} [P_n^m(\mu)]^2\,d\mu = \frac{2}{2n+1}\frac{(n+m)!}{(n-m)!}. \tag{c.11}$$

It is easily seen by combining (c.4) and (c.5) that the functions P_n^m with different n (and the same m) are orthogonal:

$$\int_{-1}^{1} P_n^m(\mu)P_k^m(\mu)\,d\mu = 0 \qquad (n \neq k). \tag{c.12}$$

The calculation of the integrals of products of three Legendre polynomials is considerably more complex.† Here we shall give the result for the integral of the product $P_l^u P_m^v P_n^w$, one of the parameters u, v, w being equal to the sum of the other two:

$$u = v+w.$$

The integral is zero except when the sum $l+m+n$ is even and each of l,

† See Gaunt, *Philosophical Transactions of the Royal Society* A 228, 192, 1929.

m, n is not less than the difference nor greater than the sum of the other two†:

$$l+m+n = 2p, \quad l+n \geqslant m \geqslant |l-n|, \quad l+m \geqslant n. \tag{c.13}$$

In this case

$$\int_{-1}^{1} P_l^{v+w} P_m^v P_n^w \, d\mu = (-1)^{p-m-w} \, 2 \frac{(m+v)!\,(n+w)!\,(l+m-n)!\,p!}{(m-v)!\,(p-l)!\,(p-m)!\,(p-n)!\,(2p+1)!} \times$$
$$\times \sum_k (-1)^k \frac{(l+v+w+k)!\,(m+n-v-w-k)!}{(l-v-w-k)!\,(m-n+v+w+k)!\,(n-w-k)!\,k!}. \tag{c.14}$$

The summation is taken over all values of k for which the factorials in the denominators are meaningful. The sum can be calculated in a general form (though there is no simple method of doing so) only in some particular cases, of which we give three:

$$\int_{-1}^{1} P_{m+n}^{v+w} P_m^v P_n^w \, d\mu = 2 \frac{(m+n+v+w)!\,(m+n)!\,(2m)!\,(2n)!}{(m-v)!\,(n-w)!\,(2m+2n+1)!\,m!\,n!}, \tag{c.15}$$

$$\int_{-1}^{1} P_l^{v+w} P_m^v P_{l+m}^w \, d\mu = (-1)^v \, 2 \frac{(l+m+w)!\,(l+m)!\,(2l)!\,(2m)!}{(l-v-w)!\,(m-v)!\,(2l+2m+1)!\,l!\,m!}, \tag{c.16}$$

$$\int_{-1}^{1} P_l P_m P_n \, d\mu = 2 \frac{(p!)^2 (m+n-l)!\,(n+l-m)!\,(l+m-n)!}{(2p+1)!\,[(p-l)!\,(p-m)!\,(p-n)!]^2}. \tag{c.17}$$

§d. The confluent hypergeometric function

The *confluent hypergeometric function* is defined by the series

$$F(\alpha, \gamma, z) = 1 + \frac{\alpha}{\gamma}\frac{z}{1!} + \frac{\alpha(\alpha+1)}{\gamma(\gamma+1)}\frac{z^2}{2!} + \ldots, \tag{d.1}$$

which converges for all finite z; the parameter α is arbitrary, while the

† When the sum $l+m+n$ is odd, the integrand is an odd function of μ, and the integral therefore vanishes. The other rules can be obtained, for example, as follows. We write P_l^{v+w} in the form (c.5) and P_m^v and P_m^w in the form (c.4). In the integral

$$\int \frac{d^{l-v-w}}{d\mu^{l-v-w}}(\mu^2-1)^l \frac{d^{m+v}}{d\mu^{m+v}}(\mu^2-1)^m \frac{d^{n+w}}{d\mu^{n+w}}(\mu^2-1)^n \, d\mu,$$

we integrate $l-v-w$ times by parts, obtaining an integral of the form

$$\int (\mu^2-1)^l \frac{d^{l-v-w}}{d\mu^{l-v-w}} \left\{ \frac{d^{m+v}}{d\mu^{m+v}}(\mu^2-1)^m \frac{d^{n+w}}{d\mu^{n+w}}(\mu^2-1)^n \right\} d\mu,$$

and this is zero if $l-v-w > [2m-(m+v)]+[2n-(n+w)]$, i.e. if $l > m+n$.

parameter γ is supposed not zero or a negative integer. If α is a negative integer (or zero), $F(\alpha, \gamma, z)$ reduces to a polynomial of degree $|\alpha|$.

The function $F(\alpha, \gamma, z)$ satisfies the differential equation

$$zu''+(\gamma-z)u'-\alpha u = 0, \tag{d.2}$$

as is easily seen by direct verification.† By the substitution $u = z^{1-\gamma}u_1$, this equation is transformed into another of the same form,

$$zu_1''+(2-\gamma-z)u_1'-(\alpha-\gamma+1)u_1 = 0. \tag{d.3}$$

Hence we see that, for non-integral γ, equation (d.2) has also the particular integral $z^{1-\gamma} F(\alpha-\gamma+1, 2-\gamma, z)$, which is linearly independent of (d.1), so that the general solution of equation (d.2) is of the form

$$u = c_1F(\alpha,\gamma,z)+c_2z^{1-\gamma}F(\alpha-\gamma+1,2-\gamma,z). \tag{d.4}$$

The second term, unlike the first, has a singular point at $z = 0$.

Equation (d.2) is of Laplace's type, and its solutions can be represented as contour integrals. Following the general method, we form the functions

$$P(t) = \gamma t-\alpha, \quad Q(t) = t(t-1), \quad Z(t) = t^{\alpha-1}(t-1)^{\gamma-\alpha-1},$$

so that

$$u = \int e^{tz}t^{\alpha-1}(t-1)^{\gamma-\alpha-1}\, dt. \tag{d.5}$$

The path of integration must be chosen so that the function $V(t) = e^{tz}t^{\alpha}(t-1)^{\gamma-\alpha}$ returns to its original value on traversing the path. Applying the same method to equation (d.3) ,we can obtain for u a contour integral of another form:

$$u = z^{1-\gamma} \int e^{tz}t^{\alpha-\gamma}(t-1)^{-\alpha}\, dt.$$

The substitution $tz \to t$ reduces this integral to the convenient form

$$u(z) = \int e^{t}(t-z)^{-\alpha}t^{\alpha-\gamma}\, dt, \tag{d.6}$$

and the function V to

$$V(t) = e^{t}t^{\alpha-\gamma+1}(t-1)^{1-\alpha}.$$

The integrand in (d.6) has in general two singular points, at $t = z$ and $t = 0$. We take a contour of integration C which passes from infinity (re $t \to -\infty$) round the two singular points in the positive direction and back to infinity (Fig. 50). This contour satisfies the required conditions, since

† The equation (d.2) with a negative integral γ does not require special discussion, since it can be reduced to a case of positive integral γ by the transformation which gives equation (d.3).

$V(t)$ vanishes at its ends. The integral (d.6), taken along the contour C, has no singular point for $z = 0$; hence it must be the same, apart from a

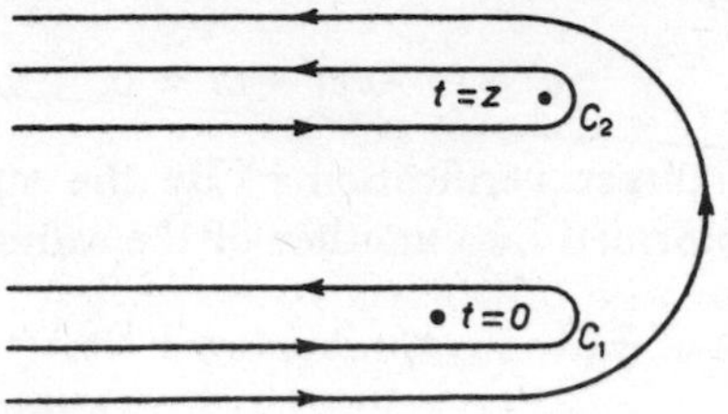

FIG. 50

constant factor, as the function $F(\alpha, \gamma, z)$, which also has no singularity. For $z = 0$ the two singular points of the integrand coincide; according to a well-known formula in the theory of the gamma function,†

$$\frac{1}{2\pi i}\int e^t t^{-\gamma}\, dt = 1/\Gamma(\gamma). \tag{d.7}$$

Since $F(\alpha, \gamma, 0) = 1$, it is evident that

$$F(\alpha,\gamma,z) = \frac{\Gamma(\gamma)}{2\pi i}\int\limits_C e^t(t-z)^{-\alpha}t^{\alpha-\gamma}\, dt. \tag{d.8}$$

The integrand in (d.5) has singular points at $t = 0$ and $t = 1$. If $\mathrm{re}(\gamma-\alpha) > 0$, and α is not a positive integer, the path of integration can be taken as a contour C' starting from the point $t = 1$, passing round the point $t = 0$ in the positive direction, and returning to $t = 1$ (Fig. 51); for $\mathrm{re}(\gamma-\alpha) > 0$,

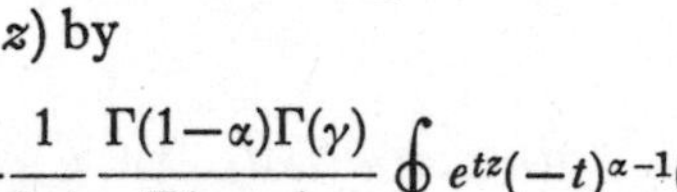

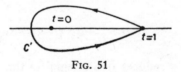

FIG. 51

the function $V(t)$ returns to its original value of zero on passing round such a contour.‡ The integral thus defined again has no singularity for $z = 0$, and is related to $F(\alpha, \gamma, z)$ by

$$F(\alpha,\gamma,z) = -\frac{1}{2\pi i}\frac{\Gamma(1-\alpha)\Gamma(\gamma)}{\Gamma(\gamma-\alpha)}\oint\limits_{C'} e^{tz}(-t)^{\alpha-1}(1-t)^{\gamma-\alpha-1}\, dt. \tag{d.9}$$

The following remark should be made concerning the integrals (d.8), (d.9). For non-integral α and γ, the integrands are not one-valued functions.

† See, for instance, WHITTAKER and WATSON, *Course of Modern Analysis*, Cambridge 1944, §12.22.

‡ If γ is a positive integer, C' can be any contour which passes round both the points $t = 0$ and $t = 1$.

Their values at each point are supposed chosen in accordance with the condition that the complex quantity which is raised to a power is taken with the argument whose absolute value is least.

We may notice the useful relation

$$F(\alpha, \gamma, z) = e^z F(\gamma-\alpha, \gamma, -z), \tag{d.10}$$

which is obtained at once by substituting $t \to t+z$ in the integral (d.8).

We have already remarked that, if $\alpha = -n$, where n is a positive integer, the function $F(\alpha, \gamma, z)$ reduces to a polynomial. A concise formula can be obtained for these polynomials. Making in the integral (d.9) the substitution $t \to 1-t/z$ and applying Cauchy's formula to the resulting integral, we find

$$F(-n, \gamma, z) = \frac{1}{\gamma(\gamma+1)\dots(\gamma+n-1)} z^{1-\gamma} e^z \frac{\mathrm{d}^n}{\mathrm{d}z^n}(e^{-z} z^{\gamma+n-1}). \tag{d.11}$$

If also $\gamma =$ a positive integer m, we have the formula

$$F(-n, m, z) = \frac{(-1)^{m-1}}{m(m+1)\dots(m+n-1)} e^z \frac{\mathrm{d}^{m+n-1}}{\mathrm{d}z^{m+n-1}}(e^{-z} z^n). \tag{d.12}$$

This formula is obtained by applying Cauchy's formula to the integral derived from (d.8) by the substitution $t \to z-t$.

The polynomials $F(-n, m, z)$, $0 \leqslant m \leqslant n$, are (apart from a constant factor) the *generalised Laguerre polynomials*, defined by

$$\begin{aligned} L_n{}^m(z) &= (-1)^m \frac{(n!)^2}{m!\,(n-m)!} F(-[n-m], m+1, z) \\ &= \frac{n!}{(n-m)!} e^z \frac{\mathrm{d}^n}{\mathrm{d}z^n}(e^{-z} z^{n-m}) \\ &= (-1)^m \frac{n!}{(n-m)!} e^z z^{-m} \frac{\mathrm{d}^{n-m}}{\mathrm{d}z^{n-m}}(e^{-z} z^n). \end{aligned} \tag{d.13}$$

The polynomials $L_n{}^m$ for $m = 0$ are denoted by $L_n(z)$ and are called simply *Laguerre polynomials*; from (d.13) we have

$$L_n(z) = e^z \frac{\mathrm{d}^n}{\mathrm{d}z^n}(e^{-z} z^n).$$

The integral representation (d.8) is convenient for obtaining the asymptotic expansion of the confluent hypergeometric function for large z. We deform the contour into two contours C_1 and C_2 (Fig. 50), which pass round the points $t = 0$ and $t = z$ respectively; the lower branch of C_2 and the upper branch of C_1 are supposed to join at infinity. To obtain an expansion in inverse powers of z, we take $(-z)^{-\alpha}$ outside the parenthesis in the integrand. In the integral along the contour C_2, we make the substitution $t \to t+z$; the contour C_2 is thereby transformed into C_1. We thus represent the formula (d.8) as

$$F(\alpha,\gamma,z) = \frac{\Gamma(\gamma)}{\Gamma(\gamma-\alpha)}(-z)^{-\alpha}G(\alpha,\alpha-\gamma+1,-z)+$$

$$+\frac{\Gamma(\gamma)}{\Gamma(\alpha)}e^z z^{\alpha-\gamma}G(\gamma-\alpha,1-\alpha,z), \tag{d.14}$$

where

$$G(\alpha,\beta,z) = \frac{\Gamma(1-\beta)}{2\pi i}\int\limits_{C_1}\left(1+\frac{t}{z}\right)^{-\alpha} t^{\beta-1}e^t\,dt. \tag{d.15}$$

In raising $-z$ and z to powers in the formula (d.14) we must take the arguments which have the smallest absolute value. Finally, expanding $(1+t/z)^{-\alpha}$ in the integrand in powers of t/z and applying formula (d.7), we have for $G(\alpha, \beta, z)$ the asymptotic series

$$G(\alpha,\beta,z) = 1+\frac{\alpha\beta}{1!z}+\frac{\alpha(\alpha+1)\beta(\beta+1)}{2!\,z^2}+\ldots. \tag{d.16}$$

Formulae (d.14) and (d.16) give the asymptotic expansion of the function $F(\alpha, \gamma, z)$.

For positive integral γ, the second term in the general solution (d.4) of equation (d.2) is either the same as the first term (if $\gamma = 1$) or meaningless (if $\gamma > 1$). In this case we can take, as a set of two linearly independent solutions, the two terms in formula (d.14), i.e. the integrals (d.8) taken along the contours C_1 and C_2 (these contours, like C, satisfy the required conditions, so that the integrals along them are solutions of equation (d.2)). The asymptotic form of these solutions is given by the formulae already obtained; it remains for us to find their expansion in ascending powers of z. To do this, we start from equation (d.14) and the analogous equation for the function $z^{1-\gamma}\,F(\alpha-\gamma+1,\ 2-\gamma,\ z)$. From these two equations we express $G(\alpha,\alpha-\gamma+1,-z)$ in terms of $F(\alpha,\gamma,z)$ and $F(\alpha-\gamma+1,\ 2-\gamma,\ z)$; we then put $\gamma = p+\epsilon$ (p being a positive integer), and pass to the limit $\epsilon \to 0$, resolving the indeterminacy by L'Hospital's rule. A rather lengthy calculation gives the following expansion:

$$G(\alpha,\alpha-p+1,-z) = -\frac{\sin\pi\alpha\,.\,\Gamma(p-\alpha)}{\pi\Gamma(p)}z^{\alpha}\times$$

$$\times\left\{\log z\,.\,F(\alpha,p,z)+\sum_{s=0}^{\infty}\frac{\Gamma(p)\Gamma(\alpha+s)[\psi(\alpha+s)-\psi(p+s)-\psi(s+1)]}{\Gamma(\alpha)\Gamma(s+p)\Gamma(s+1)}z^s+\right.$$

$$\left.+\sum_{s=1}^{p-1}(-1)^{s+1}\frac{\Gamma(s)\Gamma(\alpha-s)\Gamma(p)}{\Gamma(\alpha)\Gamma(p-s)}z^{-s}\right\}, \tag{d.17}$$

where ψ denotes the logarithmic derivative of the gamma function: $\psi(\alpha) = \Gamma'(\alpha)/\Gamma(\alpha)$.

§e. The hypergeometric function

The *hypergeometric function* is defined in the circle $|z| < 1$ by the series

$$F(\alpha,\beta,\gamma,z) = 1+\frac{\alpha\beta}{\gamma}\frac{z}{1!}+\frac{\alpha(\alpha+1)\beta(\beta+1)}{\gamma(\gamma+1)}\frac{z^2}{2!}+\dots, \tag{e.1}$$

and for $|z| > 1$ it is obtained by analytical continuation of this series. The hypergeometric function is a particular integral of the differential equation

$$z(1-z)u''+[\gamma-(\alpha+\beta+1)z]u'-\alpha\beta u = 0. \tag{e.2}$$

The parameters α and β are arbitrary, while $\gamma \neq 0, -1, -2, \dots$. The function $F(\alpha, \beta, \gamma, z)$ is evidently symmetrical with respect to the parameters α and β.† The second independent solution of equation (e.2) is

$$z^{1-\gamma}F(\beta-\gamma+1, \alpha-\gamma+1, 2-\gamma, z);$$

it has a singular point at $z = 0$.

We shall give here for reference a number of relations obeyed by the hypergeometric function.

The function $F(\alpha, \beta, \gamma, z)$ can be represented for all z, if‡ $\mathrm{re}(\gamma-\alpha) > 0$, as an integral:

$$F(\alpha,\beta,\gamma,z) = -\frac{1}{2\pi i}\frac{\Gamma(1-\alpha)\Gamma(\gamma)}{\Gamma(\gamma-\alpha)}\oint_{C'}(-t)^{\alpha-1}(1-t)^{\gamma-\alpha-1}(1-tz)^{-\beta}\,dt, \tag{e.3}$$

taken along the contour C' shown in Fig. 51. That this integral in fact satisfies equation (e.2) is easily seen by direct substitution; the constant factor is chosen so as to give unity for $z = 0$.

The substitution $u = (1-z)^{\gamma-\alpha-\beta}u_1$ in equation (e.2) leads to an equation of the same form, with parameters $\gamma-\alpha$, $\gamma-\beta$, γ in place of α, β, γ respectively. Hence we have

$$F(\alpha,\beta,\gamma,z) = (1-z)^{\gamma-\alpha-\beta}F(\gamma-\alpha,\gamma-\beta,\gamma,z); \tag{e.4}$$

both sides of this equation satisfy the same equation, and they have the same value for $z = 0$.

The substitution $t \to t/(1-z+zt)$ in the integral (e.3) leads to the following relation between hypergeometric functions with variables z and $z/(z-1)$:

$$F(\alpha,\beta,\gamma,z) = (1-z)^{-\alpha}F(\alpha,\gamma-\beta,\gamma,z/(z-1)). \tag{e.5}$$

The value of the many-valued expression $(1-z)^{-\alpha}$ in this formula (and of

† The confluent hypergeometric function is obtained from $F(\alpha, \beta, \gamma, z)$ by passing to the limit

$$F(\alpha,\gamma,z) = \lim_{\beta\to\infty} F(\alpha,\beta,\gamma,z/\beta).$$

‡ This inequality holds for all cases occurring in physical applications.

similar expressions in all the following formulae) is determined by the condition that the complex quantity which is raised to a power is taken with the argument whose absolute value is least.

Next we shall give, without proof, an important formula relating hypergeometric functions with variables z and $1/z$:

$$F(\alpha,\beta,\gamma,z) = \frac{\Gamma(\gamma)\Gamma(\beta-\alpha)}{\Gamma(\beta)\Gamma(\gamma-\alpha)}(-z)^{-\alpha}F(\alpha,\alpha+1-\gamma,\alpha+1-\beta,1/z)+$$
$$+\frac{\Gamma(\gamma)\Gamma(\alpha-\beta)}{\Gamma(\alpha)\Gamma(\gamma-\beta)}(-z)^{-\beta}F(\beta,\beta+1-\gamma,\beta+1-\alpha,1/z). \quad (e.6)$$

This formula expresses $F(\alpha, \beta, \gamma, z)$ as a series which converges for $|z| > 1$, i.e. it is the analytical continuation of the original series (e.1).

The formula

$$F(\alpha,\beta,\gamma,z) = \frac{\Gamma(\gamma)\Gamma(\gamma-\alpha-\beta)}{\Gamma(\gamma-\alpha)\Gamma(\gamma-\beta)}F(\alpha,\beta,\alpha+\beta+1-\gamma,1-z)+$$
$$+\frac{\Gamma(\gamma)\Gamma(\alpha+\beta-\gamma)}{\Gamma(\alpha)\Gamma(\beta)}(1-z)^{\gamma-\alpha-\beta}F(\gamma-\alpha,\gamma-\beta,\gamma+1-\alpha-\beta,1-z) \quad (e.7)$$

relates hypergeometric functions of z and $1-z$; it is derived similarly to formula (e.6). Combining (e.7) and (e.5) with (e.6), we obtain the relations

$$F(\alpha,\beta,\gamma,z) = \frac{\Gamma(\gamma)\Gamma(\beta-\alpha)}{\Gamma(\beta)\Gamma(\gamma-\alpha)}(1-z)^{-\alpha}F(\alpha,\gamma-\beta,\alpha+1-\beta,1/(1-z))+$$
$$+\frac{\Gamma(\gamma)\Gamma(\alpha-\beta)}{\Gamma(\alpha)\Gamma(\gamma-\beta)}(1-z)^{-\beta}F(\beta,\gamma-\alpha,\beta+1-\alpha,1/(1-z)), \quad (e.8)$$

$$F(\alpha,\beta,\gamma,z) = \frac{\Gamma(\gamma)\Gamma(\gamma-\alpha-\beta)}{\Gamma(\gamma-\beta)\Gamma(\gamma-\alpha)}z^{-\alpha}F\left(\alpha,\alpha+1-\gamma,\alpha+\beta+1-\gamma,\frac{z-1}{z}\right)+$$
$$+\frac{\Gamma(\gamma)\Gamma(\alpha+\beta-\gamma)}{\Gamma(\alpha)\Gamma(\beta)}(1-z)^{\gamma-\alpha-\beta}z^{\beta-\gamma}F\left(1-\beta,\gamma-\beta,\gamma+1-\alpha-\beta,\frac{z-1}{z}\right). \quad (e.9)$$

Each of the terms in the sums on the right of equations (e.6)–(e.9) is itself a solution of the hypergeometric equation.

If α (or β) is a negative integer or zero, $\alpha = -n$, the hypergeometric function reduces to a polynomial of the nth degree, and can be represented in the form

$$F(-n,\beta,\gamma,z) = \frac{z^{1-\gamma}(1-z)^{\gamma+n-\beta}}{\gamma(\gamma+1)\dots(\gamma+n-1)}\frac{d^n}{dz^n}[z^{\gamma+n-1}(1-z)^{\beta-\gamma}]. \quad (e.10)$$

$F(\alpha, \beta, \gamma, z)$ also reduces to a polynomial for $\alpha = \gamma+n$ and for $\alpha = n$,

$\gamma = m+1$ (n and m being positive integers, with $n \leqslant m$). The explicit forms of these polynomials can be obtained in the former case by combining (e.10) with (e.5), and in the latter case by combining it with (e.9).

§f. The calculation of integrals containing confluent hypergeometric functions

Let us consider an integral of the form

$$J_{\alpha\gamma}^{\nu} = \int_0^\infty e^{-\lambda z} z^\nu F(\alpha, \gamma, kz)\,\mathrm{d}z. \tag{f.1}$$

We assume that it converges. If this is so we must have re $\nu > -1$ and re $\lambda > |\text{re}\, k|$; if α is a negative integer, the latter condition can be replaced by re $\lambda > 0$.

The integral (f.1) is easily calculated by using for $F(\alpha, \gamma, kz)$ the integral representation (d.9) and effecting the integration over z under the contour integral:

$$J_{\alpha\gamma}^{\nu} = -\frac{1}{2\pi i}\frac{\Gamma(1-\alpha)\Gamma(\gamma)}{\Gamma(\gamma-\alpha)}\oint_{C'}\int_0^\infty e^{-(\lambda-kt)z} z^\nu (-t)^{\alpha-1}(1-t)^{\gamma-\alpha-1}\,\mathrm{d}t\mathrm{d}z$$

$$= -\frac{1}{2\pi i}\frac{\Gamma(1-\alpha)\Gamma(\gamma)}{\Gamma(\gamma-\alpha)}\lambda^{-\nu-1}\Gamma(\nu+1)\times$$

$$\times\oint_{C'}(-t)^{\alpha-1}(1-t)^{\gamma-\alpha-1}(1-kt/\lambda)^{-\nu-1}\,\mathrm{d}t.$$

Using (e.3), we have finally

$$J_{\alpha\gamma}^{\nu} = \Gamma(\nu+1)\lambda^{-\nu-1}F(\alpha, \nu+1, \gamma, k/\lambda). \tag{f.2}$$

In the cases where the function $F(\alpha, \nu+1, \gamma, k/\lambda)$ reduces to a polynomial, we have for the integral $J_{\alpha\gamma}^{\nu}$ an expression in terms of elementary functions:

$$J_{\alpha\gamma}^{\gamma+n-1} = (-1)^n\Gamma(\gamma)\frac{\mathrm{d}^n}{\mathrm{d}\lambda^n}[\lambda^{\alpha-\gamma}(\lambda-k)^{-\alpha}], \tag{f.3}$$

$$J_{-n,\gamma}^{\nu} = (-1)^n\frac{\Gamma(\nu+1)(\lambda-k)^{\gamma+n-\nu-1}}{\gamma(\gamma+1)\dots(\gamma+n-1)}\frac{\mathrm{d}^n}{\mathrm{d}\lambda^n}[\lambda^{-\nu-1}(\lambda-k)^{\nu-\gamma+1}], \tag{f.4}$$

$$J_{\alpha m}^{n} = \frac{(-1)^{m-n}}{k^{m-1}(1-\alpha)(2-\alpha)\dots(m-1-\alpha)}\times\Big\{-(m-1)!\frac{\mathrm{d}^n}{\mathrm{d}\lambda^n}[\lambda^{\alpha-1}(\lambda-k)^{m-\alpha-1}]+$$

$$+n!(m-n-1)\dots(m-1)\lambda^{\alpha-n-1}(\lambda-k)^{-1+m-n-\alpha}\frac{\mathrm{d}^{m-n-2}}{\mathrm{d}\lambda^{m-n-2}}[\lambda^{m-\alpha-1}(\lambda-k)^{\alpha-1}]\Big\}; \tag{f.5}$$

here m, n are integers, with $0 \leqslant n \leqslant m-2$.

Next, let us calculate the integral

$$J_\nu = \int_0^\infty e^{-kz} z^{\nu-1}[F(-n,\gamma,kz)]^2\,\mathrm{d}z, \tag{f.6}$$

where n is an integer and re $\nu > 0$. To calculate this, we begin with a more general integral having $e^{-\lambda z}$ instead of e^{-kz} in the integrand. We write one of the functions $F(-n, \gamma, kz)$ as a contour integral, and then integrate over z, using formula (f.4):

$$\int_0^\infty e^{-\lambda z} z^{\nu-1}[F(-n,\gamma,kz)]^2\,\mathrm{d}z = -\frac{1}{2\pi i}\frac{\Gamma(1+n)\Gamma(\gamma)}{\Gamma(\gamma+n)}\times$$

$$\times\int_0^\infty \oint_{C'} (-t)^{-n-1}(1-t)^{\gamma+n-1}e^{-(\lambda-ktz)}z^{\nu-1}F(-n,\gamma,kz)\,\mathrm{d}t\mathrm{d}z$$

$$= -\frac{1}{2\pi i}(-1)^n\frac{\Gamma(1+n)\Gamma^2(\gamma)\Gamma(\nu)}{\Gamma^2(\gamma+n)}\times$$

$$\times\oint_{C'} (\lambda-kt-k)^{\gamma+n-\nu}(-t)^{-n-1}(1-t)^{\gamma+n-1}\frac{\mathrm{d}^n}{\mathrm{d}\lambda^n}[(\lambda-kt)^{-\nu}(\lambda-kt-k)^{\nu-\gamma}]\,\mathrm{d}t.$$

The nth derivative with respect to λ can evidently be replaced by a derivative of the same order with respect to t; we then put $\lambda = k$, and thereby return to the integral J_ν:

$$J_\nu = -\frac{1}{2\pi i}\frac{\Gamma(n+1)\Gamma(\nu)\Gamma^2(\gamma)}{\Gamma^2(\gamma+n)k^\nu}\times\oint_{C'}(-t)^{\gamma-\nu-1}(1-t)^{\gamma+n-1}\frac{\mathrm{d}^n}{\mathrm{d}t^n}[(1-t)^{-\nu}(-t)^{\nu-\gamma}]\,\mathrm{d}t.$$

By integrating n times by parts, we transfer the operator $\mathrm{d}^n/\mathrm{d}t^n$ to the expression $(-t)^{\gamma-\nu-1}(1-t)^{\gamma+n-1}$, and then expand the derivative by Leibniz' formula. As a result, we obtain a sum of integrals, each of which reduces to EULER's well-known integral. We finally have the following expression for the integral required:

$$J_\nu = \frac{\Gamma(\nu)n!}{k^\nu\gamma(\gamma+1)\ldots(\gamma+n-1)}\left\{1+\frac{n(\gamma-\nu-1)(\gamma-\nu)}{1^2\gamma}+\right.$$

$$+\frac{n(n-1)(\gamma-\nu-2)(\gamma-\nu-1)(\gamma-\nu)(\gamma-\nu+1)}{1^2 2^2\gamma(\gamma+1)}+\ldots+$$

$$\left.+\frac{n(n-1)\ldots1(\gamma-\nu-n)\ldots(\gamma-\nu+n-1)}{1^2 2^2\ldots n^2\gamma(\gamma+1)\ldots(\gamma+n-1)}\right\}. \tag{f.7}$$

It is easy to see that the integrals J_ν are related by

$$J_{\gamma+p} = \frac{(\gamma-p-1)(\gamma-p)\dots(\gamma+p-1)}{k^{2p+1}} J_{\gamma-1-p}, \tag{f.8}$$

where p is any integer.

We similarly calculate the integral

$$J = \int_0^\infty e^{-\lambda z} z^{\gamma-1} F(\alpha, \gamma, kz) F(\alpha', \gamma, k'z)\, dz. \tag{f.9}$$

We represent the function $F(\alpha', \gamma, k'z)$ as a contour integral, and integrate over z, using formula (f.3) with $n = 0$:

$$J = -\frac{1}{2\pi i} \frac{\Gamma(1-\alpha')\Gamma(\gamma)}{\Gamma(\gamma-\alpha')} \oint_{C'} \int_0^\infty (-t)^{\alpha'-1}(1-t)^{\gamma-\alpha'-1} z^{\gamma-1} e^{-z(\lambda-k't)} F(\alpha, \gamma, kz)\, dz dt$$

$$= -\frac{1}{2\pi i} \frac{\Gamma(1-\alpha')\Gamma^2(\gamma)}{\Gamma(\gamma-\alpha')} \oint_{C'} (-t)^{\alpha'-1}(1-t)^{\gamma-\alpha'-1}(\lambda-k't)^{\alpha-\gamma}(\lambda-k't-k)^{-\alpha}\, dt.$$

By the substitution $t \to \lambda t/(k't+\lambda-k')$, this integral is brought to the form (e.3), giving

$$J = \Gamma(\gamma)\lambda^{\alpha+\alpha'-\gamma}(\lambda-k)^{-\alpha}(\lambda-k')^{-\alpha'} F\left(\alpha, \alpha', \gamma, \frac{kk'}{(\lambda-k)(\lambda-k')}\right). \tag{f.10}$$

If α (or α') is a negative integer, $\alpha = -n$, this expression can be rewritten, using (e.7), as

$$J = \frac{\Gamma^2(\gamma)\Gamma(\gamma+n-\alpha')}{\Gamma(\gamma+n)\Gamma(\gamma-\alpha')} \lambda^{-n+\alpha'-\gamma}(\lambda-k)^n(\lambda-k')^{-\alpha'} \times$$

$$\times F\left(-n, \alpha', -n+\alpha'+1-\gamma, \frac{\lambda(\lambda-k-k')}{(\lambda-k)(\lambda-k')}\right). \tag{f.11}$$

Finally, let us consider integrals of the form

$$J_\gamma^{sp}(\alpha, \alpha') = \int_0^\infty e^{-\frac{1}{2}(k+k')z} z^{\gamma-1+s} F(\alpha, \gamma, kz) F(\alpha', \gamma-p, k'z)\, dz. \tag{f.12}$$

The values of the parameters are supposed such that the integral converges absolutely; s and p are positive integers. The simplest of these integrals,

$J_\gamma^{00}(\alpha, \alpha')$, is, by (f.10),

$$J_\gamma^{00}(\alpha,\alpha') = 2^\gamma\Gamma(\gamma)(k+k')^{\alpha+\alpha'-\gamma}(k'-k)^{-\alpha}(k-k')^{-\alpha'}F\left(\alpha,\alpha',\gamma,-\frac{4kk'}{(k'-k)^2}\right); \quad \text{(f.13)}$$

if α (or α') is a negative integer, $\alpha = -n$, we can also write, by (f.11),

$$J_\gamma^{00}(-n,\alpha') = 2^\gamma\frac{\Gamma(\gamma)(\gamma-\alpha')(\gamma-\alpha'+1)\dots(\gamma-\alpha'+n-1)}{\gamma(\gamma+1)\dots(\gamma+n-1)}\times$$

$$\times(-1)^n(k+k')^{-n+\alpha'-\gamma}(k-k')^{n-\alpha'}F\left[-n,\alpha',\alpha'+1-n-\gamma,\left(\frac{k+k'}{k-k'}\right)^2\right]. \quad \text{(f.14)}$$

The general formula for $J_\gamma^{sp}(\alpha, \alpha')$ can be derived, but it is so complex that it cannot be used conveniently. It is more convenient to use recurrence formulae, which enable us to reduce the integrals $J_\gamma^{sp}(\alpha, \alpha')$ to the integral with $s = p = 0$. We shall give these here without proof.† The formula

$$J_\gamma^{sp}(\alpha,\alpha') = \frac{\gamma-1}{k}\{J_{\gamma-1}^{s,p-1}(\alpha,\alpha')-J_{\gamma-1}^{s,p-1}(\alpha-1,\alpha')\} \quad \text{(f.15)}$$

enables us to reduce $J_\gamma^{sp}(\alpha, \alpha')$ to the integral with $p = 0$. The formula

$$J_\gamma^{s+1,0}(\alpha,\alpha') = \frac{4}{k^2-k'^2}\{[\tfrac{1}{2}\gamma(k-k')-k\alpha+k'\alpha'-k's]J_\gamma^{s0}(\alpha,\alpha')+$$

$$+s(\gamma-1+s-2\alpha')J_\gamma^{s-1,0}(\alpha,\alpha')+2\alpha's J_\gamma^{s-1,0}(\alpha,\alpha'+1)\} \quad \text{(f.16)}$$

then makes possible the final reduction to the integral with $s = p = 0$.

---

† The derivation is given by W. Gordon, *Annalen der Physik* 2, 1031, 1929.

INDEX OF NAMES

INDEX OF SYMBOLS

INDEX OF SUBJECTS